FUNDAMENTALS OF ENGINEERING SCIENCE

The purpose of this book is to cover the engineering science content of the new general courses in engineering, which are being established following the publication of the Government White Paper *Better Opportunities in Technical Education*. The author is a practising teacher, who has borne in mind the needs of students just embarking on a career in engineering, and who has a most unusual awareness of their capabilities and of the particular difficulties they have to face. The work as a whole provides a thoroughly comprehensive picture of basic engineering science, starting with the fundamental concepts of the units of length, mass and time, and lays a firm foundation of mechanics before going on to deal with the complex but almost equally fundamental 'laws' of atomic structure, theories of electricity and so on. The final chapters deal with energy conversion and engineering materials. The development of the argument is always most carefully graded, so that at no time does the student feel himself overloaded, but retains throughout a sense of knowledge being steadily acquired and consolidated.

With the modifications to syllabuses from 1969 onwards this book now covers about half the mechanical engineering science work of the first year of the Ordinary National Certificate Course and covers all the fundamental engineering science in the four years of the Mechanical Engineering Technicians' Course. Of course, as a fundamental primer, *Fundamentals of Engineering Science* is most suitable for teachers engaged on other courses such as Motor Vehicle, Mechanical Engineering Craft and the Construction Courses.

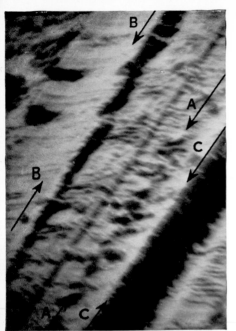

Tool steel
(hardened and ground)

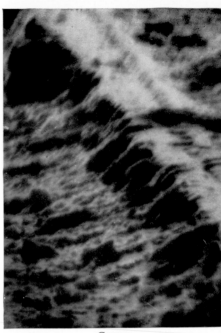

Copper
(ground)

Micrographs of metal surfaces (approx. magnification × 5000). Each surface would appear polished to the unaided eye

(Reproduced from the Proceedings of the Institution of Mechanical Engineers—'Surface Examination by Reflection Electron Microscopy', by J. S. Halliday, Ph.D.)

Mild steel
(ground)

Nickel
(ground)

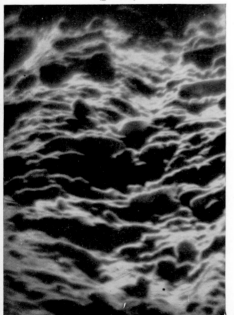

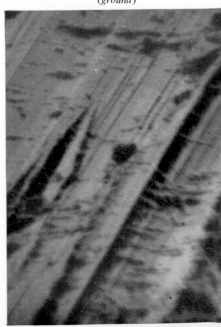

FUNDAMENTALS OF ENGINEERING SCIENCE

G. R. A. TITCOMB
B.Sc.(Eng.), C.Eng., M.I.E.E.

Formerly Head of Electrical Engineering Department
Crawley College of Further Education

Revised and metricated by
M. JACKSON
B.Sc., C.Eng., M.I.Mech.E., A.F.R.Ae.S.

Head of Mechanical Engineering Department
People's College of Further Education, Nottingham

HUTCHINSON TECHNICAL EDUCATION

HUTCHINSON EDUCATIONAL LTD

178–202 Great Portland Street, London W1

London Melbourne Sydney
Auckland Bombay Toronto
Johannesburg New York

★

First published 1961
Second Impression 1962
Second Edition 1963
Fourth Impression 1964
Third Edition 1968
Fourth Edition (revised and metricated) 1970

This book has been set in Times New Roman type
face. It has been printed offset by The Camelot
Press, Ltd., London and Southampton, and bound
by Wm. Brendon, Tiptree, Essex.

ISBN 0 09 100730 5 (Cased)
ISBN 0 09 100731 3 (Paper)

Contents

Author's Note   17

1. INTRODUCTION   19

2. FUNDAMENTAL QUANTITIES AND UNITS

2. 1   Length   24
2. 2   Mass   24
2. 3   Time   24
2. 4   Derived units   25
2. 5   Force and mass   25
2. 6   Force and pressure   27
2. 7   Density   30
2. 8   Relative density   31
2. 9   Determination of density and relative density   32
2.10   The conversion of units   33

3. VECTORS

3. 1   Scalar and vector quantities   38
3. 2   Force vectors. Vector addition   39
3. 3   Subtraction of vectors   45
3. 4   Resultant of more than two forces   48
3. 5   Equilibrium   51
3. 6   Equilibrant   52
3. 7   Experimental verification of vector-addition methods   53
3. 8   Examples   57
3. 9   Resolution of forces   62
3.10   Applications of method of resolution of forces   66
3.11   Resolution of forces without the use of scale drawings   71
3.12   Examples   74
3.13   The inclined plane   80

4. PARALLEL FORCES

4. 1	The turning effect of a force. Moments	94
4. 2	General note on compound units	97
4. 3	Equilibrium under the action of parallel forces	99
4. 4	Examples	100
4. 5	Levers	102
4. 6	Types of lever	104
4. 7	Examples	106
4. 8	Simply-supported beams	109
4. 9	Resultant of a number of parallel forces	113
4.10	Couple. Torque	116
4.11	Centre of gravity	118
4.12	Composite figures	122
4.13	The steelyard	131
4.14	Stability	135

5. FORCES APPLIED TO SOLID MATERIALS

5. 1	Tension	148
5. 2	Compression	148
5. 3	Shear	149
5. 4	Stress. Intensity of stress	150
5. 5	Strain	152
5. 6	Hooke's law	154
5. 7	Young's modulus of elasticity	156
5. 8	Modulus of rigidity	156
5. 9	Examples	157
5.10	Tensile testing of materials	161
5.11	Load-extension graph	163
5.12	Factor of safety	165
5.13	Example	166

6. WORK AND ENERGY

6. 1	Work. Units of work	174
6. 2	Examples	175

6. 3   Work diagrams   177
6. 4   Examples   179
6. 5   Work done by a variable force   182
6. 6   Example   183
6. 7   Work done by a force inclined to direction of movement   185
6. 8   Energy   188
6. 9   Potential energy   188
6.10   Strain energy   190
6.11   Kinetic energy   190
6.12   Action of a flywheel   191

7. FRICTION

7. 1   The nature of friction   195
7. 2   The laws of friction   197
7. 3   The coefficient of friction   197
7. 4   Examples   200
7. 5   Experiment to determine coefficient of friction   202
7. 6   Angle of friction   204
7. 7   Moment of frictional force   205
7. 8   Rough inclined plane   208

8. VELOCITY AND ACCELERATION

8. 1   Speed   219
8. 2   Examples   220
8. 3   Velocity   221
8. 4   Distance-time graphs   223
8. 5   Acceleration   227
8. 6   Velocity-time graphs   228
8. 7   Bodies moving with uniform acceleration   231
8. 8   Examples   234
8. 9   Motion under effects of gravity   241
8.10   Examples   243
8.11   Combination and resolution of velocities   247
8.12   Projectiles   250
8.13   Examples   250

9. FORCE, MASS AND ACCELERATION

9. 1	Force and acceleration	258
9. 2	Momentum	259
9. 3	Change of momentum	260
9. 4	Relationship between force, mass and acceleration	260
9. 5	The International units of force, mass and acceleration	262
9. 6	Examples	262
9. 7	Conversions between potential and kinetic forms of energy	264
9. 8	Examples	265

10. ANGULAR MOTION. TORQUE

10. 1	Angular measure	272
10. 2	Examples	274
10. 3	Angular velocity	277
10. 4	Examples	278
10. 5	Relationship between angular velocity and linear velocity	279
10. 6	Examples	281
10. 7	Angular acceleration	282
10. 8	Turning effect of a force. Torque	283
10. 9	Examples	285

11. POWER

11. 1	Power	290
11. 2	Power transmitted by a torque	291
11. 3	Examples	292
11. 4	Efficiency	295
11. 5	Examples	296

12. MACHINES

12. 1	Force ratio or mechanical advantage	303
12. 2	Movement ratio or velocity ratio	304
12. 3	Efficiency	304
12. 4	Relationship between load and effort	305

CONTENTS

12. 5   The lever   306
12. 6   The wheel and axle   308
12. 7   The wheel and differential axle movement   310
12. 8   Pulley systems   312
12. 9   Examples   316
12.10   The inclined plane   323
12.11   The screw-jack   324
12.12   Examples   327
12.13   Gear drives   329
12.14   Use of idler gear   331
12.15   Examples   332
12.16   Belt drives   336
12.17   Speed cones   339
12.18   Examples   340

13. ATOMIC STRUCTURE

13. 1   Atoms   352
13. 2   The electron   353
13. 3   The proton   354
13. 4   The neutron   354
13. 5   Other particles   355
13. 6   Atomic structure   355
13. 7   Solids, liquids and gases   358

14. HEAT

14. 1   The nature of heat   365
14. 2   The transmission of heat. (1) Conduction   366
14. 3   The transmission of heat. (2) Convection   367
14. 4   The transmission of heat. (3) Radiation   367
14. 5   Temperature   369
14. 6   Scales of temperature   369
14. 7   Methods of measurement of temperature   370
14. 8   Quantity of heat. Units of measurement   371
14. 9   Specific heat capacity   371
14.10   Heat energy lost or gained through change in temperature   372
14.11   Examples   373

14.12 Thermal capacity   374
14.13 Water equivalent   376
14.14 Calorimetry   377
14.15 Change of state   379
14.16 Enthalpy and specific enthalpy   380
14.17 Measurement of enthalpy of fusion or evaporation   384
14.18 Problems on mixtures   385
14.19 Expansion and contraction   391
14.20 Coefficient of linear expansion   392
14.21 Coefficient of superficial (area) expansion   396
14.22 Coefficient of cubical (volume) expansion   396
14.23 Expansion of liquids   397
14.24 Examples   398
14.25 Expansion of gases   399
14.26 The gas laws   400
14.27 Boyle's law   401
14.28 Charles' law   403
14.29 Examples   405
14.30 Combination of Boyle's law and Charles' law   408
14.31 Examples   409

15. FLUIDS

15. 1 Viscosity   421
15. 2 Fluid pressure   421
15. 3 Effect of the mass of the fluid   423
15. 4 Atmospheric pressure. The barometer   425
15. 5 The siphon   426
15. 6 Archimedes' principle   427
15. 7 The hydrometer   428
15. 8 Examples   429

16. THE ELECTRIC CIRCUIT

16. 1 Electric charge   436
16. 2 Potential   438
16. 3 Potential difference   438
16. 4 Conductors and insulators   439

16. 5   Electromotive force   441
16. 6   Simple electric circuit. Electric current flow   442
16. 7   Unit of electric current   443
16. 8   Effects of electric current   444
16. 9   Resistance   445
16.10   Symbols   447
16.11   Examples   447
16.12   Circuit diagrams   448
16.13   Energy relationships in simple electric circuits   449
16.14   Examples   451
16.15   Resistors connected in series and in parallel   452
16.16   Examples   455
16.17   Current distribution in parallel circuits   462
16.18   Series parallel circuits   465
16.19   Groupings of cells in series and in parallel   469
16.20   Resistivity   475
16.21   Examples   479
16.22   Variation of resistance with temperature   481
16.23   Examples   486
16.24   Resistance-temperature coefficient at other reference temperatures   487
16.25   Electrical power   489
16.26   Examples   491
16.27   Cost of electrical energy   492
16.28   Examples   493

17. ELECTRICAL MEASUREMENTS

17. 1   Internal resistance of a source   507
17. 2   Measurement of e.m.f. The slide-wire potentiometer   509
17. 3   Measurement of resistance. Voltmeter-ammeter method   512
17. 4   Measurement of resistance. Potentiometer method   519
17. 5   Measurement of resistance. Substitution   520
17. 6   Measurement of resistance. Alternative potentiometer method   521
17. 7   Measurement of resistance. Bridge method   522
17. 8   Measurement of resistivity   526
17. 9   Measurement of resistance-temperature coefficient   527
17.10   Calibration of meters. Voltmeters   527

17.11 Calibration of meters. Ammeters 532
17.12 Adjustment of meter range. Voltmeters 534
17.13 Adjustment of meter range. Ammeters 536
17.14 Multi-range meters 538

18. ELECTRO-CHEMISTRY

18. 1 The simple voltaic cell 550
18. 2 Theory of action of simple cell 551
18. 3 Local action 552
18. 4 Polarization 553
18. 5 The Daniell cell 554
18. 6 The Leclanché cell 556
18. 7 The Weston standard cell 558
18. 8 Primary and secondary cells 560
18. 9 The lead-acid secondary cell 560
18.10 Characteristics of the lead-acid secondary cell 563
18.11 Other types of secondary cell 567
18.12 Electrolysis 568
18.13 Electrolysis of water 569
18.14 Faraday's laws of electrolysis. Electro-chemical equivalent 571
18.15 Examples 572
18.16 Electroplating 573
18.17 Example on Faraday's laws of electrolysis 576
18.18 Energy considerations in electro-chemical reactions 577

19. ELECTROMAGNETISM

19. 1 Magnetic fields 584
19. 2 Magnetic field of a bar magnet. Lines of force 585
19. 3 Magnetic effect of an electric current. Magnetic field due to current in a straight wire 588
19. 4 Magnetic field due to current in a single-turn loop 590
19. 5 Magnetic field due to current in a solenoid 593
19. 6 Magnetic field due to current in a toroid 596
19. 7 Magnetic flux and magnetic flux density 598
19. 8 Effect of iron in a magnetic field 599
19. 9 Effect of an iron core inside a solenoid 602

19.10	Electromagnets	603
19.11	Force on a current at right angles to a magnetic field	605
19.12	Fleming's left-hand rule	609
19.13	Units of measurement of strength of magnetic field	611
19.14	Examples	612
19.15	Force on a current at other than a right angle to a magnetic field	613
19.16	Practical applications of force exerted on a current in a magnetic field	616
19.17	Force between parallel currents	619
19.18	The ampere	621
19.19	Electromagnetic induction	622
19.20	Faraday's law of electromagnetic induction	627
19.21	Lenz's law	628
19.22	Fleming's right-hand rule	630
19.23	Flux-cutting rules	631
19.24	Examples	634
19.25	Practical applications of the effects of electromagnetic induction	636

20. ALTERNATING CURRENTS

20. 1	Generation of alternating e.m.f.	646
20. 2	A cycle of an alternating waveform	653
20. 3	Period	654
20. 4	Frequency	657
20. 5	Examples	658
20. 6	Multi-polar alternators	663
20. 7	Examples	665
20. 8	Average value of an alternating current	666
20. 9	Examples	669
20.10	Heating effect of an alternating current	672
20.11	Form factor	681
20.12	Crest, or peak, factor	682

21. ELECTRICAL MEASURING INSTRUMENTS

21. 1	Ammeters and voltmeters. General	687
21. 2	Ammeters and voltmeters. Moving-coil type	687

21. 3   Ammeters and voltmeters. Moving-iron type   690
21. 4   Comparisons between moving-coil and moving-iron instruments   695
21. 5   Dynamometer (or electrodynamic) instruments   697
21. 6   Other types of instrument   700

22. ENERGY CONVERSION

22. 1   Various forms of energy. Energy conversion   705
22. 2   Conservation of energy   706
22. 3   Stored energy   707
22. 4   Efficiency of energy conversion   708
22. 5   Mechanical equivalent of heat   710
22. 6   Electrical equivalent of heat   711
22. 7   Examples   712

23. ENGINEERING MATERIALS

23. 1   Mechanical properties of materials   721
23. 2   Electrical properties of materials   723
23. 3   Ferrous metals   724
23. 4   Non-ferrous metals   726
23. 5   Plastics   730
23. 6   Ceramics   734

Appendix A: Bow's Notation   737

Appendix B: Note on Units   747

Tables   749

Answers to questions   753

Index   765

Author's Note

The purpose of this book is to cover the engineering science content of the new general courses in engineering, which are being established following the publication of the Government White Paper *Better Opportunities in Technical Education*. The sequence of presentation has been chosen so that the earlier chapters lay a foundation for the later work, but it should not be necessary to cover one chapter completely before tackling the next. The format is such that the teacher may use the book in relation to any arrangement of the syllabus he may choose. The material for the first year of a two-year course may be selected as required, and the remaining sections of the various chapters left until the second year. It is felt that a two-fold advantage is gained by this method of coverage. The teacher may more readily make modifications in the items to be dealt with in each year of the course, and further, a first-year student may be given a glimpse of the road that lies ahead. In addition, a second-year student has easy reference to earlier work for purposes of revision.

The problems of the part-time student have been particularly borne in mind during the preparation of this book. Numbers of worked examples have been included at frequent intervals throughout the book, and it is hoped that these, together with the questions for solution at the ends of the chapters, will be of assistance to those students whose work must be done with a minimum of tutorial guidance. Such students should also be encouraged to consolidate work covered during lectures by reading the appropriate parts of the book in the periods between attendances at college. The book will be of use, too, in the increasing number of secondary schools which are including engineering science in their curriculum.

From time to time, several references are made to suggested laboratory work. These suggestions are of course far from being exhaustive, but are made to emphasize to the student the importance of a practical approach to a problem wherever possible. Engineering science is by its very nature an eminently practical subject, and any course involving its study must inevitably include a considerable amount of practical work. It is hoped that some of the suggestions made may be helpful in the development of such work which, to be successful, must be both instructive and interesting.

The units used throughout the book have followed the definitions given in *The International System* (SI) *Units*, BS 3763: 1964.

Grateful acknowledgements are due to the Northern Counties Technical Examinations Council, the East Midland Educational Union, the Union of Lancashire and Cheshire Institutes, the Union of Educational Institutions, and the Surrey County Council Education Committee for permission to use questions taken from their respective examination papers at the appropriate level. These questions have been modified where necessary into SI units and therefore are not now acknowledged individually.

The author also gladly makes acknowledgement to his colleagues, both past and present. The subject-presentation in this book has been developed during several years of teaching experience, and ideas gained during discussions with colleagues will naturally have been woven into the general fabric of this experience. Finally, the author would like to express his appreciation of the encouragement given to him by Dr. T. Siklos, and of the ready help given by the publishers.

1961   G. R. A. TITCOMB

1. Introduction

This book is intended to introduce the student to the fundamental principles on which engineering is based. The aim has been to present these principles in such a way that a secure foundation may be laid for more advanced studies later. It is quite possible that some of the theory covered here will already have been encountered by the student, but no apologies are made for this. It is essential that a firm grasp of basic principles is obtained before specialized and advanced work is attempted, and these basic principles cannot be repeated too often. Engineering offers a fascinating and worthwhile career, and requires people of many different talents. It is not easy to become a good engineer, but that should be one of the main attractions of the profession. It is the sincere wish of the author that this book may help some students a little way along the road towards their qualifications, and towards an understanding of an interesting and vital subject.

In broad terms science deals with the interpretation and measurement of observed facts. It can be considered to have three main sections, Physics, Chemistry and Biology, with the science of Mathematics threading them all together. There is no firm division between the sections, and a specialist in one field should have at least a background knowledge of the others.

Physics deals with the properties of inert materials, with the way in which such materials react under certain conditions, and with the relationships between the various forms of energy.

Chemistry deals with the composition of materials, with the way in which materials may combine, and with the various methods of producing them.

Biology deals with the properties of living things, with growth of all kinds, and with the various reactions that take place during the life-cycle.

Engineering science covers those aspects of science which are, or may be, applied in some branch of engineering, and so includes mainly physical science, with some chemistry. There are some engineering applications in which a knowledge of biology is required, but these are rather specialized and will not be included in this book.

There are three main branches of engineering, each of which has its own Engineering Institution, whose object is to promote the general advancement of engineering science, and its applications. These three major professional bodies are: The Institution of Civil Engineers, The Institution of Mechanical Engineers and The Institution of Electrical Engineers. Each is incorporated by Royal Charter, and fulfils a major role of service to the engineering profession and to the community at large.

The more specialized branches of engineering, each of which could be considered as a sub-division of one of the main branches, also have separate Institutions. They include those for Building, Chemical Engineering, Metallurgy, Mining, Production Engineering, Structural Engineering, Aeronautical Engineering, Radio Engineering, Marine Engineering and Engineering Inspection. This list is given to indicate the vast range of engineering and the importance of engineering science, which can be taken as the starting point for them all.

The study of engineering science can be taken as following several parallel paths, and, in general, progress along one path depends on equivalent progress along another. Consequently, although this book has collected together certain sections into convenient chapters or series of chapters, it is not intended that the order of study should necessarily be that in which the chapters are written. The material in the book will usually be dealt with during two years of study, but the first-year student who is interested to see 'what comes next' may like to read on beyond a particular section. Indeed, it is hoped that many will do this, and so gain a broad picture of the field before studying the work in more detail.

Roughly, the work can be divided into mechanical engineering science and electrical engineering science, and diagram 1 shows an outline of the scope of this book in the form of the roots of a tree. These roots are far-spread, and the student should note that whatever specialized 'fruits' are required, they all depend on the same roots in the same soil. For example, the mechanical engineer whose electrical knowledge is weak is a less effective engineer than one who appreciates the broad principles and potentialities of electrical engineering. Similarly, the electrical engineer who does not understand the basic principles of mechanical engineering cannot be considered to be a true engineer. As engineering spreads into more and more specialized fields it is essential that a solid, broad foundation is laid before the student engineer embarks on these specialized studies.

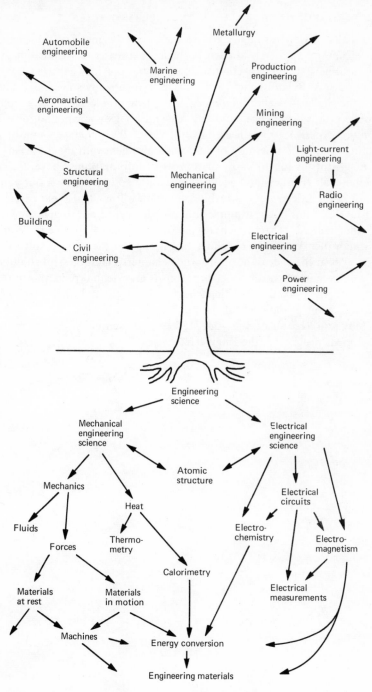

1. Some of the aspects of engineering and engineering science

Finally, a word of advice before the course begins. Try to develop an engineer's approach to each problem as it arises. Assemble all the known relevant facts, together with any useful previous experience you may possess. Relate the new problem to those already solved, and find out the similarities and differences. If the new problem is outside your own previous experience, read any relevant books you can find, or ask a more experienced engineer. Do not forget the immense value of a library, and do not hesitate to discuss the problem with the librarian— it is part of his job to know of sources of information. Above all, be methodical. Neatness and accuracy generally go together. Set out your work in an orderly, logical fashion, and you will tend to avoid careless mistakes. In this book, examples are shown worked out to give a guide to the method of approach to particular types of problem. Work through them carefully, checking each step, and then try to solve the examples at the end of the appropriate chapter. The successful solution of a large number of these set problems is an essential preparation for the time when practical problems have to be faced, and when there will be no answer at the back of the book.

May you have success in your studies, and eventually join the ranks of a great profession, the Engineers.

2. Fundamental Quantities and Units

There are at least three quantities whose existence is apparent without the aid of any instruments. They can be measured in a rather crude way by the human senses alone, and must have been known to mankind for a very long time indeed. They can be thought of as fundamental, or basic, quantities.

The first of these is LENGTH, and no instruments are needed to prove that a man's fingers are not all of the same length, or that it is not possible to touch a distant object just by stretching out an arm. Lengths could be measured by being compared with any length chosen as a standard. For example, the length of a path between two points could be measured by the number of strides required to walk between them, or by the number of times it was longer than, say, the length of an arm.

The second fundamental quantity is MASS, or the amount of material in an object. Once again, no instruments are required for anyone to reach the conclusion that the body of a fully-grown adult contains more mass than that of a newly-born baby, or that a large boulder contains more mass than a pebble. Masses can be measured by comparing them with any mass chosen as a standard, and this will usually mean comparing masses by comparing them using the earth's gravitational force. The mass of a body is not affected by changes in its shape or volume, or by any external considerations. It is a measure of the actual quantity of material in it.

The third quantity is TIME. In normal situations, it is possible to distinguish one event from a later event by the passage of time between them. Again, time can be measured by comparison with some standard time interval, such as the length of the day between sunrise and sunset, although this is not a very accurate method since the length of the day is itself not a constant time interval.

The units in which each of these quantities may be measured will be discussed in the following sections. Once these units have been established, it will be possible to proceed to base units for other quantities on them. The majority (although not all) of the units used for the measurement of quantities in science may be derived from the units used for these three fundamental quantities.

2.1. Length

The basic standard of length is the METRE (m), which was originally based on the length of the northern quadrant of the earth, the metre being taken as one ten-millionth part of this length. The metre is now measured against a standard platinum-iridium bar kept at the International Bureau of Weights and Measures at Sèvres in France. (There is a more complicated definition for exact scientific work, but it is not given here as it depends on more advanced principles.) Subdivisions or multiples of the metre are all defined with reference to simple powers of 10, and so are very conveniently associated with the decimal system. The same prefixes are used, with the same meanings, throughout the metric system, and should be remembered, as they are very frequently used in scientific measurements. These prefixes, with their standard symbols and meanings, are given in the table on page 747. Thus a millimetre (mm) is $\frac{1}{1000}$th of a metre, or 10^{-3} m, while a kilometre (km) is 1000 metres, or 10^3 m, and so on.

2.2. Mass

The basic unit of mass is the KILOGRAMME (kg). The spelling given is correct for this French word, but some English-speaking countries (notably U.S.A.) use the shorter form kilogram. This unit again measures mass by reference to a standard platinum-iridium mass of one kilogramme, kept at Sèvres.

Multiples and sub-multiples (strictly, of the gramme) follow the usual metric system. The gramme was the original mass unit, defined as the mass of water contained in a volume of one millilitre, but the kilogramme is now taken as the standard.

2.3. Time

The basic unit of time is the SECOND (s), which is taken to be $\frac{1}{86\,400}$th part of the mean (or average) solar day. (1 day = 24 × 60 × 60 = 86 400 s.)

It is interesting that the committee which set up the basic metric system in France in 1793 also put forward a 'metric time system' of 10 'hours' a day, with 100 'minutes' in an 'hour', and 100 'seconds' in a 'minute'. This system never came into extensive use, however.

The multiples of seconds—i.e. minutes, hours and so on—are well known, but the student should note that the sub-multiple prefixes of the metric system are often used for time intervals of less than a second; for example, 1 milli-second (ms) is $\frac{1}{1000}$th, or 10^{-3} s, and 1 micro-second (μs) is $\frac{1}{1\,000\,000}$th, or 10^{-6} s.

2.4. Derived units

The majority of units used in all measurements can be derived from the fundamental units defined above. Thus a complete system of units can be specified in terms of the units used for length, mass and time.

The derived units will be discussed as the quantities to be measured by them are introduced, but some of the familiar ones can be quickly dealt with now.

Any area is measured as the product of two lengths, although the relationship between an area and its easily-measured linear dimensions may be complicated. (A linear dimension is one that can be measured in a straight line.) It can thus be said that an area has the 'dimensions' of (length) × (length), or (length)^2, and so is measured in 'squared' length units.

Therefore, with the length unit of the metre (m), the unit of area is the 'squared metre' (or 'square metre'), which is abbreviated to m^2.

Any volume is basically measured as the product of three lengths, although again the actual relationship with the linear dimensions may be complicated. Thus a volume has the dimensions of (length) × (length) × (length); that is (length)^3—and so is measured in 'cubed' length units, i.e. the unit of volume is the cubed metre (or cubic metre) abbreviated to m^3.

The LITRE (l) may also be used as a unit of volume, particularly of liquids where lm^3 = 1000 litre. The litre is defined as containing 1 kg of distilled water at stated temperature and pressure.

2.5. Force and mass

The presence of a force can be detected by means of its effects. A force can be exerted to lift something, or to start it moving, or stop it from moving. A force can deflect a moving object, or make it move faster or slower. A force can bend or even break an object, or can compress or stretch it. A precise, scientific definition of a force can only really be based on the results of measuring one or more of its effects, and so such a definition will be left until this measurement is discussed in more detail (see Chapter 9, page 262). For the time being, a force may be defined as that which will have any of the effects mentioned above. The force may be exerted naturally or it may be brought about by some deliberate action. Much of engineering is concerned with the production of a force which may be exerted in a particular way and in a particular direction to fulfil a certain purpose. A force may sometimes be one of attraction, tending to bring two objects closer together, and sometimes it may be one of repulsion, tending to separate the two objects.

The earth exerts a natural force of attraction on any mass of material placed on or near it. This is only one special instance of the general force of attraction that exists between any two objects, although the reason for it is not yet fully understood. The force of attraction depends on the masses of the two objects concerned, and on the distance between them. It can be shown that the force F between two masses m_1 and m_2, which are a distance d apart, is given by

$$F = K \frac{m_1 \ m_2}{d^2} \qquad . \qquad . \qquad . \qquad \text{(i)}$$

where K is a constant. It is extremely small between any two objects normally encountered on a human scale. The force exerted by the earth is large only because of its own very large mass. The force of attraction between objects is known as a GRAVITATIONAL force, and it is such gravitational forces that maintain planets and other celestial bodies in their relative positions.

The gravitational force, or force due to 'gravity', exerted on a mass by the earth is often used to 'weigh' the mass. Since the gravitational force of the earth on an object at any one point is directly proportional to the mass of the object, it follows that the gravitational forces on different objects *at any one point on the earth* are proportional to the masses of those objects. For example, if one body has twice the mass of another body it will experience twice the gravitational force, so that a comparison of the gravitational forces on the bodies at any one point on the earth will give a comparison of the masses of the bodies. Alternatively the gravitational force on a body will extend a spring. If a mass is hung from the end of a supported spring the gravitational force on the mass will extend the spring. The extension of the spring can be calibrated so that the mass (kg) of the body can be read from the scale.

The gravitational force exerted by the earth on a given mass is not constant at all points on the earth's surface. For many purposes, this difference in force is negligible, but in order to avoid any variation in the *unit* of force, a 'standard' gravitational environment is defined. This standard gravity or standard acceleration is internationally accepted as 9·806 65 m/s² or approximately 9·81 m/s².

The unit of force called the NEWTON (N) is that force which when applied to a body having a mass of one kilogramme gives it an acceleration of one metre per second squared (1 m/s²). From this definition it follows that when a mass of one kilogramme is under the standard acceleration of 9·81 m/s², a gravitational force of 9·81 N is acting. The gravitational force on a mass of 2 kg is 19·62 N or, in general, the forces due to gravity on different objects at any one point on the earth are proportional to the masses of those objects. At other places, where the gravitational conditions are not the same as those arbitrarily chosen as standard, the gravitational force will be different but it should be noted that the mass of a body remains constant.

2.6. Force and pressure

In a non-scientific discussion, the terms 'force' and 'pressure' are often taken to mean the same thing. However, these terms have *different* meanings for scientific purposes.

The PRESSURE on a surface, or, more exactly, the INTENSITY OF PRESSURE on a surface, is measured by the FORCE PER UNIT AREA of the surface, with the area being measured at right angles to the direction of the force.

Thus, if a force of 1000 N acts at right angles to a surface having an area of 5 m², the pressure on the surface is given by

$$\text{pressure} = \frac{\text{force}}{\text{area at right angles to the force}} \qquad \text{(ii)}$$

$$= \frac{1000 \text{ N}}{5 \text{ m}^2}$$

$$= 200 \frac{\text{N}}{\text{m}^2}$$

The units of pressure are, then, those of the units of force divided by the units of area. This is referred to as 'force unit PER area unit'. For example, the above answer would be given as 200 newtons per square metre, which is usually written as 200 N/m².

This unit of PRESSURE N/m², has no SI name. It is felt by many that to give it a name would facilitate its use, and the name Pascal (Pa) is used in France. Multiple or sub-multiple units of either are also used, for example, 1000 N/m² = 1 kN/m² = 1 kPa.

Examples

(i) A force of 80 N acts uniformly over an area of 4 m². What is the pressure on the area?

$$\text{Pressure} = \frac{\text{force}}{\text{area at right angles}}$$

$$= \frac{80 \text{ N}}{4 \text{ m}^2}$$

$$= 20 \text{ N/m}^2$$

(ii) A young lady having a mass of 50 kg places her full force on the heel of one shoe. If the heel has an area of 50 mm² (approximately equivalent to an 8 mm diameter circle) find

(a) the force on the surface on which she stands

(b) the pressure on the surface on which she stands.

(a) The force on the surface

= gravitational force on the lady

= 50 (kg) × 9·81 (m/s²)

= 490·5 N

(b) The pressure on the surface

$$= \frac{\text{force}}{\text{area at right angles}}$$

$$= \frac{490 \cdot 5 \text{ N}}{50 \text{ mm}^2}$$

= 9·81 N/mm²

Since 1 000 000 mm² = 1 m²

= 9 810 000 N/m²

or 9·81 MN/m²

This example is intended to illustrate the difference between force and pressure. A force of 490 N is not a particularly large one, and most men could be expected to be able to lift a mass having a force equal to this. However, the pressure on the surface is high, and is enough to cause physical damage to such surfaces as a wooden floor. (Evidence of this can be seen on many floors, thanks to the dictates of fashion in ladies' shoes.)

(iii) The average pressure on a dam 45 m long is 40 kN/m² when the depth of the water is 8 m. Find the total force on the side of the dam, assuming it to be vertical where it is in contact with the water.

$$\text{Pressure} = \frac{\text{force}}{\text{area at right angles}}$$

$$\therefore\ 40\ 000\ \text{N/m}^2 = \frac{\text{force N}}{45 \times 8\ \text{m}^2}$$

$$\text{or} \qquad \text{force} = 40\ 000\ \frac{\text{N}}{\text{m}^2} \times 45 \times 8\text{m}^2$$

$$= 14\ 400\ 000\ \text{N}$$

$$= \underline{\underline{14\text{·}4\ \text{MN}}}$$

(iv) A force of 1 kN acts vertically downwards along a tapering rod as shown in diagram 2. The rod has a circular cross-section, and has a diameter of 50 mm at the top surface and 100 mm at the bottom surface. Find the pressure on (a) the top surface and on (b) the bottom surface.

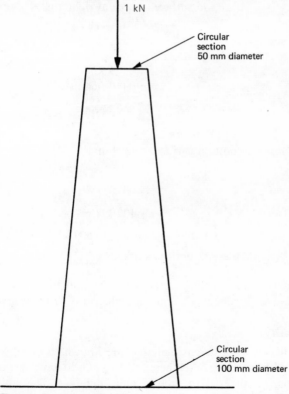

1 kN

Circular
section
50 mm diameter

Circular
section
100 mm diameter

2. Change of pressure caused by constant force—numerical example

The area of the top surface, on which the force acts at right angles, is

$$\frac{\pi}{4} \times (\text{diameter})^2$$

$$= \frac{\pi}{4} \times (50)^2 \text{ mm}^2$$

$$= 1964 \text{ mm}^2$$

The area of the bottom surface, also at right angles to the direction of the force,

$$= \frac{\pi}{4} \times (100)^2 \text{ mm}^2$$

$$= 7854 \text{ mm}^2$$

$$\text{Then pressure at top surface} = \frac{\text{force}}{\text{area at right angles}}$$

$$= \frac{1 \text{ kN}}{1964 \text{ mm}^2}$$

$$= \frac{1 \text{ kN}}{0 \cdot 001\ 964 \text{ m}^2}$$

$$= 509 \text{ kN/m}^2$$

$$\text{Pressure at bottom surface} = \frac{1 \text{ kN}}{7854 \text{ mm}^2}$$

$$= \frac{1 \text{ kN}}{0 \cdot 007\ 854 \text{ m}^2}$$

$$= 127 \text{ kN/m}^2$$

$$\text{Pressure at top surface} = \underline{509 \text{ kN/m}^2}$$

$$\text{Pressure at bottom surface} = \underline{127 \text{ kN/m}^2}$$

Note that the same force is responsible for both these two different pressures. The larger the area, the less the pressure for a given force.

2.7. Density

Equal masses of different materials are known to occupy different volumes. Although 1 kg of feathers and 1 kg of lead have the same mass, the volume of material in each is quite different. This ability of a material to 'pack' more, or less, mass into a given volume is measured by what is called its DENSITY. The density of a material is the mass of material in unit volume.

Thus, the density of a material is given by the equation:

$$\text{density} = \frac{\text{mass of material}}{\text{volume occupied by the material}} \qquad \text{(iii)}$$

The units of density will be 'mass units per volume unit'. Density is fundamentally measured in KILOGRAMMES PER CUBIC METRE (kg/m^3), although, again, other units such as g/ml^3 may also be used.

Since the density of a material depends on its volume, and the volume of a substance changes with change in temperature, the temperature at which a quoted value of density was determined should also be stated. With most solids and liquids, however, the changes in volume, and hence changes in density, are fairly small over a normal range of temperature.

2.8. Relative density

It is often necessary to appreciate the 'heaviness' of one material relative to another and therefore it is usual to compare the density of any substance with the density of water expressed in the same units.

This is known as the 'relative density' of the substance. It may be defined as the ratio:

$$\frac{\text{relative density}}{\text{of substance}} = \frac{\text{density of substance}}{\text{density of water (in the same units)}} \qquad \text{(iv)}$$

Relative density is thus a number, and has no units. Since, however, the density of water is 1 g/ml, 1 kg/l or 1 tonne/m³ (where 1 tonne = 1000 kg), the relative density of a substance is numerically equal to its density expressed in these units.

Examples

(i) The density of aluminium is 2550 kg/m³, and that of water is 1000 kg/m³. Find the relative density of aluminium.

$$\frac{\text{Relative density}}{\text{of aluminium}} = \frac{\text{density of aluminium}}{\text{density of water}}$$

$$= \frac{2550}{1000}$$

$$= 2\cdot55$$

(ii) Given that the relative density of lead is 11·3 and that the density of water is 1000 kg/m³, find the density of lead.

$$\text{Relative density of lead} = \frac{\text{density of lead}}{\text{density of water}}$$

$$\text{or } 11\cdot3 = \frac{\text{density of lead}}{1000 \text{ kg/m}^3}$$

$$\text{or density of lead} = 11\cdot3 \times 1000 \text{ kg/m}^3$$
$$= 11\ 300 \text{ kg/m}^3$$

Note that the relative density of a substance indicates the number of times that a given volume of the substance is heavier than an equal volume of water. It follows that substances whose relative density is greater than 1 will sink if placed in water, while those whose relative density is less than 1 will float in water. For example lead, as seen above, has a relative density of 11·3 and so will sink in water, while cork has a relative density of 0·25, and will float in water (see Section 15.6, page 427).

2.9. Determination of density and relative density

The density and relative density of a substance may be determined experimentally by measurement of the mass and volume of a sample of the substance. Usually the mass can readily be found by the use of some form of balance, and the volume may be measured in one of several ways.

If the sample is of regular shape, its volume can be calculated from measurement of its linear dimensions, such as the length, breadth and height of a rectangular block; the diameter and length of a cylindrical block; or the diameter of a sphere. If the sample has an irregular shape, and will sink in water, its volume may be found by partly filling a measuring cylinder with water, noting the volume of water in the cylinder from the scale on its side, and then inserting the sample. The sample, in sinking in the water, will raise the water level by an amount corresponding to the volume of the solid. Therefore, a new reading of volume from the scale on the side of the measuring cylinder will enable the volume of the sample to be calculated. If the sample is too big to go into the measuring cylinder, a suitable vessel may be filled to the brim with water, so that when the sample is placed in the vessel, water spills over the sides. This water is caught and measured in a measuring cylinder, and gives the volume of the sample direct. If the sample floats in water, a small piece of heavier material, whose volume has first been found in the way already described, may be tied to the sample with cotton (whose volume is negligible), so that sample and added mass will sink together. The volume of the added mass can then be subtracted from the total result obtained. Of course, if the sample is a liquid, its volume can be determined direct in the measuring cylinder.

Example

A quantity of lead shot was found to have a mass of 100 g. When placed in a measuring cylinder partly full of water, the water level rose from a reading of 80 ml to a reading of 88·8 ml. Estimate the density and relative density of the lead.

$$\text{Volume of lead shot} = 88\cdot8 - 80 \text{ ml} = 8\cdot8 \text{ ml}$$
$$\text{Mass of lead shot} = 100 \text{ g}$$

$$\text{Density of lead} = \frac{\text{mass}}{\text{volume}} = \frac{100 \text{ g}}{8\cdot8 \text{ ml}}$$

$$= \underline{\underline{11\cdot4 \text{ g/ml}}}$$

$$\text{Relative density of lead} = \frac{\text{density of lead}}{\text{density of water}}$$

$$= \frac{11\cdot4 \text{ g/ml}}{1 \text{ g/ml}}$$

$$= \underline{\underline{11\cdot4}}$$

2.10. The conversion of units

Now that the basic units and some of their derived units have been dealt with, conversion of a measurement in terms of one unit into a measurement in terms of another unit can be discussed. The system suggested here may seem a little cumbersome at first, but even if it is not written down in detail as given, and as used in this book, the thought processes required are the same for any method of conversion, and much confusion—and many wrong answers—can be avoided by the use of this system. The whole idea of the method is based on the use of 'unity brackets'. For a very simple example, suppose it is required to express a length of 2 km in metres. The 'conversion relationship' required here is that

$$1 \text{ km} = 1000 \text{ m}$$

B

Since these two are equal, it follows that the bracketed expression $\left(\dfrac{1000 \text{ m}}{1 \text{ km}}\right)$ has a value of 1, or unity. Since the value of any number is unchanged if it is multiplied by 1, the original length given may be written as

$$2 \text{ km} = 2 \text{ km} \times \left(\frac{1000 \text{ m}}{1 \text{ km}}\right)$$

The km units may now be thought to cancel, so that the result, written out in full, would be

$$2 \text{ km} = 2 \text{ k̶m̶} \times \left(\frac{1000 \text{ m}}{1 \text{ k̶m̶}}\right)$$
$$= 2 \times 1000 \text{ m}$$
$$= \underline{\underline{2000 \text{ m}}}$$

The method may quite safely be extended to any number of unit conversions, with any amount of complications, and the whole advantage of the method is that it makes clear 'which way up' the conversion factor should be applied.

Small numbers, as well as large numbers, are often more conveniently expressed in 'standard form' than in decimals alone. For example, the last answer can be re-written as

$$2000 \text{ m} = \underline{\underline{2 \times 10^3 \text{ m}}}$$

A number written in standard form becomes a number between 1 and 10, which is multiplied by some power of 10.

As further examples,

$$0 \cdot 000\ 000\ 001\ 45 = \frac{1 \cdot 45}{1\ 000\ 000\ 000} = \frac{1 \cdot 45}{10^9} = 1 \cdot 45 \times 10^{-9}$$
$$86\ 500\ 000 = 8 \cdot 65 \times 10\ 000\ 000 = 8 \cdot 65 \times 10^7$$

The negative power of 10 is always numerically one more than the number of '0's after the decimal point.

The positive power of 10 is always numerically one less than the total number of figures in front of the decimal point.

Examples

(i) Express 60 km/h in m/s.

Use the conversion relationships:

$$1 \text{ km} = 1000 \text{ m}$$
$$1 \text{ hr} = 60 \text{ min} = 3600 \text{ s}$$

so that

$$60 \text{ km/h} = 60 \ \frac{\text{km}}{\text{h}} \times \left(\frac{1000 \text{ m}}{1 \text{ km}}\right) \times \left(\frac{1 \text{ h}}{3600 \text{ s}}\right)$$

$$= 60 \times 1000 \times \frac{1}{3600} \ \frac{\text{m}}{\text{s}}$$

$$= 16\cdot667 \text{ m/s}$$

$$\simeq \underline{\underline{16\cdot7 \text{ m/s}}}$$

(ii) Express 200 rev/min into radians/second
    Use the conversion relationships:
$$1 \text{ rev} = 2\pi \text{ rad}$$
$$1 \text{ min} = 60 \text{ s}$$

so that

$$200 \text{ rev/min} = 200 \ \frac{\text{rev}}{\text{min}} \times \left(\frac{2\pi \text{ rad}}{1 \text{ rev}}\right) \times \left(\frac{1 \text{ min}}{60 \text{ s}}\right)$$

$$= 200 \times 2\pi \times \frac{1}{60} \text{ rad/s}$$

$$= \underline{\underline{20\cdot94 \text{ rad/s}}}$$

Further examples of this system are given throughout the worked examples in this book, and as other conversion relationships are established.

CHAPTER SUMMARY

The basic units, from which nearly all others can be derived, are those of length, mass and time.

For the International system (SI), these units are:

METRE, KILOGRAMME, SECOND

Areas are measured in squared length units; e.g. m^2.

Volumes are measured in cubed length units; e.g. m^3.

Alternative volume units may be used, especially for liquids; e.g. litre.

The gravitational force on a body is the measure of the force of attraction exerted on its mass by the earth.

This force on a given body will vary slightly depending on where it is measured, because of variation in the gravitational force of attraction at different points on or near the earth's surface.

Forces are measured in NEWTON (N). The gravitational force on a mass of 1 kg is 9·81 N.

Pressure is force per unit area at right angles to direction of force. In other words,

$$\text{pressure} = \frac{\text{force}}{\text{area at right angles}}$$

Typical units are N/m^2, kN/mm^2.

Density is mass per unit volume. In other words,

$$\text{density} = \frac{\text{mass}}{\text{volume}}$$

Typical units are kg/m^3, g/ml.

$$\text{Relative density of a material} = \frac{\text{density of material}}{\text{density of water}}$$

(both in the same units).

QUESTIONS

1. What is meant by the statement that the relative density of aluminium is 2·7? Describe an experiment to find the relative density of aluminium.

Calculate the mass of 1 m^3 of aluminium given that 1 m^3 of water has a mass of 1000 kg.

2. (a) The density of water is 1000 kg/m^3. An aluminium bar is 1·600 m long with a rectangular section 25 mm by 6 mm. Calculate the mass of the bar.

(Relative density of aluminium = 2·7).

(b) A relative density bottle has a mass of 70 g when empty, 105 g when filled with water, and 104 g when filled with another liquid. What is (i) the capacity of the bottle, and (ii) the relative density of the liquid?

3. Mercury has a relative density of 13·6. If the density of water is 1000 kg/m^3 what is the mass of 2 litres of mercury?

4. A cubical tank of 400 mm length of side is filled with oil. Calculate the mass of the oil of relative density 0·75, given that the density of water is 1000 kg/m^3.

5. The internal diameter of a cylindrical tank is 350 mm. It contains 2 litres of oil having a density of 0·8 g/ml.

Determine (a) the height of the oil in mm, (b) the mass of the oil in grams.

6. Two cylindrical rods have the same mass. One is made of iron and is 375 mm long, and the other is made of copper and is 225 mm long. If the diameter of the iron rod is 22 mm, find the diameter of the copper rod correct to three significant figures. The density of iron is 7200 kg/m^3, and of copper is 8800 kg/m^3.

7. Describe in detail how you would determine the relative density of a specimen of iron of irregular shape.

8. A relative density bottle has a mass of 80 g when empty and 125 g when filled with water. When carefully dried, and filled with oil, it is found to have a mass of 116 g. What is the relative density of the oil? If the density of water is 1 g/ml, what is the density of the oil in kg/m^3?

3. Vectors

3.1. Scalar and vector quantities

Quantities dealt with in problems in science and engineering can be placed into two broad groups—SCALAR quantities and VECTOR quantities. A scalar quantity is one which possesses a magnitude only, and no other information is required to specify it. Examples of scalar quantities are the three fundamental quantities of length, mass and time. A vector quantity is one which possesses both a magnitude and a *direction*, and both must be stated in order to specify it completely. Examples of vector quantities are the movement of a body (in a particular direction), or the force acting on a body (again, in a particular direction).

It is often useful to represent quantities graphically; that is, by lines on a drawing. These lines may be used either to enable a problem to be visualized more clearly, or to assist in calculations involved in its solution.

Any scalar quantity may be represented by the length of a line, drawn to some suitable scale. For example, the two time intervals of 10 s and 1 min could be represented by the lengths of two lines. If drawn to the same scale, these give a visual image of the relative magnitudes of the time intervals. Two such lines, together with the scale used, are shown in diagram 3.

The magnitude of a vector quantity can be represented graphically in the same way, by the length of a line drawn to some chosen scale. As has been said, however, this alone does not completely specify such a quantity, since some method of representing its direction is also required. Provided that its direction is PLANAR, that is, that it can be thought of as pointing along a flat surface or PLANE, the direction of a vector quantity can be conveniently represented by the direction of the line drawn to represent it. Such a line, whose length and direction give a graphical representation of a vector quantity, is usually called a 'plane vector', or, more simply, a 'vector'.

However, the directions of some vector quantities are not planar. For example, the end of one of the blades of a ship's propeller would follow a spiral path as the ship moved through the water, and this cannot be accurately represented by a line drawn on a plane such as a flat piece of paper. (Of course, the idea of perspective, which the artist uses when he paints, does make a three-dimensional picture possible.)

For the present, attention will be confined to planar vectors like

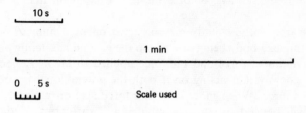

3. Graphical representation of scalar quantities

that drawn in diagram 4 to represent the path of a boat on a lake. The length of the vector in this case represents the distance moved along the path in a given time, while the inclination of the vector, and the arrowhead on the end, shows the direction of the movement. The length of

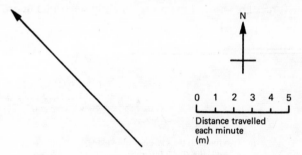

4. Plane vector representing movement of a boat on a lake

the vector is drawn to a scale of distance moved in 1 min. The direction of the vector indicates that the movement is in a north-westerly direction. (Note the length scale, and the 'direction scale' given by the compass direction.)

3.2.   Force vectors. Vector addition

Force is a vector quantity. It is necessary to specify not only the magnitude of a force, but also the direction in which it acts. For example, the gravitational force exerted on the mass of a body, which is known as the weight of the body, acts towards the centre of the earth. For most purposes this can be thought of as acting vertically downwards. If the body is to be lifted upwards, a force must be applied vertically upwards to overcome the gravitational force. If the body is to be moved sideways, a force must be exerted on it in a sideways direction.

Quite frequently, a body may be acted on by a number of forces. For example, a body being lifted from the ground has acting on it both the gravitational force and the force applied to lift it. A body being moved sideways has acting on it both the gravitational force and the sideways force. When more than one force acts on a body, the final result will depend on the magnitudes and directions of the forces being applied. The body will tend to move as if only one RESULTANT force were being applied.

Three special cases may be considered for any two forces acting on the same body.

(a) *Force in the same direction along the same line of action*

This condition is shown in diagram 5 (a), where the vectors representing the forces are shown drawn very slightly separated in order that

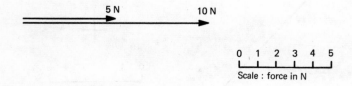

5 N   10 N

0 1 2 3 4 5

Scale : force in N

(a) Two forces in the same direction along
the same line of action

5 (a)

they may be distinguished from one another. They are to be taken as acting along the same line, through the same point in the body.

In this case, the magnitude of the resultant force is simply the arithmetical sum of the separate forces, since any effect caused by one force adds directly to the effect of the other. For the case shown, the magnitude of the resultant force would be $R = 5 + 10 = 15$ N, and the body would behave as if a single force of 15 N were being applied in the same direction as the two 'component' forces.

(b) *Forces in opposite directions along the same line of action*

This condition is shown in diagram 5 (b).

In this case, the effects of the forces are in opposition, and the magnitude of the resultant force will be the arithmetical difference between the two forces. For the case shown, the magnitude of the resultant force is $R = 10 - 5 = 5$ N, and the body would behave as if a single force of 5 N were being applied in the direction of the larger force.

The results of (a) and (b) can be combined if they are expressed in algebraic terms. The direction of a force along a given line of action can be represented as 'positive' or 'negative', with respect to an assumed direction taken as reference. Thus, if the reference, or positive

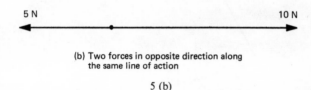

5 N   10 N

(b) Two forces in opposite direction along
the same line of action

5 (b)

direction of the forces shown in diagrams 5 (a) and (b), is taken as being from left to right along the line of action shown, the forces in (a) could be written as $+ 5$ N and $+ 10$ N respectively. The forces in (b) would then be $- 5$ N and $+ 10$ N respectively.

The magnitude of the resultant force in each case is then given by the algebraic sum of the two component forces (i.e. the sum obtained by taking their individual signs into account).

For case (a) $R = (+ 5) + (+ 10) = + 15$ N
and for case (b) $R = (- 5) + (+ 10) = + 5$ N

The magnitudes are seen to be the same as before, although now the sign of the resultant also gives its direction along the line of action (i.e. from left to right in each case, since R is positive for each).

(c) *Forces not having the same line of action*

This condition is shown in diagram 5 (c).

In this case, the resultant force cannot be calculated by simple arithmetical or algebraic means.

Although it can be calculated by mathematical methods (see Section 3.11, page 71), such methods require slightly more advanced mathematical techniques. In any case, the method given here is in itself of very great practical importance, and should be thoroughly mastered and practised.

The magnitude and direction of the resultant force in cases where different lines of action are involved can be found as follows. This method can also be justified experimentally as will be suggested later. Suppose the body on which the forces act is free to move. It is then reasonable to suppose that the distance moved in a given time will be proportional to the force exerted (this can be proved to be true for a smooth body on a smooth, flat horizontal surface). The position of the

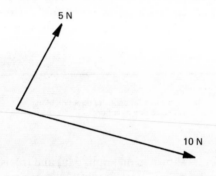

(c) Two forces having different lines of action

5 (c)

body after a given time will depend on the distance moved in that time under the action of the resultant force. It can therefore be thought of as the resultant position due to each force acting in turn for the given length of time.

Supposing the 10 N force acts first, on its own, for the given time. The body will move in the direction of the 10 N force through a distance proportional to this force, as shown by the movement vector ab in diagram 5 (d). If the 5 N force now acts, on its own, for the same given time, the body will move in the direction of the 5 N force through a distance proportional to this force, as shown by the movement vector bc in diagram 5 (d). The position of the body, now at c, is the same as it would have been if it had travelled along the line ac under the action of a force whose value is proportional to the length ac. Since all distances on this diagram will be in the same proportion to the forces responsible, the diagram may be scaled directly in N as shown. This method is known as the VECTOR ADDITION of the two forces, and the

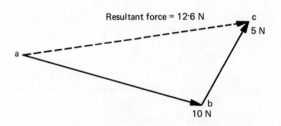

(d) Vector addition of forces having different
lines of action

5 (d)

resultant is known as their VECTOR SUM. Note that the component force vectors are drawn head to tail, and that the direction of the resultant is a to c; i.e. from 'start to finish' of the components.

This method of vector addition by scale drawing gives both the magnitude and the direction of the resultant vector.

Note that the vector sum of two vectors will always be different from their arithmetical or algebraic sum unless the vectors have the same line of action.

Example

Two forces act at a point at the same time. Their magnitudes and directions are indicated in the force vector diagram 6 (a). Use a graphical method to find the magnitude and direction of their resultant force.

The 'triangle of forces' used to find the resultant force is shown in diagram 6 (b). The same answer is obtained whichever force is taken to start with, as is shown in diagram 6 (c).

If diagrams 6 (b) and (c) are compared, it will be seen that the resultant is the diagonal of a parallelogram drawn with the two force vectors as adjacent sides. This may be referred to as the 'parallelogram of forces' for this case, and it is drawn in full in diagram 6 (d) for comparison. Note that diagram 6 (b) represents the triangle to the right of the resultant here, while diagram 6 (c) represents the triangle to the left of the resultant.

The parallelogram of forces may sometimes be preferred to the triangle of forces, since it enables the component forces to be drawn along their actual lines of action. (In the triangle of forces, one of the

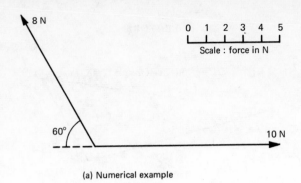

(a) Numerical example

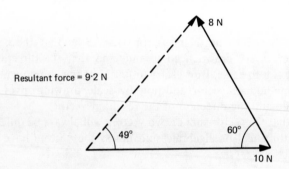

Resultant force = 9·2 N

(b) Triangle of forces to find resultant of forces
given in (a)

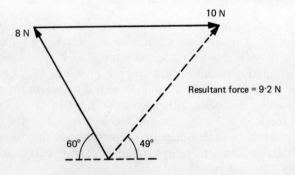

Resultant force = 9·2 N

(c) Alternative triangle of forces giving the same
result as (b)

6 (a, b, c)

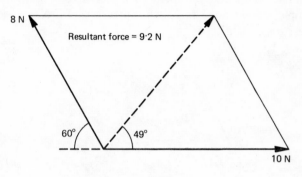

(d) Parallelogram of forces for the forces
shown in (a)

6 (d)

forces must be drawn parallel to its actual line of action, but at a distance from it.)

3.3. Subtraction of vectors

It may also be necessary to find the difference between two forces represented by vectors. As with vector addition, the process is a simple algebraic one for vectors having the same line of action. In diagram 5 (a), which is re-drawn here for convenience, it is seen that the difference between these two forces is given by $(+10) - (+5) = 5$ N. This

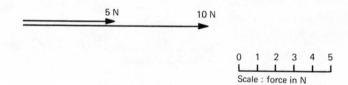

(a) Two forces in the same direction along
the same line of action

5 (a). Positive direction taken from left to right

is the same result as that given by the vector addition of opposing forces along the same line of action shown in diagram 5 (b), page 41.

This suggests an easy way for finding the difference between two vectors. The result will always be given by reversing the vector to be subtracted, and then adding this reversed vector to the other.

This method can be used even when the vectors are not in line, provided that vector addition methods are used to obtain the result. For example, consider the forces shown in diagram 5 (c), again re-drawn here for convenience.

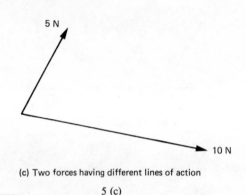

(c) Two forces having different lines of action

5 (c)

Suppose it is required to find the resultant if the 10 N force is sub-tracted from the 5 N force. The 10 N force is first reversed, and then this reversed vector is added to the 5 N force in the usual way, as shown in diagram 7.

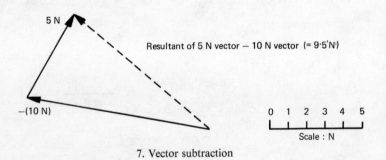

7. Vector subtraction

The same result can be obtained in another way. Instead of adding the − (10 N) force head-to-tail to the 5 N force, the 10 N force could be added tail-to-tail, as shown in diagram 8.

This shows that if a movement 'round' the triangle in the general direction of the resultant is in opposition to one particular vector, then that vector is subtracted from the other vector in the triangle. Thus, to

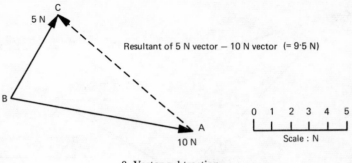

8. Vector subtraction

get from A to C (the direction of the resultant) round the triangle via B, the 'movement' from A to B is '*against*' the 10 N vector, but '*with*' the 5 N vector. The 10 N vector is then subtracted from the 5 N vector.

Example

Find the result of subtracting the force of 8 N in diagram 9 (a) from the force of 12 N shown in the same diagram.

The triangle of forces for this vector subtraction is shown in diagram 9 (b). Note that in order to get from A via B to C it is necessary to move *against* the 8 N vector.

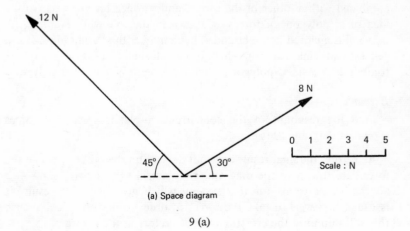

(a) Space diagram

9 (a)

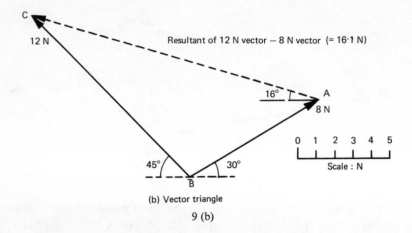

(b) Vector triangle

9 (b)

3.4. Resultant of more than two forces

Suppose more than two forces act at the same time at the same point. If all the forces act in directions which lie in the same plane (i.e. their vectors can all be drawn on the same flat piece of paper), and if all the lines of action of the forces pass through the same point, this system of forces is known as a system of CONCURRENT, CO-PLANAR FORCES. The resultant of such a system of forces can be found by an extension of the triangle of forces method used in the preceding sections. The resultant of any two of the forces can be found from the triangle obtained from their vectors, and this resultant can then be combined with another of the forces, and so on. This gives rise to the idea of a 'polygon' of forces as shown in the following example. (A polygon is a closed figure bounded by a number of straight lines. It is a general mathematical term which covers all such cases. For example, a triangle is a 3-sided polygon, while a hexagon is a 6-sided polygon.)

Example

Find the resultant of the concurrent co-planar system of forces shown in diagram 10 (a).

As before, the final result does not depend on the order in which the forces are drawn in the diagram. Diagrams 10 (b) and (c) show two alternative polygons for this system, which give the same result. It is usual, however, to take the forces in order 'round the clock', since this will minimize the crossing-over of vectors in the diagram.

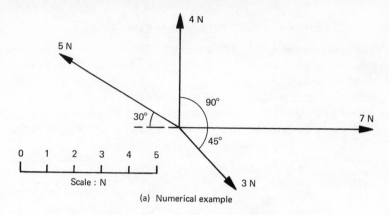

(a) Numerical example

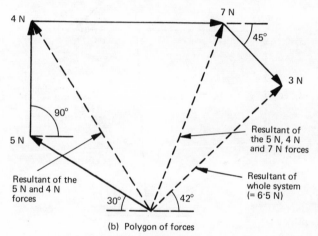

(b) Polygon of forces

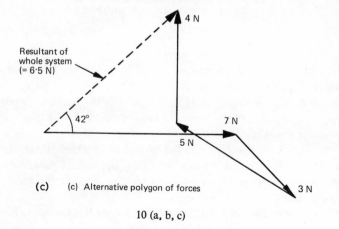

(c) Alternative polygon of forces

10 (a, b, c)

The intermediate resultants need not be drawn in every case. They are shown here to indicate how the polygon of forces is based on the triangle of forces.

If it is required to subtract one or more vectors from the others in a system of concurrent co-planar forces, the methods of Section 3.3, page 45, may be extended to cover such a case. It was shown in that

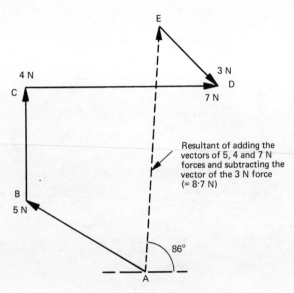

Resultant of adding the vectors of 5, 4 and 7 N forces and subtracting the vector of the 3 N force (= 8·7 N)

(d) Polygon of forces to give the subtraction of the
3 N force from the sum of the other forces

10 (d)

section that vector subtraction was given by reversing the vector to be subtracted. Alternatively, the vector could be so placed that movement round the triangle from 'start to finish' of the resultant would be *against* the direction of the vector to be subtracted. This applies equally to a vector polygon.

For example, suppose that in the system of diagram 10 (a), the 3 N force were to be subtracted from the sum of the other forces, instead of being added to it. A vector polygon to give this result is shown in diagram 10 (d).

It will be seen that in order to move from A to E (i.e. start to finish of resultant), following the route A—B—C—D—E round the polygon, it is necessary to move *against* the direction of the 3 N force, which is thus subtracted from the rest.

3.5. Equilibrium

A body is said to be in EQUILIBRIUM under a system of forces if there is no resulting tendency for the body to move. Consider again the smooth object placed on the smooth, flat horizontal surface. Since any resultant force would tend to make the object move, it follows that for a body in equilibrium the resultant of any forces acting on it must be zero. It will be seen later that if the forces are not concurrent, i.e. if their lines of action do not all pass through the same point, other conditions are also necessary for equilibrium to be maintained.

For the concurrent co-planar force systems considered so far, then, if the body on which they act is in equilibrium their resultant must be zero. This means that the polygon of forces for the system must close on itself, with the 'heads' and 'tails' of the vectors joining all the way round. It also follows that equilibrium can be achieved under the action of two forces only if these forces are equal and in opposite directions along the same line of action, as they would be, for example, along the rope held between two perfectly matched tug-of-war teams.

This last statement raises an interesting and important point. Any object on a flat horizontal table is in equilibrium, since there is no tendency for it to move up or down of its own accord. There must therefore be a force acting in opposition to the gravitational force of its own weight. In other words, the object exerts a downwards force on the table through its own weight, and the table must exert an equal upwards force on the object. This is a special example of a much more general result. If a force is applied to a body in equilibrium, and the body remains in equilibrium, then other forces must have been set up to oppose the applied force. This is referred to as the principle of 'action and reaction'. For example, if a force is applied to a brick wall, and the wall does not fall over, the wall must be exerting a 'reaction force' to keep it in equilibrium. This reaction force will automatically increase to balance an increase in the applied force—at least up to a certain maximum value, after which the reaction force can increase no more and the wall will fall over (or, at least, part of it will be moved).

In a complex system, there may be many forces and reactions to be considered. The problem may usually be simplified, however, since the conditions of equilibrium at any one point in the system can be considered and analysed separately.

3.6. Equilibrant

It has been seen that if a system of concurrent, co-planar forces is in equilibrium, their resultant must be zero. If a system of such forces has a resultant, then an additional force, known as the EQUILIBRANT for the system, will be required to maintain equilibrium. This equilibrant force must be numerically equal to the resultant, and must act in the opposite direction along the same line of action. It is thus possible to use the methods of finding the resultant of such a system, which have already been described, to find the required equilibrant for the system. Note that the equilibrant must just balance the resultant. It is an opposing equal force along the same line of action. If the resultant is a vector R, the equilibrant is the vector $-R$.

Since the resultant of any two non-parallel forces will act through the intersection of their lines of action, it follows that the equilibrant of these forces must also act through this point, in opposition to the resultant. This leads to an important result. If a body remains in equilibrium under the action of three co-planar non-parallel forces, they must be concurrent. In other words, the lines of action of the three forces must all pass through the same point.

Example

Find (a) the resultant and (b) the equilibrant of the system of forces shown in diagram 11 (a).

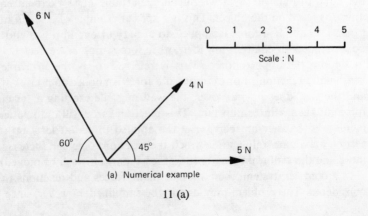

(a) Numerical example

11 (a)

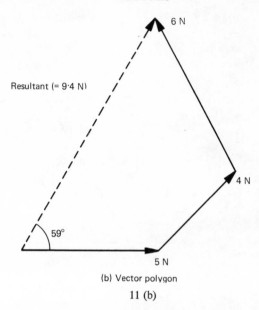

(b) Vector polygon

11 (b)

The vector polygon is shown in diagram 11 (b), while diagram 11 (c) shows the resultant and the equilibrant vectors drawn again separately. Note that the equilibrant force is the force that would just close the vector polygon on itself, so that, with the equilibrant added, the system would have a zero resultant, as is required for equilibrium. It also follows that if a system of concurrent co-planar forces acts on a body which remains in equilibrium, the reaction force set up by the body will be the same as the equilibrant force of the system.

3.7. Experimental verification of vector-addition methods

The theory of the triangle and polygon of forces may be verified by a few simple experiments, which the student should perform for himself. The equipment required consists of some known masses, some free-running pulleys mounted on a suitable vertical board, and some fine thread. If pulleys are not available, quite reasonable results can be achieved with smooth round nails driven into the board. The arrangement is indicated in diagram 12. Three lengths of thread are joined in a small knot at one end, and two of the other ends are passed over the pulleys (or nails). They are fastened to masses, which are allowed to

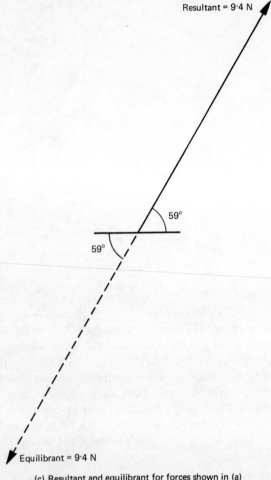

(c) Resultant and equilibrant for forces shown in (a)

11 (c)

hang freely on these threads. The third thread is also fastened to a mass, which it supports.

If the pulleys are free-running or the nails smooth, the tension in any one thread will be constant along its length. For example, mass m_1 exerts a downwards force on the end of one thread, which is transmitted by the thread to the point where the three threads are joined together. It thus exerts an outwards force away from this point, as indicated in the diagram.

When the threads are in an equilibrium position, the three directions of the threads away from their common point of intersection represent the directions of three concurrent co-planar forces in equilibrium. The magnitudes of these forces will be equal to the tensions in the threads, which in turn may be taken as equal to the gravitational forces on the

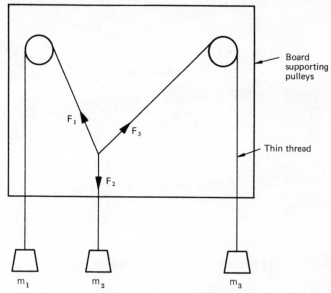

12. 'Triangle of forces' experiment

masses hung on the end of each. The forces are concurrent because their lines of action all pass through the same point—the knot joining the threads. They are co-planar forces since they all act parallel to a plane—the flat board.

If a piece of paper is then slid under the threads, their directions may be marked on the paper, to give what is known as a space diagram of the three forces. From this space diagram, a vector diagram of the forces may be drawn. This is done by vectors of lengths representing the forces being drawn to some scale, and in directions parallel to the directions of the threads. The vector diagram may conveniently be drawn directly as a triangle of forces, and it must be noticed that the vectors are drawn head to tail, so that they all point the same way

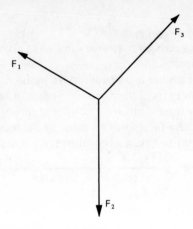

(a) Space diagram

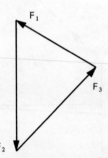

(b) Triangle of forces for space diagram shown in (a)

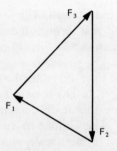

(c) Alternative triangle of forces for space
diagram shown in (a)

13 (a, b, c)

round the triangle. It does not matter which way they point—clockwise or anticlockwise—provided that they follow one another round. Since this system of forces is in equilibrium (the thread has stopped moving), the triangle of forces should close on itself so that the three forces have no resultant.

Any one of the three forces could be considered as the equilibrant of the other two, or, if its direction were reversed, as the resultant of the other two. Diagrams 13 (a), (b) and (c) show typical results. The vector triangle for (b) and (c) is drawn with vectors pointing round the triangles in opposite directions, to illustrate the type of results to be expected.

A similar method, using more threads and masses, may be used to verify the principle of the polygon of forces.

3.8. Examples

(i) A box having a mass of 100 kg is suspended in the air by means of two ropes, fastened to the same point on the box. One rope makes an angle of 30° to the horizontal and the other makes an angle of 45° to the horizontal. What is the tension in each rope?

The gravitational force on the box $= mg = 100 \times 9 \cdot 81 = 981$ N. The space diagram for this system is as shown in diagram 14 (a), and the tensions in the ropes are shown as T_1 N and T_2 N respectively. The vector triangle is drawn in the way described for the triangle of forces experiment in the previous section, except that in this case only the directions of the two tensions are known. Since the system is in equilibrium, however, it is known that the triangle must 'close' as long as all the vectors point the same way round the triangle. The triangle can then be drawn to a suitable scale, as shown in diagram 14 (b). Lines are drawn from the ends of the vector representing the force to a suitable scale. These lines, which will represent the forces in the ropes, are drawn at the appropriate angles to the gravitational force vector as indicated. The point of intersection of these lines determines the other corner of the triangle, so that the forces or tensions in the ropes, T_1 and T_2, can be measured and read off from the scale as 721 N and 879 N respectively.

Tension in rope at 30° to horizontal = <u>721 N</u>
Tension in rope at 45° to horizontal = <u><u>879 N</u></u>

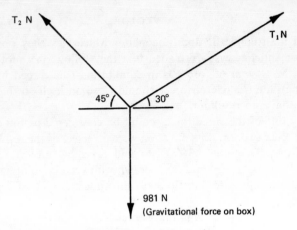

T_2 N

T_1 N

45°   30°

981 N
(Gravitational force on box)

(a) Space diagram for numerical example

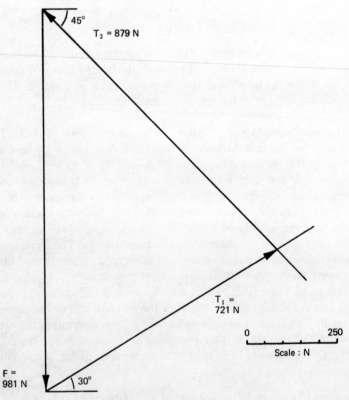

45°

T_2 = 879 N

T_1 =
721 N

0   250

Scale : N

F =
981 N

30°

(b) Vector diagram of forces for numerical example

14 (a, b)

(ii) A mass of 250 kg is to be suspended by two ropes fastened to it at the same point and at equal angles to the horizontal. If the maximum tension in each of the ropes is not to exceed 1·7 kN, find the minimum angle which the ropes can safely make to the horizontal.

The space diagram for this system is as shown in diagram 15 (a), although in this case the actual angle between the ropes and the horizontal is not yet known. The angle made by each rope and the tension in each rope are the same, however, and the tension can be assumed for the present to be the maximum safe value of 1·7 kN.

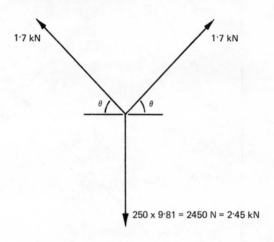

(a) Space diagram for numerical example

15 (a)

(The Greek letter θ—pronounced 'theta'—is used to represent the unknown, equal, angles. This symbol is very frequently used for angles in the way that 'x' is used for an unknown quantity in algebraic problems.)

In this case, the lengths of the three sides of the vector triangle are known. The triangle may be constructed by means of a pair of compasses, which are used to strike an arc of radius equal to the known rope tension from each end of the known force vector. The point of intersection of these arcs determines the other corner of the vector triangle, and the unknown angle can then be measured from the diagram by means of a protractor. The vector diagram is shown in diagram 15 (b).

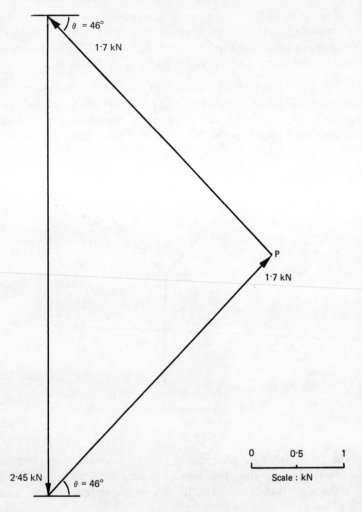

θ = 46°

1·7 kN

P

1·7 kN

2·45 kN θ = 46°

| 0 | 0·5 | 1 |

Scale : kN

(b) Vector diagram for numerical example

15 (b)

From the vector diagram, $\theta = 46°$

Minimum safe angle between each rope and the horizontal is $\underline{\underline{46°}}$

At greater angles than 46° to the horizontal, the point marked P on the vector diagram would move closer to the force vector. The vectors

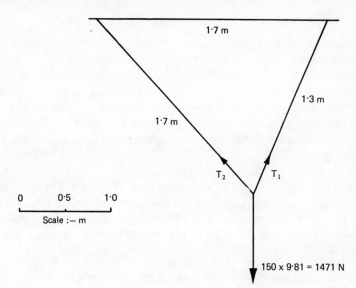

1·7 m

1·3 m

1·7 m

T_2 T_1

0   0·5   1·0

Scale :— m

150 x 9·81 = 1471 N

(a) Space diagram for numerical example,
drawn to scale to determine direction of ropes

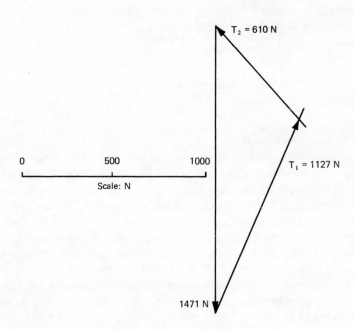

T_2 = 610 N

0   500   1000

Scale: N

T_1 = 1127 N

1471 N

(b) Vector diagram for numerical example

16 (a, b)

representing the rope tension would be shorter, and the rope tensions correspondingly less than 1·7 kN. For angles less than 46°, P would move further away from the force vector, and the lengths of the rope tension vectors would increase, indicating tensions greater than 1·7 kN. This point is of practical importance, and rope or chain slings used for lifting heavy equipment should not be at too small an angle to the horizontal. In other words, the total angle *between* the ropes should not be too great.

(iii) Two ropes are used to support a mass of 150 kg. The ropes are 1·7 m and 1·3 m long respectively, and one end of each is fastened to the same point on the mass. The other ends of the ropes are fastened to hooks 1·7 m apart on a horizontal beam. Find the tensions in the ropes.

In this case, the space diagram must first be drawn to scale so that the directions of the ropes can be found. This is done in diagram 16 (a). From the inclinations determined with the aid of the space diagram, the vector diagram can be drawn, and the tensions read off as before. This is shown in diagram 16 (b).

From the vector diagram,

Tension in the 1·7 m rope is 610 N
Tension in the 1·3 m rope is 1127 N

3.9. Resolution of forces

In the preceding sections it has been shown that two or more con-current co-planar forces can be combined to give a single resultant force. It follows from the same line of reasoning that any single force can be considered as being the resultant of a number of concurrent co-planar forces. In practice, it is often convenient to consider that a single force is the resultant of just two component forces whose direc-tions are at right angles to each other. The process of finding these component forces for a given single force is referred to as the RESOLU-TION of the single force in two perpendicular directions, or into two rectangular components. The directions chosen for the components are determined by the particular problem. Any one force can have any number of such components, and any pair at right angles to each other can be thought of as replacing the original force. Diagrams 17 (a), (b)

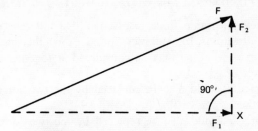

(a) Resolution of a force into two perpendicular components

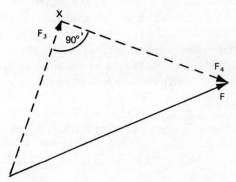

(b) Resolution of a force into two perpendicular components

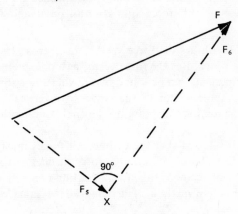

(c) Resolution of a force into two perpendicular components

17 (a, b, c)

and (c) show the same force resolved into 3 different pairs of perpendicular directions. In (a) forces F_1 and F_2 together have a resultant equal to force F, and so may be considered as together equivalent to F, or capable of replacing it.

In (b) force F could also be replaced by the two forces F_3 and F_4 acting together.

In (c) force F could also be replaced by the two forces F_5 and F_6 acting together.

The geometry of the diagrams indicates that the corner of the vector triangle marked X in each lies on the circumference of a circle drawn with the original force vector as a diameter. This follows from the geometrical theorem which proves that the angle between lines drawn from the ends of a diameter to the same point on the circumference of a circle is always a right angle. In other words 'the angle in a semi-circle is a right angle'. If the student has not yet met this theorem, he should draw a diameter in a circle and join the ends to the same point on the circumference. The angle between these two lines at the circumference can then be measured, and will be found to be 90° (i.e. a right angle) no matter where the point is taken on the circumference.

This fact gives a simple graphical method for the resolution of a force in two directions at right angles, and the method is illustrated in the following examples.

(i) A force of 10 N acts in a direction inclined at 30° above the horizontal. Resolve this force into its horizontal and vertical components.

Diagram 18 (a) shows the force vector drawn to scale, with a circle drawn round it which uses the force vector as a diameter. The required horizontal components can be found by drawing a horizontal line from one end of the force vector to the circle. The vertical component is given by the line joining this point on the circle to the other end of the original vector.

Provided it is realized that the component forces must point in the same general direction as the original force, it does not matter which end of the original vector is taken as a starting point. Diagram 18 (b) shows the alternative method of arriving at the same result for this example.

From either of these diagrams the given force is seen to have a horizontal component of 8·7 N and a vertical component of 5 N, in the directions shown in the diagrams.

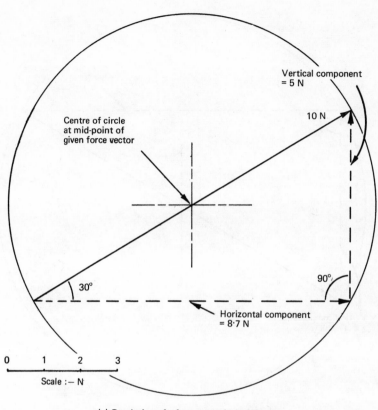

(a) Resolution of a force-numerical example

18 (a)

(ii) A force of 150 N acts vertically downwards. What component of this force acts in a direction inclined at 30° to the horizontal?

Unless specified to be otherwise, 'component' as used in the wording of this question is taken to mean 'one of the two components at right angles'.

Diagram 19 shows the construction of the force-vector diagram, by the same method as before. Only a small arc of the circle need be drawn in practice, as is indicated in this diagram.

From the diagram, the given force has a component of 75 N acting in a downwards direction at 30° to the horizontal. Note that if the given

c

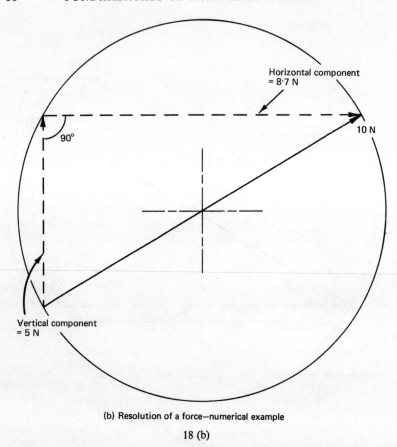

(b) Resolution of a force—numerical example

18 (b)

force is being replaced by its components, the other component of 130 N, acting in a downwards direction of 60° to the horizontal as shown, would also need to be considered.

3.10. Applications of method of resolution of forces

It is not always possible to arrange that the whole force developed by a mechanism should be applied in the particular direction required. For such a case, only the component of the force which is in the required direction may be fulfilling the purpose of the mechanism. The following example will illustrate this point.

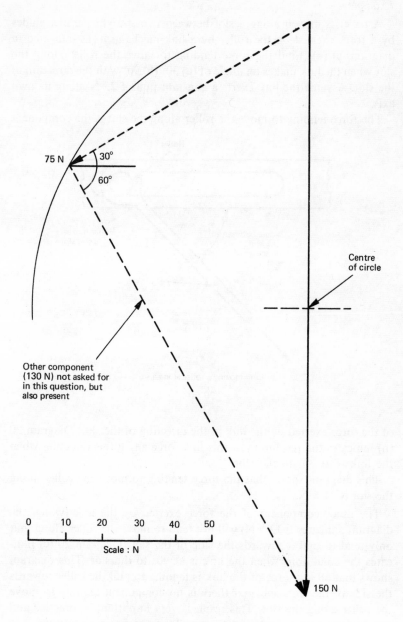

75 N

30°

60°

Centre
of circle

Other component
(130 N) not asked for
in this question, but
also present

0   10   20   30   40   50

Scale : N

150 N

19. Resolution of a force—numerical example

Example

A roller is moved along a slot between two straight parallel guides by a force exerted on the roller by a link mechanism, as indicated in diagram 20 (a). Find the force tending to move the roller along the slot when the link makes an angle of (a) 30° (b) 90° with the direction of the slot. Assume the link exerts a constant pull of 25 N along its own axis.

The force tending to move the roller along the slot is the component

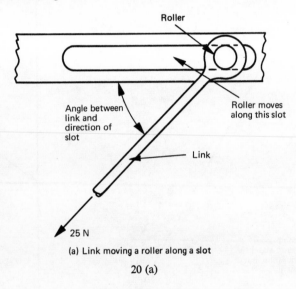

(a) Link moving a roller along a slot

20 (a)

of the force exerted by the link in the direction of the slot. Diagram 20 (b) indicates the resolution of this link force along this direction when the link is at 30° to the slot.

This diagram shows that the force tending to move the roller along the slot is 21·6 N.

The other component of the force exerted by the link (which the diagram indicates is 12·5 N) will not tend to move the roller along, but only tend to pull it towards the side of the slot. Diagram 20 (c) indicates the conditions when the link is at 90° to the slot. This diagram shows that all the force of the link is tending to pull the roller towards the side of the slot, and that there is no component tending to move the roller along the slot. This result is very important in practice and can be summarized in the statement: 'A force has no component at

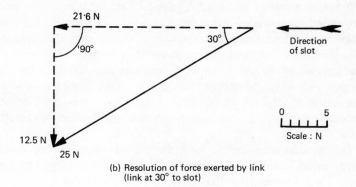

(b) Resolution of force exerted by link
(link at 30° to slot)

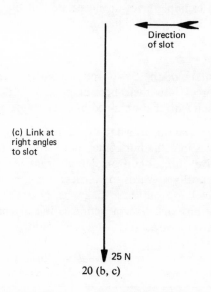

(c) Link at
right angles
to slot

25 N
20 (b, c)

right angles to its own direction.' This statement is equally true of any other vector quantity.

There is another application of the idea of resolving a force into two component forces at right angles. Although this application may seem at present to be an unnecessary complication of a simple method discussed earlier in the sections on the triangle and polygon of forces, the principle is a very important one.

It has been seen in Section 3.2, page 39, that the sum of two vectors having the same line of action is given simply by their algebraic sum. Two forces acting along different lines of action may be replaced by their components at right angles, along any convenient reference axes. The component of one force along any one axis can then be added algebraically to the component of the other force along the same axis. The results of these additions will give the components of the resultant force along these axes, and may be re-combined to find this resultant force.

This process may seem a long way round when the two original force vectors could be added by the triangle of forces method. However, it will be seen later that this is the basis of a method of vector addition by calculation. Vectors may be added by this approach without the necessity (and possible inaccuracy) of a scale drawing.

The following example gives an illustration of the method, for the present by scale-drawing techniques.

Example

Find the resultant of the two forces shown in diagram 21 (a), by resolving the forces into their horizontal and vertical components. Compare the result with that obtained by the triangle of forces method.

Diagrams 21 (b) and (c), drawn to the same scale, show the resolution of the given forces into the horizontal and vertical directions.

Taking 'positive' directions from left to right for horizontal components, and vertically upwards for vertical components, the following table can be drawn up from these diagrams. Note that the total resultant force along any one line of action is the algebraic sum of the forces along that line of action.

Force	Horizontal Component	Vertical Component
6 N	− 4·25 N	+ 4·25 N
8 N	+ 6·9 N	+ 4·0 N
Resultant	+ 2·65 N	+ 8·25 N

The resultant force thus has a horizontal component of + 2·65 N and a vertical component of + 8·25 N. These may then be added vectorially as shown in diagram 21 (d), which is drawn to the same scale as the other diagrams.

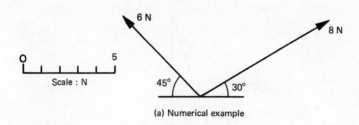

(a) Numerical example

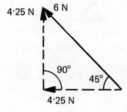

(b) Resolution of 6 N force into its horizontal and vertical components

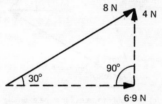

(c) Resolution of 8 N force into its horizontal and vertical components

21 (a, b, c)

Diagram 21 (e) shows the triangle of forces, drawn to the scale used for the original forces, to indicate that the same resultant is obtained.

3.11. Resolution of forces without the use of scale drawings

(This section should be omitted until a working knowledge of trigonometrical ratios has been obtained.)

Diagram 22 shows the general case of a force vector inclined at some angle to the horizontal direction. From the previous sections, it follows that the force F, represented by the vector OA, has horizontal and vertical components represented by OB and BA respectively.

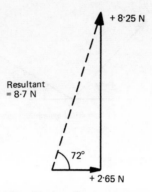

(d) Resultant of total horizontal and vertical components

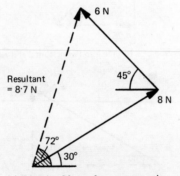

(e) Triangle of forces for same example

21 (d, e)

Since the triangle OAB is right-angled at B,

$$\frac{OB}{OA} = \text{cosine of angle } \theta \text{ (written cos } \theta)$$

and

$$\frac{BA}{OA} = \text{sine of angle } \theta \text{ (written sin } \theta)$$

These give the relationships

$$OB = OA \cos \theta$$
$$BA = OA \sin \theta$$

Since the length of line OA represents the magnitude of the force F, then the length of OB represents the magnitude of the horizontal component, and the length of BA represents the magnitude of the vertical component. Hence

horizontal component of F is $F \cos \theta$
vertical component of F is $F \sin \theta$

The values of these components may then be calculated by means of trigonometrical tables, from the values of F and θ, and it is not necessary to draw a scale vector diagram.

Example

Calculate the horizontal and vertical components of a force of 16 N acting in a direction inclined 53° upwards from the horizontal.

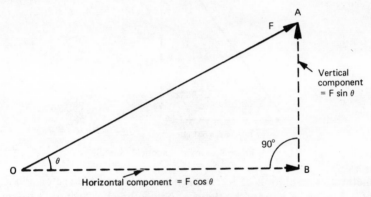

22. Components of force vector

Diagram 23 represents the force vector and its components, but although a sketch is helpful and should be drawn, it need not be drawn to scale.

From trigonometrical tables, $\cos 53° = 0.6018$ and $\sin 53° = 0.7986$ so that the horizontal component is

$$H = 16 \cos 53° \text{ N}$$
$$= 16 \times 0.6018 \text{ N}$$
$$\simeq 9.64 \text{ N}$$

The vertical component is

$$V = 16 \sin 53° \text{ N}$$
$$= 16 \times 0.7986 \text{ N}$$
$$\simeq 12.8 \text{ N}$$

Note that although the trigonometrical tables usually give values to four significant figures, engineering values are often only measured to three significant figures, except where great precision is necessary. Seven-figure tables are available, but there is no point in using these for calculations involving quantities which may not be measured to this accuracy. The number of significant figures quoted in a result should reflect the precision of the original data or of the result itself. This

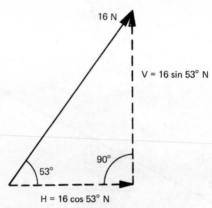

23. Force vector for numerical example

method of resolution of forces may be applied to the vector addition of a number of vectors, by the methods outlined in Section 3.10, page 66. The following examples illustrate this.

3.12. Examples

(i) Calculate the resultant of the system of forces shown in diagram 24 (a). Check the result by a scale drawing.

Choose as the positive directions those horizontally from left to right, and vertically upwards. (These are the directions usually chosen as positive, and they are the same as those used in plotting a graph.)

Each force can then be resolved into its horizontal and vertical components, by the method of the previous section. These results are shown in the following table. Note again that a force has no component at right angles to its own direction. For example, the horizontal component of the horizontal 10 N force must be 10 N. Since this 'component' is equal to the force itself, there can be no other component.

Force (N)	Horizontal Component (N)	Vertical Component (N)
10	$+ 10 \cos\ 0° = + 10\cdot0$	$+ 10 \sin\ 0° =\quad 0$
8	$+\ 8 \cos 90° =\quad 0$	$+\ 8 \sin 90° = + 8\cdot0$
3	$-\ 3 \cos 30° =\ -\ 2\cdot6$	$+\ 3 \sin 30° = + 1\cdot5$
5	$-\ 5 \cos 45° =\ -\ 3\cdot5$	$-\ 5 \sin 45° =\ -\ 3\cdot5$
6	$+\ 6 \cos 60° = +\ 3\cdot0$	$-\ 6 \sin 60° =\ -\ 5\cdot2$
Resultant	$+ 10\cdot0 + 0 - 2\cdot6 - 3\cdot5 + 3\cdot0$ $= + 6\cdot9$	$0 + 8\cdot0 + 1\cdot5 - 3\cdot5 - 5\cdot2$ $= + 0\cdot8$

For the positive directions chosen, the + or − signs for the components could be obtained directly from the standard sign conventions for the trigonometrical ratios of angles of any magnitude. The angles are then measured anticlockwise from the positive horizontal direction.

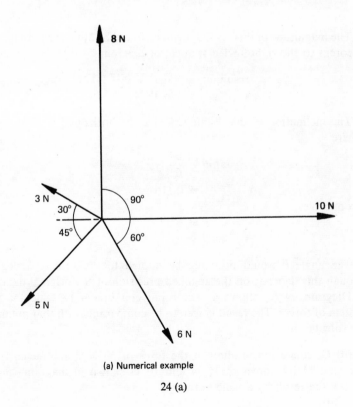

(a) Numerical example

24 (a)

For example, the 3 N force makes an angle of 150° with the positive horizontal direction. It follows from this idea that the horizontal component is 3 cos 150° = − 2·6 N, and the vertical component is 3 sin 150° = + 1·5 N. However, these signs will always be apparent from a diagram.

The resultant thus has a horizontal component of + 6·9 N and a vertical component of + 0·8 N, as shown in diagram 24 (b).

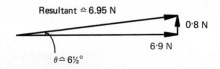

(b) Components of resultant for numerical example

24 (b)

The magnitude of this resultant can be found by applying Pythagoras' theorem to the right-angled triangle of diagram 24 (b):

$$\text{resultant} = \sqrt{6\cdot9^2 + 0\cdot8^2} \text{ N}$$
$$\backsimeq \underline{6\cdot95 \text{ N}}$$

The inclination of the resultant above the horizontal is given by θ, where

$$\tan \theta = \frac{0\cdot8}{6\cdot9}$$

$$\backsimeq 0\cdot116$$

From tables,

$$\theta \backsimeq 6°37'$$
$$\text{say } \theta \backsimeq \underline{\underline{6\tfrac{1}{2}°}}$$

The angle θ would probably be quoted to the nearest $\frac{1}{2}$ degree, though this depends on the assumed precision of the original data.

Diagram 24 (c) shows a vector polygon drawn to scale for this system of forces. The result is seen to be comparable with that obtained by calculation.

(ii) Calculate the resultant if the force of 20 N is subtracted from the sum of the forces of 15 N and 10 N shown in diagram 25 (a). Check the result by a scale drawing.

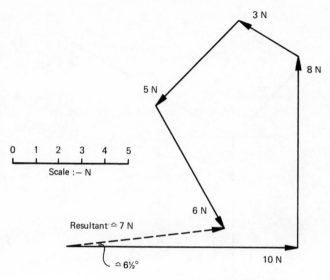

(c) Scale vector polygon for numerical example

24 (c)

Since the force of 20 N is to be subtracted from the sum of the others, it is helpful to redraw the vector diagram with the 20 N vector reversed, as shown in diagram 25 (b).

The vectors on the second vector diagram can now all be added together to give the required result.

The horizontal and vertical components are listed in the following table, with the same positive directions being used as before; i.e.

Force	Horizontal Component	Vertical Component
F_1 (= 15 N)	+ 15 cos 90° = 0 N	− 15 sin 90° = − 15·0 N
F_2 (= 10 N)	− 10 cos 45° = − 7·07 N	+ 10 sin 45° = + 7·07 N
− F_3 (= 20 N)	− 20 cos 30° = − 17·32 N	− 20 sin 30° = − 10·0 N
Resultant = $F_1 + F_2 + (- F_3)$	− 24·39 N	− 17·93 N

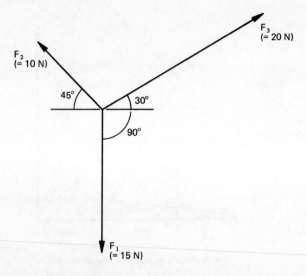

(a) Numerical example

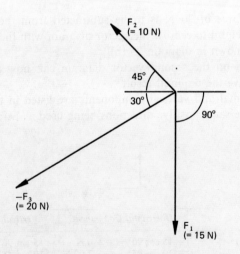

(b) Redrawn vector diagram, with the 20 N vector
reversed in direction, but still of the same
magnitude

25 (a, b)

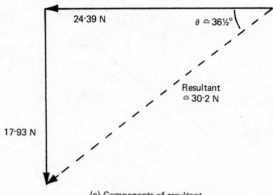

24·39 N

$\theta \simeq 36\frac{1}{2}°$

Resultant
$\simeq 30·2$ N

17·93 N

(c) Components of resultant

25 (c). In each case, the negative sign is interpreted by the
direction in which the vector is drawn

These horizontal and vertical components of the resultant are shown
in diagram 25 (c).

The magnitude of the resultant is given by

$$R = \sqrt{(24·39)^2 + (17·93)^2} \text{ N}$$
$$\simeq \underline{30·2 \text{ N}}$$

The inclination of the resultant below the horizontal is θ, where

$$\tan \theta = \frac{17·93}{24·39} \simeq 0·735$$

or $\theta \simeq 36°20'$

say $\theta \simeq \underline{36\frac{1}{2}°}$

The specification of the direction of the resultant could be given
in full by the statement that $\theta \simeq + 216\frac{1}{2}°$ or, alternatively, that
$\theta \simeq - 143\frac{1}{2}°$. This uses the idea of measuring positive angles anti-
clockwise, and negative angles clockwise from the positive horizontal
direction, as is illustrated in diagram 25 (d).

A vector polygon drawn to scale for this system of forces is shown
in diagram 25 (e). Movement round the polygon from start to finish of
the resultant vector is seen to require travelling *against* the F_3 vector,
which is therefore subtracted from the others.

Results from the vector polygon are comparable with those obtained
by calculation.

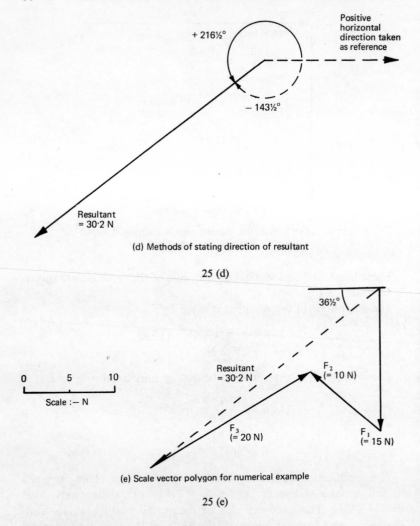

(d) Methods of stating direction of resultant

25 (d)

(e) Scale vector polygon for numerical example

25 (e)

3.13. The inclined plane

As has been said, a 'plane' is a flat surface without bumps or hollows in it. An 'inclined plane' is therefore a flat surface which is inclined at some angle to the horizontal; for example, a sheet of glass tipped up at one edge. If a smooth roller is placed on a smooth inclined plane, everyone knows that the roller will move down the plane. In order to keep the roller in equilibrium on the plane, some additional force must be applied to it. This additional force may be applied in any direction *provided it has a component acting up the incline*. The conditions for the equilibrium of such a roller will now be investigated a little further.

(a) *Investigation of equilibrium by scale drawing*

Consider the situation in diagram 26 (a), where the additional force for equilibrium, P, is shown applied parallel to the plane. The corres-

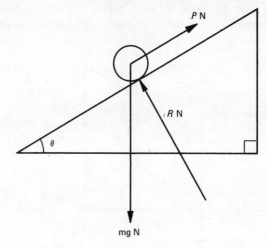

(a) Space diagram of roller on smooth inclined plane

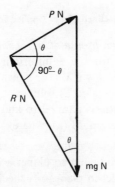

(b) Force vector diagram corresponding to conditions in (a)

26. Forces acting on roller on smooth inclined plane. (Note that the triangle of forces 'closes' if the roller is in equilibrium.)

ponding triangle of forces is shown in diagram 26 (b). Note that the reaction R set up between the roller and the plane will be at right angles to the plane. This assumes that both roller and plane are absolutely smooth, so that there is no friction between them. This is an ideal case. Modifications necessary when friction is present will be discussed later—see Section 7.8, page 208.

Diagrams 27 (a) and (b), and 28 (a) and (b), show corresponding space and vector diagrams for cases where the applied force is horizontal or at some other angle α (pronounced 'alpha') to the inclined plane.

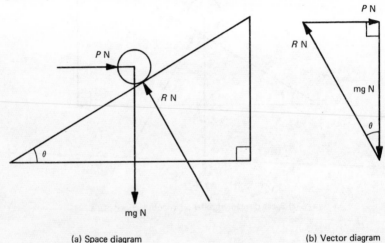

(a) Space diagram   (b) Vector diagram

27. Roller on smooth inclined plane. Applied force horizontal

(b) *Investigation of equilibrium by use of trigonometrical ratios*

The conditions necessary for the equilibrium of the roller on the smooth inclined plane (or for any mass for which the effects of friction can be neglected) can be calculated as follows:

Resolve all forces in directions parallel to and perpendicular to the inclined plane. Refer to diagram 28 (a), where

component of mg parallel to plane	$= mg \sin \theta$
„ „ mg perpendicular to plane	$= mg \cos \theta$
„ „ P parallel to plane	$= P \cos \alpha$
„ „ P perpendicular to plane	$= P \sin \alpha$
„ „ R parallel to plane	$= 0$ (neglecting friction)
„ „ R perpendicular to plane	$= R$

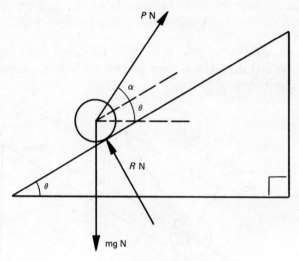

(a) Space diagram

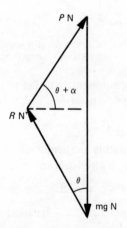

(b) Vector diagram

28. Roller on smooth inclined
plane. Applied force at angle
α to inclined plane

These various components are shown in diagram 29. R and $mg \cos \theta$ act in direct opposition, but are shown slightly separated for clarity.

For equilibrium to exist there must be no resultant force on the roller, so that the algebraic sum of any one 'set' of components in a given direction must be zero.

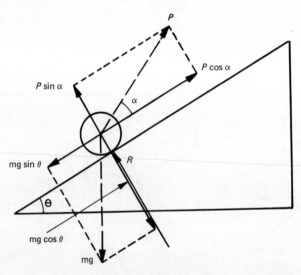

29. Components of forces parallel to, and perpendicular to, the smooth inclined plane

Thus, taking the components parallel to the plane, and choosing the direction up the plane as positive,

$$P \cos \alpha - mg \sin \theta = 0$$

Taking the components perpendicular to the plane, and choosing the direction upwards away from the plane as positive,

$$P \sin \alpha + R - mg \cos \theta = 0$$

These two equations can then be used to calculate any unknown values in a particular problem.

Two special cases of importance are:

(i) when P is parallel to the plane, and $\alpha = 0$,
(ii) when P is horizontal, and $\alpha = -\theta$.

(i) When P is parallel to the plane the above two equations become

$$P - mg \sin \theta = 0, \text{ or } \underline{P = mg \sin \theta}$$
$$\text{and } 0 + R - mg \cos \theta = 0, \text{ or } \underline{R = mg \cos \theta}$$

(ii) When P is horizontal, the above two equations become

$$P \cos \theta - mg \sin \theta = 0, \text{ or } \underline{P = mg \tan \theta}$$
$$\text{and } -P \sin \theta + R - mg \cos \theta = 0, \text{ or } R = \underline{P \sin \theta + mg \cos \theta}$$

The following example illustrates these points.

Example

A roller is held in equilibrium on a smooth inclined plane by a horizontal force P. If the plane makes an angle of 30° to the horizontal and the gravitational force F on the roller is 10 N, find the value of P and the reaction force between the roller and the plane.

(a) Graphical solution

The space diagram is shown in diagram 30 (a), and the corresponding force-vector diagram in 30 (b). Note that the vector of F is drawn vertically downwards to a suitable scale. Lines are then drawn from each end of this vector parallel to P, and parallel to R (i.e. perpendicular to the plane) as shown. The intersection of these two lines gives the other corner of the triangle of forces.

From the scale vector diagram,

$$P = 5 \cdot 75 \text{ N}$$
$$R = 11 \cdot 5 \text{ N}$$

(b) Trigonometrical solution

Resolve forces parallel with, and perpendicular to, the plane.

Component of F parallel with plane $= 10 \sin 30° = 5 \cdot 0$ N
,,   ,, F perpendicular to plane $= 10 \cos 30° = 8 \cdot 66$ N
,,   ,, P parallel with plane $= P \cos 30° = 0 \cdot 866 \, P$ N
,,   ,, P perpendicular to plane $= P \sin 30° = 0 \cdot 5 \, P$ N
,,   ,, R parallel with plane $=$ 0
,,   ,, R perpendicular to plane $=$ R N

These components are shown drawn in diagram 31.

Since the roller is in equilibrium, opposing forces along the same line of action must be equal. Equating opposing forces parallel to the plane,

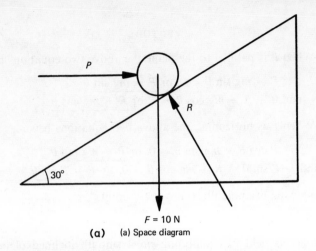

P

R

30°

$F = 10$ N

(a) (a) Space diagram

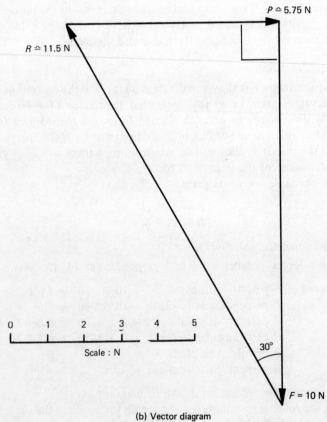

$P \simeq 5.75$ N

$R \simeq 11.5$ N

0   1   2   3   4   5

Scale : N

30°

$F = 10$ N

(b) Vector diagram

30. Smooth inclined plane—numerical problem

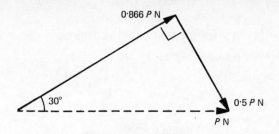

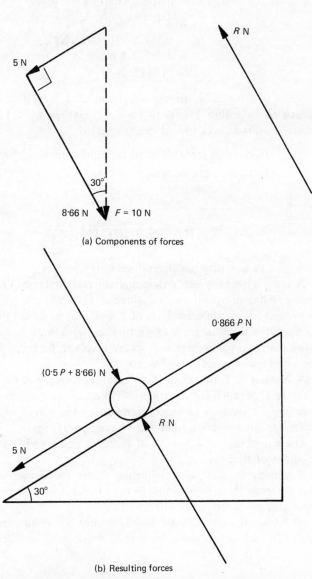

(a) Components of forces

(b) Resulting forces

31. Components of forces parallel with, and perpendicular to, the plane

$$0.866\ P = 5\ \text{N}$$

or
$$P = \frac{5}{0.866}\ \text{N}$$

$$= 5.77\ \text{N}$$

Equating opposing forces perpendicular to the plane,

$$(0.5\ P + 8.66) = R\ \text{N}$$

or
$$R = 0.5 \times 5.77 + 8.66\ \text{N}$$

$$= 2.885 + 8.66\ \text{N}$$

$$= 11.5(45)\ \text{N}$$

Since it is unlikely, to say the least, that these forces would be measured to within 1 part in about 11 000, or even 1100, the last figures in this answer should not be quoted.

Horizontal force required for equilibrium $\simeq$ 5.75 N

Reaction force at surface of plane $\simeq$ 11.5 N

CHAPTER SUMMARY

A SCALAR quantity has magnitude only.

A VECTOR quantity has both magnitude and direction. Vectors having the same line of action may be added algebraically.

Vectors having different lines of action may be added or subtracted by use of a parallelogram of vectors, or by a triangle of vectors. If more than two component vectors are involved, their resultant may be found by use of a polygon of vectors.

A body is in equilibrium if no resultant force acts on it. (But see Chapter 4, page 94, for a further condition.)

If a body remains in equilibrium under the action of a force, an equal opposing reaction force must have been set up.

The equilibrant of a system of forces is equal and opposite to the resultant of that system.

If a body remains in equilibrium under the action of three co-planar forces, these forces must be concurrent; i.e., their lines of action must all pass through the same point.

A vector quantity can be resolved into two components at right angles to each other, either by a scale drawing or by calculation, e.g.

A force F has a component equal to $F \cos \theta$ in a direction inclined at an angle θ to the direction of the force.

A vector quantity has no component in a direction perpendicular to its own direction.

For a body of mass m held in equilibrium by a force P on a smooth plane inclined at θ to the horizontal,

(a) If P is parallel with the plane, $P = mg \sin \theta$, and the reaction force at right angles to the plane is $R = mg \cos \theta$.

(b) If P is horizontal, $P = mg \tan \theta$ and the reaction force at right angles to the plane is $R = P \sin \theta + mg \cos \theta$.

QUESTIONS

1. Two forces of 2·25 N and 3 N are acting at a point and are inclined to one another at an angle of 90°. Find graphically the magnitude and direction of (a) the equilibrant, (b) the resultant of the two forces.

2. The diagram shows a simple jib crane the vertical post of which is 3 m long, the jib 5·7 m long and the tie-rope 3·7 m long. Find graphically the forces on the jib and tie when a load of 30 kN is applied to the end of the jib.

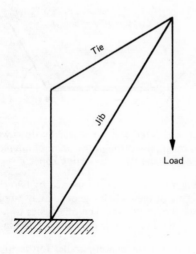

3. The diagram shows a linkage, known as a toggle joint, with which material at M is compressed by a slider S due to a constant effort of 1·2 kN applied vertically at B as shown.

For the position when BD is 100 mm, determine graphically (a) the force in each link AB and BC, (b) the compressive force exerted on the material and the vertical thrust exerted by the slider S on the guide.

(Friction is to be ignored.)

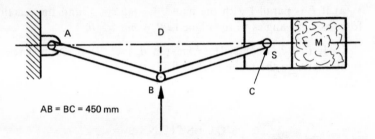

AB = BC = 450 mm

4. (a) State the conditions for the equilibrium of three non-parallel forces acting in the same plane.

(b) A non-uniform beam AB, 3 m long and having a mass of 50 kg, is supported by two ropes attached to its ends. The beam is horizontal and the direction of the ropes is as shown in the diagram. Using a graphical construction, determine the position of the centre of gravity of the beam and the tension in each rope.

(Hint: The gravitational force will act vertically downwards through the centre of gravity. This must pass through the point of intersection of the lines of action of the tensions in the two supporting ropes.)

5. A machine having a mass of 3 t is supported by two chains attached to the same point on it. One of these chains goes to an eye-bolt in the wall and is inclined at 30° above the horizontal. The other goes to a hook in the roof and is inclined at 45° to the horizontal. Find the tension in each chain.

6. State the conditions for three non-parallel forces to maintain a rigid body in equilibrium.

The gravitational force on a uniform rod AB is 250 N. It is smoothly hinged at A and is maintained at an angle of 45° above the horizontal by a cord attached to the rod at B and to a point C as shown in the diagram. If AC = AB and AD = DB, draw a diagram showing clearly the direction of the reaction at the hinge.

By drawing a triangle of forces, determine the value of this reaction and the tension in the cord.

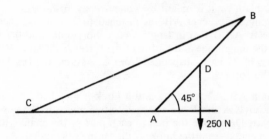

7. Represent by means of a diagram four forces all pulling away from a point. The first is 4 N acting east, the second 4 N acting 60° north of east, the third 1 N acting 60° north of west and the fourth 3 N acting west. Then graphically or otherwise find a single force which will balance all the above forces.

8. (a) Explain what is meant by the 'resultant' of a number of forces.

(b) A mass of 2 t is raised by a rope which passes around an overhead pulley. Obtain the resultant force acting on the pulley when the load is slowly lifted,

(i) by the free end being pulled vertically downwards,

(ii) by the free end being pulled horizontally.

9. (a) State the principle known as 'Polygon of Forces'.

(b) A force of 10 N is held in equilibrium at a point O by three forces A, B and C, acting at 60°, 120° and X° respectively, measured in a clockwise direction from the line of action of the 10 N load. If A is 20 N and B is 40 N, find the value of C and the angle X.

10. Define the terms 'Resultant' and 'Equilibrant' applied to a system of forces.

The following forces act on a body: 10 N due north, 8 N due east, 5 N 30° south of west, 12 N south-east, all forces pulling. Find the resultant in magnitude and direction.

11. A beam AB is 8 m long and hinged at A. It is kept horizontal by a tie rod BC, the point C being 2 m vertically above A. A vertical downwards force of 2·5 kN is applied to B. Calculate the pull in the tie rod and the thrust along the beam.

12. State the principle of the triangle of forces. A mass of 12 t is suspended from two ropes which make angles of 10° and 70° with the horizontal. Determine the force in each rope.

13. A body having a mass of 20 kg is supported on a smooth plane inclined at 30° to the horizontal. Determine the magnitude of the force necessary to keep the body in equilibrium, (a) when the direction of the force is parallel with the plane, (b) when it is horizontal.

14. (a) Explain what is meant by 'concurrency' of forces.

(b) A triangular bracket ABC is fastened to a wall with AB vertical, A being above B. AB is 1 m in length, AC is horizontal and 0·7 m in length. Determine the magnitude and nature of the forces in AC and BC respectively when a mass of 75 kg is suspended from C. Assume the bracket to be pin-jointed at the corners.

15. A chain AB is 2·5 m long and a hook is attached at a point C, 1 m from A. The ends A and B are attached to two points in the same horizontal line 2 m apart. Determine the pull in each part of the chain when a load of 20 kN is suspended from the hook. If the permissible pull in the chain is not to exceed 30 kN, what is the maximum load which may be hung from the hook?

16. Four forces act at a point and have the following magnitudes and directions, the angles being measured anticlockwise from the positive horizontal direction from left to right.

$$10 \text{ N}, 0°; \ 20 \text{ N}, 90°; \ 15 \text{ N}, 150°; \ 10 \text{ N}, 210°$$

Find the magnitude and direction of the resultant force if (i) all the forces are added together, (ii) if the 20 N force is subtracted from the sum of the other three.

17. (a) Explain what is meant by a 'polygon of forces'.

(b) Find graphically the resultant of the following forces which all act at a point. The angles are measured in an anticlockwise direction from a horizontal left-to-right reference direction:

$$8 \text{ N}, 45°; \ 6 \text{ N}, 120°; \ 10 \text{ N}, 240°; \ 5 \text{ N}, 300°$$

What would be the resultant if a fifth force of 4 N at 180° were to be subtracted from the sum of these forces?

18. Two forces act at a point. The first is 15 N and acts upwards at 30° to the horizontal, to the right. The second is 20 N and acts upwards at 45° to the horizontal, to the left. Find the horizontal and vertical components of the resultant of these two forces.

19. A roller of mass m kg is held in equilibrium on a smooth plane inclined at 20° to the horizontal by a force of 600 N acting in a horizontal direction. Find the value of the mass m and also the reaction force between the plane and the roller.

20. (a) Explain what is meant by the resolution of a force into two components at right angles to one another.

(b) A certain force has a component of 5 N in a direction inclined at 30° to its own direction. Find the other component at right angles to the one given.

21. A mass of 1 kg is hung by means of a thread, and a horizontal force of 15 N is then applied to the mass. Find the tension in the thread. If the thread will break when the tension in it exceeds 25 N, find the greatest possible inclination of the thread to the vertical due to the effect of a horizontal force applied to the mass.

22. A truck of mass 500 kg is to be pulled up an incline of 1 in 4 (i.e. 1 m vertical rise for a distance of 4 m measured up the slope). Neglecting the effects of friction, find the least force required (a) when it is applied parallel with the plane, (b) when it is applied at an angle of 30° to the horizontal.

23. The gravitational force on a roller is 8 N and it is held in equilibrium on a smooth plane inclined at X° to the horizontal by a force of 2 N applied parallel with the plane. Find the value of the angle X°. What force would be necessary to maintain the roller in equilibrium if the force were to be applied horizontally?

24. A mass of 5 kg is hung from the junction B of two strings AB and BC. If AB = 50 mm and BC = 75 mm, find the tensions in these strings if the points A and C are held at the same horizontal level and (i) 75 mm apart, (ii) 100 mm apart.

25. A ship is being towed by two tugs using cables. One cable is at an angle of 30° on one side of the line of movement of the ship, and has a tension of 750 kN. The other cable is at an angle of 45° on the other side of the line of movement of the ship, and has a tension of 1 MN. Find the resultant force acting on the ship along its line of movement. What sideways force, if any, is being applied to the ship?

4. Parallel Forces

In Chapter 3, forces were considered whose lines of action all passed through the same point, and whose vectors all lay in the same flat surface, or plane.

Not all forces are like this in practice, however. For example, if a number of masses are arranged in a horizontal line, the gravitational forces exerted on them will all be vertically downwards. These parallel forces cannot be combined in the same way as concurrent co-planar forces, and this chapter is concerned with the way in which the effects of such parallel forces may be combined.

4.1. The turning effect of a force. Moments

When a door is pushed at the handle side, the line of action of the force does not pass through the hinges of the door. Since the hinge-fastening prevents the door from moving bodily in the direction of the applied force, the result is that the door turns on its hinges. In more general terms, a force will have a turning effect about any point not directly in its line of action.

The turning effect of a force can quite easily be shown to depend on the perpendicular distance between the line of action of the force and the point considered. For example, a person holding the handle of a door need exert only quite a small force to oppose the turning effect produced by someone else pushing much harder but nearer to the hinge. If the edge of the door is pushed so that the line of action passes through the hinge, no turning effect is produced, since the distance between the line of action and the point about which turning could take place is then zero. These forces are illustrated in diagram 32.

This turning effect is called the (turning) MOMENT of the force about the point, and may be measured as the product of the force and the *perpendicular distance* between its line of action and the point considered. Thus a force F whose line of action passes at a perpendicular distance d from a point P will have a moment about P of $F \times d$. This is illustrated in diagram 33.

The units in which the moment of a force is measured are:

(force units) × (length units) i.e. newton metres (Nm)

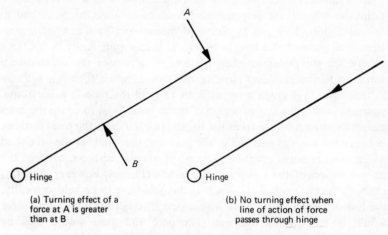

(a) Turning effect of a force at A is greater than at B

(b) No turning effect when line of action of force passes through hinge

32. Turning effect of a force

Note that a statement concerning the moment of a force must also mention the point about which the moment is calculated. For cases

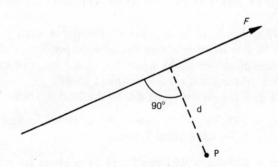

33. Turning moment of a force

such as the door mentioned earlier, where the moment of the force about the hinge may actually cause the door to turn on the hinge, the point about which rotation may take place is called the FULCRUM. The name hinge has too specialized a meaning for more general use, although, of course, the hinge forms the fulcrum for the door.

It is important to remember that the moment of a force about a point depends on the *perpendicular* distance between the point and its line of action. This can be simply demonstrated by means of a mass tied on to the end of a long pole. The pole can quite easily be held in a nearly upright position, when the line of action of the gravitational force on the mass passes close to the hands, which form the fulcrum in this case. It is much more difficult to hold the pole in a horizontal position, where the line of action of the gravitational force on the mass passes at some distance from the hands. In each case, the total distance between the mass at one end of the pole and the hands at the other end of the pole remains constant. The perpendicular distance between the line of action of the force and the hands changes, however, and this changes the moment of the force. If the pole were to be held vertically, the line of action of the force would pass through the hands, and there would be no turning moment. The pole and mass would then be balanced. These conditions are illustrated in diagram 34.

Example

A jib crane has an arm (the 'jib') 13 m long, and lifts a load having a mass of 2 t. Find the turning moment which will tend to topple the crane when the jib makes an angle of (a) 60°, (b) 30° to the horizontal.

Diagram 35 shows a scale drawing of the jib in each position. Measurement of this drawing shows that the perpendicular distance between the line of action of the force due to the mass of the load and the fulcrum of the jib is (a) 6·5 m, (b) 11·25 m.

The turning moment on the crane due to the load is, then

(a) Moment = 2000 kg × 9·81 m/s^2 × 6·5 m about fulcrum
    = 127·6 kNm about fulcrum

(b) Moment = 2000 kg × 9·81 m/s^2 × 11·25 m about fulcrum
    = 221 kNm about fulcrum

The crane would have to resist this turning moment in each case, or else it would topple over. In practice there is a maximum safe load which can be lifted by the crane for any given working radius of the jib. If this load were exceeded for a given radius, or if the radius were exceeded for a given load, the resulting moment would be increased and the crane might be pulled over.

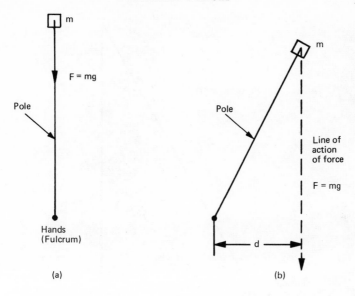

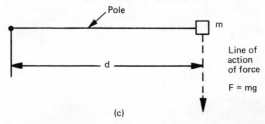

34. Effect of perpendicular distance between fulcrum and line of action of force

    (a) No turning moment—line of action passes through fulcrum
    (b) Small turning moment—distance d is small
    (c) Maximum turning moment—distance d is large

4.2. General note on compound units

It has been seen that various units derived from the fundamental units for length, mass and time may involve compounds of these units. For example,

the unit of pressure is the N/m^2
the unit of density is the kg/m^3
the unit of moment is the Nm.

D

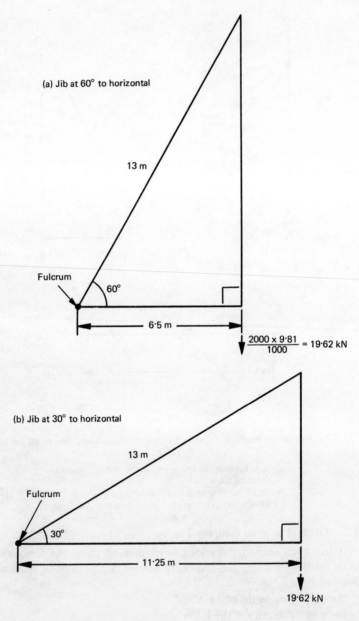

(a) Jib at 60° to horizontal

13 m

Fulcrum

60°

6·5 m

$\frac{2000 \times 9·81}{1000}$ = 19·62 kN

(b) Jib at 30° to horizontal

13 m

Fulcrum

30°

11·25 m

19·62 kN

35 (a, b)

It is important to realize the fundamental significance of the sign '/' used in these compound units. The sign '/' is used to mean PER, and implies the *division* of the unit in front of the sign by the unit following the sign. Thus N/m^2 means NEWTONS per SQUARE METRE, and the result is found by *dividing* a force by an area. Similarly, kg/m^3 means KILO-GRAMMES *per* CUBIC METRE, and the result is found by *dividing* a mass by a volume. On the other hand, the absence of a sign between the unit symbols implies the product of the two units, and means that the unit in front is *multiplied* by the following unit. Thus Nm means NEWTONS × METRES, and the result is found by *multiplying* a force by a distance. Occasionally a hyphen may be used for this purpose.

This distinction is very important, and should be clearly understood.

4.3. Equilibrium under the action of parallel forces

A body is said to be in equilibrium if there is no tendency for it to move under the action of the forces applied to it. In Section 3.5, page 51, it was seen that this condition requires that the resultant force acting on the body should be zero. It can now be seen that a further condition is necessary. If a body is to be in equilibrium, the total *moment* of the forces acting on the body must also be zero. For example, consider the bar shown in diagram 36. The bar is pivoted at a fulcrum A, and forces of 2 N and 3 N are applied to it at points B and C as shown. There will be a reaction force (see Section 3.5, page 51) of 5 N acting upwards at the fulcrum as shown, so that the total down-wards force on the bar is equal to the total upwards force on the bar, and the resultant force on the bar is zero. However, the 2 N force exerts a moment about the fulcrum which tends to rotate the bar in an anti-clockwise direction, while the moment of the 3 N force acts in a clockwise direction about the fulcrum.

These moments can then be written

$$\text{ANTI-CLOCKWISE moment about fulcrum (A)} = 2\ N \times 5\ m$$
$$= 10\ Nm$$
$$\text{CLOCKWISE moment about fulcrum (A)} = 3\ N \times 3\ m$$
$$= 9\ Nm$$

There will be no moment about A due to the reaction force at the ful-crum, since the line of action of this force passes through A. This means

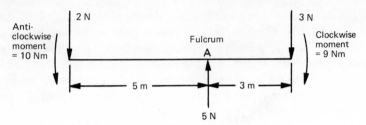

36. Pivoted bar—not in equilibrium

that there is a resultant turning moment about the fulcrum of

$$(10 - 9) \text{ Nm} = 1 \text{ Nm}$$

in an anti-clockwise direction. The bar will therefore tend to rotate in this direction, and so will not be in equilibrium. For equilibrium to be maintained, the clockwise and anti-clockwise moments about the fulcrum must balance each other, so that the resulting moment about the fulcrum will be zero. This can be stated as a PRINCIPLE OF MOMENTS:

'A body free to rotate about a fulcrum will be in equilibrium only if the resultant force acting on the body is zero *and* if the sum of the clockwise moments about the fulcrum is equal to the sum of the anti-clockwise moments about the fulcrum.'

4.4. Examples

(i) Two boys, one of mass 21 kg and the other 28 kg, sit one on each end of a plank which is pivoted about a fulcrum at its centre. If the smaller boy sits at a distance of 2 m from the fulcrum, how far away on the other side of the fulcrum must the larger boy sit in order for the plank just to balance horizontally?

The conditions are as shown in diagram 37.
Let the distance of larger boy from fulcrum be x metres. Then

anti-clockwise moment
    about fulcrum $= 21 \times 9 \cdot 81 \times 2$ Nm
                  $= 412$ Nm

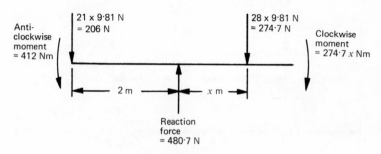

37. Numerical example

and   clockwise moment
            about fulcrum $= 274 \cdot 7 \, x$ Nm

For the plank to balance horizontally, in equilibrium,

            clockwise moment $=$ anti-clockwise moment
            about fulcrum   about fulcrum

or $274 \cdot 7 \, x$ Nm $= 412$ Nm

or $x = \dfrac{412}{274 \cdot 7}$

                    $= 1 \cdot 5$ m

Larger boy must sit <u>1·5 m</u> away from fulcrum.

Note that a smaller distance is required to give the same moment for the larger force.

(ii) Find the value of the force F N shown in diagram 38, if the beam is just to balance in a horizontal position about the fulcrum at A.

The reaction at A is equal to the total downwards force on the beam; i.e., in this case $(10 + F)$ N. This reaction has no moment about the fulcrum, however.

$$\text{Total anti-clockwise} \atop \text{moment about A} = \left(\frac{3 \times 150 + 5 \times 75}{1000} \right) \text{Nm}$$

$$= \left(\frac{450 + 375}{1000} \right) \text{Nm}$$

$$= 0 \cdot 825 \text{ Nm}$$

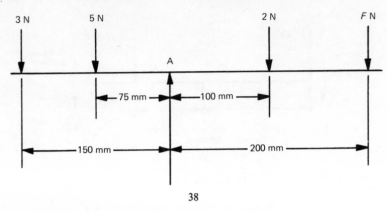

38

$$\text{Total clockwise} \atop \text{moment about A} = \left(\frac{2 \times 100 + F \times 200}{1000}\right) \text{Nm}$$

$$= 0\cdot2 + 0\cdot2F \text{ Nm}$$

$$\text{But total clockwise} \atop \text{moment about A} = \frac{\text{total anti-clockwise}}{\text{moment about A}}$$

$$\therefore\ 0\cdot2 + 0\cdot2\,F = 0\cdot825$$
$$\text{or} \qquad 0\cdot2\,F = 0\cdot625$$
$$\text{or} \qquad\quad F = 3\cdot125 \text{ N}$$

Required value of force F to balance the beam about A is $\underline{3\cdot125 \text{ N.}}$

4.5. Levers

One very common application of the principle of the moment of a force about a point may be found in the lever. With its help, a small force may be used to counterbalance a larger force. Also, since the small force must move through a greater distance than the larger force, the lever can be used as a simple 'movement amplifier'. It can also be used for comparing two masses, as in a lever balance, and in the case of the bell-crank lever it may be used to modify the direction in which a force is exerted. These various examples are illustrated in diagram 39.

In diagram 39 (a), the 'heel' of the crowbar acts as the fulcrum. At the point when the load is just balanced,

$$F \times \text{a} = P \times \text{b} \quad \text{or} \quad P = \frac{\text{a}}{\text{b}} \times F$$

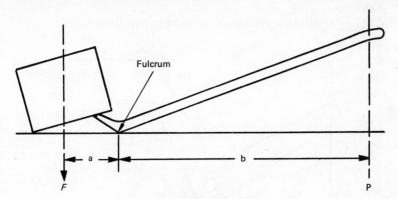

(a) Crowbar used to lift heavy loads

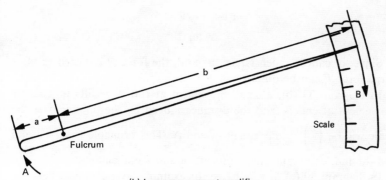

(b) Lever as movement amplifier

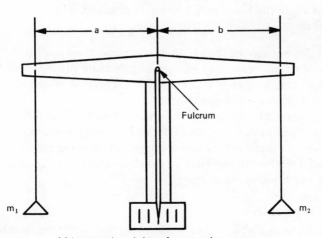

(c) Lever used as a balance for comparing masses

39 (a, b, c)

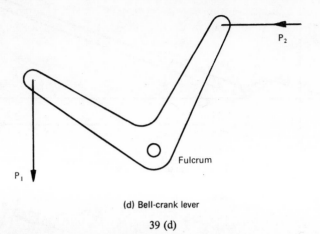

(d) Bell-crank lever

39 (d)

Since 'b' can be much larger than 'a', the force P required to lift a large force F can be quite small.

In diagram 39 (b), a small movement at end A results in a larger movement at end B, and the distance moved by the pointer over the scale will be $\left(\dfrac{b}{a}\right) \times$ movement of end A. This principle is very useful for the indication and measurement of small movements.

In diagram 39 (c), if a = b, as, for example, in a chemical balance, the beam will balance only when $m_1 = m_2$. Alternatively, m_2 may be moved along the beam until balance is obtained, when

$$m_1 g \times a = m_2 g \times b$$

From this m_2 may be found, when m_1, a and b are known. A pointer attached to the beam may be used to give more precise indication of balance. This pointer is really another application of the idea of the lever as a movement amplifier.

In diagram 39 (d), the force P_1 in the first wire sets up force P_2 in the wire at right angles as shown. If the lever is symmetrical, $P_1 = P_2$. This lever is useful where only a limited travel is required, and where possible slackness in the wires on which no pull is exerted might make the use of a pulley inconvenient.

4.6.   Types of lever

The force applied to a lever is called the effort, while the force tending to turn the lever in the opposite direction is called the load.

It has been found convenient to subdivide levers into groups, according to the relative positions of the fulcrum, the load and the effort.

(a) *Levers of the first order*

This sub-division has the fulcrum placed between the load and the effort, as shown in diagram 40 (a).

Each of the examples shown in diagram 39 is of this type. Any movement of load and effort is in opposite directions, but the load and effort must be applied in the same direction. The relative values of load and effort depend on their relative distances from the fulcrum, but the load can be made many times greater than the effort if the effort is applied much further away from the fulcrum.

(b) *Levers of the second order*

This sub-division has the load placed between fulcrum and effort, as shown in diagram 40 (b).

Typical examples of these are a garden wheel-barrow and a pair of nutcrackers. Any movement of load and effort is in the same direction, but the load and effort must be applied in opposite directions. The relative values of load and effort again depend on their relative distances from the fulcrum, but since it is further from the fulcrum, the effort will always be less than the load. It follows that the load in a wheel-barrow should be kept as nearly over the wheel as possible if the minimum of effort is to be made.

(c) *Levers of the third order*

This sub-division has the effort placed between the load and the fulcrum, as is shown in diagram 40 (c).

Typical examples are a steam safety valve, where the effort is provided by the force of the steam in a boiler against the valve, and the human forearm, where the effort is provided by the muscle attached closer to the fulcrum—the elbow joint—than is a load held in the hand. Any movement of load and effort is in the same direction, but the load and effort must be applied in opposite directions. Relative values of load and effort again depend on their distances from the fulcrum, but since it is closer to the fulcrum, the effort will always be greater than the load. Since the load moves further than the effort, this type could also be used to give movement amplification.

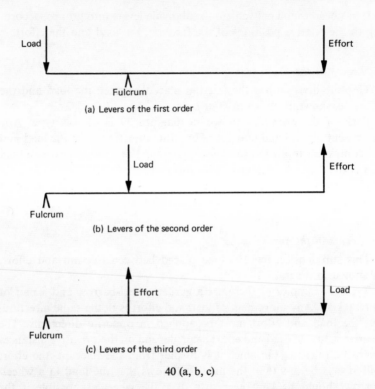

(a) Levers of the first order

(b) Levers of the second order

(c) Levers of the third order

40 (a, b, c)

4.7. Examples

(a) *Levers of the first order*

A straight bar is rested on a small block as shown in diagram 41, and is used as a lever to raise a load of 5 kN. Find the effort required if this is exerted at the point shown, and (i) acting vertically downwards, (ii) acting at right angles to the bar.

Anti-clockwise moment about fulcrum, due to load

$$= 5000 \text{ N} \times 0.05 \text{ m}$$
$$= 250 \text{ Nm}$$

For effort E_a N applied vertically downwards, clockwise moment about fulcrum

$$= E_a \times 0.8 \text{ Nm}$$

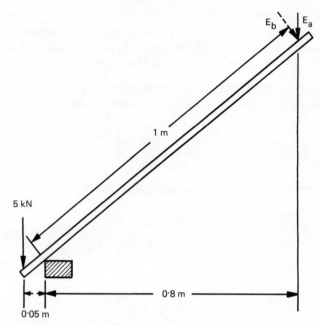

41. Lever of the first order—numerical example

Equating these moments,

$$0.8 \, E_a = 250$$
$$E_a = 312.5 \text{ N}$$

For effort E_b N, applied at right angles to the bar, the clockwise moment about the fulcrum

$$= E_b \times 1 \text{ Nm}$$

This is again required to balance the anti-clockwise moment about the fulcrum due to the load, so that

$$E_b = 250$$
$$E_b = 250 \text{ N}$$

The required efforts are 312.5 N vertically downwards

or   250 N at right angles to the bar.

In each case, very slightly more effort would be required to actually lift the load. The given values would bring the load to the point of just being lifted.

(b) *Levers of the second order*

The nutcrackers having the dimensions shown in diagram 42 are being used to crack a nut. If the force required to crack the nut is 250 N, what effort must be applied at the points shown?

Consider the upper arm of the nutcrackers.
Anti-clockwise moment about fulcrum due to load

$$= \left(\frac{250 \times 25}{1000}\right) \text{Nm}$$

$$= 6 \cdot 25 \text{ Nm}$$

Clockwise moment about fulcrum due to effort

$$= E \times \frac{125}{1000} \text{ Nm}$$

$$= 0 \cdot 125 \, E \text{ Nm}$$

Equating these moments,

$$0 \cdot 125 \, E = 6 \cdot 25$$
$$E = 50 \text{ N}$$

A similar result would be obtained for the lower arm, so that the required effort at the points shown is 50 N.

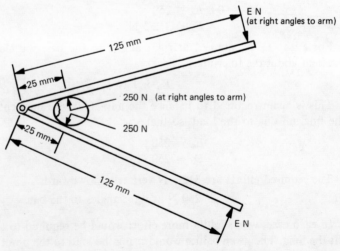

42. Lever of the second order—numerical example

If the lower arm were rested against, say, a table, at the point of application of the effort, and while the effort was applied to the upper arm only, a reaction force of 50 N would be developed by the table on the lower arm at the point of contact.

(c) *Levers of the third order*

A man's forearm has the dimensions shown in diagram 43. What effort must be made by his arm muscles when he holds a mass of 2·5 kg in his hand, with his forearm held horizontally?

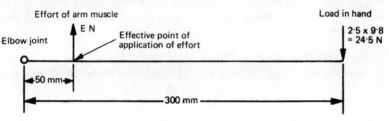

43. Lever of the third order—numerical example

Clockwise moment about fulcrum due to load

$$= \left(24 \cdot 5 \times \frac{300}{1000}\right) \text{Nm}$$

$$= 7 \cdot 35 \text{ Nm}$$

Anti-clockwise moment about fulcrum due to effort

$$= E \times \left(\frac{50}{1000}\right) \text{Nm}$$

$$= 0 \cdot 05 \, E \text{ Nm}$$

Equating these moments,

$$0 \cdot 05 \, E = 7 \cdot 35$$
$$E = 147 \text{ N}$$

Required effort exerted by arm muscles = <u>147 N</u>.

4.8. Simply-supported beams

If a beam is just rested horizontally on two supports, the supporting forces or reactions will be vertical; i.e. perpendicular to the beam. Such an arrangement is called a 'simply-supported' beam.

If the beam is to be in equilibrium, then both the conditions mentioned in Section 4.3, page 99, must be fulfilled. The total force acting on the beam must be zero, and the clockwise moments of the forces about either of the supports must equal the anti-clockwise moments about that support. These two facts enable the reactions at the supports to be determined when the loading of the beam is known. The following examples illustrate the method used.

Examples

(i) A light beam rests horizontally on two supports 3 m apart, and is loaded by vertical forces acting as shown in diagram 44. Find the reaction force at each support.

The reaction forces at A and B will be vertically upwards (assuming the beam to be in equilibrium). Let these reaction forces be R_A and R_B

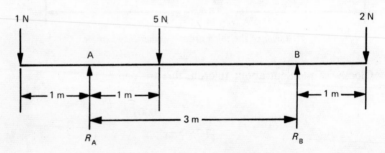

44. Simply-supported beam—numerical example

N respectively. Calculate the moments of each of the forces about one of the supports, say A. This is called 'taking moments about A'. Then

moment of 1 N force about A = 1 N × 1 m anti-clockwise
= 1 Nm anti-clockwise

Moment of R_A about A = 0, since it acts through A

Moment of 5 N force about A = 5 × 1 Nm clockwise
= 5 Nm clockwise

Moment of R_B about A = R_B × 3 Nm anti-clockwise

Moment of 2 N force about A = 2 × 4 Nm clockwise
= 8 Nm clockwise

Then the total anti-clockwise moment about A

$$= 1 + 3\,R_B \text{ Nm}$$

and the total clockwise moment about A

$$= 5 + 8 \text{ Nm}$$
$$= 13 \text{ Nm}$$

For the beam to be in equilibrium, these moments must be equal.

$$\therefore\ 1 + 3\,R_B = 13$$
$$3\,R_B = 12$$
$$R_B = 4$$

But total downwards force = total upwards force,

or $1 + 5 + 2 = R_A + R_B$

or $R_A + R_B = 8$

giving $R_A = 8 - R_B$
$$= 4$$

This answer would also be given if moments were taken about B. In this case, the reactions at each support are equal, and each reaction force is 4 N vertically upwards.

(ii) A light beam rests horizontally on two supports, A and B, which are spaced 4 m apart. It is loaded by vertical forces as shown in diagram 45. Find the reactions at each support.

If an added force of 8 N is then applied at a point on the beam 'overhanging' the support at B, find the distance from B at which this force must be applied in order for the beam to be brought to the point of tipping up.

Let the reactions be R_A and R_B N as shown.

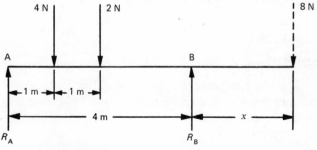

45. Simply-supported beam—numerical example

Following the same method as in the previous example, take moments about A.

Total anti-clockwise moment about A

$= R_B \times 4$ Nm (in this case only R_B exerts an anti-clockwise moment about A)

Total clockwise moment about A

$= 4 \times 1 + 2 \times 2$ Nm (due to the vertical loads)
$= 8$ Nm

Equating these moments,

$$4 R_B = 8$$
$$R_B = 2$$

But

$$R_A + R_B = 4 + 2 = 6$$
$$\therefore R_A = 6 - R_B$$
$$= 4$$

(This answer could also be found by taking moments about B.)

For the loads first considered, the reaction forces are 4 N at A and 2 N at B.

Now consider the effect of adding the force of 8 N to the right of B as shown. Simple experiment will indicate that this force will tend to tip the beam up, using B as the fulcrum and lifting the beam away from the support at A. Just at the point when this is about to happen the reaction force at A will be reduced to zero, so that it is no longer supporting the beam. The beam is then really balancing at point B. The required distance x can then be found most conveniently by equating moments about B.

Then, total anti-clockwise moment about B

$= 4 \times 3 + 2 \times 2$ Nm
$= 16$ Nm

and total clockwise moment about B

$= 8 \times x$ Nm (since R_A, which would normally give a clockwise moment about B, is assumed to have been reduced to zero).

Equating these moments,

$$8 x = 16$$
$$x = 2$$

The beam is on the point of tipping when the 8 N force is 2 m away from B on the other side from A.

At this point, $R_A = 0$, so that the total reaction force occurs at B, and

$$R_B = 4 + 2 + 8 = 14 \text{ N}$$

If the 8 N force were applied at very slightly more than 2 m from B, the beam would tip up; i.e. it would no longer be in equilibrium.

4.9. Resultant of a number of parallel forces

It has been seen that parallel forces cannot be added in the same way as are concurrent co-planar forces. However, the principle of moments may be used to find the resultant of a number of parallel forces, and the line of action of this resultant. The magnitude of the resultant will simply be the algebraic sum of the forces.

The line of action of the resultant can be found by equating the moment of the resultant about any convenient point, to the algebraic sum of the moments of the individual forces about that point. This follows from the fact that the effect of the resultant force must be the same as the total effect of all the individual forces acting together. The method used is illustrated in the following examples.

Examples

(i) A locomotive has four pairs of wheels in line, mounted on four parallel axles. The distances between successive axles are 1·7 m, 3 m and 1·7 m. The loadings on the axles are 40 kN (front), 120 kN, 160 kN and 40 kN (rear) respectively. If the locomotive stands on a level track, find the total load on the rails, and the distance from the front axle at which it acts.

The loads on the rails are indicated in diagram 46, where F kN represents the total load, assumed to act a distance x m from the front axle.

The total load F kN will be equal to the sum of the individual axle-loads, so that

$$F = 40 + 120 + 160 + 40$$
$$= 360 \text{ kN}$$

Taking moments about the point of the track where the front wheel

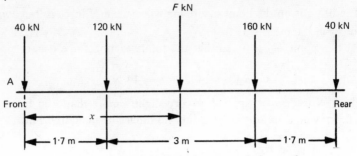

46. Axle loadings of locomotive—numerical example

rests (A on diagram 46), total clockwise moment about A due to individual axle-loads

$$= 120 \times 1 \cdot 7 + 160 \times 4 \cdot 7 + 40 \times 6 \cdot 4 \text{ kNm}$$
$$= 204 + 752 + 256 \text{ kNm}$$
$$= 1212 \text{ kNm}$$

This must be equal to the clockwise moment produced about A by the resultant load F kN:

$$F \times x = 1212$$
or $$360\,x = 1212$$

$$x = \frac{1212}{360} = 3 \cdot 37 \text{ m}$$

The total load on the rails is equivalent to a load of 360 kN acting at a point 3·37 m behind the front axle.

(ii) A light beam AB is acted on by vertical forces as shown in diagram 47. Find the total force on the beam, and the point about which the beam would balance.

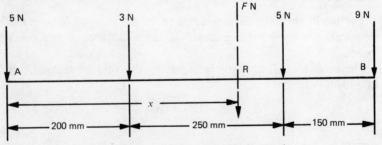

47. Forces on a beam—numerical example

The diagram shows the total force as F N acting at R, at an assumed distance of x m from end A. The total resultant force F

$$= 5 + 3 + 5 + 9 = \underline{22 \text{ N}}$$

Taking moments about A, total clockwise moment about A due to individual forces

$$= 3 \times 0.200 + 5 \times 0.450 + 9 \times 0.600 \text{ Nm}$$
$$= 0.6 + 2.25 + 5.4 \text{ Nm}$$
$$= 8.25 \text{ Nm}$$

This must be equal to the total clockwise moment about A due to the resultant force, $F \times x$ Nm. Then

$$F \times x = 8.25$$
$$\text{or} \quad 22 \, x = 8.25$$
$$x = \underline{0.375 \text{ m}} \text{ or } \underline{375 \text{ mm}}$$

The resultant force on the beam is $\underline{\underline{22 \text{ N}}}$ acting at a point $\underline{\underline{375 \text{ mm}}}$ from end A.

It follows that the beam would balance (i.e. be in equilibrium) if an equilibrant force, equal and opposite to this resultant, were applied to the beam. Thus, if a support were placed 375 mm from end A, the reaction at the support would be 22 N, and the beam would balance about this support.

As a check, the clockwise and anti-clockwise moments about the point of action of the resultant may be compared.

Thus, clockwise moment about R (if $x = 0.375$ m)

$$= 5 \times 0.075 + 9 \times 0.225 \text{ Nm}$$
$$= 0.375 + 2.025 \text{ Nm}$$
$$= 2.4 \text{ Nm}$$

and the anti-clockwise moment about R

$$= 5 \times 0.375 + 3 \times 0.175 \text{ Nm}$$
$$= 1.875 + 0.525 \text{ Nm}$$
$$= 2.4 \text{ Nm}$$

which again indicates that the beam would balance at R.

This result is true in every such case. That is, the total clockwise moment is equal to the total anti-clockwise moment about a point in the line of action of the resultant of a number of parallel forces.

4.10. Couple. Torque

When the key of a clockwork mechanism is turned to wind up the spring, equal and opposite forces are applied at the ends of the key, as shown in diagram 48.

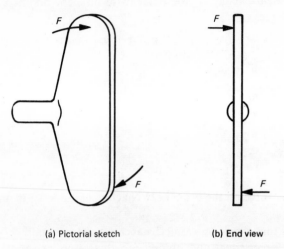

(a) Pictorial sketch   (b) End view

48. Forces applied to a key to wind up a clockwork spring

Since the two forces are equal and in opposite directions, the total resultant force is zero, and there is no tendency for the key to move bodily sideways. There is, however, a resultant moment which will turn the key about its axis.

Two forces acting in this way are said to form a COUPLE, and the resultant moment of the couple is called the TORQUE produced by the couple. Note that a couple consists of *equal* forces, whose lines of action are parallel but in opposite directions. A torque is the pure turning moment which will result, and which will tend to twist the body on which it acts without tending to move it sideways.

The torque produced by a couple is the same about *any* point in the plane containing the lines of action of the forces forming the couple. This can be proved by reference to diagram 49. The two forces forming the couple are shown marked F in this diagram, and the distance between their parallel lines of action is d. A line is drawn perpendicular to the lines of action, and two points P and Q are shown on this line. P lies between the forces at a distance of x_1 from one of them, while Q is outside both forces, at a distance of x_2 from one of them. The total

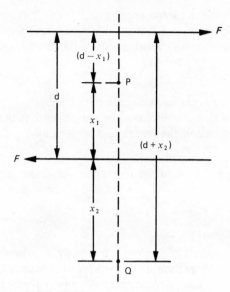

49. Resultant moment, or torque of a couple

moment about either P or Q is $F \times$ d, and is in the same 'sense' for either (clockwise in this case).

Take moments about P. Both forces produce a clockwise moment about P, the total clockwise moment being

$$F \times x_1 + F \times (d - x_1)$$
$$= F \times x_1 + F \times d - F \times x_1$$
$$= F \times d$$

Take moments about Q. The upper force produces a clockwise moment about Q of

$$F \times (d + x_2)$$

The lower force produces an anti-clockwise moment about Q of

$$F \times x_2$$

The resulting *clockwise* moment about Q is equal to
(clockwise moment) − (anti-clockwise moment)

$$= F \times (d + x_2) - F \times x_2$$
$$= F \times d + F \times x_2 - F \times x_2$$
$$= F \times d$$

The torque is thus the same about either P or Q, in magnitude and also in 'sense' (clockwise in this case). The same result would have been obtained if Q had been on the other side of the two forces.

Summary

The torque of a couple, each component of which is a force *F*, whose parallel lines of action are separated by a distance d, is the same about any point in the plane of the forces, and is given by

$$\text{torque} = F \times d$$

or   torque = (one of the forces) × (perpendicular distance between the forces)

4.11. Centre of gravity

The mass, or amount of material in a body, can be thought of as being made up of a large number of particles. (In Chapter 13, on atomic structure, it is seen that this statement is literally true.) Each particle will have its own mass and so will experience its own gravitational force. As long as the body is small compared with the size of the earth, these gravitational forces can be taken as parallel. The resultant of all these parallel forces will be the total gravitational force on the whole body, and will have a particular line of action through the body.

This force can thus be considered to act at a point in the body, which is known as the body's CENTRE OF GRAVITY (c.g.), or sometimes as its 'centre of mass'. The body will act as if all its mass were concentrated at its centre of gravity, so that its gravitational force will always act through this point, whatever the position in which the body may be.

The position of the centre of gravity of a body could be found by finding the line of action of the resultant force of all the parallel forces acting on the particles of which it is composed. More advanced mathematical techniques are available which enable this to be done, but it would be a tedious process without them. Fortunately, however, it is possible to find the position of the centre of gravity of a body fairly simply, by experiment.

First consider the case of a thin flat sheet of uniform thickness, known as a LAMINA. If this sheet is suspended from a point near its edge, it will swing until it reaches a point of equilibrium. When it is in equilibrium, the total force acting on it must be zero, and the total moment about its point of suspension must also be zero; i.e. clockwise moment equal to anti-clockwise moment. This means that the resultant force due to its mass must act in a vertical line through its point of suspension, as shown in diagram 50 (a). A line drawn on the plate, vertically downwards from its point of suspension, must therefore pass through its centre of gravity. If the lamina is then suspended from another point near its edge, a vertical line drawn downwards from this second point will also pass through its centre of gravity. Since it lies on both lines, the centre of gravity must be at their point of inter-section, as shown in diagram 50 (b). As a check on the result, a vertical line drawn downwards from any other point of suspension should pass through the same point of intersection.

The student should carry out this simple experiment. The vertical line is best drawn from a second thread attached to the same point of suspension, and with a small mass tied to its other end. It should be found that the lamina can be balanced in any position about its centre of gravity, say on the end of a pencil placed at that point. This follows from the fact that the gravitational force produces no moment about a support at its centre of gravity.

There are some shapes of lamina for which the position of the centre of gravity can be found by inspection. These include the symmetrical shapes such as rectangles and circles. The material in a uniform rec-tangular lamina is evenly arranged on each side of a line drawn down the centre, parallel to one side of the rectangle. It follows that the moments about this line of all the particles on one side of it will balance the moments of all the particles on the other side. This means that the centre of gravity must lie on the line. The same is true of a line drawn down the centre and parallel to any side of the rectangle. The centre of gravity is thus at the intersection of these lines. It can be shown by geometry that this point is also given by the intersection of the diagonals. Similar reasoning shows that the centre of gravity of a circular lamina is at the centre of the circle.

These points are illustrated in diagram 51, which also shows that the centre of gravity of a triangular lamina lies at the point of intersection of the lines drawn from a corner (apex) to the mid-point of the opposite side. This line is known as a 'median' of the triangle. The centre of gravity for each thin strip lies at its centre, so that G lies on a line drawn through these centre points, as shown. Since this is true for strips drawn parallel to any side, G lies at the intersection of all such lines—the medians. This point can be shown to lie one-third of the way up from the base along any median.

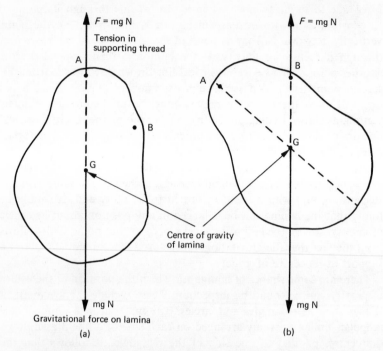

50. Determination of the position of the centre of gravity of a lamina

When only a shape or area is considered, the term CENTROID, or 'centre of area', is used for the point where the c.g. of a lamina of that shape would lie. This is because an area has no mass, so that it cannot experience a gravitational force. The term 'centre of *gravity*' would therefore be inappropriate.

It may be rather more difficult to determine the position of the centre of gravity of a solid object not in the form of a lamina. Again, however, for some regular shapes the position can be seen by inspection. For example, it is fairly easy to see that the centre of gravity of a sphere will lie at the centre of the sphere; that the centre of gravity of a rectangular block will lie at the intersection of its body diagonals; and that the centre of gravity of a cylinder lies on its axis, half-way along its length. It is less easy to see why the centre of gravity of a cone lies on its axis, a quarter of the way up from its base. This could be checked by a simple experiment similar in technique to that used for the lamina.

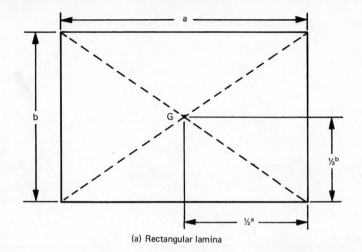

(a) Rectangular lamina

(b) Lamina in the shape of a parallelogram

(c) Circular lamina

51. Centre of gravity for laminae of various shapes

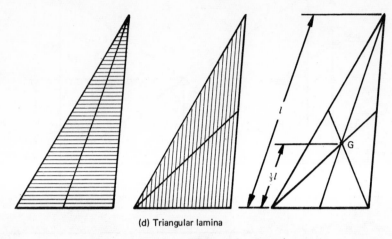

(d) Triangular lamina

51. Centre of gravity for laminae of various shapes

If a cone is suspended from a point on the rim of its base, it will hang so that its centre of gravity is vertically below the point of suspension. A beam of light, as parallel as possible, could be arranged to shine on to the suspended cone, at right angles to its axis, so that it would cast a triangular shadow on to a screen behind it. The outline of this triangle, and the shadow of the suspending thread, could be drawn in on the screen. If the line of the thread (which will be vertical) is extended downwards, it should be found to intersect the axis at a point a quarter of the way up from the base. Diagram 52 illustrates the position of the centre of gravity of some regular-shaped solids.

4.12.   Composite figures

The centre of gravity of a solid made up from the shapes considered, or the centroid of an area built up in this way, can be found by means of the principle of moments. In this connection, the moment of an area about an axis can be calculated just as if the area were a force acting through its centroid. The method used to find the centroid of a composite area or the centre of gravity of a composite solid is indicated in the following examples.

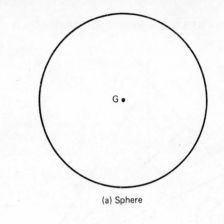

(a) Sphere

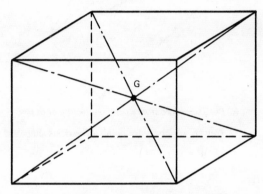

(b) Rectangular block

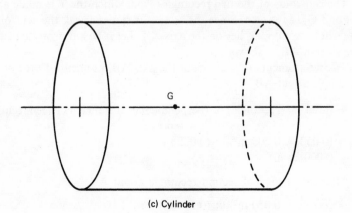

(c) Cylinder

52. Centre of gravity for solids of various shapes

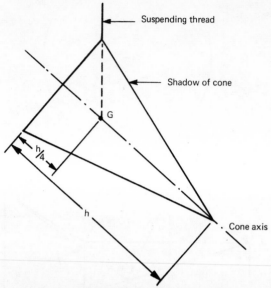

— Suspending thread

— Shadow of cone

G

$h/4$

h

· Cone axis

(d) Cone suspended from a point on the trim of its base

52. Centre of gravity for solids of various shapes

Examples

(i) Find the centroid of the T-section shown in diagram 53.

The centroids of the two rectangles from which the T is made are at G_1 and G_2, as shown. Since the section is symmetrical, the centroid of the whole section, G, lies on the axis XX. Let it be $\bar{x}$ m from the end of the section AB as shown.

Taking moments of area about the axis AB, moment of area of first rectangle about AB

= (area of rectangle) × (perpendicular distance between centroid
and axis)

= (0·050 × 0·200 m²) × (0·025 m)

= 0·000 25 m³

Moment of area of second rectangle about AB

= (0·200 × 0·050 m²) × (0·150 m)

= 0·001 5 m³

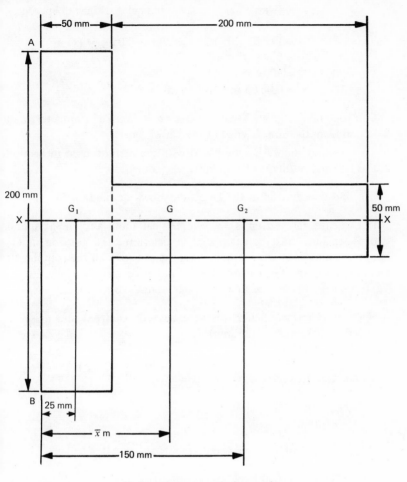

53. T-section—numerical example

Total moment of area of whole section about AB

$$= 0.000\ 25 + 0.001\ 5\ \text{m}^3$$
$$= 0.001\ 75\ \text{m}^3$$

But this will be equal to the moment of the whole area acting at its centroid, about AB

$$= \text{(whole area)} \times \text{(perpendicular distance between centroid and axis)}$$
$$= (0 \cdot 050 \times 0 \cdot 200 + 0 \cdot 200 \times 0 \cdot 050) \times (\bar{x}) \text{ m}^3$$
$$= 0 \cdot 000 \ 02 \ \bar{x} \text{ m}^3$$
$$\therefore \ 0 \cdot 000 \ 02 \ \bar{x} = 0 \cdot 001 \ 75$$
$$\bar{x} = 0 \cdot 087 \ 5 \text{ m} = 87 \cdot 5 \text{ mm}$$

Centroid of the given T-section lies on its axis of symmetry, and 87·5 mm from the outside edge of the bar of the T.

This method should be compared with the method used in Section 4.9 to find the resultant of a number of parallel forces.

(ii) Find the centroid of the L-section shown in diagram 54.

In this case, the section is not symmetrical about any one axis, and two dimensions must be calculated to determine the position of G; i.e. both $\bar{x}$ and $\bar{y}$, as shown. As before, the centroids of the component rectangles, G_1 and G_2, can be inserted at the centre of each rectangle. Then moment of area of first rectangle about AB

$$= \text{(area)} \times \text{(perpendicular distance between centroid and axis)}$$
$$= (50 \times 200 \text{ mm}^2) \times (25 \text{ mm})$$
$$= 250 \ 000 \text{ mm}^3$$

Moment of area of second rectangle about AB

$$= (100 \times 50 \text{ mm}^2) \times (100 \text{ mm})$$
$$= 500 \ 000 \text{ mm}^3$$

Total moment of area of whole section about AB

$$= 250 \ 000 + 500 \ 000 \text{ mm}^3$$
$$= 750 \ 000 \text{ mm}^3$$

But this must be equal to (whole area) $\times \bar{x}$

$$\therefore \ (50 \times 200 + 100 \times 50) \times \bar{x} = 750 \ 000$$
$$\text{or} \qquad\qquad 15 \ 000 \ \bar{x} = 750 \ 000$$
$$\bar{x} = \underline{50}$$

Taking moments of area about BC in a similar way, moment of area of whole section about BC

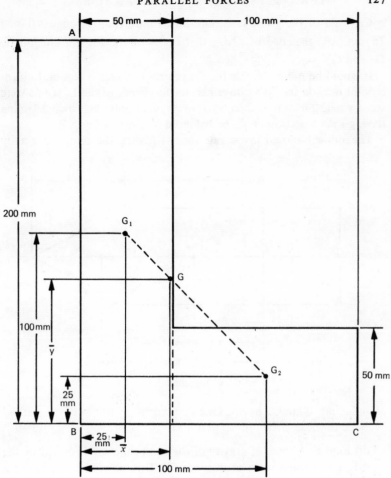

54. L-section—numerical example

$$= (50 \times 200 \text{ mm}^2) \times (100 \text{ mm}) + (100 \times 50 \text{ mm}^2) \times (25 \text{ mm})$$
$$= 1\ 000\ 000\ +\ 125\ 000 \text{ mm}^3$$
$$= 1\ 125\ 000 \text{ mm}^3$$

This must be equal to (whole area) $\times \bar{y}$:

$$(50 \times 200 + 100 \times 50) \times \bar{y} = 1\ 125\ 000$$
$$\text{or} \qquad\qquad 15\ 000\ \bar{y} = 1\ 125\ 000$$
$$\bar{y} = \underline{75}$$

Centroid of the given L-section lies 50 mm from the edge AB, and 75 mm from the edge BC. Note that G lies on the straight line joining G_1 and G_2.

It would be quite possible for the centroid of such a section to lie at a point outside the area altogether, in the corner of the L. If this were so, it would mean that there was no physical point at which a lamina having such a section could be balanced in any position.

The student should investigate this by finding the centre of gravity

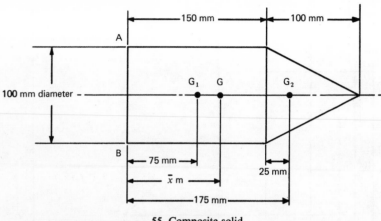

55. Composite solid

of an L-shaped lamina having long thin 'arms', by means of the method of suspension described in Section 4.11.

(iii) Find the centre of gravity of the composite solid formed by the cylinder and cone shown in diagram 55. The material has a uniform density, so that masses are proportional to volumes.

The centres of gravity G_1 and G_2 of the cylinder and cone can be marked as shown. The centre of gravity of the whole solid, G, can be seen to lie on the axis of the solid. Assume it is $\bar{x}$ mm from AB as shown.

Since the density is uniform, so that masses are proportional to volumes, 'moments of volumes' can be taken here. Take moments of volume about the axis AB.

The moment of volume of the cylinder about AB

$$= \text{(volume of cylinder)} \times \text{(perpendicular distance between centroid and axis)}$$

$$= \left[\pi \times \left(\frac{100}{2} \right)^2 \times 150 \text{ mm}^3 \right] \times \left(75 \text{ mm} \right)$$

$$= 28\ 125\ 000\ \pi \text{ mm}^4$$

Moment of volume of the cone about AB

$$= \left[\tfrac{1}{3} \pi \left(\frac{100}{2} \right)^2 \times 100 \text{ mm}^3 \right] \times \left(175 \text{ mm} \right)$$

$$= 14\ 580\ 000\ \pi \text{ mm}^4$$

Total moment of volume of the whole solid about AB

$$= 28\ 125\ 000\ \pi + 14\ 580\ 000\ \pi \text{ mm}^4$$
$$= 42\ 705\ 000\ \pi \text{ mm}^4$$

But this must equal the moment of the whole volume acting at G about axis AB

$$= \text{(total volume)} \times \text{(perpendicular distance between centroid and axis)}$$

$$= \left[\pi \times \left(\frac{100}{2} \right)^2 \times 150 + \tfrac{1}{3} \pi \left(\frac{100}{2} \right)^2 \times 100 \right] \times \bar{x} \text{ mm}^4$$

$$= (375\ 000\ \pi + 83\ 300\ \pi)\ \bar{x} \text{ mm}^4$$

$$= 458\ 300\ \pi\ \bar{x} \text{ mm}^4$$

$$\therefore\ 458\ 300\ \pi\ \bar{x} = 42\ 705\ 000\ \pi$$

or

$$\bar{x} = \frac{42\ 705\ 000}{458\ 300}$$

$$= 93 \cdot 2$$

The centroid of the given solid lies on its axis of symmetry, and 93·2 mm from the axis AB.

(iv) A rectangular bar, 150 mm × 50 mm × 25 mm, has a 25 mm diameter hole drilled in the 50 mm face. The centre of the hole lies on the line along the centre of the bar, and is 50 mm from one end. (See diagram 56.) Find the centre of gravity of the bar.

Since the bar is of uniform thickness and is symmetrical about the line XX, which runs along the centre, G_1, G_2 and G all lie on this line. They indicate the centres of gravity of the undrilled bar, of the material removed by drilling and of the drilled bar respectively. Further,

E

volumes, and hence masses, are in this case proportional to the areas measured on the 150 mm × 50 mm face.

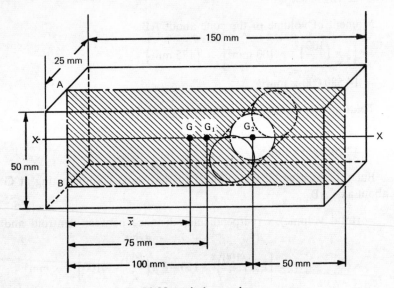

56. Numerical example

Take moments of area on this face about axis AB.
Moment of area of undrilled bar about AB

$$= (150 \times 50 \text{ mm}^2) \times (75 \text{ mm})$$
$$= 577\ 500 \text{ mm}^3$$

Moment of area of material removed, about AB

$$= \left[\pi \times \left(\frac{25}{2} \right)^2 \text{mm}^2 \right] \times \left(100 \text{ mm} \right)$$
$$= 15\ 625\ \pi \text{ mm}^3 = 49\ 100 \text{ mm}^3$$

Then moment of area of drilled bar about AB

$$= 577\ 500 - 49\ 100 \text{ mm}^3$$
$$= 528\ 400 \text{ mm}^3$$

But this must equal the moment of area of the drilled bar acting through G, about AB

$$= \text{(area of drilled bar)} \times \bar{x}$$

$$= \left[150 \times 50 - \pi \times \left(\frac{25}{2} \right)^2 \right] \times \bar{x} \text{ mm}^3$$

$$= (7500 - 491) \bar{x} \text{ mm}^3$$

$$= 7009 \bar{x} \text{ mm}^3$$

$$\therefore \quad 7009 \bar{x} = 528\,400$$

$$\bar{x} = 75 \cdot 4 \text{ mm}$$

The centre of gravity of the drilled bar lies <u>75·4 mm</u> from the end containing AB, and at a depth of <u>12·5 mm</u> into the bar.

4.13. The steelyard

The steelyard is a device which has been used for comparing masses since Roman times. It works on the principle of balancing the moments about a fulcrum of a known and an unknown mass. One form of a steelyard is shown in diagram 57. It is seen to consist of a lever supported at its fulcrum in some suitable manner. The unknown mass is placed on one side of the fulcrum in a scale pan. On the other side of the fulcrum a movable mass is hung from the arm, which is marked with a scale so that the position of the mass can be read off. The distance between the movable mass and the fulcrum determines the moment exerted by this mass about the fulcrum. Since this moment (clockwise in diagram 57) balances the moment of the unknown mass about the fulcrum (anti-clockwise in diagram 57), the position of the moving mass depends on the value of the unknown mass. The scale on the arm can then be marked off directly in units of mass.

Since the lever or arm of the steelyard will usually be fairly substantial, its own mass cannot be neglected. It is arranged that the centre of gravity of the arm and scale pan alone (without either the unknown or the movable mass) should lie at a point on the same side of the fulcrum as the scale pan. This is shown at G. Extra thickness of material may be added on this side of the fulcrum to ensure that G is at a suitable point. The movable mass can then be placed in position, near the fulcrum on the other side, so that the lever just balances without any mass being added in the pan. This position of the moving mass will form the zero of the scale on the arm. The marking of this scale can be calculated as shown in the next example.

It should be noted that the steelyard—and any other similar balancing arrangement—fundamentally compares an unknown mass with a movable known mass. Wherever the same steelyard is used with the same masses balance will be obtained, even though changes occur in the gravitational force exerted on each. The gravitational force per unit mass will be *the same for each mass* on the steelyard, so that balance is still obtained. A spring balance, on the other hand, will measure FORCE,

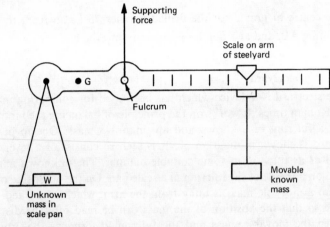

57. Steelyard

and therefore the actual gravitational force. The reading on an accurate spring balance for the same mass weighed in different places would thus change if the gravitational force per unit mass changed.

Example

The arm and scale pan of a steelyard have a mass of 4 kg. The centre of gravity lies at a distance of 50 mm from the fulcrum, on the same side as the scale pan, which is 125 mm from the fulcrum. The movable mass is 2 kg. Find the distance of the movable mass from the fulcrum if the steelyard is just to balance with (a) no mass added to the scale pan, (b) 5 kg added to the scale pan, (c) 10 kg added to the scale pan.

The steelyard is shown in skeleton form in diagram 58, where the various masses and distances are shown for (a), with no mass added in the scale pan.

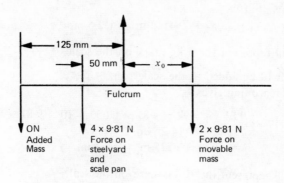

58. Steelyard—numerical example

(a) With no mass added.
Take moments about the fulcrum. Anti-clockwise moment about fulcrum due to the force on the steelyard and scale pan

$$= 4 \times 9\cdot81 \times 0\cdot050 \text{ Nm}$$
$$= 1\cdot962 \text{ Nm}$$

Clockwise moment about fulcrum due to the movable mass

$$= 2 \times 9\cdot81 \times x_0 \text{ Nm}$$

If the steelyard is to balance, these moments must be equal.

$$\therefore \ 19\cdot62 \, x_0 = 1\cdot962$$
$$x_0 = 0\cdot100 \text{ m} = \underline{\underline{100 \text{ mm}}}$$

This will represent the zero of the scale.

(b) With 5 kg added to the scale pan.
Take moments about the fulcrum. Total anti-clockwise moment about fulcrum due to the force on the steelyard and scale pan, together with the added mass in the pan,

$$= 4 \times 9\cdot81 \times 0\cdot050 + 5 \times 9\cdot81 \times 0\cdot125 \text{ Nm}$$
$$= 8\cdot09 \text{ Nm}$$

Clockwise moment about fulcrum due to the movable mass

$$= 2 \times 9\cdot81 \times x_5 \text{ Nm, where } x_5 = \text{new distance from fulcrum}$$

Again, these moments must be equal for the steelyard to balance.

$$19.62 \, x_5 = 8.09$$
$$x_5 = 0.4125 \text{ m} = \underline{\underline{412.5 \text{ mm}}}$$

This will represent the 5 kg mark on the scale.

(c) With 10 kg added to the scale pan.
Similar reasoning gives

$$2 \times 9.81 \, x_{10} = 4 \times 9.81 \times 0.050 + 10 \times 9.81 \times 0.125 \text{ Nm}$$
$$= 14.2 \text{ Nm}$$
$$x_{10} = 0.725 \text{ m} = \underline{\underline{725 \text{ mm}}}$$

This will represent the 10 kg mark on the scale.

Note that the distance between the zero and the 5 kg mark on the scale is

$$412.5 - 100 = 312.5 \text{ mm}$$

The distance between the zero and the 10 kg mark on the scale is

$$725 - 100 = 625 \text{ mm}$$

Note that this is twice the distance between zero and the 5 kg mark.

The scale along the arm will be uniform, with equal increases in distance *from the zero* representing equal increases in mass added to the scale pan. Therefore, once two points have been found, preferably at each end of the possible range, the rest of the scale can be marked out evenly. The scale for the steelyard in this example is shown in diagram 59.

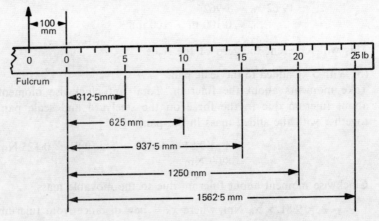

59. Scale for steelyard—numerical example

It is relatively easy to make a simple steelyard, and the student should make up a scale from two points obtained by balancing known masses in the scale pan. The scale can then be checked against other known masses.

4.14. Stability

It is easy to stand some things upright—for example, a rectangular block will stand on any one of its faces, and a cone will stand on its

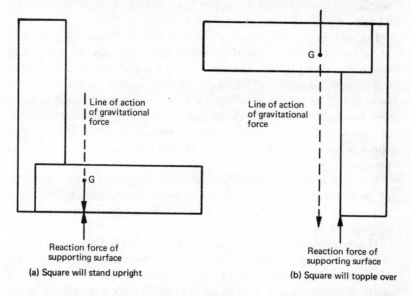

Line of action of gravitational force

G

Reaction force of supporting surface

(a) Square will stand upright

Line of action of gravitational force

G

Reaction force of supporting surface

(b) Square will topple over

60. Engineer's square standing on edge

base. It is much more difficult to make some other things stand upright in this way—for example, a long pole on its end, or a cone on its point. If anything is to stand upright, the line of action of its gravitational force, which will pass through its centre of gravity, must come within its base. If this is not so, the force will produce an unbalanced moment about a point in its base, and it will topple over.

In diagram 60 (a) and (b), two conditions are shown for an engineer's square standing on different edges. In (a), the line of action of the gravitational force falls within the base on which the square is standing. The square will stand up. In (b), the line of action of the force falls outside the base on which the square is standing. The square will fall over.

In case (a), the reaction force of the surface on which the square is standing will pass upwards through G. Therefore, no resultant force, and no resultant moment, acts on the square. In case (b), the reaction force of the surface can only pass across the point of contact with the surface. Thus although the total resultant force is zero, there is a resultant moment which will cause the square to topple over. In other words, the gravitational force and the reaction force form a couple, whose torque will cause the square to fall.

If a rectangular block is slowly tipped over on to one edge, the line of action of its gravitational force will move towards the edge on to which it is being tipped. The line of action can eventually be made to fall outside this edge, and the block will then tip over on to the adjacent face. It will be necessary to apply a considerable disturbance to cause this, however, if the length of the face on which it originally stood is of about the same size as the other dimensions of the block. If the disturbance is only very slight, the block will fall back again into its original position.

If a cone is made to stand up on its point, however, so that its centre of gravity is vertically over the point, only a very small disturbance is required to make the cone fall over. These conditions are shown in diagram 61 (a) and (b).

If a body returns to its original position after a *slight* disturbance, it is said to be in STABLE EQUILIBRIUM, as in the case of the rectangular block. If a body continues to move towards a new position after a slight disturbance, it is said to be in UNSTABLE EQUILIBRIUM, as in the case of the cone standing on its point. If a slight disturbance does not change the body's condition of equilibrium at all, so that it stays where the slight disturbance has moved it, it is said to be in NEUTRAL EQUILIBRIUM. An example of this last state is a round ball lying on a flat surface, which is shown in diagram 61 (c).

Diagram 61 shows the effect of the disturbance on the position of the centre of gravity. This gives a direct guide to the state of equilibrium.

For stable equilibrium (diagram 61 (a)), the disturbance makes the centre of gravity *rise*. For unstable equilibrium (diagram 61 (b)), the disturbance makes the centre of gravity *fall*. For neutral equilibrium (diagram 61 (c)), the disturbance does not alter the height of the centre of gravity.

Note that if the rectangular block were balanced about its edge in

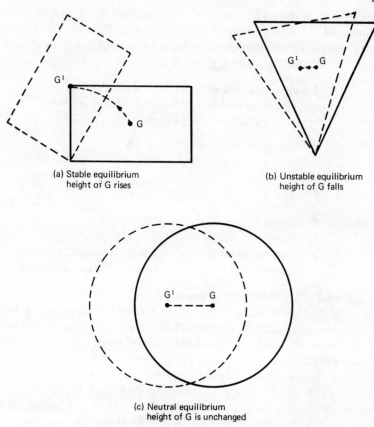

(a) Stable equilibrium
height of G rises

(b) Unstable equilibrium
height of G falls

(c) Neutral equilibrium
height of G is unchanged

61. States of equilibrium

the position shown dotted in diagram 61 (a), any further disturbance would lower its centre of gravity, so that in this position the block would be in unstable equilibrium.

CHAPTER SUMMARY

The moment of a force about a point

= (force) × (perpendicular distance between the point and the line of action of the force)

Usual unit is Nm.

If a body is in equilibrium, the total resultant force and the total moment of any forces acting about any point in the body are zero. In other words, for equilibrium, total clockwise moment = total anti-clockwise moment about any point in the body.

> Levers of the first order: Load—Fulcrum—Effort
> Levers of the second order: Fulcrum—Load—Effort
> Levers of the third order: Fulcrum—Effort—Load.

For any lever in equilibrium,

$$F \times a = P \times b$$

or $\qquad P = \dfrac{a}{b} \times F$

where P = effort
$\qquad\quad F$ = load
$\qquad\quad a$ = perpendicular distance between load and fulcrum
$\qquad\quad b$ = perpendicular distance between effort and fulcrum.

The resultant of a number of parallel forces is equal to the algebraic sum of the forces. It will act along a line parallel with the line of action of the forces such that the moment of the resultant is equal to the sum of the moments of the forces about a given point. The sum of the moments of a system of parallel forces about a point on the line of action of their resultant is zero.

Two equal forces acting in opposite directions along different, parallel, lines of action form a couple. The moment, or torque, of a couple about any point in its plane is $F \times d$, where

$\qquad F$ = each of the parallel opposing forces
$\qquad d$ = perpendicular distance between their lines of action.

The centre of gravity of a body is the point through which the gravitational force on the body acts.

The centroid of an area is at the same point as the centre of gravity of a uniform thin lamina having the same shape.

A body in stable equilibrium will return to its original position after a slight disturbance. A slight movement will raise the height of the centre of gravity.

A body in unstable equilibrium will continue to move towards a new position after a slight disturbance. A slight movement will lower the height of the centre of gravity.

A body in neutral equilibrium will remain in the position to which it is moved by a slight disturbance. Any slight movement does not affect the height of the centre of gravity.

QUESTIONS

1. (i) What is understood by (a) force, (b) moment of a force?

(ii) A strong metre rule AB, whose mass can be neglected, is pivoted at the end A and a 7 N force acts downwards at the end B. Calculate the force required to be applied vertically upwards at a point C on the rule 350 mm from A in order to hold the rule in a horizontal position. Give a sketch illustrating a practical example of a lever in which the effort is applied at a point between the load and the fulcrum.

2. (a) What is meant by the moment of force about a point? How is it measured?

(b) A weathervane is balanced about the point P, as shown in the diagram. The respective masses of the tail, shaft and head can be regarded as acting at the points A, B, C as shown in the diagram.

Calculate the mass of the head.

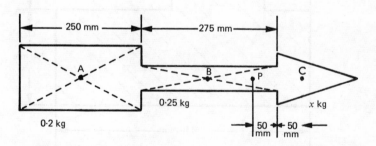

3. Give two practical examples of levers with accompanying diagrams to show the position of the effort, load and fulcrum in each case.

4. A beam 4 m long is simply supported at its two ends, A and B. It carries loading forces of 20 kN, 1·3 m from A; 40 kN, 2 m from A; and 60 kN, 2·7 m from A. Calculate the reactions at A and B.

5. Determine the position of the centroid of the section shown in the diagram, and state its distances from OX and OY.

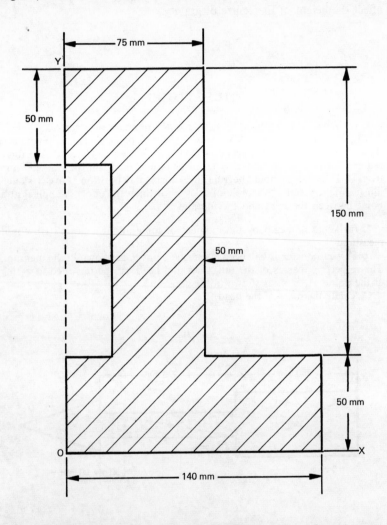

6. A manufacturer's instruction manual states that a certain nut on an engine must be tightened to a torque of 4·5 Nm by means of a box spanner.

What force would have to be applied to the ends of a tommy bar 180 mm long

(a) if the bar protruded equally from the spanner on each side, and

(b) if the spanner were at one end of the bar?

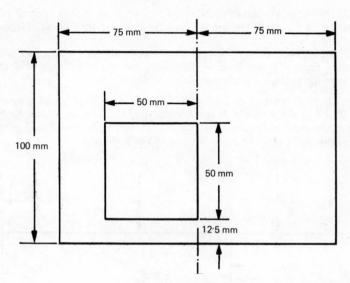

7. (a) Describe briefly an experimental method of finding the centre of gravity of a thin plate of uniform thickness.

(b) The diagram shows a 150 mm by 100 mm rectangular plate of uniform thickness, out of which a 50 mm square hole has been cut. Determine the position of the centre of gravity of the plate relative to the left-hand edge and the bottom of the plate.

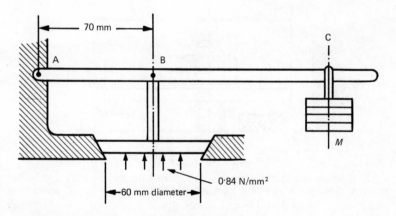

8. In the lever safety valve shown in the diagram, the distance AB from the hinge to the centre line of the valve is 70 mm, the effective diameter of the valve being 60 mm.

(a) If the valve is designed to blow off at a pressure of 0·84 N/mm² and the mass *m* on the end of the arm at C is 40 kg, find the distance AC. Neglect the mass of the arm.

(b) If the distance AC is 400 mm and the mass of the arm is 4 kg, its centre of gravity being 175 mm from A, determine the necessary mass *m* if the valve is to lift at the same pressure of 0·84 N/mm².

9. (a) Explain what is meant by the moment of a force about a point.

(b) The diagram shows a beam AB carrying loads of 60 N and 80 N. It is required that the beam shall balance on a single knife edge. Ignoring the mass of the beam, determine the position of the knife edge.

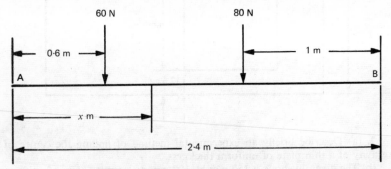

10. A component is clamped to a drilling-machine table as shown in the diagram. Calculate the forces on the component and the packing piece at the points A and B respectively, if the force exerted by the bolt is 2·25 kN.

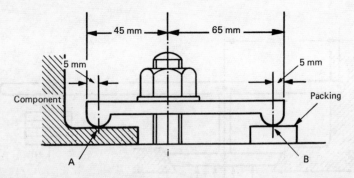

11. A horizontal beam AC is 10 m long. Its supports are at A and B, 8 m from A. The beam carries a load of 40 kN at 2·5 m from A, another of 30 kN at 4 m from A and one of 20 kN at C.

(a) Determine the reactions at the supports.

(b) If an additional upwards load of 20 kN is applied at 5 m from A, determine the load now required to be applied at C in order that the reaction at A may be zero.

12. Explain what is meant by the term 'centre of gravity'. The diagram shows the plan view of a steel forging of uniform cross section. The forging has to be lifted vertically by means of an eye-bolt. Determine the position of the eye-bolt from OA and OB so that the face OAB will remain horizontal.

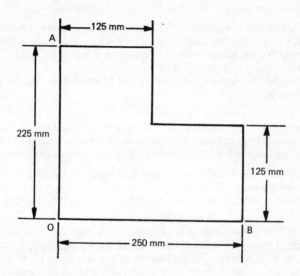

13. A horizontal lever OA is pivoted at O and supported by a chain at end A. The lever is 2 m long, has a mass of 60 kg, and the centre of gravity is 0·7 m from A. By considering the moments of the forces acting, find the tension in the chain (a) when the chain is vertical, (b) when the chain is inclined at 45° towards the lever.

14. (a) Define the moment of a force.

(b) In an experiment to verify the principle of moments, a horizontal uniform beam 2 m long was supported at each end and a load of 30 N was placed 0·5 m from the left-hand support. The reaction at the right-hand support was found to be 12·5 N. Find (i) the mass of the beam, and (ii) the reaction at the left-hand support.

15. (a) Describe, with the aid of a diagram, one application of the lever.

(b) A uniform beam of mass 1·5 kg/m, 3 m long, supports a force of 50 N at one end and 125 N at the other. It is supported 1·2 m from the 125 N force. Calculate the value of the mass that must be hung at the centre for the beam to balance.

16. (a) Define 'force'. State the unit in which it should be measured.

(b) A uniform heavy plank 11 m long and having a mass of 40 kg projects 3 m horizontally from the top of a cliff edge. How far can a man of mass 80 kg move along the plank before it tips?

17. Define 'moment of a force'.

A motor lorry has a wheel base of 3 m. The engine has a mass of 250 kg and has its centre of gravity 0·6 m behind the front axle. The mass of the remainder of the lorry (500 kg) may be considered as imposing equal loads on the two axles. How far from the back axle must a load of 1250 kg be placed in order to limit the total back axle loading to 11 kN?

18. A 1 m rule has a mass of 0·15 kg and is suspended horizontally by two vertical strings attached respectively at the 0·125 m and the 0·750 m marks. A mass of 0·2 kg hangs at the 0·25 m mark. Find

(a) the tension in each string

(b) to what mark the 0·2 kg mass must be moved so that the tensions in the strings are interchanged.

19. State the 'principle of moments'.

A metre rule AB has a mass of 0·05 kg and is pivoted at C, 0·4 m from one end. A mass of 0·02 kg hangs vertically at A. Determine the point of application of a vertical force of 0·1 N which will maintain the rule in a horizontal position.

20. A beam AB is 3 m long and is simply supported at its ends. In addition to its own mass of 150 kg, it also carries a load acting at 1 m from A. The reaction at B is found to be 900 N. Calculate the value of the load, and the reaction at A.

21. A horizontal beam AB of uniform section and 5 m long rests on supports at its ends. The beam has a mass of 400 kg and carries a load of 20 kN at a point 1·25 m from A, and a load of 10 kN at a point 1·5 m from B. Find the reactions of the supports. At what point should the load of 20 kN be applied to make the reactions of the supports equal?

22. (a) Define 'moment of a force'.

(b) A light rod AB is pivoted at A and hangs vertically. A force of 25 N is applied at C along a line of action CD. C is 400 mm below A, D is to the left of the rod and the angle ACD is 135°. A horizontal force EF of 20 N is applied at E, 500 mm below A, and F is to the right of the rod. Where must a horizontal force of 15 N be applied to prevent rotation of the rod?

23. (a) State the 'principle of moments'.

(b) A uniform rod 1·3 m long, carries a force of 50 N at one end and a force of 300 N at the other end. It is found that the rod balances about a point 0·3 m from the 300 N force. What is the mass of the rod?

24. A circular plate of diameter 125 mm and thickness 12 mm has a hole of diameter 50 mm drilled in it at a distance of 12 mm from one edge. In this hole is fixed a shaft of the same material 300 mm long, 50 mm diameter, and projecting 288 mm on one side of the plate. Find the distance of the centre of gravity of the assembly from the centre of the plate on the flush face.

25. A metal bar, of circular cross-sectional area and overall length 250 mm, is 20 mm diameter for a length of 125 mm, and then tapers to a point in the length of the remaining 125 mm. Find the position of the centre of gravity of the bar.

26. The outside dimensions of an angle-iron section are 125 mm by 100 mm and it is 12 mm thick. If all the corners are sharp, determine the centre of gravity of a thin section of this angle-iron and state its position relative to the two outside edges.

27. A bar of metal 600 mm long has been turned down to three parallel portions as follows

	Length	Mass
Section A	150 mm	4·15 kg
Section B	200 mm	3·55 kg
Section C	250 mm	2·5 kg

Find the distance of the centre of gravity of the bar from the Section C end.

28. A shaft consists of a parallel portion 150 mm diameter and 600 mm long with a 100 mm diameter bearing journal 150 mm long at each end, making an overall length of 900 mm. A 50 mm diameter hole is bored centrally at one end only, to a depth of 250 mm. Determine the position of the centre of gravity of the shaft.

29. (a) Distinguish between the terms 'centroid of area' and 'centre of gravity' of a body.

(b) The end piece for a pre-cast concrete shed, with a 0·6 m by 0·6 m opening for a window, is shown in the diagram. The piece has a mass of 450 kg and it can be assumed to act at the centroid of the area shown. During erection, a chain is attached to the apex point A at 45° to the horizontal when the end piece is lying flat on horizontal ground. The pull in the chain causes the piece to rotate about the edge BC. Determine the pull in the chain when the apex A has just left the ground.

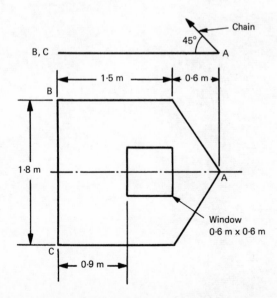

30. A lever ABCD, pivoted at B, is shown in the diagram. If forces act at A and C, in the directions shown, calculate the value of the force F to keep the lever in equilibrium. Hence draw a polygon of forces to determine the reaction at B in magnitude and direction.

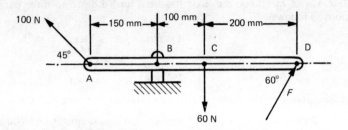

31. Two men A and B are carrying a 1 kN load slung from a light-weight pole measuring 3 m between the points of support.

(a) When the load is slung 1·2 m from A, how much force is he supporting?

(b) How far from A must the load be slung for him to be supporting 250 N?

(c) How much force is B supporting in each case?

5. Forces Applied to Solid Materials

If a force is applied to a solid material, reaction forces are set up in the material to oppose the force applied to it. These reaction forces are brought about by the opposition exerted by the material to any attempt to change its shape or volume. For example, if a straight beam is rested horizontally on two supports, and a downwards force is applied between the supports, the beam will set up reaction forces opposing the applied force. It has been seen in Section 4.8, page 109, that these reaction forces are transmitted to the supports, equilibrium being maintained when the total reaction force is equal to the total applied force, and when the total moment acting on the beam about either of the supports is zero. In setting up the reaction forces transmitted to the supports, however, the beam will bend. Some distortion must take place to call into action the forces resisting the distortion.

As another example, consider the behaviour of a coil spring under the action of an applied force. The spring will set up an opposing force if it is stretched, and equilibrium will be reached when the force exerted by the spring is equal and opposite to the applied force which tends to stretch it. But the spring will be stretched in the process. Again, some distortion is necessary in order that the opposing reaction may be brought into being.

There is a limit to which the reaction force may increase. This limit depends on the material of the object concerned, its shape and size and the way in which the force is applied. A point will eventually be reached, however, when the reaction force can increase no more. After this, a further increase in applied force will cause the object to break, or otherwise fail to oppose the total applied force to remain in equilibrium. Both this failing limit and the distortion produced by a given force vary widely with the material used. A wooden beam will bend more for a given load, and will break at a lower load, than a steel beam of the same size and shape. A length of rubber will stretch more for a given mass hung from it, and will break for a smaller value of such mass, than a length of steel of the same dimensions. In some cases, the distortion produced may be so small as to be barely noticeable, but this distortion must take place if the reaction force is to be set up. For example, the distortion which takes place when a small mass is hung from a length of steel bar cannot be seen with the unaided eye, but accurate measurement will show that the bar has in fact stretched slightly.

The following sections deal with some aspects of the distortion of solid materials under the action of various applied forces.

5.1. Tension

A material is said to be in TENSION if the forces applied to it tend to stretch the material. For example, if a mass is hung on the end of a

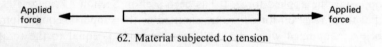

62. Material subjected to tension

length of rubber, the rubber is in tension. The rope of a crane lifting a weight is in tension. The rope between two tug-of-war teams is in tension. These conditions are represented in diagram 62.

A 'tensile' force—i.e., one producing tension—will increase the length of the material on which it acts.

5.2. Compression

A material is said to be in COMPRESSION if the forces applied to it tend to compress or squeeze it. For example, if a rubber eraser is squeezed

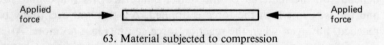

63. Material subjected to compression

between the fingers, the rubber is in compression. The supports of a simply-supported beam are in compression. The legs of a chair are in compression when someone sits on the chair. These conditions are represented in diagram 63.

A 'compression' force—i.e., one producing compression—will decrease the length of the material on which it acts.

5.3. Shear

A material is said to be in SHEAR if the forces applied to it tend to slide one face of the material over an adjacent face. For example, the rivets holding two flat pieces of metal close together are in shear if a tensile force is applied between the plates. A piece of paper fails in shear when it is cut cleanly by a pair of scissors. A shaft subjected to a pure torque is subjected to a shearing force.

These conditions are represented in diagram 64.

In practice, a material may be subjected to a combination of tension, compression and shear. For example, a simply-supported beam will be

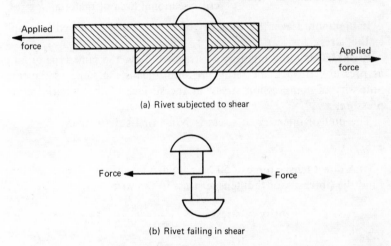

(a) Rivet subjected to shear

(b) Rivet failing in shear

64. Material subjected to shear

in tension along the outside edges of the bend which a load will produce on it. The inside edges of the bend will, however, be in compression. (This may be seen most readily on a block of rubber such as an eraser. If this is bent, two lines drawn on the outside face of the bend are seen to move apart as this face stretches under tension. Two similar lines on the inside face of the bend will be seen to move together as this face compresses.) In addition, the beam material will be subjected to shear underneath the points of application of the load. Any study of these more complicated conditions must be based on a previous study of the effects of 'pure' or 'direct' tension, compression or shear.

5.4. Stress. Intensity of stress

When a material is subjected to forces which tend to cause distortion, the material is said to be in a state of STRESS. The intensity of this stress will depend on the magnitude and direction of the applied force, and the cross-sectional area of the material withstanding the stress. For direct tensile or compressive stresses, this area is measured at right angles to the direction of the force. For shear stress, the area will be that of the adjacent faces which the stress is tending to slide over one another.

Then

$$\text{intensity of stress} = \frac{\text{applied force or 'load'}}{\text{cross-sectional area of material}} \cdot \qquad \text{(i)}$$

In common usage, the 'intensity of stress' is often referred to simply as the 'stress'.

It will be seen that intensity of stress will have the same type of units as pressure. In fact, the term 'pressure' means the same as the term 'intensity of compression stress' at the surface of the material under pressure.

The unit of intensity of stress is N/m^2 or its derivatives.

Examples

(i) A direct tensile force of 50 N is applied to a wire of diameter 2 mm. Find the (intensity of the) tensile stress in the wire.

$$\text{Intensity of stress} = \frac{\text{load}}{\text{cross-sectional area}}$$

$$= \frac{50 \text{ N}}{\frac{\pi}{4} \times 2^2 \text{ mm}^2}$$

$$= \underline{15\cdot91 \text{ N/mm}^2}$$

(ii) A man who has a mass of 75 kg sits on a chair in such a way that the reaction at each of the four chair legs is the same. If each leg has a cross-sectional area of 650 mm², find the compressive stress in each leg of the chair.

Assume that none of the force is carried by the man's feet.

Since each chair leg produces the same reaction force, the compressive force on each leg $= \dfrac{75}{4} \times 9\cdot81 = 183\cdot8 \text{ N}$.

Then

(intensity of) compressive stress $= \dfrac{\text{load}}{\text{cross-sectional area}}$

$$= \dfrac{183 \cdot 8 \text{ N}}{650 \text{ mm}^2}$$

$$= \underline{\underline{0 \cdot 283 \text{ N/mm}^2}}$$

(iii) A rivet of 10 mm diameter is subjected to a shear force of 1000 N. Find the shear stress in the rivet.

(Intensity of) shear stress $= \dfrac{\text{load}}{\text{cross-sectional area}}$

$$= \dfrac{1000 \text{ N}}{\dfrac{\pi}{4} \times 10^2 \text{ mm}^2}$$

$$= \underline{\underline{12 \cdot 72 \text{ N/mm}^2}}$$

Note that in each of the above examples, there must be two equal opposing forces acting on the body if equilibrium is to be maintained. For example, consider the tensile force applied to the wire of (i). Some equal resisting force must have been applied to the other end of the wire or it would have moved bodily in the direction of the applied force. This would in turn be the reaction force at the point where the end of the wire is fixed. The conditions are shown in diagram 65.

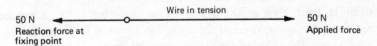

65. Forces acting on wire in tension

The tension in the wire is said to be 50 N (note NOT 100 N). For the wire to be in equilibrium, both forces must be present. The applied force on the wire is pulling at the fixing with a force of 50 N, and the fixing is pulling back on the wire with an equal force. This is another illustration of the equality of action and reaction under equilibrium conditions. Every particle of the wire can be thought of as pulling on the adjacent particle with a force of 50 N. The second particle then pulls back on the first particle with an equal force.

The tension in a wire or rope under equilibrium will thus be equal at all points along its length, provided no other forces act on it. This tension is equal to the force applied at either end. Similar remarks could be made concerning compressive and shear forces.

5.5. Strain

It has been seen that when a force is applied to a body which resists the force, some distortion of the shape of the body must occur. This distortion is measured by what is called the STRAIN.

For a material under tensile or compressive stress, the strain is measured by the fraction:

$$\text{strain} = \frac{\text{change in length}}{\text{original length}} \qquad \text{(ii)}$$

Thus, if a bar 3 m long is stretched under tension until its length increased by 0·9 mm, the tensile strain would be given by

$$\frac{0\cdot9 \text{ mm}}{3 \text{ m} \times \left(\dfrac{1000 \text{ mm}}{1 \text{ m}}\right)}, \text{ or } 0\cdot000\ 3$$

If a block 150 mm high is compressed by 0·05 mm under the action of a compressive force, the compressive strain would be given by

$$\frac{0\cdot05 \text{ mm}}{150 \text{ mm}}, \text{ or } 0\cdot000\ 33$$

Note that the units of length used in calculating the strain must be the same for the change in length and for the original length. The strain is, then, a ratio; that is, it has no units, but is just a number. Since the strain would equal the change in length if the original length were 1 unit, the value of the strain gives the change in length per unit length.

For example, if the strain in a particular case were 0·000 2, then this would mean that a length of 1 mm would change by 0·000 2 mm, or a length of 1 m would change by 0·000 2 m, or a length of 1 km would change by 0·000 2 km—always assuming, of course, that the conditions of stress were the same in each case.

This definition of strain applies to tensile or compressive strain. In the case of shear strain, it is not only a change in length that is considered. Shear stress tends to make one face of the material slide over an adjacent face. The resulting strain can be visualized as follows.

Consider a pile of thin, flat metal plates, held together by springs passed through holes in the plates. If the top of the pile were pushed sideways, the adjacent plates would slide over each other, and the whole pile would take on a distorted shape as shown in diagram 66.

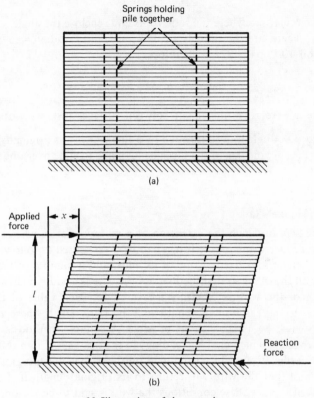

66. Illustration of shear strain

The shear strain is measured by the ratio $\frac{x}{l}$, where x is the relative movement between the top surface and the bottom surface, and l is the perpendicular distance between these surfaces. It is sometimes convenient to measure shear strain in terms of the inclination of the side of the block to its original direction, and this is shown as angle γ in diagram 66. (γ is a Greek letter, often used to mean an angle. It is pronounced 'gamma'.) Angle γ is usually very small for normal cases of shear strain, and it can be shown that the ratio $\frac{x}{l}$ is equal to the angle γ measured in radians. An angle γ in radians is defined by the ratio

$$\gamma = \frac{\text{arc length}}{\text{radius}}$$

for a circular arc where the radii to its ends enclose the angle γ between them. There are 2π radians in $360°$, so that 1 radian $\simeq 57·3°$. (See Section 10.1, page 272.) Therefore,

$$\text{shear strain} = \frac{x}{l} = \underline{\gamma \text{ radians}} \quad . \quad . \quad . \quad \text{(iii)}$$

where x = relative movement between surfaces distance l apart

and γ = angle moved through by a line which was originally perpendicular to the faces being made to slide over one another.

5.6. Hooke's law

The way in which the extension of a material varies when it is subjected to increasing tensile forces can be investigated as follows. A wire of the material is fixed at one of its ends, and a number of masses are hung on the other so that the load on the wire is steadily increased. The length of the wire is carefully measured for each value of the load. Since the increases in its length may be fairly small, these measurements must be as accurate as possible. A suitable method is to use a vernier scale, which enables readings to the nearest 0·2 mm to be made fairly easily. Provided that the load on the wire is not too great, it will be found that the wire will return to its original length if the load is removed. Under these conditions the wire is said to be elastic.

From the readings taken during this experiment, which the student should perform for himself, the values of the tensile stress and the corresponding tensile strain can be calculated, by means of the relationships

$$\text{tensile stress} = \frac{\text{tensile force on wire}}{\text{cross-sectional area of wire}}$$

$$\text{tensile strain} = \frac{\text{extension of wire}}{\text{original length of wire}}$$

If a graph of these values is plotted, it is found to be a straight line, as shown in diagram 67.

If too great a stress is applied to the wire, this graph will depart from a straight line, and the wire will cease to be in an elastic state. The maximum stress that can be applied before the material of the wire takes on a permanent strain is known as the ELASTIC LIMIT.

For stresses below the elastic limit, the wire will return to its original length if the load is removed. Once the stress has exceeded the elastic

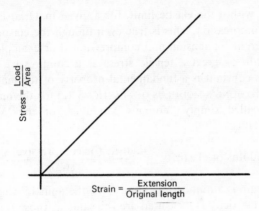

67. Graph of stress/strain for a wire in
tension

limit, a permanent strain or deformation will take place, and the wire will not return to its original length if the load is removed.

From these results it follows that, *provided the elastic limit is not exceeded*, the strain produced is directly proportional to the stress producing it. This means that if the stress is doubled, the strain will be doubled. This may be expressed by the relationship:

$$\frac{\text{stress}}{\text{strain}} = \text{constant} \ . \qquad . \qquad . \qquad . \qquad \text{(iv)}$$

Although the test is more difficult to carry out without special apparatus, a similar result can be obtained for a material in compression or in shear. These results are stated in Hooke's law (named after the scientist who first reported this relationship in about 1700).

'Within the elastic limit, the strain produced is directly proportional to the stress producing it.'

Strictly, the LIMIT OF PROPORTIONALITY, up to which $\dfrac{\text{stress}}{\text{strain}}$ = constant, may differ from the elastic limit. For a material such as steel, however, the two limits are practically the same.

5.7. Young's modulus of elasticity

For most materials, the constant ratio $\dfrac{\text{stress}}{\text{strain}}$ is found to have the same value, within the elastic limit, for a given material under either tension or compression. This is true even though the elastic limit may be very different for tension and compression. For example, cast iron cannot sustain as great a tensile stress as a compressive stress. The value of this constant is a fundamental property of the material itself, and is called YOUNG'S MODULUS OF ELASTICITY (E) for the material. It is sometimes called simply 'Young's Modulus', or the 'Modulus of Elasticity'. Thus

$$\text{Young's modulus of elasticity} = \frac{\text{tensile (or compressive) stress}}{\text{strain}} \quad \text{(v)}$$

Since the strain is a number, without units, the units in which Young's modulus of elasticity is measured are the same as those for stress; i.e. force per unit area. The unit generally used is kN/mm^2.

5.8. Modulus of rigidity

For shear stress, the constant ratio $\dfrac{\text{stress}}{\text{strain}}$ for a given material is found to be different from Young's modulus of elasticity. This ratio for shear stress is called the MODULUS OF RIGIDITY (G) for the material. Thus

$$\text{modulus of rigidity} = \frac{\text{shear stress}}{\text{strain}} \quad \cdot \quad \cdot \quad \cdot \quad \text{(vi)}$$

The units in which the modulus of rigidity is measured are also those of stress, and again the unit kN/mm^2 is generally used. The table on p. 157 gives typical values of the modulus of elasticity and the modulus of rigidity (known as the 'elastic constants') for some of the more common engineering materials. Note that, in general, the modulus of rigidity is less than that of elasticity. This shows that most materials require a smaller shear stress than tensile or compressive stress to produce a given strain.

Material	Young's Modulus of Elasticity E, kN/mm²	Modulus of Rigidity G, kN/mm²
Wrought iron	190	83
Steel	205	90
Cast iron	110	48
Copper	96	39
Brass	83	37
Wood	9·6	0·55

Typical average values of the elastic constants.

The actual values may vary with the composition or heat treatment of the material.

5.9. Examples

(i) A wire 3m long and 3·15 mm diameter is extended by 0·9 mm when a tensile force of 200 N is applied to it. Calculate Young's modulus of elasticity for the material of the wire, assuming that the elastic limit has not been exceeded.

$$\text{Cross-sectional area of wire} = \frac{\pi}{4} \times (3·15)^2 \text{ mm}^2$$

$$= 7·79 \text{ mm}^2$$

$$\text{Tensile stress in wire} = \frac{\text{load}}{\text{cross-sectional area}}$$

$$= \frac{200 \text{ N}}{7·79 \text{ mm}^2}$$

$$= 25·7 \text{ N/mm}^2$$

$$\text{Original length of wire} = 3 \text{ m}$$

$$= 3000 \text{ mm}$$

$$\text{Extension of wire} = 0·9 \text{ mm}$$

$$\text{Tensile strain in wire} = \frac{\text{extension}}{\text{original length}}$$

$$= \frac{0 \cdot 9}{3000}$$

$$= 0 \cdot 000\ 3$$

Then Young's modulus
of elasticity $= \dfrac{\text{stress}}{\text{strain}}$

$$= \frac{25 \cdot 7\ \text{N/mm}^2}{0 \cdot 000\ 3}$$

$$= 85\ 700\ \text{N/mm}^2$$

Modulus of elasticity of
wire material $= \underline{85 \cdot 7\ \text{kN/mm}^2}$

(ii) What will be the extension of a steel rod having a diameter of 11·28 mm and a length of 200 mm if a tensile force of 10 kN is applied to it? Take E for steel as 205 kN/mm².

Cross-sectional area of rod $= \dfrac{\pi}{4} \times (11 \cdot 28)^2\ \text{mm}^2$

$$= 100\ \text{mm}^2$$

Tensile stress in rod $= \dfrac{\text{load}}{\text{cross-sectional area}}$

$$= \frac{10\ \text{kN}}{100\ \text{mm}^2}$$

$$= 0 \cdot 1\ \text{kN/mm}^2$$

But $\qquad E = \dfrac{\text{stress}}{\text{strain}}$

or $\qquad 205 = \dfrac{0 \cdot 1}{\text{strain}}\ \text{kN/mm}^2$

$\therefore \qquad \text{strain} = \dfrac{0 \cdot 1}{205}$

$$= 0 \cdot 000\ 487$$

But $\qquad \text{strain} = \dfrac{\text{extension}}{\text{original length}}$

$$= \frac{\text{extension (mm)}}{200\ \text{(mm)}}$$

$$\therefore \frac{\text{extension (mm)}}{200 \text{ (mm)}} = 0.000\ 487$$

$$\text{Extension} = 200 \times 0.000\ 487 \text{ mm}$$
$$= 0.097\ 4 \text{ mm}$$
$$\simeq 0.1 \text{ mm}$$
$$\text{Extension of bar} = \underline{0.1 \text{ mm}}$$

It would be very difficult to measure the extension any more accurately than is implied by this answer.

(iii) A brass cylinder has a diameter of 25 mm and a height of 50 mm. The cylinder supports a compressive load of 20 kN. By how much does the cylinder shorten when the load is applied?

Take E for brass as 83 kN/mm².

$$\text{Cross-sectional area of cylinder} = \frac{\pi}{4} \times 25^2 \text{ mm}^2$$

$$= 491 \text{ mm}^2$$

$$\text{Compressive stress in cylinder} = \frac{\text{load}}{\text{cross-sectional area}}$$

$$= \frac{20 \text{ kN}}{491 \text{ mm}^2}$$

$$= 0.040\ 7 \text{ kN/mm}^2$$

$$\therefore \quad E = 83 = \frac{\text{stress}}{\text{strain}} \text{ kN/mm}^2$$

$$= \frac{0.040\ 7}{\text{strain}} \text{ kN/mm}^2$$

$$\text{Compressive strain in cylinder} = \frac{0.040\ 7}{83}$$

$$= 0.000\ 491$$

$$\therefore \quad \frac{\text{compression}}{\text{original length}} = 0.000\ 491 \ (= \text{compressive strain})$$

$$\text{or} \quad \text{compression} = 50 \times 0.000\ 491 \text{ mm}$$
$$= 0.024\ 5 \text{ mm}$$
$$\simeq 0.02 \text{ mm}$$

Cylinder shortens by $\underline{0.02 \text{ mm}}$.

(iv) Three plates are held together by two cylindrical rivets, as shown in diagram 68. If a direct pull of 5 kN is applied between one plate and the other two, as shown, estimate the diameter of the rivets. The shear stress in the rivets is not to exceed 40 N/mm².

As seen from the diagram, if the plates are to be pulled apart, each rivet would have to shear twice; i.e., across two faces each.

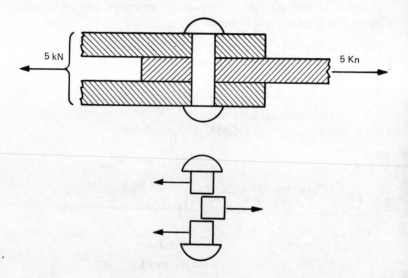

68. Rivet in *double* shear—numerical example

Let the diameter of each rivet be d mm.
Then the total area resisting shear

$$= 4 \times \frac{\pi}{4} \times d^2 \, mm^2 \text{ (2 rivets, each in double shear)}$$

$$= \pi d^2 \, mm^2$$

total shear force $= 5 \, kN$

$$\therefore \text{ shear stress} = \frac{5 \, kN}{\pi d^2 \, mm^2}$$

But this has a value of about 40 N/mm²

i.e. $$40 = \frac{5000}{\pi d^2}$$

or
$$d^2 = \frac{5000}{40\pi}$$
$$= 39\cdot8$$
$$d = 6\cdot30$$
$$\text{Diameter of rivets} = \underline{6\cdot30 \text{ mm}}$$

(v) A square hole having 12 mm sides is to be punched out of a metal plate 1·6 mm thick. The shear stress required to cause fracture is 350 N/mm². What force must be applied to the punching die? What would be the compressive stress in the punch?

Area of metal to be sheared

$$= (\text{perimeter of hole}) \times (\text{thickness of metal plate})$$
$$= 4 \times 12 \times 1\cdot6 \text{ mm}^2$$
$$= 76\cdot8 \text{ mm}^2$$

If the shear stress is to be 350 N/mm², then

$$350 = \frac{\text{force on punch}}{\text{area resisting shear}} \text{ N/mm}^2$$

or   force on punch $= 350 \times 76\cdot8$ N
$$= 26\ 850 \text{ N} = \underline{26\cdot85 \text{ kN}}$$

Cross-sectional area of punch $= 12 \times 12 \text{ mm}^2$
$$= 144 \text{ mm}^2$$

Compressive stress in punch $= \dfrac{\text{load}}{\text{cross-sectional area}}$

$$= \frac{26\ 850 \text{ N}}{144 \text{ mm}^2}$$

$$= 186\cdot5 \text{ N/mm}^2$$

Force required on punch $= \underline{26\cdot85 \text{ kN}}$
Compressive stress in punch $= \underline{186\cdot5 \text{ N/mm}^2}$

5.10. Tensile testing of materials

In addition to the value of Young's modulus of elasticity, there are other properties of a material which may be determined by a tensile test, and which may be used as a measure of the quality of the material. These other properties will be discussed more fully a little later, but they include the elastic limit, and the load required to cause fracture.

Variations in the composition and heat treatment of the material can cause quite considerable variations in such properties, and it is common industrial practice to specify the values required of a material for a particular application. These values are checked by a tensile test, which is carried out to destruction on a sample of the material.

In order that such tests may be used for the purpose of comparison, certain standard shapes and sizes have been specified for samples used as the test pieces. One very commonly used standard test piece for tensile tests, as detailed in a British Standard Specification, is illustrated in diagram 69.

The diameter of 11·28 mm² has been chosen in order that the cross-sectional area of the test piece shall be 100 mm². Other diameters may be used for other standard test pieces.

From the size of the sample given here, it is evident that the tensile-testing machine must be capable of exerting forces of many kilonewtons in order to break such a sample of, say, high-tensile steel (which will require a stress of the order of 1·5 kN/mm² to produce fracture). Since it may be required to apply the load in small, accurately measured steps, these machines may be large, complex and expensive. Many will also possess the facility of applying the load at a controllable, measured rate, as this may also determine the behaviour of the material being tested. Furthermore, it is usual to arrange that the machine is capable

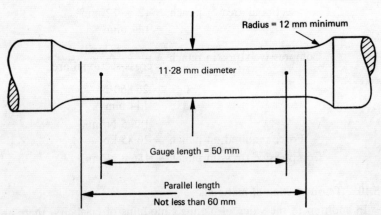

Radius = 12 mm minimum

11·28 mm diameter

Gauge length = 50 mm

Parallel length
Not less than 60 mm

69. A standard tensile test piece

of applying compressive loads to differently shaped samples, although special machines are also available for these compression tests.

It is not proposed to give constructional details for a tensile-testing machine here, but the student should inspect such a machine and at least see a tensile test carried out to destruction on a sample if this is at all possible.

5.11. Load-extension graph

If a graph is plotted of the results of a tensile test to destruction on a sample of material, the general shape of the graph will be as shown in diagram 70, although differences in detail will be found between the graphs for different types of material.

As the load is first applied to the test piece, the extension increases proportionally to the load until point A is reached. This represents the 'elastic' condition of the material, and if the load were to be removed at any time up to this point, a negligible permanent extension would be found; i.e., the material would return to its original length for all practical purposes. Beyond this elastic limit, however, the extension produced results in a permanent strain. (Strictly, the elastic limit may not coincide with the limit of proportionality, but few of these 'points' can be sharply defined in a practical case.)

At some load just beyond the elastic limit, a more rapid stretching of the material takes place quite suddenly with no increase in load. This is shown at point B, which is known as the YIELD POINT of the material. Beyond the yield point, the extension increases rapidly with increasing load, for a material such as mild steel. In this region the material is said to be DUCTILE, and is in a 'plastic' condition where it stretches much more under a given increase in load than is the case during the 'elastic' stage up to point A. Any extension during this ductile stage is quite permanent

At the maximum load (point C in diagram 70), the cross-sectional area of the sample will decrease at a point usually about half-way between the ends, forming a 'waist'. This reduction in cross-sectional area will give an increase in the tensile stress at the waist, and the material would fracture at this point if the load were to be sustained. If, however, the load is carefully reduced as shown in the graph, further extension occurs up to the final point of fracture, at D. Diagram 71 shows the appearance of the two parts of the broken test piece when placed side by side after fracture.

The true value of stress required to break the sample would be given by (load to cause fracture) ÷ (cross-sectional area at the point of fracture). However, it is standard industrial practice to relate all values of stress during this test to the original cross-sectional area of the test piece, and the maximum or breaking stress is always taken as (maximum load, at point C in the diagram) ÷ (original cross-sectional area).

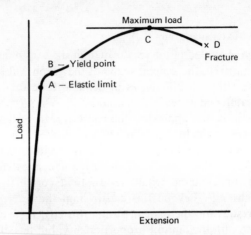

70. Typical load-extension graph for a ductile material. (Not to scale)

This value is known as the ULTIMATE TENSILE STRESS (or sometimes 'ultimate tensile strength') for the material. In other words,

$$\text{ultimate tensile stress} = \frac{\text{maximum load}}{\text{original cross-sectional area}} . \qquad \text{(vii)}$$

The total increase in length, measured after fracture with the broken ends fitted together, is an indication of the permanent strain given to the material, mainly during its ductile state. It is usually measured in terms of

$$\frac{\text{percentage}}{\text{elongation}} = \frac{\text{elongation during test to destruction}}{\text{original length}} \times 100\% \qquad \text{(viii)}$$

This value is a measure of the 'ductility' of the material. A ductile material will have a fairly high value of percentage elongation. Typical values of percentage elongation for ductile materials such as mild steel, copper, brass, aluminium, silver and gold may be between 15 and 75%. Wide variations are, however, possible because of differences in composition and heat treatment.

On the other hand, brittle materials such as cast iron, hardened steels and some special alloys, have very low values of percentage elongation—of the order of 2% or less. Such materials have a negligible ductile stage during a tensile test to destruction. Very little if any waist is formed in the specimen, and fracture may occur without any marked yield point being noticeable. A typical load-extension graph for a brittle material is shown in diagram 72.

The properties of ductility or brittleness, together with certain other physical properties of materials, are considered in Chapter 23.

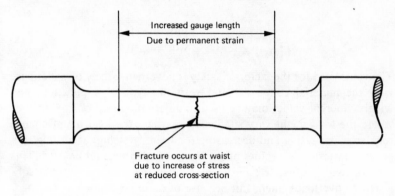

71. Test piece after fracture

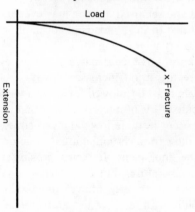

72. Typical load-extension graph for a brittle material. (Not to scale)

5.12. Factor of safety

For most practical applications, the stress in the material concerned must not be allowed to exceed the elastic limit. Otherwise, permanent strain will be suffered by the material, with consequent permanent change in its physical dimensions. A maximum 'safe' working stress is used in design calculations, and the value of this working stress is derived from the ultimate tensile stress of the material by means of a number known as the FACTOR OF SAFETY. Then

$$\text{working stress} = \frac{\text{ultimate stress}}{\text{factor of safety}} \qquad . \qquad . \qquad \text{(ix)}$$

or

$$\text{factor of safety} = \frac{\text{ultimate stress}}{\text{working stress}} \qquad . \qquad . \qquad \text{(x)}$$

The value used for the factor of safety is governed largely by experience with the material concerned and with the type of application, and widely different values may be used in different cases. For applications where the load might vary suddenly, or where the load might change regularly, increasing and decreasing (or even reversing) according to a general pattern, high values of the factor of safety would be used. This type of load is often referred to as a 'live' load, and a material subjected to live loads might fail because of an effect known as FATIGUE. It is found that if a stress whose value may be well below the ultimate is repeatedly applied and removed, fatigue may eventually cause fracture. For material subjected to steady loads of constant value ('dead' loads), a lower factor of safety might be used.

Another effect known as CREEP may also occur, especially at higher temperatures. Here the strain increases slowly at constant values of stress, and this again must be allowed for when a value for the factor of safety is being decided. It is of interest to note that under some circumstances creep can occur at quite low values of stress, and the designer may be forced to allow for a certain amount of deformation during the working life of the equipment. It seems possible that creep occurs with stress at all temperatures, but the effect is usually of importance only at high temperatures (say above about 300°C), where creep increases very rapidly with temperature and stress.

5.13. Example

A tie-bar in a steel structure (that is, a bar under tension in the structure) is of rectangular section 50 mm × 30 mm. The extension measured in a 250 mm length of the tie-bar when load was applied to the structure was 0·1 mm.

Find (i) the tensile stress in the tie-bar
  (ii) the tensile force acting on the tie-bar
  (iii) the factor of safety used.
Take E as 205 kN/mm² and the ultimate tensile stress as 460 N/mm².

$$\text{Strain in tie-bar} = \frac{\text{extension}}{\text{original length}}$$

$$= \frac{0 \cdot 1 \text{ mm}}{250 \text{ mm}}$$

$$= 0 \cdot 000 \, 4$$

$$\text{Modulus of elasticity E} = \frac{\text{stress}}{\text{strain}}$$

$$\therefore \text{ stress} = \text{E} \times \text{strain}$$
$$= 205 \times 0 \cdot 000 \, 4 \text{ kN/mm}^2$$
$$= 0 \cdot 082 \text{ kN/mm}^2 = 82 \text{ N/mm}^2$$

$$\text{Stress} = \frac{\text{load}}{\text{cross-sectional area}}$$

$$\therefore \text{ load} = \text{stress} \times \text{cross-sectional area}$$
$$= (0 \cdot 082 \text{ kN/mm}^2) \times (50 \times 30 \text{ mm}^2)$$
$$= 123 \text{ kN}$$

$$\text{Factor of safety} = \frac{\text{ultimate stress}}{\text{working stress}}$$

$$= \frac{460 \text{ N/mm}^2}{82 \text{ N/mm}^2}$$

$$= 5 \cdot 62$$

For the given tie-bar, (i) tensile stress $= 82 \text{ N/mm}^2$
        (ii) tensile force $= 123 \text{ kN}$
        (iii) factor of safety $= 5 \cdot 62$

CHAPTER SUMMARY

If a material is in tension, it is stretched by the applied forces.
If a material is in compression, it is compressed by the applied forces.
If a material is in shear, adjacent faces in the material tend to slide
over one another.

$$\text{Stress} = \frac{\text{force}}{\text{cross-sectional area}}. \text{ Typical unit is N/mm}^2.$$

$$\text{Tensile or compressive strain} = \frac{\text{change in length}}{\text{original length}}$$

$$\text{Shear strain} = \frac{\text{relative movement of two faces parallel to applied forces}}{\text{perpendicular distance between the faces}}$$

$$= \gamma \text{ radians}$$

where γ is the inclination of a line originally perpendicular to the applied forces in the plane containing them.

Hooke's law: strain $\propto$ stress up to limit of proportionality

i.e.
$$\frac{\text{stress}}{\text{strain}} = \text{constant up to limit of proportionality}$$

$$= \text{Young's modulus of elasticity (E) for the material concerned.}$$

$$\frac{\text{shear stress}}{\text{shear strain}} = \text{modulus of rigidity (G) for the material concerned.}$$

Elastic limit – greatest stress for which strain is not permanent.

Limit of
proportionality – greatest stress for which strain $\propto$ stress
Yield point – stress at which strain increases suddenly without increase in stress.

$$\text{Ultimate tensile stress} = \frac{\text{maximum tensile load}}{\text{original cross-sectional area}}$$

$$\text{Percentage elongation} = \frac{\text{elongation during test to destruction}}{\text{original length}} \times 100\%.$$

A ductile material has a pronounced yield point and significant percentage elongation.

A brittle material has no pronounced yield point and very little percentage elongation.

$$\text{Factor of safety} = \frac{\text{ultimate stress}}{\text{working stress}}$$

QUESTIONS

1. (a) Describe an experiment using a spiral spring to find the relationship between the load applied and extension it produced.

(b) If a spiral spring is 300 mm long when unloaded and a force of 50 N extends it 50 mm, what force is necessary to give the spring a length of 450 mm?

2. In a laboratory experiment a wire of diameter 1 mm and original length 2·25 m was subjected to increasing loads, and the extension was measured with a vernier for each load, with the following results:

Load in N	30	55	80	105	130	155
Vernier reading in mm	0·5	1·5	2·75	3·75	4·87	5·75

Plot a load/extension graph, and from it determine the value of Young's modulus of elasticity for the material of the wire.

3. (a) Explain what is meant by (i) Hooke's law, (ii) Young's modulus of elasticity.

(b) A tie-bar, of rectangular cross-section and 3 m long, is to carry a load of 75 kN. If the thickness of the bar is 16 mm and the tensile stress is to be limited to 120 N/mm², determine the necessary width of the bar.

If E for the material is 205 kN/mm², calculate the extension that would occur due to this load.

4. (a) Give three different examples on a motor vehicle where the part is subjected to (i) a tensile stress, (ii) a shear stress, (iii) a compressive stress.

(b) A brake rod is 10 mm diameter and is subjected to a pull of 1·5 kN when the brake is applied. Calculate the stress in the rod during braking.

5. A 22 mm diameter punch and die produce blanks from nickel sheet 3 mm thick having a shear strength of 370 N/mm².

Calculate (a) the force required for the operation, and (b) the stress in the punch.

6. A mild-steel bush 50 mm outside diameter, 30 mm bore, and 125 mm long is placed vertically in a press and subjected to a vertical load of 50 kN. Find (a) the stress, (b) the decrease in length.

E for mild steel is 205 kN/mm².

7. The following results were obtained in the experimental determination of Young's modulus for mild steel wire:

Load in N	0	50	100	150	200	250	300
Extension in mm	0	1·1	1·9	2·7	3·5	4·3	5·1

Plot the load/extension graph and state what may be deduced from its character.

If the initial length of the wire was 2·3 m and its diameter 0·94 mm, evaluate Young's modulus for mild steel from the graph.

8. (a) Draw a neat sketch of a typical load/elongation diagram to the point of fracture for mild steel, showing (i) the maximum load point, (ii) the yield point.

(b) A shaft is connected to another shaft through a flanged coupling by four bolts equally spaced on a 300 mm diameter pitch circle. If the shafts transmit a torque of 2·5 kNm, and the shear stress in the bolts is not to exceed 30 N/mm², calculate the required bolt diameter to the nearest 1 mm.

9. (a) Define Young's modulus and the modulus of rigidity.

(b) A bar of a certain metal is 1 m long and 50 mm diameter. When subjected to a tensile load of 25 kN the change of length is 0·065 mm. Calculate Young's modulus for the material.

(c) A block of rubber 500 mm long, 20 mm wide and 400 mm high has its lower face fixed and its upper face subjected to a pull of 400 N parallel to the face. The upper face is found to move 20 mm relative to the lower face. Calculate the modulus of rigidity for rubber.

10. Define the term 'Elasticity'.

A hollow cast-iron column of square cross-section 2·4 m long has its internal sides measuring 150 mm and is to carry a load of 1 MN. If the safe working stress is to be limited to 110 N/mm², calculate:

(a) the area of metal required to carry the load,

(b) the thickness of the walls of the column.

If the value of E for the material is 110 kN/mm², by how much will the column shorten under the load of 1 MN?

11. State Hooke's law and sketch the graph connecting the two quantities with which this law is concerned.

A tie-bar of rectangular cross-section is to carry a load of 75 kN. If the thickness of the bar is 16 mm and the tensile stress is to be limited to 120 N/mm², determine the necessary width of the bar. If it is found that the bar extends 0·06 mm over a 100 mm length, determine the value of the modulus of elasticity.

12. (a) (i) State the relationship that exists between 'force' and 'extension' when an elastic material is loaded within the limit of proportionality.

(ii) Describe how this relationship may be demonstrated using a loaded spring.

(b) A bar of steel is in tension and it extends 0·05 mm due to a load of 10 kN.

(i) Find the probable extension due to a load of 12 kN if the loading is within the limit of proportionality.

(ii) If the bar is 330 mm long and has a cross-sectional area of 320 mm², find the value of Young's modulus in kN/mm².

13. (a) Distinguish between hardness and brittleness in a material.

(b) A vertical steel rod 3 m long carries a load of 20 kN. If the extension of the rod is not to exceed 0·2 mm, calculate (i) the minimum possible cross-sectional area of the rod, (ii) the tensile stress in the rod.

(Assume E for the steel to be 205 kN/mm².)

14. A piece of elastic is hung from one end and various loads are attached at the other. The following table shows the length of elastic for given loads:

F (load in N)	0·6	1·2	1·8	2·4	3·0	6·0
l (length in mm)	530	550	570	590	610	710

Show that F and l are connected by a law of the type l = aF + b, and find the values of a and b.

What will be the length of the elastic (a) with no load, and (b) with a load of 13·5 N? What assumptions have you made to arrive at your answer to part (b)?

15. (a) Explain, by reference to one example of each in engineering practice, what is meant by tensile, compressive and shear force.

(b) The return spring of a valve has a stiffness of 8 kN/m. How far will the valve open when the applied force is 90 N? What applied force will cause the valve to open 7·5 mm?

16. (a) Describe how you would obtain a load/extension graph for a specimen of steel wire.

(b) Explain what is meant by the 'elastic limit' for such a specimen.

(c) The extension of a wire 3 m long for a load of 60 N is 1·17 mm. Determine the length of the wire when the load is 90 N, stating any assumptions made.

17. Explain the meaning of the terms 'stress', 'strain' and 'modulus of elasticity'.

A pull of 1 kN is applied to a wire operating a machine by remote control. The wire is 21 m long and 130 mm² cross-sectional area. If the movement at the machine end must be 50 mm, find the movement required at the operator's end.

Assume E = 205 kN/mm².

18. What is meant by the terms 'elastic limit' and 'factor of safety'?

A metal tube of outside diameter 75 mm and length 1·65 m is to carry a compressive load of 60 kN. If the allowable axial stress is 75 N/mm², calculate the inside diameter of the tube.

If the modulus of elasticity for the material is 90 kN/mm², by how much will the tube shorten under this load?

19. Define the following terms: (a) yield stress; (b) modulus of elasticity; (c) factor of safety. In a tensile test on a sample of steel in the form of a bar 300 mm long and of circular section of diameter 26 mm, the readings obtained were as follows:

Applied load (kN)	7·05	14·12	21·2	28·25	35·32	42·4	49·45	56·5
Extension (mm)	0·025	0·046	0·063	0·086	0·104	0·124	0·147	0·163

Plot a stress/strain graph for this material and hence determine the modulus of elasticity. Use it to find the extension produced on the same specimen by a load of 40 kN.

20. Define the following terms:
(a) yield stress, (b) ultimate tensile strength,
(c) factor of safety, (d) modulus of elasticity.
The ultimate stress for a certain steel is 450 N/mm². What is the maximum load which a rod 50 mm diameter can carry with a factor of safety of 5? If the rod is 1·5 m long, determine the extension under this loading.
(Modulus of elasticity = 200 kN/mm².)

21. Explain with diagrams what is meant by tensile stress and shear stress.
The ultimate shear stress for the sheet steel from which armature laminations are made is 280 N/mm². Determine the force necessary to punch an annular ring 300 mm internal and 450 mm external diameter from a sheet of material 0·63 mm thick.

22. Define the terms 'modulus of elasticity' and 'modulus of rigidity'.
Calculate the force required to punch a hole 75 mm diameter in a steel sheet 1·25 mm thick, if the shear strength of the material is 420 N/mm². What mean compressive stress is set up in the punch during this operation?

23. Define (a) modulus of elasticity, (b) yield point.
A mild steel specimen of diameter 11·28 mm was found to have an extension on a 200 mm gauge length of 0·15 mm when a load of 15 kN was applied. Determine Young's modulus for the material, assuming the load to lie below the elastic limit. If a load of 60 kN produced an extension of 0·75 mm, determine whether the stress will still be within the elastic limit.

24. A tubular strut carries a load of 27·5 kN. The outer diameter is 30 mm and the ultimate compressive stress for the material is 320 N/mm². Using a factor of safety of 5, calculate the inside diameter of the tube. If the original length of the strut is 250 mm, determine its length when loaded. The modulus of elasticity is 83 kN/mm².

25. The following results were obtained during a tensile test on a steel test piece of 11·28 mm diameter and 50 mm gauge length:

Load in kN	2·5	7·5	12·5	17·5	22·5	27·5	30	32·5	34	35
Extension μm	5	18	31	44	55	67	80	86	97	153

Maximum load reached during test to fracture = 45·25 kN.
Final distance between gauge points = 70 mm.
Final diameter of bar at point of fracture = 7·4 mm.

From these results determine:
(a) Young's modulus of elasticity for the steel,
(b) the stress at the limit of proportionality,
(c) the ultimate tensile stress,
(d) the percentage elongation,
(e) the percentage contraction of area.

26. Sketch a typical stress/strain curve as would be obtained in a tensile test on a ductile material. Mark on this figure the elastic limit stress and ultimate stress. In such a test, a specimen of diameter 11·28 mm gave an extension of 0·31 mm on a gauge length of 200 mm at the elastic limit load of 31 kN. Determine the elastic limit stress and Young's modulus for the material.

27. What is meant by (i) stress, (ii) strain, (iii) modulus of elasticity, (iv) factor of safety, (v) ultimate tensile stress, (vi) yield point?

A flat steel tie-bar 4·5 m long, is found to be 2·4 mm short. It is sprung into place by means of drifts driven into holes in the ends of the bar.

Determine (a) the stress in the bar,

(b) the factor of safety if the material of the tie-bar has an ultimate tensile stress of 450 N/mm².

Take E for the material as 205 kN/mm².

6. Work and Energy

The terms 'work' and 'energy' are probably already familiar to the student in a general way. Expressions such as 'man at work' or 'an energy-giving food' are in fairly common use, and give a general impression of the meaning of the terms. However, work and energy have been given much more precise scientific meanings than these rather vague statements imply, and the purpose of this chapter is to state and explain these more exact meanings.

6.1. Work. Units of work

If a body moves as a result of a force being applied to it, the force is said to do work on the body. The amount of work done is measured by the product of the applied force and the distance moved in the direction of the force. In other words,

$$\text{work done} = (\text{force}) \times (\text{distance moved in the direction of the force}) \qquad . \qquad . \qquad . \qquad \text{(i)}$$

Thus the same amount of work is done when the point of application of a force of 1 N moves through a distance of 30 m in the direction of the force, as when the point of application of a force of 10 kN moves through a distance of 3 mm in the direction of the force. If either the force or the distance moved in the direction of the force are zero, no work is done. For example, if the resistance to motion were zero, no force would be needed to maintain movement, and no work would be done. Equally, a man pushing hard against a heavy truck without managing to move it at all does no work in the strict scientific sense, even though he may feel tired afterwards. Both the force and movement in the direction of the force are necessary if work is to be accomplished.

Work is done in overcoming resistance to movement. If the resistance to movement is small, the work done can only be relatively small. This may be illustrated, for example, in terms of the difference between driving a nail into seasoned oak or into a block of moist putty.

Work is said to be done *on* the body responsible for the resisting force *by* the force which overcomes that resistance. For example, a man pushing a truck against the forces resisting its motion does work on the truck, provided he moves it in the direction of his applied force. A man trying to stop a truck moving towards him by pushing against it has work done on him by the truck. Similarly, a man lifting a heavy weight does work against the gravitational force exerted on the mass of material he is lifting. A man lowering a heavy mass slowly has work done on him by the gravitational force. It is interesting to note that if work done *by* the man is thought of as being 'positive', while work done *on* the man is negative, the total work done in lifting and lowering a heavy weight is zero.

The units in which work is measured are those of (force units) × (length units), i.e. newton metres. In the SI system of units work and energy are measured in joules to distinguish from the units for the moment of a force, which are dimensionally the same (see Section 4.1, page 94) 1 joule = 1 newton metre, 1 J = 1 Nm.

6.2. Examples

(i) Find the work done when a force of 20 N moves through a distance of 10 m along its line of action.

$$\begin{aligned}
\text{Work done} &= \text{force} \times \text{distance moved in direction of force} \\
&= 20 \text{ N} \times 10 \text{ m} \\
&= \underline{\underline{200 \text{ J}}}
\end{aligned}$$

(ii) A body is moved through a distance of 5 m against a constant force of 2 kN which opposes its motion. What is the work done?

A force of 2 kN must be applied to the body to overcome the resistive forces. (Strictly, a slightly greater force would be required if the body were stationary to begin with, see Chapter 9, page 258.)

$$\begin{aligned}
\text{Work done} &= \text{force} \times \text{distance moved in direction of force} \\
&= 2 \text{ kN} \times 5 \text{ m} \\
&= 10 \text{ kNm} \\
&= \underline{\underline{10 \text{ kJ}}}
\end{aligned}$$

Note that this is either the work done *by* the required applied force, or the work done *on* the body against the action of the resisting force.

(iii) A man lifts a mass of 25 kg from ground level to a height of 1·4 m. What is the work done?

In order to overcome the gravitational force of 25 × 9·81 = 245 N acting vertically downwards the man must exert a force of 245 N vertically upwards.

$$\text{Work done} = \text{force} \times \text{distance moved in direction of force}$$
$$= 245 \text{ N} \times 1\cdot4 \text{ m}$$
$$= 343 \text{ J}$$

(iv) A man rolls a barrel having a mass of 100 kg up an incline of 10° to the horizontal. Find the work done in rolling the barrel 30 m up the slope, neglecting any forces opposing the motion other than on the mass of the barrel.

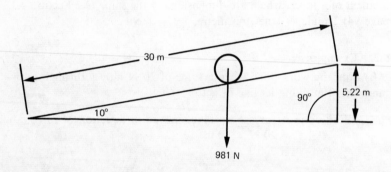

73. Mass being moved up incline—numerical example

In this case, the movement is not entirely in the direction of the force to be overcome (see diagram 73).

If all other opposing forces are neglected, work is only done in this case against the gravitational force of 981 N; and the distance moved must be measured along the line of action of this force. The barrel is seen to be moved only 5·22 m against the 981 N force. (This distance can be found by a scale drawing, or by the use of suitable mathematical tables.) Then

$$\text{work done} = \text{force} \times \text{distance moved in direction of force}$$
$$= 981 \text{ N} \times 5\cdot22 \text{ m}$$
$$= 5120 \text{ J} = 5\cdot12 \text{ kJ}$$

(v) If, in the previous example, an additional force of 250 N acts down the incline to oppose the movement of the barrel, what would then be the total work done?

With the additional resistive force, since this acts *down the incline*, the barrel is moved through 30 m against this resistive force. In other words,

work done against additional resistive force = 250 N × 30 m

= 7500 J = 7·5 kJ

From the previous answer,

work done in raising height of barrel = 5·12 kJ

∴ Total work done = 12·62 kJ

6.3. Work diagrams

It is sometimes convenient to use a diagram to represent the work done by a force. The diagram can take the form of a graph of the applied force against distance moved in the direction of the force. Diagram 74 shows the result where the applied force is constant.

On this diagram, a length measured vertically—parallel to the 'force' axis—will represent a force, to whatever scale is used for that axis. A length measured horizontally—parallel to the 'distance' axis—will

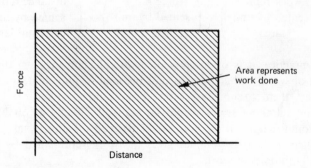

74. Work diagram for a constant force

represent a distance moved in the direction of the force, again to whatever scale is used for the axis.

Since a vertical length multiplied by a horizontal length on this diagram represents an area, this area must represent the result of (force) × (distance moved in direction of force). In other words, an area on this diagram will represent work done. This fact gives the diagram its name.

The scale on which the area represents work done will depend on the scales chosen for the force and distance axes. For example, suppose 20 mm along the force axis represents a force of 50 N, while 20 mm along the distance axis represents a movement of 2 m in the direction of the force. Then an area of 400 mm² on the diagram could be obtained as

$$400 \text{ mm}^2 = (20 \text{ mm vertically}) \times (20 \text{ mm horizontally})$$

so that   400 mm² represents (50 N) × (2 m)

or   400 mm² represents 100 J

The 400 mm² of area could equally well be obtained as (10 mm vertically) × (40 mm horizontally), and this gives the same scale for area:

$$400 \text{ mm}^2 = (10 \text{ mm vertically}) \times (40 \text{ mm horizontally})$$

so that   400 mm² represents (25 N) × (4 m)

or   400 mm² represents 100 J as before.

The scale for work represented by unit area is thus seen to be equal to the product of the scales for the two axes:

$$\begin{pmatrix} \text{work repre-} \\ \text{sented by unit} \\ \text{area} \end{pmatrix} = \begin{pmatrix} \text{force repre-} \\ \text{sented by unit} \\ \text{vertical length} \end{pmatrix} \times \begin{pmatrix} \text{distance repre-} \\ \text{sented by unit} \\ \text{horizontal length} \end{pmatrix}$$

In practice, it is often convenient to calculate the area directly in units of work, rather than to find the area in mm² first, and then to convert them to units of work. For example, a vertical height of 20 mm on these scales would be read off directly as 50 N; and a horizontal length of 20 mm would be read off directly as 2 m. The product of these two values gives the work represented by the area directly in units of work.

These points are illustrated in diagram 75.

The area of each diagram is the same, and represents the same amount of work done.

(a) Area = 100 N × 1 m = 100 J

(b) Area = 50 N × 2 m = 100 J

(c) Area = 25 N × 4 m = 100 J

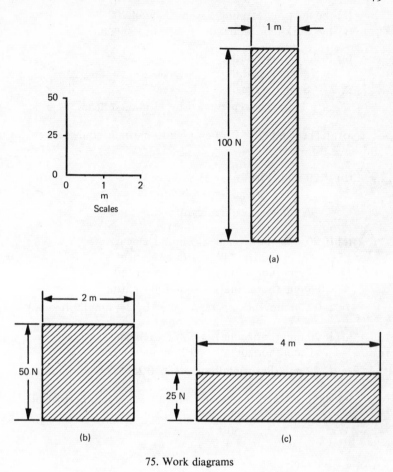

75. Work diagrams

6.4. Examples

(1) A work diagram has the following scales:

Vertical scale: 20 mm represents 10 N force.

Horizontal scale: 20 mm represents 5 m movement in direction of force. Find

    (a) the vertical distance representing a force of 6 N

    (b) the force represented by a vertical distance of 96 mm

    (c) the horizontal distance representing a movement of 0·6 m in the direction of the force

    (d) the movement represented by a horizontal distance of 29 mm

(e) the area representing a work done of 100 J

(f) the work represented by an area of 1000 mm²

(a) If 20 mm (vertical) $\equiv$ 10 N force

$\frac{20}{10}$ mm (vertical) $\equiv$ 1 N force

$\therefore$ 2 × 6 mm (vertical) $\equiv$ 6 N force

$\therefore$ 6 N force is represented by <u>12 mm</u> (vertical)

(NOTE: The symbol $\equiv$ is often used to mean 'is equivalent to', as in this case.)

(b) If 20 mm (vertical) $\equiv$ 10 N force

1 mm (vertical) $\equiv$ 0·5 N force

$\therefore$ 96 mm (vertical) represents <u>48 N</u> force

(c) If 20 mm (horizontal $\equiv$ 5 m movement

$\frac{20}{5}$ mm (horizontal) $\equiv$ 1 m movement

4 mm (horizontal) $\equiv$ 1 m movement

4 × 0·6 mm (horizontal) $\equiv$ 0·6 m movement

$\therefore$ 0·6 m movement is represented by <u>2·4 mm</u> (horizontal)

(d) If 20 mm (horizontal) $\equiv$ 5 m movement

1 mm (horizontal) $\equiv$ 0·25 m movement

$\therefore$ 29 mm (horizontal) represents 0·25 × 29 = <u>7·25 m</u>

(e) 400 mm² area $\equiv$ (20 mm vertical) × (20 mm horizontal)

$\equiv$ (10 N) × (5 m)

$\equiv$ 50 J

$\therefore$ $\frac{400}{50}$ mm² area $\equiv$ 1 J

or 8 × 100 mm² area $\equiv$ 100 J

$\therefore$ 100 J work done is represented by an area of <u>800 mm²</u>

(f) From this,

$$400 \text{ mm}^2 \text{ area} \equiv 50 \text{ J}$$

$$\therefore 1000 \text{ mm}^2 \text{ area} \equiv \frac{1000}{400} \times 50 \text{ J}$$

$$\therefore 1000 \text{ mm}^2 \text{ area represents } \underline{125 \text{ J}} \text{ work done.}$$

(ii) An area of 1000 mm² on a work diagram represents work done of 50 J. If the force scale on the diagram is 20 mm $\equiv$ 10 N, find the distance scale.

$$1000 \text{ mm}^2 \text{ area} \equiv 50 \text{ J}$$
$$\therefore\ 400 \text{ mm}^2 \text{ area} \equiv 20 \text{ J}$$

Let the distance scale be 20 mm $\equiv x$ m distance moved. Then

$$400 \text{ mm}^2 \text{ area} \equiv (20 \text{ mm vertical}) \times (20 \text{ mm horizontal})$$
$$\equiv (10 \text{ N}) \times (x \text{ m})$$
$$\equiv 10\ x \text{ J}$$
$$\therefore\ 10\ x \equiv 20$$
$$\therefore\ x \equiv 2$$

Distance scale is $\underline{\underline{20 \text{ mm} \equiv 2 \text{ m}}}$ movement in direction of force.

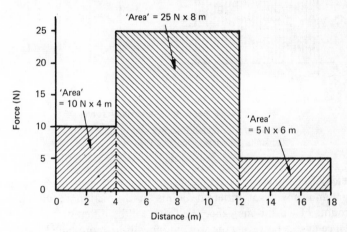

76. Work diagram—numerical example

(iii) The force resisting the movement of part of a mechanism changes suddenly at points in the movement, as shown in diagram 76. Find the total work done in moving the part over its full range of movement.

The total work done will be represented by the total area enclosed by this work diagram. In this case, it is appropriate to calculate the area directly in terms of the units of work which it represents. Then

total work done = total area under force-distance graph
$$= (10 \text{ N} \times 4 \text{ m}) + (25 \text{ N} \times 8 \text{ m}) + (5 \text{ N} \times 6 \text{ m})$$
$$= 40 + 200 + 30 \text{ Nm}$$
$$= 270 \text{ J}$$

Total work done in moving part over full range = $\underline{\underline{270 \text{ J}}}$

6.5.   Work done by a variable force

In many practical cases, the value of the force applied to move a body varies as the body moves. For example, the force required to

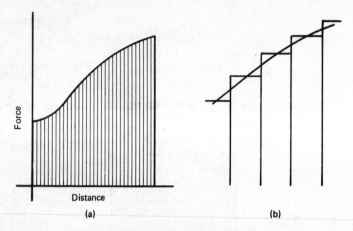

77. Work diagram for a variable force

(a) Diagram divided into number of thin strips
(b) Enlarged view of part of (a)

stretch a spring will increase as the spring is stretched. This means that equal movements at different points in the action require different amounts of work done, since the force will be different.

Once again, however, the work done will be represented by the area enclosed by the work diagram drawn for the particular case. This follows from the idea that an area bounded by a curve can be split up into a very large number of very thin rectangular strips, as is shown in diagram 77. The area of each narrow rectangle would represent the work done by a force whose value remained constant for the short distance of movement represented by the width of the rectangle. If the rectangles were made very narrow indeed—too narrow to draw on a diagram—the actual variation of the force over the very small distance then represented would be quite negligible. The sum of the areas of all these rectangles (in other words, the area under the curve) would then represent the total work done by the variable force.

If the rectangles are made very thin indeed, the difference between the stepped outline of the rectangle and the smooth outline of the curve becomes quite negligible. In other words, the area under the curve becomes equal to the sum of the areas of all the rectangles. This will represent the work done by the variable force.

Any available method may be used for estimating the area under a curved graph. Typical among these are 'counting squares' or the use of the mid-ordinate rule.

6.6. Example

A mass of 50 kg is hung on the end of a chain weighing 1·5 kg per metre length. The other end of the chain is attached to a drum. Find the work done in winding the chain round the drum to raise the mass from a vertical distance of 40 m below the drum to a vertical distance of 10 m below the drum.

The arrangement is sketched in diagram 78 for the two extreme positions and one intermediate position.

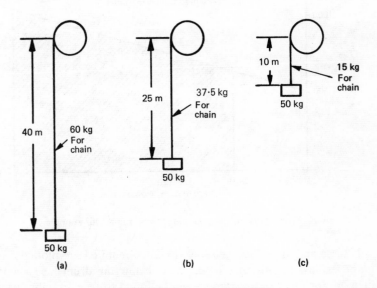

78. Variable force—numerical example

It is seen from this diagram that the force required to raise the mass changes as the height of the mass changes, because of the decreasing length of chain that has to be lifted with the mass. Values of the force can be found for any given position of the mass. For example, for the three positions shown in diagram 78:

(a) At 40 m below drum,
$$\text{force required} = (50 + 60 \text{ kg}) \times (9 \cdot 81 \text{ m/s}^2)$$
$$= 1079 \text{ N}$$

(b) At 25 m below drum,
$$\text{force required} = (50 + 37 \cdot 5 \text{ kg}) \times (9 \cdot 81 \text{ m/s}^2)$$
$$= 858 \text{ N}$$

(c) At 10 ft below drum,
$$\text{force required} = (50 + 15 \text{ kg}) \times (9 \cdot 81 \text{ m/s}^2)$$
$$= 637 \text{ N}$$

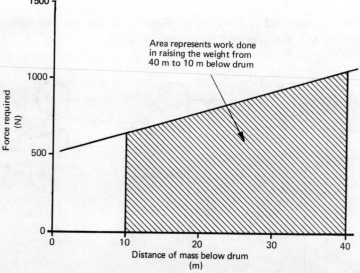

Area represents work done in raising the weight from 40 m to 10 m below drum

79. Work diagram for a variable force—numerical example

If these and any other values of the force required are plotted on a graph against the distance of the mass below the drum (i.e. a work diagram for this case), the graph will be found to be a straight line as shown in diagram 79.

The work done in raising the mass from 40 m to 10 m below the drum is then represented by the area under this work diagram between these two values of distance (shown shaded in diagram 79). In this case there is no need to use any of the approximate methods of finding the area, such as the mid-ordinate rule, since the required area is simply a trapezium.

Work done = area under graph

$$= \tfrac{1}{2} \begin{pmatrix} \text{sum of parallel} \\ \text{sides} \end{pmatrix} \times \begin{pmatrix} \text{perpendicular distance} \\ \text{between parallel sides} \end{pmatrix}$$

$$= \tfrac{1}{2} (1079 \text{ N} + 637 \text{ N}) \times (40 \text{ m} - 10 \text{ m})$$

$$= \tfrac{1}{2} \times 1716 \text{ N} \times 30 \text{ m}$$

$$= 25\,740 \text{ Nm}$$

Work done in lifting weight = <u>25·74 kJ</u>

6.7. Work done by a force inclined to direction of movement

(This section should be omitted until a working knowledge of trigonometrical ratios has been obtained.)

In the definition of work done by a force given in Section 6.1, page 174, it was seen that the value of work done is given by

work done = (force) × (distance moved in direction of force)

An earlier example in this chapter (example iv, section 6.2, page 175) has shown that the movement of a body may not be directly along the line of action of an applied force, and has stressed that the work done depends only on the force and the distance moved in the direction of the force. This point will be considered in a more general way in this section.

Suppose a force F is applied to a body at some angle θ to its permissible direction of motion (the body might be moved between rails, or might be a ship with its rudder set along a definite line, for example). The conditions will be as shown in diagram 80.

The force F can be resolved into its two rectangular components of

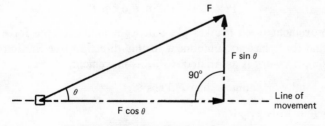

80. Force inclined to direction of movement.

$F \cos \theta$ and $F \sin \theta$ are the two components of F in the directions shown

$F \cos \theta$ along the line of movement and $F \sin \theta$ at right angles to the line of movement, as shown in diagram 80. The component $F \cos \theta$ acts along the line of movement, so that if the movement along this line is d, the work done is $(F \cos \theta) \times d$, or $F d \cos \theta$. The component $F \sin \theta$ acts at right angles to the line of movement, and since no motion takes place in this direction, this component does not do work. The total work done is then $F d \cos \theta$. The same result may be obtained in an alternative way, which might be more easily visualized in certain cases.

The movement d along its restricted line could be thought of as being caused by a movement of d $\cos \theta$ along the line of action of the force, plus a movement of d $\sin \theta$ at right angles to the direction of the force. This idea is shown in diagram 81.

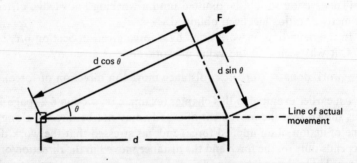

81. Force inclined to direction of movement

The body may be considered to have reached its final position as a result of the movements d $\cos \theta$ and d $\sin \theta$, as shown. Then, since the body moves a distance d $\cos \theta$ in the direction of the force F, the work done is

$$F \times (d \cos \theta), \text{ or } F d \cos \theta$$

The movement d $\sin \theta$ takes place at right angles to the force, and since the force has no component in this direction (see Section 3.10, page 66), no work is associated with this movement.

The total work done is then $\underline{\underline{F d \cos \theta}}$.   .   .   (ii)

where F = force applied
    d = distance moved
    θ = angle between direction of force and direction of movement.

Example

Find the work done and the tractive effort required to move a train having a mass of 300 tonne up a slope 400 m long having a gradient of 1 in 75. The tractive resistance is 60 N per tonne mass of the train.

Two forces must be overcome by the tractive effort of the engine in this case. The first is the opposing component of the gravitational force on the train, which tends to roll it backwards down the slope. The second is the opposing force due to the resistance to motion (called the 'tractive resistance' in this question). The conditions are as shown in diagram 82.

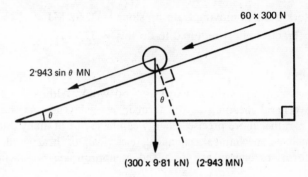

82. Force inclined to direction of movement

The gradient, given as 1 in 75, is taken to be a vertical rise of 1 unit for each 75 units moved up the slope; in other words $\sin \theta = \frac{1}{75}$.

In this case, θ is the angle between the direction of the force and the perpendicular to the direction of movement. Therefore, $2 \cdot 943 \cos \theta$ MN acts perpendicularly to the track, and does not involve any work done.

The component of force opposing motion is $2 \cdot 943 \sin \theta$ MN

$$\text{or} \quad 2 \cdot 943 \times \frac{1}{75} \text{ MN}$$

$$= 39 \cdot 3 \text{ kN}$$

The tractive resistance opposing motion

$$= 60 \times 300 \text{ N}$$
$$= 18 \text{ kN}$$

Then total tractive effort

$$= 39 \cdot 3 + 18 \text{ kN}$$
$$= 57 \cdot 3 \text{ kN}$$

This is the force required, acting up the slope, to move the train up the slope.

The distance moved up the slope (in the direction of this force) is 400 m.

$$\text{Then work done} = 57 \cdot 3 \text{ kN} \times 400 \text{ m}$$
$$= 22\,920 \text{ kNm}$$

Work done in moving train up slope = 22·92 MJ
Tractive effort required to do this = 57·3 kN

6.8. Energy

Energy is defined as the CAPACITY TO DO WORK. Although this has the same general meaning as the term in everyday use, its scientific meaning is rather more precise. Energy can have one of many different forms, such as mechanical, chemical, electrical, or heat; and these various forms of energy are discussed at appropriate points in this book.

Recent advances in science have shown that mass is yet another form of energy, and that the release of nuclear energy is brought about by the transformation of mass into energy. Energy may be converted from one of its forms into another form, but it can neither be created nor destroyed. The principles of energy conversion are dealt with in more detail in Chapter 22, but the basic idea of energy conversion lies behind much of engineering science. Some of the mechanical forms of energy are considered in the following sections.

The units in which energy is measured are the same as those of the work that it is capable of performing. Thus, the basic unit is the JOULE (newton metre).

6.9. Potential energy

Suppose that a mass of 1 kg lying at ground level is picked up and placed on a shelf 5 m above ground level. An upwards force of 9·81 N must have been exerted on the mass, and an amount of work of 9·81 N × 5 m or 49·05 J done on it, to raise its position. This work is 'stored' in the weight by virtue of its new position above the 'reference' —ground level. The mass is then said to possess a POTENTIAL ENERGY of 49·05 J. It is capable of doing 49·05 J of work if it is allowed to fall back to ground level again, under the action of its gravitational force. For example, it would be capable of lifting up another mass of 1 kg to the same height of 5 m as it itself returned to ground level (although in practice some of its potential energy would be converted into some other form in the mechanism of the arrangement, so that the second 1 kg would not quite rise 5 m).

Notice that the potential energy of the mass is stated with reference to some 'datum' or reference level. This is often taken as ground level, but need not be so. For example, if a hole 10 m deep were dug beneath the shelf carrying the 1 kg weight, the potential energy of the weight when referred to the bottom of the hole would be $9·81 \text{ N} \times 15 \text{ m} = 147·05 \text{ J}$. This has not really increased its total potential energy, however, although of course it could do more work in falling to the bottom of the hole.

Fundamentally, potential energy should be measured with reference to the centre of mass of the earth. Any object possesses some potential energy, provided it is removed from this centre of mass, at which the gravitational forces may be assumed to act. However, this is rather a remote point, and it is not very convenient to measure heights from the centre of mass of the earth. Consequently, it is usual to name a particular datum level when considering the potential energy possessed by a body.

The water in a reservoir behind a dam possesses potential energy. This can be converted into electrical energy by the water flowing through turbines placed at the foot of the dam, which drive electrical generators. Since the potential energy of the water is available from natural sources in this readily convertible form, the cost of producing electrical energy by this hydro-electric means is relatively small. Unfortunately, in this country the potential energy available in this form is insufficient to meet the demand for energy in its electrical form.

A meteorite possesses potential energy in relation to the earth by virtue of its position in the stratosphere. Usually, this energy is converted to heat energy by the motion of the meteorite through the air surrounding the earth, and the heat energy produced is enough to vaporize the material of the meteorite before it strikes the earth. The larger ones survive, however, and can do work in overcoming the resistive forces of the ground when they strike it.

The potential energy possessed by a body of mass m at a height h above the datum or reference level is equal to the work done in raising it to that height, and so is equal to

$$mgh \qquad . \qquad . \qquad . \qquad \text{(iii)}$$

6.10   Strain energy

Strain energy is, in a sense, another form of potential energy. If a spring is stretched within its elastic limit, the work done in stretching the spring is stored as strain energy in the material of the spring. This energy is capable of doing work if the spring is released and allowed to return to its original unstressed state. It is the strain energy stored in the wound-up clockspring that does work against the forces opposing motion in the mechanism of the clock.

If the spring is stretched beyond its elastic limit, work is done on the spring to produce permanent deformation. If the material is taken to breaking point, all the work done, including that stored at one stage as strain energy, is used in this way, and eventually converted to other forms such as heat. For example, a tensile test piece will be found to be quite warm immediately after fracture. Some of the energy will also have been released as a sound wave at the instant of fracture.

The strain energy possessed by a body whose strained condition is reversible, so that the strain will disappear if the straining force is removed, is equal to the work done by the force producing the strain.

6.11.   Kinetic energy

A body in motion is said to possess KINETIC ENERGY by virtue of its mass and its speed of movement. This energy can be made available to do work if the moving body is brought to rest or is slowed down. An express train at high speed possesses considerable kinetic energy, and can do large amounts of work as the train is stopped. This is especially evident if the train is brought to a sudden stop in a collison. The kinetic energy is then released very quickly, and work may be done in distorting the material of whatever it is that the train has struck. Again, eventually the energy in this case is converted to heat energy, or into the energy of a sound wave.

The particles of water in a moving jet possess kinetic energy, and this is available to do work in turning the blades of a water turbine which is struck by the jet. In the case of the hydro-electric system mentioned earlier, the potential energy of the water behind the dam is first largely converted to the kinetic energy of a moving stream of water. As this stream of water strikes the blades of the water turbine it is turned into the kinetic energy of rotation of the turbine wheel, which in turn is converted to electrical energy in the electrical generator.

The precise relationship between the kinetic energy of a given body, its mass and its speed of movement, is discussed later, in Section 9.7, page 264.

6.12. Action of a flywheel

A flywheel is a fairly heavy wheel fitted to a shaft in order to minimize rapid variations in its speed of rotation. The flywheel acts as a store of energy in the form of its kinetic energy of rotation. If the load on a shaft fluctuates, the speed of the shaft will tend to vary. If the speed tends to fall because of an increase in load, the kinetic energy of the flywheel will tend to decrease with the speed. The difference in stored energy associated with this speed change is then made available to do work on the load, and thus to assist the motor driving the load. The resulting fall in speed is then less than it would have been if the driving motor had had to drive alone against the increased load. If the speed tends to rise because of a reduction in load, the kinetic energy of the flywheel must be increased because of its higher speed. This increase in energy must be supplied by the driving motor, and represents an additional load on this motor. The resulting rise in speed is then less than it would have been without the flywheel.

The flywheel will act in a similar way to 'damp out' the effects of variation in the driving torque developed by the motor. The speed of rotation of the shaft will then vary much less than it would otherwise have done.

CHAPTER SUMMARY

Work done by a force

= (force) × (distance moved in direction of force).

Units are J (Nm), kJ.

The area enclosed by a graph of force against distance moved in the direction of the force represents the work done.

If the point of application of a force F moves through a distance d

inclined at angle θ to the line of action of the force, the work done is F d cos θ.

Energy is the capacity to do work, and is measured in the same units as work.

The potential energy of a body of mass m at a height h above a given datum is equal to the work done in raising that mass to that height from the datum. In other words,

$$\text{potential energy} = mgh$$

The strain energy possessed by a material subjected to strain is equal to the work done in producing that strain, provided the elastic limit has not been exceeded.

The kinetic energy possessed by a body is due to its mass and the speed at which it is moving. (See Chapter 9, page 264, for the relationship between kinetic energy, mass and speed.)

A flywheel can store energy as kinetic energy of rotation.

QUESTIONS

1. Calculate in joules the work done in each of the following cases:
(a) A mass of 4 kg is lifted to a height of 20 m
(b) a trolley is pulled with a force of 30 N for a distance of 9 m
(c) 300 litres of water (1 litre of water has a mass of 1 kg) are pumped from the bottom of a well 21 m deep.

2. Define the term 'work', stating the mechanical units in which it is usually expressed. Explain how it may be represented graphically.

The force acting on a body varies uniformly from 0 to 50 N while it moves 1 m. The force then remains constant at 50 N while the body moves a further 1·5 m, and then decreases uniformly to zero over a final distance of 1·25 m. Calculate, with the aid of a suitable diagram, the total work done over the distance of 3·75 m and the average value of the force.

3. In a metal-shaping machine the force varies throughout the cutting operation as shown:

Force F N	0	330	450	520	565	595	600
Distance s mm	0	10	20	30	40	50	60

(a) Construct a graph of force against distance using the scales 20 mm to 10 mm, and 20 mm to 100 N.

(b) Obtain from the graph the total work done during the 60 mm cutting stroke.

(c) What is the mean force during the cutting stroke?

4. During an experiment on the effect of a varying force on a spring, the following results were obtained:

Load N	0	100	200	300	400	500
Extension mm	0	33	67	99	131	165

Plot the graph, with values of the load plotted vertically and the extension horizontally, using scales of 20 mm to 20 mm, and 20 mm to 100 N. From this graph deduce the stiffness of the spring (i.e. load for unit extension), and also the strain energy stored in the spring when it is extended by 125 mm.

5. The force on a ram pulling a broach through a hole varies as shown in the table:

Travel (mm)	0	12·5	25	37·5	50	75	100	125	150
Force (kN)	6	10·9	14·5	17·6	20	22·5	22	18·7	12

Plot the force/distance graph and from it find the total work done in J.

6. A crane lifts a load of mass 750 kg. When the load is at ground level it is supported by ropes 18 m long which together have a mass of 6 kg/m. The load is then raised 12 m.

Calculate the total work done by the crane.

7. An elastic material, which obeys Hooke's law, requires a pull of 200 N to stretch the material by 25 mm. Calculate (a) the work done in stretching the material 20 mm, and (b) the additional work required to stretch the material a further 20 mm. Illustrate your answer by means of a load/extension diagram, drawn to scale.

8. A mass of 150 kg is pulled up a plane inclined at 25° to the horizontal. A force of 4 N/kg acts down the plane opposing motion. Find (a) the work done against gravity, (b) the total work done, when the mass is pulled for a distance of 20 m measured up the plane.

9. A body is moved up a smooth plane inclined at 15° to the horizontal. If the work done in moving the body for a distance of 30 m up the plane is 750 J, find the mass of the body.

What is the potential energy of the body relative to its original starting position if it is allowed to slide back down the plane for a distance of 7·5 m?

What happens to this energy if the body slides back to its original starting position?

G

10. A constant force of 125 N acts on a point in a mechanism. The point moves along a track such that the angle between the force and the direction of movement varies as shown in the following table:

Angle between direction of movement and direction of force	0°	10°	20°	30°	25°	20°	10°
Distance moved (mm)	0	25	50	75	100	125	150

Find the work done by the force in moving the point through the 150 mm of travel.

11. A car moving with a kinetic energy of 120 kJ is allowed to free-wheel to a stop against an opposing force of 2·5 kN. How far will the car travel before coming to rest?

12. A load having a mass of 100 kg is raised by winding a chain, attached to the load, round a drum. The chain has a mass of 0·75 kg/m. If the load is initially 30 m below the axis of the drum, find the work done in raising it to a position 3 m below this axis. What is then the potential energy of the load?

13. A spring has a stiffness of 900 N/m. Find the work done in extending the spring by 75 mm.

14. In a tensile test on a steel wire beyond the elastic limit, the load was first steadily increased up to its maximum value and then steadily reduced to zero again. The following readings of load and extension were obtained:

Load (N)	0	100	200	300	400	300	200	100	0
Extension (mm)	0	0·45	0·92	1·38	2·12	1·55	1·08	0·60	0·15

Find the work done in producing the permanent extension of 0·15 mm on the wire.

15. The results of a load/extension test on a spring are as follows:

Load (N)	0	100	200	300	400	500
Extension (mm)	0	5	10·5	15·4	20·5	25·5

Plot the load/extension graph and deduce the stiffness of the spring.

What will be the extension when the spring stores a strain energy of 4·5 J?

7. Friction

If a surface is moved over another surface with which it is in contact, a resistance is set up opposing this motion. The value of the resistance will depend on the materials involved, the condition of the two surfaces, and the force holding the surfaces in contact; but the opposition to motion will always be present. This resistance to movement is said to be the result of FRICTION between the surfaces.

It is found that these frictional forces opposing motion are usually slightly greater before one surface starts to move over the other than after this movement has started. In other words, it requires a slightly greater force to start one surface moving over the other than it does to keep it moving. These two are known as STATIC FRICTION (sometimes called, colloquially but graphically, 'stiction') and SLIDING FRICTION. The force due to static friction is slightly greater than that due to sliding friction.

7.1. The nature of friction

Although the ground and polished surface of a hardened steel block may appear quite flat to the unaided eye, a powerful microscope will reveal tiny 'hills and dales' in the surface. Similar inspection of the surface of any other solid material, however finely finished, will show similar results. (See frontispiece.) Thus, when two surfaces are brought into contact with one another they will first touch only at a few points, where the 'hills' of one surface meet those of the other. The situation has been compared with that of a model of the Alps placed upside down on a model of the Himalayas.

Since so few points are actually in contact over such a small area, the pressure at these points is enormous, even with quite small forces holding the surfaces together. In fact, the pressures are great enough for the respective peaks to be squashed together in a form of 'cold weld', one surface flowing into the other so that they become joined. Normally this happens at only a few points, until the resistive forces set up at these points of contact are equal and opposite to the force holding the surfaces in contact. If the force between the surfaces is increased, the two sets of 'hills' are pushed a little further into one another, and a few more points are welded together until once again the resistive forces balance the applied forces. If two highly polished surfaces are brought into close contact; for example if two slip gauges, such as are used for the accurate measurement of the length of a gap, are 'wrung' together under pressure, the adhesion of one surface to another becomes very strong indeed. In fact, they may become extremely difficult, if not impossible, to separate without physical damage. (Since slip gauges are fairly expensive, the student is *not* recommended to try this—unless he wants to buy his own.)

It follows that the force required to overcome static friction is the force necessary to shear the welded junctions formed in the way described. Note that if the two surfaces are both very hard, greater pressures are required to cause a given amount of distortion. This means that fewer welds will be necessary to oppose a given force between such surfaces, and that the frictional forces will be smaller.

When the surfaces move in relation to one another, the conditions, in addition to the welding that occurs, will be rather like a plough being pulled across a piece of ground. In addition to a 'scraping' action, the surfaces will be separated slightly as one 'hill' rides over a 'hill' on the adjacent surface. Small particles of each surface will be physically transferred to the other during the process. This can be seen by inspection of a shaft and its bearing which have been allowed to run 'dry' (i.e. without any lubricant) for some time. If one surface is very much harder than the other, the majority of the transfer will take place from the softer to the harder surface. The effect can be compared with that of pulling a steel gramophone needle across an aluminium surface. The force required to pull these 'ploughs' across each other represents the force of sliding friction.

If the solid surfaces are separated by a film of a liquid such as oil, the oil flows between the two sets of hills and dales so that no welding takes place between the surfaces. The force required to move the surfaces in relation to one another is then much less, and is only that required to cause the particles of the oil to slide over one another. This 'viscous' resistance depends on the thickness or 'viscosity' of the oil. (Treacle has a high viscosity, while the viscosity of water is much less.) Liquids used as lubricants must, however, have sufficient viscosity to resist being squeezed out from between the two surfaces by the force holding them together. If this were to happen, the lubricating film would be broken, the surfaces would come into physical contact and the frictional forces would be greatly increased. The viscosity of a fluid tends to decrease rapidly with increase in temperature (compare hot treacle with cold treacle), and the problem of effective lubrication becomes more difficult as the temperature of the surfaces rises.

7.2. The laws of friction

As a result of many experiments carried out on different kinds of surfaces in rubbing contact, and with different forces between the surfaces, it has been found that frictional forces behave approximately in accordance with the following statements or 'laws'. These statements should be taken for what they are; that is, as the approximate rules which seem to govern most of the cases of friction investigated. They are mostly not fundamental laws in the sense that the equality of the reaction forces and applied forces for a body in equilibrium appears to be a fundamental law.

(i) The frictional force always opposes the direction of motion, or the direction in which a body is tending to move. (This law *does* seem to be a fundamental one.)

(ii) The sliding frictional force opposing motion, once motion has started, is proportional to the forces at right angles to the rubbing surfaces, which tend to hold these together. Thus if the forces at right angles to the surfaces are doubled, the sliding frictional force is also doubled.

(iii) The sliding frictional force is independent of the area of the surfaces concerned. Thus two pairs of surfaces of the same materials in the same condition and with the same force between them, but having different areas, will experience the same frictional forces opposing motion.

(iv) For low speeds of relative motion of the surfaces, the frictional force is independent of the speed. (The frictional force between unlubricated metallic surfaces decreases at higher values of rubbing speed.)

7.3. The coefficient of friction

Suppose that a block of mass m rests on a flat horizontal surface as shown in diagram 83. A reaction force equal and opposite to the gravitational force on the mass m will be set up by the surface against the block, so that it remains in equilibrium. Suppose that a force P is then applied to the block in a direction parallel to the surface, as shown. If this applied force P is steadily increased from zero, the block will not move at first, when P is small. This is because the frictional force F will oppose the applied force P, and will increase as P increases, thus preventing the block from moving. If P is increased further, however, a point will be reached where it is equal to the maximum frictional force possible under the conditions. This maximum frictional force is called the force of static friction between the surfaces under these conditions. If P is increased very slightly above this value, the block will start to move in the direction of P, and it will usually be found that P can then be reduced slightly to keep the block just moving steadily over the surface. The value of P is then equal to the force of sliding friction.

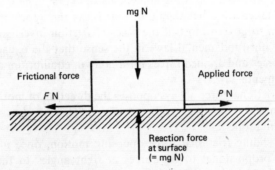

83. Frictional force between horizontal surfaces

Note that the sliding frictional force represents the maximum value of frictional force possible under the particular conditions. If an applied force of less than this limiting value is applied to the block, the block will not move. However, in this case the opposing frictional force is then only equal and opposite to the applied force. The full value of the sliding frictional force only appears when the block is moving over the surface. (Note that the limiting or 'static' friction may be slightly more than the sliding friction.)

From the statement or 'law' (ii) in the previous Section (7.2), it is seen that the value of this sliding frictional force is proportional to the forces at right angles to the surfaces and tending to hold them in contact. In diagram 83 the forces at right angles to the surfaces are the equal, opposing forces due to the weight and the reaction of the surface. If the reaction force at right angles to the surface is R_n (equal in this case to the gravitational force mg) then the sliding frictional force F is such that

$$F \propto R_n$$

($\propto$ is mathematical shorthand for 'is proportional to')

This means that if R_n is doubled, F is doubled, or, if R_n is halved, F is halved and so on. The relationship can be expressed in another way:

$$\frac{F}{R_n} = \text{a constant}$$

For example, if $F = 2$ N when $R_n = 10$ N, then when R_n is increased to 20 N, F is increased to 4 N; or, when R_n is decreased to 5 N, F is decreased to 1 N. In each case, the value of $\frac{F}{R_n}$ is the same (0·2 for figures given). This constant value of $\frac{F}{R_n}$ for any particular case is called the COEFFICIENT OF FRICTION (symbol μ—a Greek letter pronounced 'mew'). In other words

$$\text{coefficient of friction} = \frac{\text{sliding frictional force}}{\text{force between surfaces}}$$

$$\text{or } \mu = \frac{F}{R_n}$$

$$\text{or } F = \mu R_n \qquad . \qquad . \qquad . \qquad \text{(i)}$$

Since the forces F and R_n are expressed in the same units, the coefficient of friction μ is just a number, and does not possess units of its own.

Note that only one of the forces holding the surfaces together need be considered here (in this case, the reaction force at right angles to the surface). Since the surfaces are moving *across* one another, and not *towards* one another, there must always be equal and opposite forces between them.

It is important to notice from the statement or 'law' (iii) in Section 7.2 that the *area* of the block in contact with the horizontal surface *does not affect the sliding frictional force*. This follows from the explanation given in Section 7.1 of the nature of the frictional force. No matter how large the areas of the two surfaces that are rubbing together, actual physical contact will still only occur at those few points where the hills of one surface touch the hills of the other. When enough hills have been squashed together to set up sufficient reaction force between the surfaces to balance the applied force, equilibrium is reached. This will be reached for the same *effective* area of contact for any given applied force, whatever the *apparent* area available for contact. The sliding frictional force thus depends only on the applied force between the surfaces, and not on the apparent area of contact.

The value of the cofficient of friction will depend very much on the condition of the surfaces (smooth, rough, presence of small amounts of moisture or oil, etc.) as well as on the materials concerned. The following table gives the approximate values that might be expected for some surface 'pairs':

Surfaces	Coefficient of friction
Timber on timber	$0.5 - 0.2$
Timber on metals	$0.6 - 0.2$
Metals on metals (dry)	$0.25 - 0.15$
Oiled metal surfaces	$0.2 - 0.05$
Brake lining on metal	$0.5 - 0.7$

Approximate values of coefficient of friction

7.4. Examples

(i) A horizontal force of 49 N is required to slide a wooden packing case over a horizontal floor at a steady rate. If the coefficient of friction between packing case and floor is 0·5, find the mass of the packing case.

$$F = \mu R_n$$

In this case, $\qquad F = 49 \text{ N and } \mu = 0.5$

$$\therefore \quad 49 = 0.5 \times R_n$$

or $\qquad R_n = 98 \text{ N}$

The packing case has a mass of $\dfrac{98}{9.81} \simeq \underline{\underline{10 \text{ kg}}}$

(ii) Find the least force that a housewife need apply to an electric iron having a mass of 2·5 kg to move it over an ironing board if the coefficient of friction between the surfaces is 0·25.

$$F = \mu R_n$$

In this case, $\qquad \mu = 0.25, R_n = 2.5 \times 9.81 = 24.5 \text{ N}$

$$\therefore \quad F = 0.25 \times 24.5$$

$$= 6.15$$

Least force required is $\underline{\underline{6.15 \text{ N}}}$

(iii) A man who has a mass of 75 kg stands on a floor, and the coefficient of friction between the soles of his shoes and the floor is 0·5. A wooden packing case stands on the same floor, and the coefficient of friction between the packing case and the floor is 0·3. Find the maximum mass the packing case can be if the man is to be able to pull it along by means of a horizontal rope, without his shoes slipping on the floor.

The maximum horizontal force which the man can exert without his shoes slipping on the floor is

F = (coefficient of friction between shoes and floor) × (reaction force)
   = 0·5 × 75 × 9·81 N
   = 368 N

This means that the greatest frictional force between packing case and floor which he can overcome is 368 N. But

$$F = \mu R_n \text{ for the packing case on the floor}$$
$$\therefore \quad 368 = 0 \cdot 3 \, R_n$$
$$\text{or} \quad R_n = 1227 \text{ N}$$

Greatest mass of packing case is $\dfrac{1227}{9 \cdot 81}$ = 125 kg

Note that if the man inclined the rope upwards, his pull would have a vertical component. This would cause the reaction between the floor and his shoes to increase, and the reaction between the floor and the packing case to decrease. As a result, he would be able to pull along a rather heavier packing case without his shoes slipping, since the limiting frictional force at his shoes would increase because of the increased reaction force, and that at the packing case would decrease. (This would make an interesting experiment.)

(iv) A body of mass 50 kg lies on a horizontal surface. Find the work done in sliding this body for a distance of 15 m over the surface if the coefficient of friction between the surfaces in contact is 0·1.

The frictional force to be overcome is

$$F = 0 \cdot 1 \times 50 \times 9 \cdot 81 \text{ N}$$
$$= 49 \cdot 05 \text{ N}$$

This force must be moved through a distance of 15 m along its line of action.

$$\text{Work done} = 49 \cdot 05 \text{ N} \times 15 \text{ m}$$
$$= 735 \cdot 8 \text{ J}$$

(v) A stone is thrown with a kinetic energy of 30 J on to a horizontal surface, so that it slides along the surface without bouncing. If the stone has a mass of 0·25 kg and the coefficient of friction between the stone and the surface is 0·2, find how far the stone slides before coming to rest.

In this case, the kinetic energy of the stone does work in overcoming the frictional force at the surface, the work done being equal to

(frictional force) × (distance moved against this force)

If the stone comes to rest, all the kinetic energy of the stone will have been released.

$$\text{Friction force } F = \mu R_n$$
$$= 0·2 \times 0·25 \times 9·81 \text{ N}$$
$$= 0·490\ 5 \text{ N}$$

If the distance travelled by the stone is x m, then work done against friction

$$= 0·490\ 5 \text{ N} \times x \text{ m}$$
$$= 0·490\ 5\ x \text{ J}$$

This is equal to the original kinetic energy of the stone. In other words,

$$0·490\ 5\ x = 30$$

or $$x = 61·2 \text{ m}$$

The stone will slide 61·2 m before coming to rest.

(If the stone were to bounce on the surface, some of the kinetic energy would be used in straining the material of the surface, and not all of this energy would be returned to the stone as it left the surface after bouncing. There would thus be less total energy available to do work against friction, and the stone would not slide so far. This could also form an experiment, with suitable apparatus.)

7.5. Experiment to determine coefficient of friction

The student should investigate the effects of friction by further suitable experiments. In addition to those suggested in the previous section, the following method is frequently used to estimate the value of the coefficient of friction between given surfaces.

A small pulley is arranged at the end of a flat horizontal surface, as shown in diagram 84. A string passes over the pulley and is attached at one end to a block on the flat surface, and at the other end to a mass-carrier.

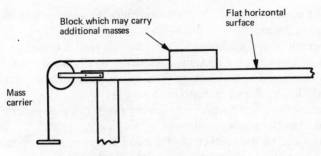

84. Estimation of coefficient of friction

Masses are added to the mass-carrier until the block just moves at a steady rate over the surface. If the mass on the carrier is too great, the block will move at an increasing speed. If the mass on the carrier is too small, the block will not move at all. Because of the slight difference between static and sliding friction, it may be necessary to disturb

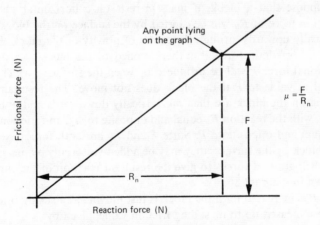

85. Estimation of coefficient of friction

the system slightly, perhaps by a light tap on the surface or by a small additional push on the block, in order to start the block moving when the value of the applied force is just sufficient to keep it moving. Added mass on the block will enable the effect of increased reaction force to be investigated.

A block of the same mass and material, but of different apparent area of contact, should be found to require the same pull to overcome frictional forces.

A graph of the gravitational force on the carrier (equal to the pull required to overcome friction) against the total gravitational force of the block (equal to the reaction force between the surfaces) should be a straight line as shown in diagram 85.

The coefficient of friction between the two surfaces in contact is then found from the graph as indicated in this diagram.

The value of the coefficient of friction is measured by measuring F and R_n for any convenient point on the graph. Then

$$\mu = \frac{F}{R_n}$$

7.6. Angle of friction

(This section should be omitted until a working knowledge of trigonometrical ratios has been gained.)

Suppose that a block of mass m rests on a horizontal surface. A reaction force of R_n will be exerted by the surface on the block, acting vertically upwards through the centre of gravity of the block. Suppose that a horizontal force P is then applied to the block. An opposing frictional force F will be produced between the surfaces, which will be equal in value to P if the block does not move. The resultant forces acting on the block are then mg vertically downwards and P horizontally, with the reaction R_n equal and opposite to mg, and frictional force F equal and opposite to P. Since F and R_n are both forces exerted on the block by the surface, they may be added vectorially by means of the parallelogram of forces to give the resultant reaction of the surface, as shown in diagram 86.

If P is increased until the block is just moving at a steady rate, F will have increased up to its sliding friction value, given by

$$F = \mu R_n$$

The angle φ between the direction of the resultant reaction and the vertical, as shown in diagram 86, will then have its maximum value. Since F and R_n are at right angles, it follows from diagram 86 that

$$\tan \varphi = \frac{F}{R_n}$$

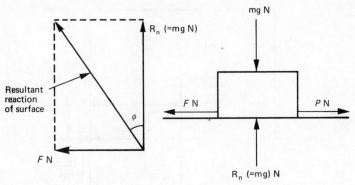

86. Forces acting on a block on a rough horizontal surface

or $\qquad \tan \varphi = \dfrac{\mu R_n}{R_n}$ since $F = \mu R_n$ for this condition

$\therefore \qquad \underline{\tan \varphi = \mu}$ . . . . . (ii)

This maximum value of angle φ, defined by $\tan \varphi = \mu$, is called the ANGLE OF FRICTION.

Summary

The resultant reaction between a rough surface and the surface of a body sliding over it is inclined backwards to the direction of motion through an angle φ, such that $\tan \varphi = \mu$, the coefficient of friction between the surfaces. This angle of 'backwards inclination' to the vertical is known as the angle of friction.

7.7. Moment of frictional force

The frictional force acts at the sliding surfaces of contact, and parallel to these surfaces. If the applied force acts parallel to the sliding surfaces but at a distance from them, the frictional force and the applied force will set up a couple which tends to topple the body. The resulting behaviour of the body will depend on its mass and dimensions, the point of application of the applied force and the coefficient of friction for the surfaces. These will determine whether the body will slide along the surface or will topple over.

The general conditions are indicated for a simple rectangular block in diagram 87. If the maximum moment of the couple due to the

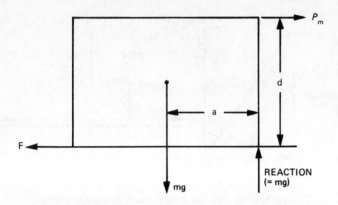

87. Sliding or toppling conditions for rectangular block.

If $P_m \times d$ is greater than $mg \times a$ the block will topple over.
If $P_m \times d$ is less than $mg \times a$ the block will slide.

Note that P_m is the maximum applied force before sliding can take place, and will be equal to the limiting frictional force $F = \mu R_n$

applied force P and frictional force F is greater than the maximum moment of the opposing couple due to the force mg and the reaction R_n at the front bottom corner of the block, the block will topple over. If the maximum moment of the couple due to P and F is less than the maximum opposing moment of the couple due to mg and R_n, then the block will slide.

Example

A rectangular block of mass 5 kg has dimensions 50 mm × 100 mm × 125 mm. It stands on a horizontal surface on a 50 mm × 100 mm face, and the coefficient of friction between the surfaces in contact is 0·3. A steadily increasing horizontal force is applied to the top edge of the block (a) at right angles to a 50 mm edge, (b) at right angles to a 100 mm edge. Find, for each case, whether the block will eventually slide on the horizontal surface or whether it will topple over.

The two arrangements are shown in diagram 88 (a) and (b).

(a) *Force applied at right angles to upper 50 mm edge*

Assume that the block is about to topple over on its front lower edge, so that all the reaction of the surface appears, as shown, at this edge. This will give the maximum possible moment of the couple opposing the toppling moment which is acting on the block.

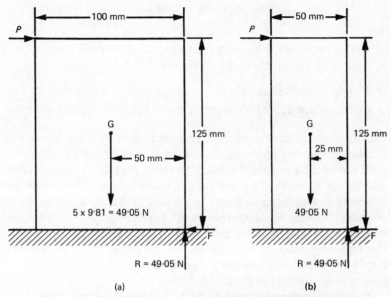

88. Sliding or toppling of rectangular block—numerical example

The maximum possible moment of the couple tending to topple the block will occur when the frictional force F has its limiting value.

$$\text{Maximum value of } F = \mu R_n$$
$$= 0 \cdot 3 \times 49 \cdot 05 \text{ N}$$
$$= 14 \cdot 72 \text{ N}$$

This equals the maximum value of P before sliding would occur, so that

$$\text{maximum toppling moment} = 14 \cdot 72 \text{ N} \times 0 \cdot 125 \text{ m}$$
$$= 1 \cdot 84 \text{ Nm}$$
$$\text{Maximum moment opposing toppling} = 49 \cdot 05 \text{ N} \times 0 \cdot 050 \text{ m}$$
$$= 2 \cdot 452 \text{ Nm}$$

∴ Maximum opposing moment is greater than maximum toppling moment, so that the block will slide over the horizontal surface.

(b) *Force applied at right angles to upper 100 mm edge*

Following the same method as before,

$$\text{maximum toppling moment} = 1 \cdot 84 \text{ Nm}$$

(since maximum frictional force, and hence maximum value of P before sliding would start, are still the same).

$$\text{Maximum moment opposing toppling} = 49 \cdot 05 \text{ N} \times 0 \cdot 025 \text{ m}$$
$$= 1 \cdot 23 \text{ Nm}$$

∴ Maximum toppling moment is now greater than maximum opposing moment, and the block would topple over.

With force applied at right angles to upper 50 mm edge, <u>block slides</u>.
With force applied at right angles to upper 100 mm edge, <u>block topples</u>.

Note that, in each case, the opposing moments would increase steadily and equally to one another as the applied force P was increased, until one of these moments reaches its maximum value. A further slight increase of P above the value for this maximum will mean that the opposing moments can no longer be equal, and the block will no longer be in equilibrium. Some movement will take place, and the block will slide if the toppling moment had reached its maximum first, or topple if the opposing moment had reached its maximum first. (If the two maximum values were to occur at the same value of P, the block would tend to slide along on its front edge.)

A simple experiment could be devised along these lines to estimate the coefficient of friction between the surface of a block and a given horizontal surface. A horizontal force could be applied at various heights up the side of the block until the block was on the point of sliding and toppling at the same time. If the mass of the block is m kg, the horizontal distance between its centre of gravity and its lower front edge is a m, and the height at which the horizontal force needs to be applied to cause simultaneous sliding and toppling effects is h m, then

$$\text{maximum toppling moment} = F \times h \text{ Nm}$$
$$= \mu R_n \times h \text{ Nm}$$
$$\text{maximum opposing moment} = R_n \times a \text{ Nm}$$

But in this case these are equal, since sliding and toppling tend to occur at the same point, so that

$$\mu R_n \times h = R_n \times a$$

or
$$\mu = \frac{a}{h}$$

7.8.   Rough inclined plane

In Section 3.13, page 80, the equilibrium conditions of a body on a smooth, frictionless, inclined plane were considered. It can now be seen that a frictional force will also exist between the surfaces in contact, opposing any motion between them.

(a) *Motion up the plane*

Consider the example of a body of mass m which rests on a rough plane where the coefficient of friction between the surfaces is μ. Let the plane be inclined at angle θ to the horizontal, and suppose a force P acts on the body so that it is about to move up the plane. Take two special cases, (i) when P acts parallel to the plane, (ii) when P acts horizontally.

(i) P parallel to the plane

The conditions are as shown in the space diagram 89, where R_n is the reaction perpendicular to the plane.

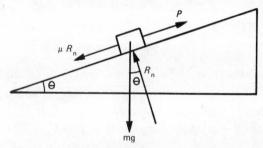

89. Rough inclined plane. Body about to move up the plane. P parallel to plane

Equating opposing components of forces parallel to the plane,

$$P = mg \sin \theta + \mu R_n \qquad . \qquad . \qquad \text{(iii)}$$

Equating opposing components of forces perpendicular to the plane,

$$R_n = mg \cos \theta \qquad . \qquad . \qquad . \qquad \text{(iv)}$$

Substituting the value of R_n given by equation (iv) in equation (iii):

$$P = mg \sin \theta + \mu mg \cos \theta$$
$$\underline{P = mg (\sin \theta + \mu \cos \theta)} \qquad . \qquad . \qquad \text{(v)}$$

(ii) P horizontal

The conditions are as shown in the space diagram 90, where again R_n is the reaction perpendicular to the plane.

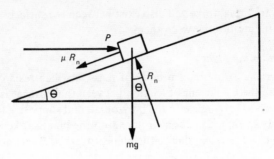

90. Rough inclined plane. Body about to move up the
plane. P horizontal

Again equating opposing components of forces parallel to the plane,

$$P \cos \theta = mg \sin \theta + \mu R_n \qquad . \qquad . \qquad \text{(vi)}$$

Equating opposing components of forces perpendicular to the plane,

$$R_n = mg \cos \theta + P \sin \theta \qquad . \qquad . \qquad \text{(vii)}$$

Substituting the value of R_n from equation (vii) in equation (vi),

$$P \cos \theta = mg \sin \theta + \mu (mg \cos \theta + P \sin \theta)$$

or $\qquad P \cos \theta - \mu P \sin \theta = mg \sin \theta + \mu mg \cos \theta$

or $\qquad P (\cos \theta - \mu \sin \theta) = mg (\sin \theta + \mu \cos \theta)$

or $\qquad\qquad P = \dfrac{mg (\sin \theta + \mu \cos \theta)}{(\cos \theta - \mu \sin \theta)} \qquad . \qquad . \qquad \text{(viii)}$

(b) *Motion down the plane*

Assume that the body would slip down the plane unless an additional applied force held it in equilibrium. The conditions will be similar to those already considered *except* that the frictional force now acts up the plane to oppose motion down the plane. Once again, two special cases will be considered, for applied force P (i) parallel to the plane and (ii) horizontal.

(i) *P parallel to plane*

The conditions are as shown in the space diagram 91, where R_n is the reaction perpendicular to the plane.

Equating opposing components of forces parallel to the plane,

$$P + \mu R_n = mg \sin \theta . \qquad . \qquad . \qquad \text{(ix)}$$

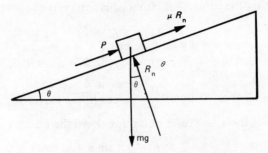

91. Rough inclined plane. Body about to move down
the plane. *P* parallel to plane

Equating opposing components of forces perpendicular to the plane,

$$R_n = mg \cos \theta \ . \qquad . \qquad . \qquad \text{(x)}$$

Substituting the value of R_n from equation (x) in equation (ix)

$$P + \mu mg \cos \theta = mg \sin \theta$$
$$\underline{\underline{P = mg\, (\sin \theta - \mu \cos \theta)}} \qquad . \qquad \text{(xi)}$$

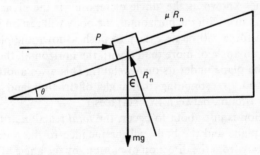

92. Rough inclined plane. Body about to move down
the plane. *P* horizontal

(ii) *P* horizontal

The conditions are as shown in the space diagram 92, where R_n is the reaction perpendicular to the plane.

Equating opposing components of forces parallel to the plane,

$$P \cos \theta + \mu R_n = mg \sin \theta \ . \qquad . \qquad . \qquad \text{(xii)}$$

Equating opposing components of forces perpendicular to the plane,

$$R_n = P \sin \theta + mg \cos \theta \qquad . \qquad \text{(xiii)}$$

Substituting the value of R_n from equation (xiii) in equation (xii),

$$P \cos \theta + \mu(P \sin \theta + mg \cos \theta) = mg \sin \theta$$

or $$P \cos \theta + \mu P \sin \theta = mg \sin \theta - \mu mg \cos \theta$$

or $$P (\cos \theta + \mu \sin \theta) = mg (\sin \theta - \mu \cos \theta)$$

or $$P = \frac{mg (\sin \theta - \mu \cos \theta)}{(\cos \theta + \mu \sin \theta)} . \qquad . \quad \text{(xiv)}$$

In either of these two cases of motion down the plane,

$$P = 0 \text{ if } \sin \theta - \mu \cos \theta = 0$$

i.e. if $$\sin \theta = \mu \cos \theta$$

or $$\tan \theta = \mu$$

But the coefficient of friction $\mu = \tan \varphi$ where φ is the angle of friction, so that

$$P = 0 \text{ if } \tan = \tan \varphi$$

or $$\theta = \varphi$$

This means that the body will just be on the point of slipping down the plane under its own gravitational force if the inclination of the plane is equal to the angle of friction. For this reason, the angle of friction φ is also sometimes known as the 'angle of repose'. If the plane makes an angle of less than φ with the horizontal, the body will rest on it in equilibrium, and a force will be necessary to push it down the plane. If the plane makes an angle of more than φ with the horizontal, the body will slide down the plane under its own weight. (This gives another experimental method of estimating the angle of friction and hence the coefficient of friction between two surfaces.)

When motion is just about to occur, the *total* reaction at the surface between the plane and the body will be inclined to the normal to the plane, and away from the direction of motion, by the angle of friction φ. This fact enables a graphical solution to be drawn for the problems considered above, provided that the case is one of limiting friction; i.e. that motion up or down the plane is just about to take place.

Diagrams 93, 94, 95 and 96 show the space diagrams and corresponding force-vector diagrams for motion about to occur up the plane and down the plane respectively, for each of the special cases of the direction of force P.

Note from the force-vector triangle in diagram 94 that

$$\frac{P}{mg} = \tan (\theta + \varphi) \text{ or } P = mg \tan (\theta + \varphi)$$

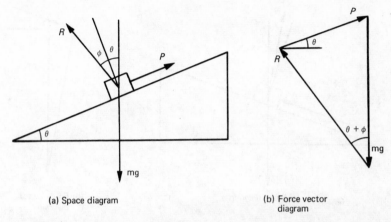

(a) Space diagram   (b) Force vector diagram

93. Rough inclined plane. Body about to move up the plane. *P* parallel to plane

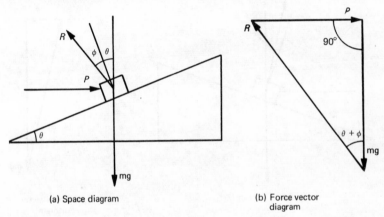

(a) Space diagram   (b) Force vector diagram

94. Rough inclined plane. Body about to move up the plane. *P* horizontal

This gives another expression for *P*, alternative to that developed previously for this case.

Note from the force-vector triangle in diagram 96 that

$$\frac{P}{mg} = \tan(\theta - \varphi) \text{ or } P = mg \tan(\theta - \varphi)$$

This gives another expression for *P*, alternative to that developed previously for this case.

If $\theta = \varphi$, $(\theta - \varphi) = 0$ and *R* vertically opposes *mg*, so that *P* = 0

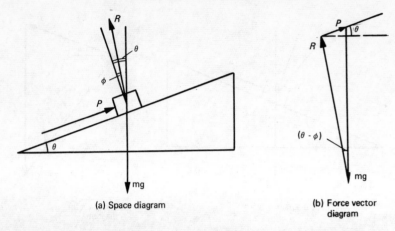

(a) Space diagram

(b) Force vector diagram

95. Rough inclined plane. Body about to move down the plane. *P* parallel to plane

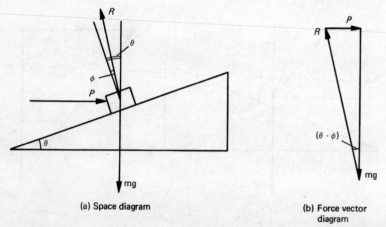

(a) Space diagram

(b) Force vector diagram

96. Rough inclined plane. Body about to move down the plane. *P* horizontal

in each case of motion down the plane. If θ is less than φ, the direction of *P* is reversed, so that the body must be pushed down the plane.

CHAPTER SUMMARY

No solid surfaces are absolutely flat, so that two surfaces in contact touch only at a few points. Frictional forces are due to cold welding at these points. Frictional force always opposes motion and is independent of apparent area of contact.

$$F = \mu R_n$$

where
F = limiting frictional force
R_n = force holding surfaces in contact
μ = coefficient of friction.

When sliding is just about to take place, the resultant reaction is inclined backwards to the direction in which motion is about to occur. The reaction then makes an angle φ with the perpendicular to the surfaces, where

$$\tan \varphi = \mu$$

φ is known as the angle of friction.

For a body of mass m resting on a rough plane inclined at angle θ to the horizontal and acted on by a force P,

(a) When motion is about to occur up the plane:

    (i)   If P is parallel to the plane,
$$P = mg (\sin \theta + \mu \cos \theta)$$

    (ii) If P is horizontal,

$$P = \frac{mg (\sin \theta + \mu \cos \theta)}{\cos \theta - \mu \sin \theta}$$

or $P = mg \tan (\theta + \varphi)$ where $\mu = \tan \varphi$

(b) When motion is about to occur down the plane:

    (i)   If P is parallel to the plane,
$$P = mg (\sin \theta - \mu \cos \theta)$$

    (ii) If P is horizontal,

$$P = \frac{mg (\sin \theta - \mu \cos \theta)}{\cos \theta + \mu \sin \theta}$$

or $P = mg \tan (\theta - \varphi)$ where $\mu = \tan \varphi$

If θ is less than φ, the body will rest on the plane without slipping.

If θ is greater than φ, the body will slide down the plane, in the absence of any external force.

If $\theta = \varphi$, the body will just be on the point of slipping down the plane.

QUESTIONS

1. A block of material which rests on a horizontal surface is to be moved by a force of 2·5 kN inclined at an angle of 30° to the surface.

(i) Determine either graphically or by calculation (a) the force component acting in the direction of motion of the block, (b) the vertical force component.

(ii) Find the work done in moving the block a horizontal distance of 1 m.

(iii) If the mass of the block is 770 kg find the normal reaction between the block and the surface on which it rests (i.e. the reaction perpendicular to the surface).

(iv) Determine the coefficient of friction between the block and the surface if the block is just moved at constant speed by this applied force.

(v) After lubrication of the surface, it is found that a block of mass 1350 kg can just be moved by the same force acting in the same manner. What is the new value of the coefficient of friction?

2. A machine having a mass of 500 kg rests on a horizontal floor, and in order to move it a pull is applied by means of a rope attached to the machine and inclined upwards at 20° to the horizontal. It is found that a pull of 750 N is just sufficient to move the machine. Determine:

(a) the horizontal effect of the pull,

(b) the vertical force between the machine and the floor,

(c) the coefficient of friction between machine and floor.

3. (a) An object of mass 30 kg rests on a rough horizontal plane and the coefficient of friction between the surfaces is 0·15. Calculate the least horizontal force required just to move the object. If the object is now moved across the surface for a distance of 20 m, what work is done against friction?

(b) Give three examples of the useful application of friction.

4. A metal box having a mass of 100 kg is pulled along a level plane, at uniform speed, by a horizontal rope applying a force of 325 N. An additional mass of 40 kg is now added to the box. What must be the force in the rope to move the box at uniform speed?

If the rope will not transmit a force of more than 500 N, what is the greatest mass which can be added to the box?

5. (a) Define 'coefficient of friction' and describe how you would determine its value for a given pair of materials.

(b) A brake is applied to the rim of a wheel with a force of 2·5 kN, and the coefficient of friction between rim and brake shoe is 0·4. Calculate the force of friction tending to stop the wheel.

6. (a) Explain the meaning of the term 'coefficient of friction'.

(b) A workpiece is held in a clamp by a balanced lever, as shown in the diagram. If the workpiece has to withstand a vertical thrust of 280 N as shown, determine the minimum force that must be applied to the lever to hold the piece firmly by means of friction. The coefficient of friction between the material of the workpiece and the material of the clamp is 0·16.

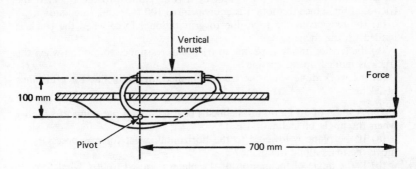

7. Define the term 'coefficient of friction'.

The coefficient of friction for a 150 mm diameter shaft rotating in a bearing at 200 rev/min is 0·02. If the load on the bearing is 20 kN, calculate:

(a) the friction torque on the shaft,

(b) the work done per second against friction in the bearing.

8. A rotor on a shaft of 75 mm diameter has a mass of 750 kg. The shaft is running in plain bearings, the coefficient of friction between journal and bearing being 0·04. If the shaft rotates at 500 rev/min, calculate the energy absorbed per second in overcoming friction.

9. (a) During an experiment to determine the coefficient of friction for a brake fabric, the following results were obtained:

Normal force between surfaces (N)	5	15	27·5	35	45	50
Force to overcome friction (N)	2	6·1	11	13·9	18·1	20

Plot a graph and from it determine the coefficient of friction.

(b) A brake drum of 1·2 m diameter is rotating at 500 rev/min and the brake block is lined with a fabric whose coefficient of friction is 0·4. Calculate the work done by the brake block in bringing the drum to rest in two minutes if the average normal force between block and drum is 1·25 kN.

10. A machine of mass 275 kg rests on a plane which is inclined at 13° to the horizontal. If the coefficient of friction between the machine and the plane is 0·29, determine either graphically or by calculation:

(a) the minimum force, parallel to the plane, required to move the machine up at a constant speed,

(b) the minimum force, parallel to the plane, required to pull the machine down at a constant speed,

(c) the horizontal force necessary to move the machine up the plane.

11. Explain the meaning of 'limiting friction'.

A truck which has a mass of 10 tonne is to be hauled up an incline making an angle of 42° with the horizontal by a rope parallel to the track. If the frictional resistance to motion is equivalent to 100 N/tonne, calculate:

(a) the tension in the rope due to gravitational force when the truck is hauled up the incline,

(b) the tension in the rope due to frictional resistance to motion when the truck is hauled up the incline,

(c) the work done when the truck is hauled up the incline for a distance of 24 m.

12. A mass of 30 kg on an inclined plane is just on the point of slipping when the angle of inclination is 15°.

(a) If the plane is lowered to the horizontal, what force is necessary to move the mass along the plane?

(b) If the angle of inclination of the plane is raised to 30°, what force is necessary to prevent the block slipping down the plane?

13. A block of mass 50 kg slides at uniform speed down a plane inclined at 12° to the horizontal. What is the coefficient of friction between the surfaces in contact? What force parallel to the plane is required to move the block at uniform speed up the plane?

14. It is found by experiment that a 20-kg cast-iron block, placed on a smooth steel plane, is just on the point of sliding when the inclination of the plane to the horizontal is 10°. If the angle of the plane is increased to 35°, what force, parallel to the plane, would be needed to push the block up the plane at a constant speed?

15. A body of mass 4 kg rests on an inclined surface and it is found that in order to move the body up the plane a force of 15 N, acting parallel to the plane, is required. To move the body down the plane a force of 5 N, acting parallel to the plane, is required. Calculate the inclination of the plane and the value of the coefficient of friction between the body and the plane.

8. Velocity and Acceleration

The study of the way in which bodies move, if the mass of the body and the forces necessary to cause motion are neglected, is called KINEMATICS. It is this type of study that will be introduced in this chapter. Later on, in Chapter 9, page 258, the effects of the mass of the moving body and the forces acting on it will be studied, but it is necessary first to have a basis on which to work.

8.1. Speed

Most people have an idea of what is meant by the SPEED of a body, and will know at least one unit in which it can be measured, in these days of restricted areas and speed limits. Consider just what is meant by a speed of 50 kilometres per hour. It means, of course, that if a car travels at this constant speed for an hour, it will cover a distance of 50 kilometres. But it is not necessary to measure the distance travelled by the car in an hour before the speed at which it is travelling can be measured. If the speed of the car is constant at 50 kilometres per hour at all times, it would travel a distance of

	25 kilometres in 0·5 h
or	12·5 kilometres in 0·25 h
or	5 kilometres in 0·1 h (6 min)
or	0·5 kilometres in 0·01 h (36 seconds)

and so on.

For each of these cases, the speed is given by dividing the distance travelled by the time taken. Thus

$$\frac{25}{0·5} = \frac{12·5}{0·25} = \frac{5}{0·1} = \frac{0·5}{0·01} = 50 \text{ kilometres per hour}$$

The speed of an object is, then, given by

$$\text{speed} = \frac{\text{distance travelled}}{\text{time taken}}$$

If the speed changes during the time interval over which the distance is measured, this equation will give the *average* speed during this time. For example, if a train takes 2 h to cover a distance of 120 kilometres, its average speed is $\dfrac{120 \text{ km}}{2 \text{ h}}$, or 60 km/h (where km/h is shorthand for 'kilometres per hour'). The train will almost certainly have travelled at greater speeds than this for parts of the journey, to make up for those times when it has to travel slowly up gradients or over restricted sections of the track.

Speed can be thought of as the rate at which the distance of a moving body from its starting point is increasing. In other words,

$$\text{speed} = \text{rate of increase of distance}$$

For example, for a car moving at a steady 50 km/h along a straight road, the distance travelled increases at the rate of 50 kilometres in every hour.

The units in which speed is measured are those of (distance units) ÷ (time units). The fundamental unit of speed is the METRE PER SECOND (m/s), although, again, multiple and sub-multiple units may be used.

8.2. Examples

(i) Convert a speed of 60 km/h into units of m/s

$$60 \text{ km/h} = 60 \,\frac{\text{km}}{\text{h}}$$

$$= 60 \,\frac{\text{km}}{\text{h}} \times \left(\frac{1000 \text{ m}}{1 \text{ km}}\right) \times \left(\frac{1 \text{ h}}{60 \text{ min}}\right) \times \left(\frac{1 \text{ min}}{60 \text{ s}}\right)$$

$$= 60 \times 1000 \times \frac{1}{60} \times \frac{1}{60} \,\frac{\text{m}}{\text{s}}$$

$$= \underline{16{\cdot}7 \text{ m/s}}$$

This is a useful result to remember as a 'conversion relationship'.

(ii) A train leaves a station at 1356 hours and arrives at another station 80 km away at 1503 hours. What is its average speed for the journey?

Time taken for journey = 15 h 3 min − 13 h 56 min

= 1 h 7 min

= 67 min

$$\text{Speed} = \frac{\text{distance travelled}}{\text{time taken}}$$

$$= \frac{80 \text{ km}}{67 \text{ min}}$$

$$= \frac{80 \text{ km}}{67 \text{ min}} \times \left(\frac{60 \text{ min}}{1 \text{ h}}\right)$$

$$= 71 \cdot 7 \text{ km/h}$$

Average speed of train over the journey = $\underline{71 \cdot 7 \text{ km/h}}$

(iii) The distance between two points on a straight road in a 50 km/h zone is 200 m. What is the minimum time taken by a car travelling between these points without exceeding the speed limit?

$$\text{Speed} = \frac{\text{distance travelled}}{\text{time taken}}$$

$$\therefore \qquad \text{time taken} = \frac{\text{distance travelled}}{\text{speed}}$$

Then, for a car travelling at 50 km/h for a distance of 200 m

$$\text{time taken} = \frac{200 \text{ m}}{50 \text{ km/h}}$$

$$= \frac{200 \text{ m}}{50 \text{ km/h}} \times \left(\frac{60 \text{ km/h}}{16 \cdot 7 \text{ m/s}}\right)$$

$$= \frac{200}{50} \times \frac{60}{16 \cdot 7} \text{ s}$$

$$= 14 \cdot 4 \text{ s}$$

Minimum time required to travel the distance is $\underline{14 \cdot 4 \text{ s}}$.

8.3. Velocity

In common non-scientific usage, 'velocity' is often taken as meaning the same thing as speed. However, a special significance is given to the term velocity for scientific purposes. The velocity of a moving body is concerned not only with 'how fast is the body moving?', but also with 'in what direction is the body moving?' In other words, the velocity of a body is its speed in a particular direction, so that

VELOCITY IS A VECTOR QUANTITY
SPEED IS A SCALAR QUANTITY

(See Section 3.1, page 38.)

Speed is the 'number part' or 'magnitude' of velocity. The speed of a moving body changes only if the rate of increase of distance changes. The velocity of a moving body changes if *either* the speed *or* the direction changes. A car may travel round a curved track at a constant speed, but its velocity will change each time its direction changes. The importance of a change in *velocity* will be seen more clearly in Chapter 9, when the effects of the mass of the moving body are considered.

The direction of a particular velocity may be specified in any suitable way. For the movement of large objects like ships, aeroplanes and trains, it may be convenient to use the points of the compass. For other purposes, as with forces (see Section 3.2, page 39) and other vector quantities, it may be more convenient to choose and state a reference direction. A particular direction may then be specified in terms of the angle made with this reference direction. With this idea, a 'negative' velocity would be a velocity in a direction opposite to that chosen as reference.

For example, if due north is chosen as reference direction, a velocity in a direction due south would be said to be negative. A velocity due west would be said to be at an angle of 90° to the reference, and a velocity due east would be at 270°, or – 90°, to the reference. For this purpose, 'positive' angles are measured in an anti-clockwise direction from the reference, and 'negative' angles are measured in a clockwise direction from the reference. Examples are given in diagram 97. If due north is used as the reference direction,

(a) is a velocity of + 30 km/h, or 30 km/h in reference direction,
(b) is a velocity of – 30 km/h, or 30 km/h at 180° to reference,
(c) is a velocity of 30 km/h at + 135° (or – 225°) to reference,
(d) is a velocity of 30 km/h at + 225° (or – 135°) to reference.

It is usual to quote the angle to reference in terms of its smallest numerical value; i.e. + 135° for (c) and – 135° for (d).

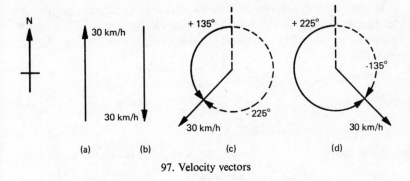

97. Velocity vectors

8.4. Distance-time graphs

If the distance travelled by a moving body is plotted on a graph against the time at which it was measured, the resulting distance-time graph gives a picture of the motion. For example, if the body moves with a constant velocity, the rate of increase of distance is a constant,

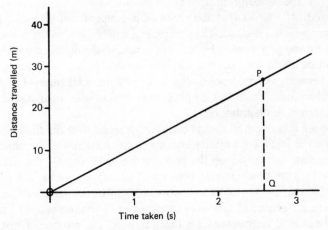

98. Distance-time graph for body moving with a constant velocity of 10 m/s in a given direction

and the graph will be a straight line. This will be so because the distance increases by the same amount for equal intervals of time. If the constant velocity is 10 m/s in a certain direction, then the distance moved in that direction will be 10 m after 1 s, 20 m after 2 s, 30 m after 3 s, and so on. The graph would then be as given in diagram 98.

If any point P is taken on this straight-line, or 'linear', graph, and lengths PQ and OQ are measured as shown, by means of the appropriate scales, then PQ represents the distance travelled in time OQ

$$\text{or} \qquad \text{speed} = \frac{\text{distance travelled}}{\text{time taken}}$$

$$= \frac{PQ}{OQ}$$

Since the velocity is constant, the speed is also constant, and the same answer will be obtained from the fraction or ratio $\frac{PQ}{OQ}$, wherever the point P is taken on the graph. The ratio $\frac{PQ}{OQ}$ is called the 'slope' of the graph, and its value will be constant for a straight-line graph.

The slope of a distance-time graph is thus equal to the speed of movement (or the velocity in the direction in which the distances are measured). It follows that the speed of movement can be found for a body for which a distance-time graph is available.

If the speed of a moving body is not constant, the distance-time graph will not be a straight line, but will be a curve. The value of the *average* speed between any two points (i.e. over any required interval of time) can still be found from this graph, however. Consider the distance-time graph shown in diagram 99.

Suppose it is required to find the average speed over the time interval between the instant 2 s after starting and the instant 4 s after starting. These points are shown on the graph as points P and Q. The distance travelled in the time interval between P and Q is represented on the graph by the *vertical* distance between them (QR), which is seen to represent a distance of (20 − 5) m, or 15 m. The time taken to travel this distance is represented on the graph by the *horizontal* distance between the points P and Q (PR), which is seen to represent a time of (4 − 2) s, or 2 s. The *average* speed between P and Q is, then,

$$\text{average speed} = \frac{\text{distance travelled}}{\text{time taken}}$$

$$= \frac{QR}{PR}$$

$$= \frac{15 \text{ m}}{2 \text{ s}}$$

$$= \underline{7 \cdot 5 \text{ m/s}}$$

Notice that this average speed, $\frac{QR}{PR}$, is the slope of the straight line PQ.

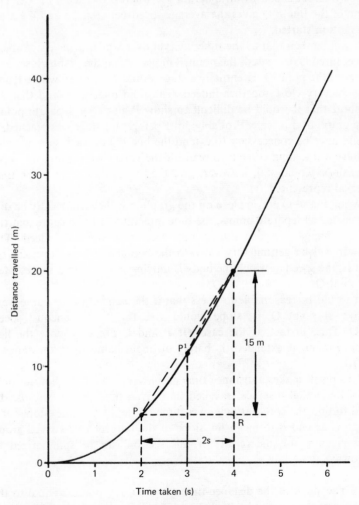

99. Distance-time graph for body moving at a changing speed. (Speed increasing)

H

Suppose that this average speed were measured over a shorter and shorter time interval—say between 3 s and 4 s after starting, then between 3·5 s and 4 s after starting, then between 3·75 s and 4 s after starting, and so on. Each of these average speeds would be given by the slope of the appropriate line PQ, where the point P was taken on the graph as being at the beginning of the required interval. One such reduced interval is shown on diagram 99, where P′ is taken at 3 s. The slope of the line P′Q gives the average speed between 3 s and 4 s after the motion started.

It will be seen that as the time interval over which the average speed is measured is decreased, the point P moves along the graph closer and closer to the point Q. Eventually a stage would be reached where P and Q were very close together indeed. The time interval would then be so short that it would be difficult to show P and Q as separate points on a graph of this scale. Probably, long before this stage was reached, it would have been necessary to extend the line PQ on each side in order to have a line long enough to read off the values to measure its slope. This slope would still, however, give the average speed over the time interval represented.

When P and Q are so close on the graph that they can hardly be distinguished as separate points, the time interval will be so short that the actual change in speed during this time is very small indeed. The answer will be getting very close to the actual speed at the point Q; that is, the speed at which the body is moving at the instant represented by point Q.

It would be reasonable to guess that if the *tangent* to the curve were drawn at point Q, its slope would give this 'instantaneous' speed at Q. This, in fact, is the case. (If P and Q are very close the line joining them, if extended, is barely distinguishable from the tangent at Q.)

This result makes a distance-time graph very useful, since it not only gives the actual distance travelled in a given time, but it can also be used to find the speed at any given time. If the idea of the 'slope' of a graph is extended to mean the slope of the tangent to a curved graph at a given point, the results of this section can be summarized as follows:

'The slope of the distance-time graph at any point is equal to the speed of the moving body at that point, or to the velocity of the body in the direction in which the distance is measured.'

8.5. Acceleration

If the velocity of a body changes, the body is said to 'accelerate'. It will be easier at first to consider a change in velocity caused by a change in speed, with the direction remaining constant. For example, if the speed of a car in a certain direction is

> 10 km/h at a certain time
> and 11 km/h 1 min later
> and 12 km/h 1 min later still
> and 13 km/h 1 min later still
> and so on,

the car would be said to have an ACCELERATION of 1 kilometre per hour every minute, in the direction of the car's velocity.

Notice that, like velocity, ACCELERATION IS A VECTOR QUANTITY. The direction in which the velocity changes is important, as well as the amount by which it changes in a given time. For example, if the result for the above car moving in a constant direction had been

> 30 km/h at a certain time
> 29 km/h 1 min later
> 28 km/h 1 min later still
> 27 km/h 1 min later still
> and so on,

then the car could be said to have a 'negative' acceleration of 1 kilometre per hour every minute in the direction of the car's velocity. The term 'negative acceleration' may be taken to mean the same as a positive RETARDATION.

The units in which the 'number part' or 'magnitude' of an acceleration are measured are those of (units of speed) ÷ (units of time). For example, in the case of the accelerating car, the car would be said to have an acceleration of 1 km/h per minute.

The fundamental unit of acceleration is the (METRE PER SECOND) PER SECOND. The brackets are usually omitted, and the unit is referred to as the METRE PER SECOND SQUARED, written as m/s^2.

Then, for a car having an acceleration of 2 m/s^2 in the direction of its movement, its velocity increases by 2 m/s every second.

In many practical cases, the acceleration of a body is not constant. Graphical methods may sometimes be of use in such cases, and these will be considered in the next section.

8.6. Velocity-time graphs

If the velocity of a body in a particular direction is constant, it has been seen that the distance moved, measured in the direction of the velocity, increases at a constant rate. Thus, if the velocity is 10 m/s in a

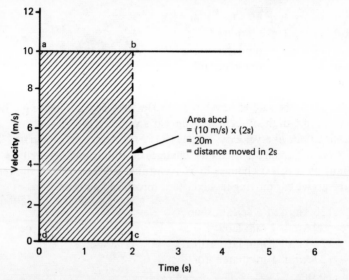

100. Velocity-time graph for a body moving at a constant velocity of 10 m/s

certain direction, the body moves in that direction for a distance of 10 m in 1 s, 20 m in 2 s, 30 m in 3 s, and so on.

A graph drawn of velocity against time is shown in diagram 100, for a body moving with a constant velocity of 10 m/s in a given direction. Since

$$\text{velocity} = \frac{\text{distance moved in direction of velocity}}{\text{time taken}}$$

then if the velocity is constant, or 'uniform', the distance moved increases uniformly with time, or

distance moved in
     direction of velocity = uniform velocity × time

As is seen in this example, the distance moved is doubled if the time considered is doubled, and so on.

The product (uniform velocity) × (time) is now represented by an area on the velocity-time graph. For example, the product (10 m/s) × (2 s) is represented by the area of the rectangle abcd in diagram 100. It follows that areas under a velocity-time graph represent distances moved in the time interval concerned. The student will notice that this follows the same sort of reasoning as was used to show that the area under a force-distance graph or 'work diagram' represents the work done by the force. (See Section 6.3, page 177.) Just as was shown to be

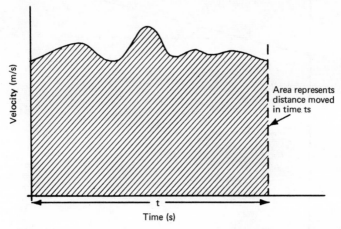

101. Velocity-time graph for a body having non-uniform motion

the case for a work diagram, the area under a velocity-time graph still represents the distance moved in the time considered even when the velocity varies. Thus, diagram 101 shows the velocity-time graph for a case when the velocity changes in a very complicated way. The area under this graph still represents the total distance moved in the direction of the velocity, and may be estimated by any suitable method, such as counting squares or mid-ordinate rule.

Next, consider the special case when the velocity increases uniformly; i.e., the case of uniform acceleration. Suppose that the body starts moving at 10 m/s, and has a uniform acceleration of 2 m/s^2. At the end of the first second, the velocity will be 12 m/s; at the end of the next second, the velocity will be 14 m/s; and so on. The velocity-time graph will be a sloping straight line as shown in diagram 102.

For any two points P and Q chosen on this graph, the *vertical* distance

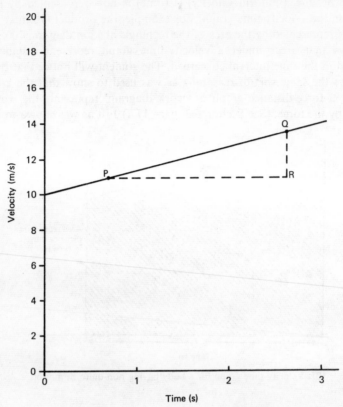

102. Velocity-time graph for body having uniform acceleration

between them (QR) represents the increase in velocity acquired during the time interval represented by the *horizontal* distance between them (PR). Then, the acceleration of the body is given by

$$\text{acceleration} = \frac{\text{increase in velocity}}{\text{time taken}}$$

$$= \frac{QR}{PR}$$

$$= \text{slope of line PQ}$$

For the case considered, the velocity-time graph is a straight line having a constant slope (which must follow from the fact that the acceleration is constant).

Just as in the case of the curved distance-time graph, the slope of a curved velocity-time graph is found at any point by measuring the slope of the tangent to the graph at that point. For example, the motion represented by diagram 101 has a non-uniform acceleration, since the slope of this graph is continually changing.

Summary

    (a) The area under a velocity-time graph over a given time interval represents the distance moved in the direction of the velocity in that time.

    (b) The slope of a velocity-time graph at any point represents the acceleration in the direction of the velocity at that point.

8.7. Bodies moving with uniform acceleration

In order that mathematical equations may be obtained to represent the motion of a body, some symbols must be used for the various quantities concerned. These are collected together and stated below for convenience of reference:

    s = distance moved by the body
    t = time, measured from the starting instant $t = 0$
    u = initial, or starting velocity
    v = final velocity after time t
    a = constant, linear, acceleration.

Linear acceleration means 'acceleration along a straight line'.

Any compatible units may be used for these quantities. For example, if s were measured in km, and t in hours, u and v would be in km/h and a would be in km/h². However, in what follows it will be assumed that the 'fundamental' units are used. Thus,

    s is measured in METRES (m)
    t is measured in SECONDS (s)
    u and v are measured in METRES PER SECOND (m/s)
    a is measured in METRES PER SECOND SQUARED (m/s²)

Diagram 103 shows the velocity-time graph for a body moving with uniform acceleration, and applies these symbols.

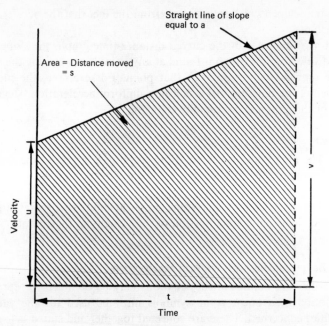

103. General velocity-time graph for a body moving with constant acceleration

As seen in the previous section, the area under this graph represents the distance travelled. Since the graph is a trapezium, its area is given by

$$\text{area} = \tfrac{1}{2} \begin{pmatrix} \text{sum of parallel} \\ \text{sides} \end{pmatrix} \times \begin{pmatrix} \text{perpendicular distance} \\ \text{between parallel sides} \end{pmatrix}$$

$$\text{or } s = \tfrac{1}{2}(u + v) \times t \quad . \quad . \quad . \quad . \quad . \quad \text{(i)}$$

This would also be equal to the distance travelled by a body moving for time t with a velocity equal to the *average* velocity $\tfrac{1}{2}(u + v)$.

The constant slope of this velocity-time graph is equal to the constant acceleration a. The total increase in velocity during time t is $(v - u)$, so that the acceleration is

$$a = \frac{(v - u)}{t} \quad . \quad . \quad . \quad . \quad . \quad . \quad \text{(ii)}$$

The two equations (i) and (ii) represent the general equations of motion of a body moving with uniform linear acceleration. These equations may also be written in slightly different form, as follows:

From equation (ii)

$$a = \frac{(v - u)}{t}$$

or $at = v - u$

or $\underline{v = u + at}$.   .   .   .   .   .   (iii)

From equation (i)

$$s = \tfrac{1}{2}(u + v) \times t$$

Substituting the value of v given by equation (iii),

$$s = \tfrac{1}{2}(u + u + at) \times t$$
$$= \tfrac{1}{2}(2u + at) \times t$$
$$= (u + \tfrac{1}{2}at) \times t$$

or $\underline{s = ut + \tfrac{1}{2}at^2}$.   .   .   .   .   (iv)

Re-writing equation (ii) in a different way,

$$a = \frac{(v - u)}{t}$$

or $$t = \frac{(v - u)}{a}$$

Substitute this expression for t in equation (iv). Then

$$s = u\left(\frac{v - u}{a}\right) + \tfrac{1}{2}a\left(\frac{v - u}{a}\right)^2$$

$$= \frac{uv - u^2}{a} + \tfrac{1}{2}a\,\frac{v^2 - 2uv + u^2}{a^2}$$

Express the R.H.S. over the common denominator $2a$. Then

$$s = \frac{2(uv - u^2) + (v^2 - 2uv + u^2)}{2a}$$

or $2as = 2uv - 2u^2 + v^2 - 2uv + u^2$

or $2as = v^2 - u^2$

or $\underline{v^2 = u^2 + 2as}$.   .   .   .   .   (v)

The equations of linear motion are very important, and should be remembered. They are all collected together in the following summary for reference:

Motion under constant linear acceleration

$$s = \tfrac{1}{2} (u + v) t \qquad \cdot \qquad \cdot \qquad \cdot \qquad \cdot \qquad \cdot \qquad \text{(i)}$$

$$a = \frac{(v - u)}{t} \qquad \cdot \qquad \cdot \qquad \cdot \qquad \cdot \qquad \cdot \qquad \text{(ii)}$$

$$v = u + at \qquad \cdot \qquad \cdot \qquad \cdot \qquad \cdot \qquad \cdot \qquad \text{(iii)}$$

$$s = ut + \tfrac{1}{2}at^2 \qquad \cdot \qquad \cdot \qquad \cdot \qquad \cdot \qquad \text{(iv)}$$

$$v^2 = u^2 + 2as \qquad \cdot \qquad \cdot \qquad \cdot \qquad \cdot \qquad \text{(v)}$$

Note: (a) if velocity is uniform, $v = u$ and $a = 0$,

(b) a will be positive if acceleration acts in the direction of u,

(c) a will be negative if acceleration acts in a direction opposite to u (i.e. if retardation takes place).

8.8. Examples

(i) A car accelerates uniformly from rest (standstill) to a speed of 15 km/h in 10 s. Find

(a) the acceleration, in m/s^2,

(b) the distance covered during this period, in m.

First convert the final speed in km/h to a speed in m/s. Then

$$15 \text{ km/h} = 15 \; \cancel{\text{km/h}} \times \left(\frac{16 \cdot 7 \text{ m/s}}{60 \; \cancel{\text{km/h}}} \right)$$

$$= 4 \cdot 17 \text{ m/s}$$

For this case,

$$u = 0, v = 4 \cdot 17 \text{ m/s}, t = 10 \text{ s},$$

and the values of a and s are required.

Select an equation involving the known quantities and *one* of the unknown quantities. Thus

$$v = u + at \qquad \cdot \qquad \cdot \qquad \cdot \qquad \cdot \qquad \cdot \qquad \text{(iii)}$$

$$4 \cdot 17 = 0 + a \times 10$$

or $$a = \frac{4 \cdot 17}{10} \text{ m/s}^2$$

$$= 0 \cdot 417 \text{ m/s}^2$$

Also $$s = \tfrac{1}{2} (u + v) t \qquad \cdot \qquad \cdot \qquad \cdot \qquad \cdot \qquad \text{(i)}$$

$$= \tfrac{1}{2} (0 + 4 \cdot 17) \times 10 \text{ m}$$

$$= 20 \cdot 85 \text{ m}$$

Acceleration of car $= \underline{0 \cdot 417 \text{ m/s}^2}$

Distance covered in first 15 s $= \underline{20 \cdot 85 \text{ m}}$

(ii) The brakes of a car can slow it down at a rate of 7 m/s². (a) What distance is travelled before the car is stopped from a speed of 50 km/h? (b) If the brakes are applied at a distance of 7 m from an obstacle when the car is travelling at 50 km/h, at what speed will it hit the obstacle?

(a) First convert the speed from km/h to m/s. Then

$$50 \text{ km/h} = 50 \text{ km/h} \times \left(\frac{16 \cdot 7 \text{ m/s}}{60 \text{ km/h}} \right)$$

$$= 13 \cdot 9 \text{ m/s}$$

In this case,

$$u = 13 \cdot 9 \text{ m/s}, v = 0 \text{ (the car has stopped)},$$
$$a = -7 \text{ m/s}^2 \text{ (retardation, against direction of velocity)}.$$

The value of s is required. Then

$$v^2 = u^2 + 2as \qquad . \qquad . \qquad . \qquad . \qquad . \qquad \text{(v)}$$
$$0 = 13 \cdot 9^2 - 2 \times 7 \, s$$

$$s = \frac{193}{14} \text{ m}$$

or $\quad 14s = (13 \cdot 9)^2 \text{ m}$
$$= \underline{13 \cdot 8 \text{ m}}$$

For (b),

$$u = 13 \cdot 9 \text{ m/s}, a = -7 \text{ m/s}^2, s = 7 \text{ m}$$

and the value of v is required. Then

$$v^2 = u^2 + 2as \qquad . \qquad . \qquad . \qquad . \qquad \text{(v)}$$
or $\quad v^2 = (13 \cdot 9)^2 - 2 \times 7 \times 7 \text{ (m/s)}^2$
$$= 193 - 98 \text{ (m/s)}^2$$
$$= 95 \text{ (m/s}^2)$$
or $\quad v = \sqrt{95} \text{ m/s}$
$$= \underline{9 \cdot 75 \text{ m/s}} \text{ (about 35 km/h)}$$

Stopping distance from 50 km/h = $\underline{13 \cdot 8 \text{ m}}$
Speed after braking for 7 m = $\underline{9 \cdot 75 \text{ m/s} \text{ (35 km/h)}}$

(iii) A train starts from rest at a station A with a uniform acceleration of 1 m/s², which is maintained for 30 s. The train then travels at a uniform speed for 10 min, and finally slows down at a steady retardation of $1 \cdot 5$ m/s^2 and comes to rest again at station B. What is the distance between the two stations?

Here the problem is really in three sections:

(a) Find s and v when $u = 0$, $a = 1$ m/s^2, $t = 30$ s
(b) Find s when $u =$ value found for v in (a), $a = 0$ and $t = 10$ min
(c) Find s when $u =$ same value as in (b), $v = 0$ and $a = -1 \cdot 5$ m/s^2.

These three values of s together give the required distance between stations.

A velocity-time graph for this problem is shown in diagram 104.

(a) For first acceleration period, ($u = 0$, $a = 1$ m/s^2, $t = 30$ s)

$$s = ut + \tfrac{1}{2}at^2 \quad . \qquad . \qquad . \qquad . \qquad . \qquad \text{(iv)}$$
$$= 0 + \tfrac{1}{2} \times 1 \times (30)^2 \text{ m}$$
$$= \underline{450 \text{ m}}$$

$$v_{max} = u + at \quad . \qquad . \qquad . \qquad . \qquad . \qquad \text{(iii)}$$
$$= 0 + 1 \times 30 \text{ m/s}$$
$$= \underline{30 \text{ m/s}}$$

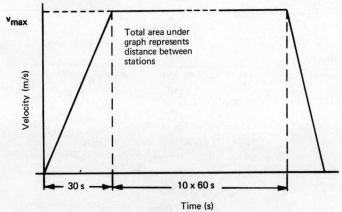

104. Velocity-time graph—numerical example

(b) For period of uniform speed, ($u = v_{max} = 30$ m/s, $a = 0$, $t = 10 \times 60$ s)

$$s = v_{max} t$$
$$= 30 \text{ m/s} \times (10 \times 60 \text{ s})$$
$$= \underline{18\,000 \text{ m}}$$

(c) For final retardation period ($u = 30$ m/s, $v = 0$, $a = -1.5$ m/s^2)

$$v^2 = u^2 + 2as \qquad \qquad \qquad \qquad \text{(v)}$$
$$0 = (30)^2 - 2 \times 1.5s$$
$$3s = 900 \text{ m}$$
$$s = \underline{300 \text{ m}}$$

Total distance travelled

$$= 450 + 18\ 000 + 300 \text{ m}$$
$$= 18\ 750 \text{ m}$$
$$= 18.75 \text{ km}$$

Distance between stations A and B $= \underline{\underline{18.75 \text{ km}}}$

This distance could also be found from the area under a velocity-time graph drawn to scale for the problem. The first part of such a graph for this problem would be a straight line having a slope equal to the acceleration of 1 m/s^2. This would be continued for a horizontal distance equivalent to 30 s. The velocity could then be drawn as a constant height of v_{max} for a distance equivalent to 600 s, followed by a steady decrease at a rate of 1.5 m/s^2. The area, representing the distance required, could then be found by measurement (see diagram 104).

(iv) Two telegraph poles A and B at the side of a railway track are 50 m apart. A train which has a uniform acceleration passes pole A at a speed of 70 km/h, and passes pole B 2 s later. What is the acceleration of the train, and how fast is it moving as it passes B?

First convert the speed at A into m/s:

$$70 \text{ km/h} = 70 \ \cancel{\text{km/h}} \times \left(\frac{16.7 \text{ m/s}}{60 \ \cancel{\text{km/h}}} \right)$$
$$= 19.44 \text{ m/s}$$

Then, in this case, $u = 19.44$ m/s, $s = 50$ m, $t = 2$ s and the values of a and v are required.

$$s = ut + \tfrac{1}{2} at^2 \qquad \qquad \qquad \text{(iv)}$$
$$50 = 19.44 \times 2 + \tfrac{1}{2}a \times 4$$
$$50 = 38.88 + 2a$$
$$2a = 11.12$$
$$a = \underline{5.56 \text{ m/s}^2}$$

Also $\quad s = \tfrac{1}{2}(u + v)t \qquad \qquad \qquad \text{(i)}$
$$50 = \tfrac{1}{2}(19.44 + v) \times 2$$
$$v = \underline{30.56 \text{ m/s}} \text{ (about 110 km/h)}$$

Acceleration of train is 5·56 m/s²

Speed at which it passes B is 30·56 m/s or 110 km/h

(v) The velocity of a vehicle changes uniformly from 50 km/h to 30 km/h in 25 s. Draw a velocity-time diagram to show this change, and use it to determine:

(a) the deceleration in m/s²,
(b) the distance travelled in the 25 s,
(c) the further time required to bring the vehicle to rest if the deceleration is maintained uniform.

Express the given velocities in m/s:

$$\text{Initial velocity, } u = 50 \text{ km/h} \times \left(\frac{16\cdot7\,\text{m/s}}{60\,\text{km/hr}}\right)$$

$$= 13\cdot9 \text{ m/s}$$

$$\text{Final velocity, } v = 30 \text{ km/h} \times \left(\frac{16\cdot7\,\text{m/s}}{60\,\text{km/h}}\right)$$

$$= 8\cdot33 \text{ m/s}$$

The velocity-time diagram is then shown in diagram 105.

$$a = \frac{8\cdot33 - 13\cdot9}{25} \text{ m/s}^2$$

$$= -\frac{5\cdot57}{25} \text{ m/s}^2$$

$$= -0\cdot223 \text{ m/s}^2$$

The negative sign indicates that it is a deceleration.

The distance travelled will be represented by the area under the velocity-time graph, which in this case is the area of a trapezium.

$$\text{Area} = \tfrac{1}{2}\left(\begin{array}{c}\text{sum of parallel} \\ \text{sides}\end{array}\right) \times \left(\begin{array}{c}\text{perpendicular distance} \\ \text{between them}\end{array}\right)$$

$$\therefore \text{ distance} = \tfrac{1}{2}(13\cdot9 + 8\cdot33)\,(\text{m/s}) \times 25 \text{ s}$$
$$= \tfrac{1}{2} \times 22\cdot23 \times 25 \text{ m}$$
$$= 278 \text{ m}$$

If the further time to reduce velocity to zero is t s, then from similar triangles on the velocity-time diagram,

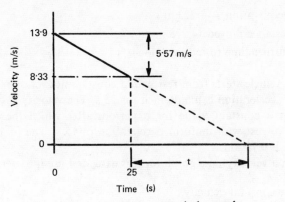

105. Velocity-time graph—numerical example

$$\frac{t}{8\cdot 33} = \frac{25}{5\cdot 57}$$

or $\quad t = \dfrac{25 \times 8\cdot 33}{5\cdot 57}$ s

$\qquad = 37\cdot 4$ s

The same answers could be obtained by the use of the equations of linear motion, as follows:

$\qquad u = 13\cdot 9$ m/s, $v = 8\cdot 33$ m/s, $t = 25$ s

$\qquad v = u + at$. $\qquad$. $\qquad$. $\qquad$. $\qquad$. $\qquad$ (iii)

$\qquad 8\cdot 33 = 13\cdot 9 + a \times 25$

or $\quad a = \dfrac{8\cdot 33 - 13\cdot 9}{25} = -0\cdot 223$ m/s^2 as before

$\qquad s = ut + \tfrac{1}{2}at^2$ $\qquad$. $\qquad$. $\qquad$. $\qquad$. $\qquad$ (iv)

$\qquad = 13\cdot 9 \times 25 - \tfrac{1}{2}0\cdot 223 \times 625$

$\qquad = 347\cdot 5 - 69\cdot 5$ m

$\qquad = 278$ m as before

If $\qquad v = 0, u = 8\cdot 33$ m/s, and $a = -0\cdot 223$ m/s^2

$\qquad v = u + at$. $\qquad$. $\qquad$. $\qquad$. $\qquad$. $\qquad$ (iii)

$\qquad 0 = 8\cdot 33 - 0\cdot 223\, t$

$\qquad t = \dfrac{8\cdot 33}{0\cdot 223}$

$\qquad = 37\cdot 4$ s as before

(a) Deceleration = 0·223 m/s²

(b) Distance moved = 278 m

(c) Further time to reduce velocity to zero = 37·4 s

(vi) A vehicle starts from rest with a constant acceleration of 1 m/s², and this acceleration is maintained for 25 s. The velocity is then maintained at a constant value for a period, after which the vehicle is brought to rest with uniform deceleration in 15 s. The total distance travelled is 0·75 km.

Sketch a velocity-time graph for this case, and use it to determine:

(a) the constant velocity,

(b) the deceleration,

(c) the total time for the journey.

The velocity-time graph is shown in diagram 106.

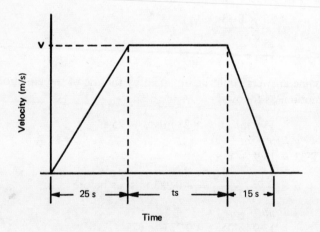

106. Velocity-time graph—numerical example

The constant velocity, v m/s, will be given by

$$v = u + at .$$.   .   (iii)

$$= 0 + 1 \times 25$$

$$= 25 \text{ m/s}$$

The deceleration, $- a$ m/s², will be given by

$$0 = 25 + a \times 15$$

$$a = - \frac{25}{15} \text{ m/s}^2$$

$$= - 1 \cdot 667 \text{ m/s}^2$$

Let t s be the time for which the velocity is maintained constant.

Total distance travelled = area under velocity-time graph

$$= \tfrac{1}{2} \{(25 + t + 15) + t\} \text{ (s)} \times 25 \text{ (m/s)}$$

$$= \tfrac{1}{2} (40 + 2t) \times 25 \text{ m}$$

But this distance is given as 0·75 km (= 750 m)

$$\tfrac{1}{2} (40 + 2t) \times 25 = 750$$

$$40 + 2t = \frac{750 \times 2}{25} = 60$$

$$2t = 60 - 40$$

$$= 20$$

$$t = 10 \text{ s}$$

Total time for journey $= t + 40$ s

$$= 50 \text{ s}$$

(a) Constant velocity = 25 m/s

(b) Deceleration = 1·667 m/s²

(c) Total time taken = 50 s

8.9. Motion under effects of gravity

An Italian scientist named Galileo (1564–1642) discovered the fact that two bodies of different weights released from the same height at the same time reach the ground together. He correctly deduced that this means that the acceleration due to gravity is independent of the weight of the body on which it acts. Legend has it that he carried out these experiments by dropping the two weights from the famous leaning tower at Pisa, in Italy. What is quite certain, however, is that for putting forward this and other conclusions concerning the motion of bodies, and in particular the motion of the stars and planets, he was bitterly persecuted by the Inquisition. At that time such ideas were considered heresy, and Galileo was forced to deny publicly theories which, from his own observations, he knew to be correct. Fortunately, the

Inquisition could not completely suppress Galileo's work, which can be considered to be the basic foundation for many modern theories of motion. This particular result is important to the discussion of the motion of bodies under the effects of gravity.

The acceleration due to gravity is a constant at any particular point on the earth's surface. It is, however, found to vary slightly between different points, and at different heights above the earth. In London, the acceleration due to gravity is 9·813 m/s^2; at the equator, 9·786 m/s^2; at the North pole, 9·828 m/s^2 (all at sea level). The value frequently used in practical calculation is 9·81 m/s^2, or 9·8 m/s^2 when the accuracy of the other measurements does not warrant the use of a more precise value. This acceleration due to gravity is usually represented by g.

Summary

The acceleration due to gravity acts vertically downwards, and is independent of the weight of the body on which it acts. Its value varies slightly at different points and heights on the earth's surface, but may usually be taken as $g = 9·81$ m/s^2. (For the exact definition of units, a standard gravitational environment has been formulated for which $g = 9·806\ 65$ m/s^2. This standard value is usually represented by g_n.)

When dealing with problems concerning the motion of bodies under the effects of gravity, it is important to adopt some convention concerning the sign to be given to distances, velocities and accelerations. Some direction must be assumed and stated to be the positive reference direction. In this book, *the positive direction will be vertically upwards*. This means that a positive distance is one measured in an upwards direction from the starting point. Similarly, velocities and accelerations will be positive when they are in an upwards direction. Since the acceleration due to gravity always acts vertically downwards, for the sign convention positive upwards g is taken as a negative number.

It is important to note the effect of this sign convention on the value calculated for a distance. The value of 's' in the formulae of Section 8.7 gives the total distance between the starting point and finishing point after any time interval t. If in that time a body has moved up to its maximum height and fallen back to the ground, the total distance between starting and finishing points would be *zero*. The value given for s would be 0, even though the body may have moved a considerable distance through the air on its travels. The point is that it moved through equal positive and negative distances, which will add up to zero. In fact, if a stone is thrown vertically upwards from the edge of a cliff so that it falls into the sea, the distance between starting and finishing points would be negative. The following examples should make this point clear.

8.10. Examples

(i) A stone is thrown vertically upwards with a velocity of 12 m/s. Find the greatest height reached, the time required to reach this height, and the total time before the stone reaches the ground again. How fast is the stone travelling when it hits the ground?

(Remember—POSITIVE UPWARDS.)

In this case, $u = +12$ m/s, $v = 0$ (at highest point reached, just before stone starts to fall again), $a = g = -9{\cdot}81$ m/s².

Then
$$v^2 = u^2 + 2ag \qquad . \qquad . \qquad . \qquad . \qquad \text{(v)}$$
$$0 = 12^2 - 2 \times 9{\cdot}81\ s$$
$$19{\cdot}62s = 144 \text{ m}$$
$$s = \underline{7{\cdot}33 \text{ m}}$$

Also
$$v = u + at . \qquad . \qquad . \qquad . \qquad . \qquad \text{(iii)}$$
$$0 = 12 - 9{\cdot}81t$$
$$9{\cdot}81t = 12$$
$$t = \underline{1{\cdot}22 \text{ s}}$$

For the total journey up and down, $s = 0$, $u = +12$ m/s, $a = g = -9{\cdot}81$ m/s² as before. Then

$$s = ut + \tfrac{1}{2}at^2 \qquad . \qquad . \qquad . \qquad . \qquad \text{(iv)}$$
$$0 = 12t - \tfrac{1}{2} \times 9{\cdot}81 \times t^2$$
or $\quad 4{\cdot}905t^2 = 12t$

$$t = \frac{12}{4{\cdot}905} \text{ or } 0 \text{ s}$$

$$t = \underline{2{\cdot}44 \text{ s}}$$

(The answer $t = 0$ applies before the stone leaves the ground for the first time.)

Also
$$v^2 = u^2 + 2as \qquad . \qquad . \qquad . \qquad . \qquad \text{(v)}$$
or
$$v^2 = 12^2 - 2 \times 9{\cdot}81 \times 0$$
or
$$v = 144$$
$$v = \pm 12 \text{ m/s}$$

The choice between the $+$ or $-$ signs may not be clear, so check by using the result for t

$$
\begin{aligned}
v = u + at \; . \qquad . \qquad . \qquad . \qquad . \qquad &\text{(iii)}\\
= 12 - 9 \cdot 81 \times 2 \cdot 44 &\\
= 12 - 24 &\\
= \underline{-\;12 \text{ m/s}} &
\end{aligned}
$$

> Greatest height reached $= \underline{\underline{7 \cdot 33 \text{ m}}}$
>
> Time to reach this height $= \underline{\underline{1 \cdot 22 \text{ s}}}$
>
> Total time in the air $= \underline{2 \cdot 44 \text{ s}}$
>
> Velocity when striking the ground $= \underline{-\;12 \text{ m/s}}$

Note from these results that the stone takes the same time to come down to the ground from its highest point as it takes to reach this point from the ground (total time in the air is twice the time taken to reach the highest point). Also, the stone returns to the ground with the same speed at which it left the ground, although, of course, the direction is reversed.

(ii) A stone is dropped into a well. The splash of the stone hitting the water at the bottom of the well is heard 2·56 s after the stone is dropped. If the surface of the water in the well is 30 m from the top of the well, estimate the speed of sound in air.

In this case, $u = 0$ m/s, $a = g = -9·81$ m/s², $s = -30$ m.
The time taken for the stone to reach the water surface is required first, and this is given by

$$
s = ut + \tfrac{1}{2}at^2 \qquad . \qquad . \qquad . \qquad . \qquad . \qquad \text{(iv)}
$$
$$
\text{or} \; -30 = 0 - \tfrac{1}{2} \times 9·81 t^2
$$
$$
\text{or} \qquad t^2 = \frac{60}{9·81} \; (= 6·12)
$$
$$
t = 2·47 \text{ s}
$$

The difference between this time and the time before the splash is heard will be the time taken for the sound to travel 30 m up the well at its own velocity (constant); i.e. (2·56 − 2·47) s, or 0·09 s.

If the velocity of sound in air is v_{air} m/s, then

$$v_{air} = \frac{\text{distance travelled}}{\text{time taken}}$$

$$= \frac{30 \text{ m}}{0 \cdot 09 \text{ s}}$$

$$\simeq 334 \text{ m/s}$$

Velocity of sound in air $\simeq$ 334 m/s

(The accuracy of the result depends on the accuracy of the measurements given.)

(iii) A ball is thrown vertically up in the air from the edge of a cliff 24·5 m high, so that when it falls down again it just misses the edge and falls on to the base of the cliff. If the initial vertical velocity was 19·6 m/s, how long will it take the ball to reach the foot of the cliff, and what is its velocity when it does so?

In this case, $u = + 19 \cdot 6$ m/s, $a = g = - 9 \cdot 81$ m/s², $s = - 24 \cdot 5$ m (since the ball ends up 24·5 m *below* its starting point).
It is required to find t and v. Then

$$s = ut + \tfrac{1}{2}at^2 \qquad . \qquad . \qquad \text{(iv)}$$

or $\qquad\qquad\qquad - 24 \cdot 5 = 19 \cdot 6t - \tfrac{1}{2} \times 9 \cdot 81 \times t^2$

or $\qquad 4 \cdot 905t^2 - 19 \cdot 6t - 24 \cdot 5 = 0$

or $\qquad\qquad\qquad t^2 - 4t - 5 = 0$

or $\qquad\qquad\qquad (t - 5)(t + 1) = 0$

$$t = 5 \text{ or } - 1 \text{ s}$$

In this case the negative answer is not applicable and so the required time $t = 5$ s.

Using this value of t,

$$v = u + at \qquad . \qquad . \qquad . \qquad \text{(iii)}$$
$$= 19 \cdot 6 - 9 \cdot 81 \times 5 \text{ m/s}$$
$$= 19 \cdot 6 - 49 \cdot 05 \text{ m/s}$$
$$= - 29 \cdot 45 \text{ m/s}$$

Time taken for ball to reach the base of the cliff = 5 s
Velocity on striking ground at base of the cliff = $- 29 \cdot 45$ m/s
(the negative value indicating a *downwards* velocity)

This example could also be solved in two parts:

(a) the motion up to the maximum height,
(b) the motion from its maximum height to the base of the cliff.

Thus, for (a) $u = + 19 \cdot 6$ m/s, $a = g = - 9 \cdot 81$ m/s^2, $v = 0$ (at top of the flight). Then

$$v = u + at \qquad . \qquad . \qquad . \qquad . \qquad \text{(iii)}$$

or $\qquad\qquad\qquad 0 = 19 \cdot 6 - 9 \cdot 81 t$

or $\qquad\qquad\qquad t = 2$ s (time to reach max. height)

Also,

$$v^2 = u^2 + 2as \qquad . \qquad . \qquad . \qquad . \qquad \text{(v)}$$

or $\qquad\qquad\qquad 0 = 19 \cdot 6^2 - 2 \times 9 \cdot 81 \times s$

or $\qquad\qquad 19 \cdot 62 s = 19 \cdot 6^2$

$\qquad\qquad\qquad s = 19 \cdot 6$ m (max. height reached)

For (b) $u = 0$, $a = g = - 9 \cdot 81$ m/s^2, $s = - (24 \cdot 5 + 19 \cdot 6) = - 44 \cdot 1$ m.

Then

$$v^2 = u^2 + 2as \qquad . \qquad . \qquad . \qquad . \qquad \text{(v)}$$
$$v^2 = 0 - 2 \times 9 \cdot 81 \times (- 44 \cdot 1)$$
$$= + 19 \cdot 62 \times 44 \cdot 1$$
$$= 867$$
$$v = \pm 29 \cdot 45 \text{ m/s}$$

In this case the ball is obviously moving downwards, so that

$$v = - 29 \cdot 45 \text{ m/s (velocity on striking ground at base of cliff)}$$

Also

$$s = ut^2 + \tfrac{1}{2}at^2 \qquad . \qquad . \qquad . \qquad . \qquad \text{(iv)}$$
$$- 44 \cdot 1 = 0 - \tfrac{1}{2} \times 9 \cdot 81 \times t^2$$

or $\qquad\qquad\qquad t^2 = \dfrac{44 \cdot 1}{4 \cdot 905} (= 9)$

$\qquad\qquad\qquad t = 3$ s (time to fall to base of cliff from max. height)

Time for upwards and downwards movement $= 2 + 3 = \underline{\underline{5 \text{ s}}}$

Velocity on striking ground at base of cliff $= \underline{- 29 \cdot 45 \text{ m/s}}$

These are the results already obtained rather more directly by the first method given.

8.11.   Combination and resolution of velocities

Both velocity and acceleration are VECTOR quantities, having direction as well as magnitude. In this respect they are similar to forces, and so can be combined and resolved in the same ways as those described for forces in Chapter 3, page 38.

If the velocities or accelerations concerned have the same line of action, then the result is obtained by the simple algebraic sum of these velocities. For example, if an ascending escalator moves upwards at

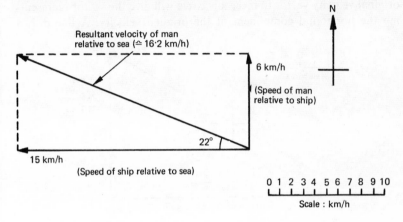

107. Resultant of two velocities

6 km/h, a man walking up the escalator at 5 km/h is carried upwards 'through the air' at 6 + 5 = 11 km/h. If the man runs down this escalator at 7 km/h, he is carried upwards at 6 – 7 = – 1 km/h (i.e. he moves downwards at 1 km/h).

If the velocities or accelerations concerned do not have the same line of action, then vector methods must be used as already described for forces in Chapter 3, page 38. For example, if a ship is sailing due west at 15 km/h and a man on the ship walks across the deck in a due northerly direction at 6 km/h, he will be carried over the sea at a velocity equal to the vector sum of these two. This resultant velocity of the man 'over' the sea is known as his velocity 'relative to' the sea. It is shown by the resultant velocity vector in diagram 107. The man will move relative to the sea at a resultant velocity of about 16·2 km/h, in a direction about 22° N of W.

Vector methods can also be used to find the components of a velocity or acceleration in two given directions at right angles to each other. First, using the method given in Section 3.9, page 62, suppose that the component velocities are required in the horizontal and vertical directions for a velocity of 20 m/s having a direction inclined 30° upwards from the horizontal.

A vector is drawn to represent the original velocity to some suitable scale, as shown in diagram 108. Part of a circle can then be drawn with this vector as a diameter. A horizontal line drawn from the start of the original velocity vector to meet this circle will give the vector representing the horizontal component of the original velocity. A line drawn

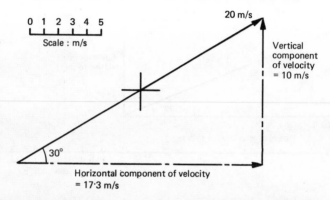

108. Resolution of a velocity into its horizontal and vertical components

vertically from this point on the circle to the finish of the original vector will be the vector representing the required vertical component of velocity.

For a visual idea of the meaning of these two components of a velocity, suppose that the original velocity in diagram 108 represents the velocity of a rocket leaving the ground. To an observer in a balloon vertically far above the path of the rocket, it would seem to be travelling horizontally at 17·3 m/s, since the observer would not be able to distinguish movement directly towards himself. Similarly, to an observer at some distance away on the ground in the direction of the horizontal movement, the rocket would appear to be travelling vertically at 10 m/s.

This effect can also be demonstrated by a small white dot painted on the edge of a wheel. If the wheel is rotated and viewed along its edge at some distance, the spot will appear to be moving along a straight line. (If viewed from too near, perspective becomes apparent and the spot can be seen to be moving first towards and then away from the viewer. If one eye is closed, the perspective effect is lost and only the component of the velocity is seen.)

If the student is familiar with the use of trigonometrical ratios, he should recognize that the horizontal component of velocity in diagram 108 is given by

$$20 \cos 30° \text{ m/s} (= 20 \times 0.866 = 17.32 \text{ m/s})$$

The vertical component is given by

$$20 \sin 30° \text{ m/s} (= 20 \times 0.5 = 10 \text{ m/s})$$

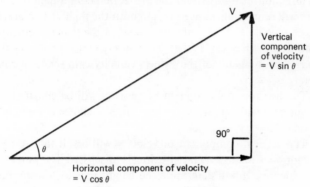

109. Resolution of a velocity into its horizontal and vertical components

These results are similar to those obtained for the components of forces in Section 3.11, page 71. For the general case of a velocity v in a direction inclined at $\theta°$ to the horizontal,

$$\text{horizontal component of velocity} = v \cos \theta$$
$$\text{vertical component of velocity} = v \sin \theta$$

These are shown in diagram 109.

Note that, in terms of components at right angles to each other (called 'rectangular components'), a velocity or an acceleration will have no component at right angles to its direction. This can be seen by viewing an object moving either directly towards or directly away from the observer. Again, provided that no perspective effects are obvious, the object would then appear to be stationary. This effect can sometimes be obtained on a long straight stretch of a railway track, when an oncoming train in the distance does not appear to be moving. It is also the reason why, to a cricketer waiting to take a high catch, the ball appears to hang in the air.

8.12.   Projectiles

If a stone is thrown at an angle other than a right angle to the ground, it will move in both a vertical and a horizontal direction. If the effects of wind resistance are neglected, the only acceleration acting on the stone while it is in the air is the acceleration due to gravity. Since this acts vertically downwards, it will have no component in the horizontal direction. It follows that the horizontal component of the stone's velocity will remain unchanged throughout the flight, as no acceleration acts to change it. The vertical component of the stone's velocity will be changed in the same way as that for a purely vertical movement.

The two components of the stone's velocity can, then, be considered separately.

(a) The horizontal component of velocity will be constant throughout, and will determine the horizontal distance covered in a given time.

(b) The vertical component of velocity will result in a total vertical motion similar to that previously discussed for purely vertical velocities. It will determine the height reached during flight and also the time spent in the air before the stone hits the ground.

8.13.   Examples

(i) A stone is thrown upwards at 24·5 m/s in a direction inclined at 53° to the vertical. Find

(a) the time the stone is in the air
(b) the greatest height reached
(c) the horizontal distance covered
(d) the angle at which it hits the ground.

The velocity-vector diagram is shown in diagram 110, which is drawn to scale.

Either from this diagram, or by trigonometrical calculation, the two velocity components are:

$$\text{horizontal component} = 14\cdot7 \text{ m/s}$$
$$(= 24\cdot5 \cos 53° \simeq 24\cdot5 \times 0\cdot6)$$
$$\text{vertical component} = 19\cdot6 \text{ m/s}$$
$$(= 24\cdot5 \sin 53° \simeq 24\cdot4 \times 0\cdot8)$$

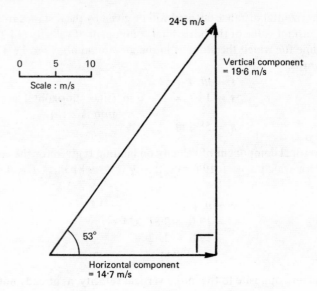

24·5 m/s

Vertical component
= 19·6 m/s

0   5   10
Scale : m/s

53°

Horizontal component
= 14·7 m/s

110. Components of velocity—numerical example

Consider the vertical component first. For the total time spent in the air, $u = +19\cdot6$ m/s, $a = g = -9\cdot81$ m/s^2 and $s = 0$ (total distance above starting point when stone hits the ground again).

Then

$$s = ut + \tfrac{1}{2}at^2 \qquad . \qquad . \qquad . \qquad (iv)$$
$$0 = 19\cdot6t - \tfrac{1}{2}9\cdot81t^2$$
or
$$4\cdot905t^2 = 19\cdot6t$$
$$t = 4 \text{ or } 0 \text{ s}$$

Neglecting the zero answer (which is for the first time the total distance $s = 0$; i.e. before it is thrown), the total time in the air is 4 s.

The greatest height reached is also determined by the vertical component of velocity, and to find this put $u = +19\cdot6$ m/s, $a = g = -9\cdot81$ m/s, $v = 0$ (at highest point).

Then

$$v^2 = u^2 + 2as \qquad . \qquad . \qquad . \qquad (v)$$
$$0 = 19\cdot6^2 - 2 \times 9\cdot81 \, s$$
or
$$19\cdot6 \, s = (19\cdot6)^2$$
$$s = \underline{\underline{19\cdot6 \text{ m}}}$$

The horizontal distance covered will be given by the distance travelled at the constant value of the horizontal component of velocity (14·7 m/s), in the time for which the stone is in the air (found above to be 4 s). In other words,

$$s = ut + \tfrac{1}{2}at^2 \qquad . \qquad . \qquad . \qquad . \qquad \text{(iv)}$$

or $\qquad\qquad s = 14·7 \times 4 + 0$ m (since horizontal acceleration is zero)

or $\qquad\qquad s = \underline{\underline{58·8 \text{ m}}}$

The vertical component of velocity on landing is given for the vertical motion for which $u = +19·6$ m/s, $a = g = -9·81$ m/s², $t = 4$ s.

Then

$$v = u + at \qquad . \qquad . \qquad . \qquad . \qquad \text{(iii)}$$
$$= 19·6 - 9·81 \times 4$$
$$= 19·6 - 39·2$$
$$= \underline{-19·6 \text{ m/s}}$$

i.e. equal and opposite to the initial vertical velocity, as already noted in example (i), Section 8.10.

The horizontal component will be constant throughout at 14·7 m/s, so that the components of the velocity of the stone when it hits the ground are as shown in diagram 111.

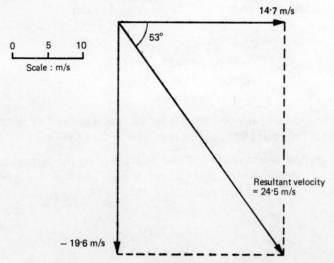

111. Resultant velocity of stone as it hits the ground again—numerical example

The resultant velocity is seen to be 24·5 m/s at an angle of 53° to the horizontal, directed towards the ground (compare this with the initial velocity).

(ii) A shell is fired horizontally from the top of a cliff towards the sea, whose surface is 19·6 m below the cliff top. If the muzzle velocity of the shell is 1200 m/s, find how far from the base of the cliff the shell will strike the surface of the sea.

In this case, the initial vertical component of the velocity is zero, since the shell is fired horizontally. Considering the vertical motion first,

$$u = 0, a = g = -9·81 \text{ m/s}^2, s = -19·6 \text{ m}$$

Then

$$s = ut + \tfrac{1}{2}at^2 \qquad\qquad\qquad\qquad\text{(iv)}$$
$$-19·6 = 0 - \tfrac{1}{2} \times 9·81t^2$$
$$4·905t^2 = 19·6$$
$$t^2 = 4$$
$$t = \pm 2 \text{ s}$$

(The negative answer may be neglected here.)

It follows that the shell is in the air for 2 s, so that the horizontal distance travelled at a constant horizontal velocity of 1200 m/s is

$$s = ut + \tfrac{1}{2}at^2 \quad . \qquad . \qquad . \qquad . \qquad \text{(iv)}$$
$$s = 1200 \times 2 + 0 \text{ m}$$
$$= 2400 \text{ m}$$

The shell strikes the sea 2400 m or 2·4 km from the base of the cliff.

CHAPTER SUMMARY

Velocity is a vector quantity, of which speed is the magnitude.

$$\text{Average speed} = \frac{\text{distance travelled}}{\text{time taken}}$$

Typical units are km/h, m/s.

The slope of a graph of distance against time is equal to the instantaneous speed at the point concerned.

Acceleration is the rate of change of velocity, and is also a vector quantity.

$$\text{Average acceleration} = \frac{\text{change in velocity}}{\text{time for change}}$$

Units are m/s².

The area enclosed by a graph of velocity against time is equal to the total distance travelled in the direction of the velocity.

The slope of a velocity-time graph at a point is equal to the instantaneous acceleration at that point.

For a body moving with uniform acceleration,

$$s = \tfrac{1}{2}(u + v)\,t \qquad s = \text{distance travelled}$$
$$a = \frac{(v - u)}{t} \qquad u = \text{initial velocity}$$
$$\qquad\qquad v = \text{final velocity}$$
$$v = u + at \qquad a = \text{acceleration}$$
$$s = ut + \tfrac{1}{2}at^2 \qquad t = \text{time taken}$$
$$v^2 = u^2 + 2as$$

For a body falling under gravity, choose vertically upwards direction as positive. Then the above equations may be applied where

$$a = -g \simeq -9{\cdot}81 \text{ m/s}^2$$

The acceleration due to gravity (g) varies from point to point on or near the earth's surface, being about 9·813 m/s² for this country.

Velocities and accelerations, being vector quantities, may be combined and resolved by similar vector methods to those used for force vectors; e.g. parallelogram of velocities.

The component of a velocity v in a direction inclined at angle θ to its own direction is $v \cos \theta$.

If air resistance is neglected, the only acceleration acting on a simple projectile is that due to gravity, so that its horizontal component of velocity remains constant throughout its flight.

QUESTIONS

1. An overhead travelling crane is moving at its maximum speed of 5 m/s. What must be the constant retardation in order to bring the crane to rest in a distance of 50 m? How long will it take to come to rest?

2. A vehicle is accelerated at 1·5 m/s² from a speed of 25 km/h. Calculate:
(a) the time required to attain a speed of 75 km/h,
(b) the distance travelled in this time.
If the vehicle is now retarded uniformly until it comes to rest after travelling a further 400 m, calculate the retardation in m/s².

3. A body starts from rest and accelerates uniformly for 24 s by which time a velocity of 10 m/s has been reached. This velocity is maintained until the body has travelled a distance of 360 m from rest. Find the distance travelled in the first 24 s, and the time taken to cover the distance of 360 m.

If the body is then decelerated at 0·5 m/s², find the total time taken and the total distance covered from start to rest.

4. A stone is dropped down a pit and hits the bottom 4½ s later. Calculate:
(a) the depth of the pit,
(b) the speed of the stone just before it strikes the bottom of the pit.

If the stone had been thrown down the pit with an initial velocity of 24 m/s, what time would elapse before striking the bottom?

5. A rocket having a mass of 25 kg is fired vertically upwards and uses 5 MJ of energy in doing work against gravity during the ascent. Determine:
(a) the maximum height attained,
(b) the velocity of the rocket 3·5 s after commencing its downward fall,
(c) the vertical distance travelled by the rocket during the first 5 s of its downward fall.

6. A stone is projected upwards with a velocity of 24 m/s at an elevation of 60° to the horizontal. Determine, 2 s after its projection, (a) the vertical component of its velocity at this instant, (b) the magnitude and direction of its actual velocity.

7. A jet of water issues horizontally with a velocity of 5 m/s from a pipe 7 m above the ground. At what distance, from a point vertically below the pipe opening, will the jet strike the ground? What is the final velocity of the jet?

8. A car starting from a point A, and having uniformly accelerated motion in a straight line, travels from B to C, a distance of 180 m, in 20 s and from C to D, a distance of 540 m, in 30 s. Determine:
(a) its acceleration,
(b) its speed when it is at B,
(c) the distance from A to B.

9. A train 140 m long starts from rest at a station and accelerates at a constant rate. After travelling a distance of 525 m it enters a tunnel 700 m long. The rear of the train leaves the tunnel 2 min after the train started from the station. Calculate:
(a) the speed of the train in km/h when the locomotive enters the tunnel,
(b) the speed of the train in km/h when the rear leaves the tunnel,
(c) the time taken for the locomotive to pass through the tunnel.

10. A train starts from rest and increases speed at a uniform rate to reach 100 km/h in 2 min. It then travels at this constant speed for 10 min, after which the speed is decreased at a uniform rate until the train comes to rest. The total distance travelled by the train is 21 km.

(a) Sketch, not necessarily to scale, a speed-time diagram to illustrate the above sequence.

(b) Find the time taken for the train to come to rest from maximum speed.

(c) Calculate the average speed of the train in km/h.

11. (a) Define 'acceleration'.

(b) A train starts from rest with an acceleration of 0·4 m/s² which remains constant until the speed is 50 km/h.

The train then travels with a uniform speed during the next 1·75 min and is then brought to rest in 20 s, the deceleration being constant during this latter period. Find the total distance travelled.

12. A train takes 3·75 min to travel between two stations 2·4 km apart, starting from and finishing at rest. For the first 30 s the train has uniform acceleration, and for the last 20 s it has uniform retardation, the speed being constant for the rest of the time. Sketch the velocity-time diagram, and from it determine (a) the uniform velocity in km/h, (b) the acceleration in m/s² and (c) the retardation in m/s² of the train.

(Hint: Express the area under the velocity-time graph in terms of the constant speed. This will be equal to 2·4 km, the distance travelled.)

13. A car is in motion and accelerates at 0·75 m/s² for 15 s until its velocity is 50 km/h. This velocity is maintained for 800 m, and then for a period of 10 s uniform retardation takes place, bringing the car to rest.

Determine (a) the initial velocity of the car, (b) the retardation whilst the car is coming to rest.

Draw a velocity-time graph, indicating the principal values, and use this graph to find the total distance travelled.

14. A train moving with an initial velocity of 16 km/h is accelerated uniformly at 2 m/s² until a velocity of 80 km/h is attained. It continues with this uniform speed for some time and is then brought to rest with a uniform retardation of 1·25 m/s². The total distance travelled is 5 km. Calculate:

(a) the distance moved through during the accelerating period,

(b) the time during which the train moves at uniform speed,

(c) the time taken for the whole journey.

15. In a test a guided missile is fired vertically upwards and is moving at 600 m/s at a height of 1500 m. At this point its direction of motion is changed instantaneously to 60° to the vertical and simultaneously control is stopped, free flight resulting.

Neglecting air resistance, determine:

(a) the maximum height attained,

(b) the time of free flight,

(c) the horizontal range.

16. A train takes 5 min to travel from one station to another 2·5 km away. It receives a constant acceleration during the first 35 s, and a constant retardation during the final 20 s, the train running at constant speed during the remaining time. Calculate the uniform speed, the acceleration and the deceleration. Draw a speed-time graph and use the graph to determine the distance travelled during the first minute of the train's motion.

17. A train, when leaving a station, accelerates uniformly from rest, travelling 1·5 km in 125 s during acceleration. It then moves with uniform speed for 6 min and is finally brought to rest at the next station with uniform retardation during 40 s. Calculate:

(a) the value of the uniform speed, in km/h,

(b) the distance between the stations, in km.

18. (a) Define 'speed' and 'velocity'.

(b) A vehicle starts from a point A and travels due north covering 12 km in 30 min before turning due east when it maintains a steady speed of 50 km/h for 20 min; it then turns and travels 30° S of E at 145 km/h for 10 min when it arrives at point B.

Find (i) the steady speed in km/h while travelling due north,

(ii) the total distance travelled in km,

(iii) the average speed in km/h during the round journey,

(iv) the direct distance between A and B.

19. Find, by calculation and then by drawing to scale, the resultant of velocities 16 km/h in the direction N 20° E and 24 km/h in the direction N 42° W.

20. A river, 72 m wide, is flowing at 5 km/h when a man, who can row in still water at 6·5 km/h, leaves one bank intending to row to a point 36 m downstream on the other bank. He steers straight towards that point and keeps that direction.

Calculate how far downstream he will strike the other bank and how long it will take him to cross.

21. A speed-boat, with a speed of 55 km/h relative to the water, covers a circuit ABC which is in the form of a right-angled triangle. Point B is due west of, and 15 km from, point A. BC, the hypotenuse of the triangle, is 18·5 km long and point C is due north of point A. A 11 km/h current is running in a direction due north. Determine (a) the course to be set on each leg of the circuit so that the boat sails exactly from A to B to C and back to A, (b) the time taken to sail round the circuit, (c) the average speed over the whole journey.

(Hint: For a triangle of velocities for any one leg of the circuit, the resultant velocity obtained from that of the boat and that of the current must point in the required direction from point to point of the circuit.)

I

9. Force, Mass and Acceleration

Chapter 8 has dealt with a study of the motion of a body in which no account was taken of the mass of the body or the forces required to cause motion. It was shown that the acceleration due to gravity was independent of the mass of the body concerned, but it will be seen later that this is because the gravitational force is itself proportional to the mass. For the more general case of motion due to an applied force, the force is *not* proportional to the mass of the body on which it acts. Here, the acceleration produced by a given force depends on the mass of the body concerned. The study of motion which takes account of mass and the force required to cause it to move is called KINETICS. This study will be introduced in the following sections of this chapter.

9.1. Force and acceleration

A resultant force acting on a body will cause the body to accelerate in the direction of the force. For example, an unsupported stone will accelerate downwards under the influence of the resultant gravitational force acting on it. If a truck is pushed steadily with a force greater than the opposing frictional forces, the truck will accelerate steadily. If the truck starts from a 'rest' or 'standstill' position, a greater force is necessary to start it moving than to keep it moving at a steady pace once it has started. The opposing frictional forces can be assumed to be constant throughout, and so the extra force is required to accelerate the truck from zero velocity at standstill to whatever velocity it has when it is moving. Once the truck is moving, only the frictional forces have to be balanced to keep it travelling at the same velocity. If the applied force is greater than the opposing frictional forces, the truck will continue to accelerate in the direction of the resultant force. If the applied force is less than the opposing frictional forces, the direction of the resultant force will oppose the motion and the truck will decelerate —that is, it will have a negative acceleration.

Whenever a resultant force acts on a body, the body will accelerate in the direction of this force. Whenever a body accelerates in a particular direction, there must be a resultant force acting in that direction. If no resultant force acts, the body will be in a state of equilibrium.

These facts are combined in what is known as Newton's first law of motion:

'A body remains in a state of rest, or of uniform motion in a straight line, unless it is acted on by some external resultant force.'

(Newton's first law of motion can be used to define a force as being 'that which changes or tends to change the state of rest, or of uniform motion, of a body'.)

The value of the acceleration produced when a resultant force acts on a body will depend on the mass of the body concerned. If the truck mentioned earlier is full of coal, it requires more force to start it moving with a given acceleration than would be necessary if the truck were empty. Similarly, a larger force is required to stop a moving truck in a given time if it is full than if it is empty.

A body having mass is said to have INERTIA, the value of which can be measured in terms of its mass. It is the mass or inertia of a body which tends to make it stay in a state of rest or of uniform motion. This inertia, or sluggishness of response, means that any change in its velocity cannot take place instantaneously as soon as a force is applied to it. The larger the mass of the body, the smaller the acceleration produced by a given force, and the greater the time required for the velocity of the body to change by a given amount.

9.2. Momentum

The momentum of a body is defined as the product of its mass and its velocity. Since it is concerned with velocity, momentum is a vector quantity, having a direction as well as a magnitude. In other words,

$$\text{MOMENTUM} = \text{MASS} \times \text{VELOCITY}$$
$$\text{and is a VECTOR QUANTITY}$$

The units in which momentum is measured are those of

$$\text{(units of mass)} \times \text{(units of velocity)}$$
$$\text{kg} \qquad \times \qquad \text{m/s}$$

i.e. units of momentum are kg m/s.

Whenever the momentum of a body changes, a force must be involved which either causes, or is caused by, the change. For example, the momentum of a truck moving along straight horizontal rails will decrease as a result of the opposing frictional forces. If such a truck hits some buffers, its momentum is changed as the velocity is reduced to zero, or even reversed if the truck bounces back from the buffers. The result is a force acting on the buffers, which may be considerable if the initial momentum of the truck is high because it has large mass, high velocity or both.

9.3.   Change of momentum

Change in momentum is, then, always accompanied by a force. The value of this force will depend on the rate at which the momentum is changed. For example, if the moving truck strikes 'solid' buffers, the deceleration is very great, the velocity of the truck is quickly reduced to zero and the force of the impact is large. If the buffers are sprung so that they 'give' with the oncoming truck, the velocity is changed less rapidly and the force will be less. For another example, if a cricketer catches a fast-moving cricket ball with hands held stiffly, the ball will sting the hands much more than if they are moved along the direction of flight as the ball enters them. In each of the examples quoted, the force is greater when the momentum is changed more quickly. This effect is stated in what is known as Newton's second law of motion:

'The rate of change of momentum is proportional to the force producing the change, and is in the direction of this force.'

9.4.   Relationship between force, mass and acceleration

Let a body of mass m undergo a change in velocity from u to v in a time t, under the action of a constant external resultant force F.

$$\text{The initial momentum} = (\text{mass}) \times (\text{velocity})$$
$$= m\,u$$
$$\text{Final momentum} = m\,v$$
$$\text{Change in momentum} = (\text{final value}) - (\text{initial value})$$
$$= m\,v - m\,u$$
$$= m\,(v - u)$$

Since this takes place in time t,

$$\begin{array}{r}\text{rate of change}\\ \text{of momentum}\end{array} = \frac{\text{change in momentum}}{\text{time taken}}$$

$$= \frac{m\,(v - u)}{t} \qquad . \qquad . \qquad . \qquad \text{(i)}$$

From Newton's second law of motion,

(force) is proportional to (rate of change of momentum)

or
$$F \propto \frac{m\,(v\,-\,u)}{t} \qquad . \qquad . \qquad . \qquad \text{(ii)}$$

But since the force F is constant, the acceleration produced, a, is also constant, so that

$$v = u + at \qquad \text{(iii) page 234}$$

or
$$at = v - u$$

$$a = \frac{(v\,-\,u)}{t}$$

Substituting in (ii) gives

$$F \propto ma \qquad . \qquad . \qquad . \qquad \text{(iii)}$$

This may be taken as a statement of Newton's second law in terms of mathematical symbols.

Since the interpretation of this relationship is of very great importance, it may be worthwhile to discuss its meaning more fully before going on further. If one quantity is proportional to another, and if the value of one is doubled, then the value of the other is also doubled. Similarly, if one is halved, the other is halved as well. Now this same result is true if the value of one quantity *is equal to* the value of the other quantity *multiplied by some constant*. For example

suppose $y = 3x$
Then when $x = 2$, $y = 6$
or when $x = 4$, $y = 12$
or when $x = 1$, $y = 3$ and so on.

In other words, y is proportional to x, or, in symbols,

$$y \propto x$$

A similar relationship between corresponding values of x and y would be given for any other value of the constant multiplier. For example

if $y = 5x$
Then when $x = 2$, $y = 10$
or when $x = 4$, $y = 20$
or when $x = 1$, $y = 5$, and so on.

Once again, doubling x will double y, and halving x will halve y.

It follows that any relationship like $y \propto x$ can always be written as $y = kx$ where k is some constant. k is known as the 'constant of proportionality', and its value will depend on the exact relationship between the values of the proportional quantities.

For example, if $y \propto x$, and $y = 8$ when $x = 10$,

$$\text{then, since } y = kx$$
$$8 = k \times 10$$
$$\text{or } k = 0\cdot8 \text{ for this case.}$$

Note that once again doubling x will double y, and so on. Then, since $F \propto ma$, the relationship may be written

$$F = kma \qquad . \qquad . \qquad . \qquad \text{(iv)}$$

The value of the constant of proportionality, k, will depend on the number values of F, m and a, or, in other words, on the units used to measure these quantities.

9.5.　The International units of force, mass and acceleration

The (SI) system of units using the NEWTON, KILOGRAMME and METRE/SECOND^2 for the units of force, mass and acceleration is an absolute or dynamical system of units. This means that a force of one newton acting on a mass of one kilogramme produces an acceleration of 1 m/s^2. This relationship is taken as the definition of the absolute unit of force, the Newton. In other words, for these units,

$$F = ma$$

or force (N) $= 1$ (N s^2/kg m) $\times$ mass (kg) $\times$ acceleration (m/s^2)　　(v)
therefore 1 N $= 1$ kg m/s^2.

9.6.　Examples

(i) Find the acceleration produced when a force of 10 N acts on a mass of 4 kg.

$$\text{Force (N)} = \text{mass (kg)} \times \text{acceleration (m/s}^2)$$
$$10 = 4 \times a$$
$$a = \underline{2\cdot5 \text{ m/s}^2}$$
$$\text{Acceleration produced} = \underline{\underline{2\cdot5 \text{ m/s}^2}}$$

(ii) A resultant force acting on a body of mass 60 kg, produces an acceleration of 7 m/s^2. What is the value of this resultant force?

$$\text{Force (N)} = \text{mass (kg)} \times \text{acceleration (m/s}^2)$$
$$= 60 \times 7 \text{ N}$$
$$\text{Force} = 420 \text{ N}$$
$$\text{The resultant force} = \underline{420 \text{ N}}$$

(iii) A force of 20 N acts on a body to produce an acceleration of 5 m/s². What is the mass of the body?

$$\text{Force (N)} = \text{mass (kg)} \times \text{acceleration (m/s}^2)$$
$$20 = m \times 5$$
$$m = 4 \text{ kg}$$
$$\text{Mass of body} = \underline{4 \text{ kg.}}$$

(iv) What constant force will increase the velocity of a mass of 5 kg from 15 m/s to 23 m/s in 10 s? How far would the mass travel in this time?

$$u = +15 \text{ m/s}, v = +23 \text{ m/s}, t = 10 \text{ s}$$

Then

$$v = u + at$$
$$23 = 15 + a \times 10$$
$$10a = 23 - 15$$

$$a = \frac{8}{10} \text{ m/s}^2$$

$$= 0 \cdot 8 \text{ m/s}^2$$

Distance travelled in the 10 s is given by

$$s = \tfrac{1}{2}(u + v)\,t$$
$$= \tfrac{1}{2}(15 + 23) \times 10 \text{ m}$$
$$= \tfrac{1}{2} \times 38 \times 10 \text{ m}$$
$$= \underline{190 \text{ m}}$$
$$\text{Force (N)} = \text{mass (kg)} \times \text{acceleration (m/s}^2)$$
$$= 5 \times 0 \cdot 8 \text{ N}$$
$$= \underline{4 \cdot 0 \text{ N}}$$

This force would act in the same direction as the velocity in order to produce the (positive) acceleration required.

$$\text{Accelerating force required} = \underline{4 \text{ N}}$$
$$\text{Distance travelled} = \underline{190 \text{ m}}$$

9.7. Conversions between potential and kinetic forms of energy

In Section 6.9, on page 188, it was explained how a mass may 'store' mechanical energy in the form of potential energy. The potential energy of a mass is measured as the product of its mass, the acceleration due to gravity and its vertical height above some datum or reference level. This is equal to the work done in raising the mass from the reference level up to its position.

If the mass is allowed to fall under its own gravitational force, its potential energy is converted into kinetic energy. (See Section 6.11 on page 192.) The kinetic energy of a body is due to its mass and its velocity. From the principle of the conservation of energy, it follows that the potential energy given up by a body in falling freely through a certain height is converted to kinetic energy in the moving body. Thus the total energy possessed by a freely-falling body, which is the sum of its potential energy and its kinetic energy, will be constant. In other words,

$$\text{(potential energy)} + \text{(kinetic energy)} = \text{constant}$$

provided that no work is done on or by the body.

Suppose a body of mass m (kg) is allowed to fall freely from a height of h m. Then for this case,

$$u = 0, a = -g \text{ m/s}^2.$$

When the body has fallen through the h m back to its datum level, the distance travelled $s = -h$ m, with positive taken as upwards, as before. The final velocity v would then be given by

$$v^2 = u^2 + 2as$$
$$\text{or } v^2 = 0 + 2 \times (-g) \times (-h)$$
$$\text{or } v^2 = 2gh$$
$$\text{or } v = \sqrt{2gh} \text{ m/s} . \qquad . \qquad . \qquad . \qquad \text{(vi)}$$

Alternatively, the height fallen through may be expressed in terms of the velocity attained:

$$h = \frac{v^2}{2g} \text{ m} \qquad . \qquad . \qquad . \qquad . \qquad . \qquad \text{(vii)}$$

Initially, the body was stationary at a height of h m above datum, so that all its energy was stored as potential energy relative to datum.

At the end of its fall, the body possesses no potential energy relative to datum, and so all its energy must then be stored as kinetic energy. Since no work is done by the falling body,

> total energy before fall = total energy after fall

or

> (initial potential energy) + (initial kinetic energy)
> = (final potential energy) + (final kinetic energy)

so that

$$mgh \text{ (J)} + 0 = 0 + \text{final kinetic energy}$$

It is known that kinetic energy depends on velocity, so expressing h in terms of v from equation (vii),

$$\text{final kinetic energy} = mg \times \frac{v^2}{2g} \text{ J}$$

$$= \tfrac{1}{2} mv^2 \text{ J} \qquad . \qquad . \quad \text{(viii)}$$

This gives the relationship between kinetic energy, mass and velocity.

9.8. Examples

(i) A body of mass 30 kg is raised to a height of 3 m above the ground, and then allowed to fall freely back to the ground. What are the values of its potential energy and kinetic energy (a) before it starts to fall, (b) when it has fallen by 1 m, (c) when it reaches the ground again?

Explain where this energy came from, and what happens to it after the body hits the ground.

(a) Before starting to fall,

$$\text{potential energy} = mgh$$
$$= 30 \text{ (kg)} \times 9 \cdot 81 \text{ (m/s}^2) \times 3 \text{ (m)}$$
$$= 833 \text{ J}$$

$$\text{Kinetic energy} = 0 \text{ (the body is stationary)}$$

(b) After falling 1 m,
potential energy *decreases* by

$$mg \times \text{(fall in height)} = 30 \text{ (kg)} \times 9 \cdot 81 \text{ (m/s}^2) \times 1 \text{ (m)}$$
$$= 294 \text{ J}$$
$$\text{Potential energy remaining} = 883 - 294 \text{ J}$$
$$= 589 \text{ J}$$

(Alternatively, the body is still $(3 - 1) = 2$ m above ground, so that

$$\text{potential energy} = 30 \times 9\cdot81 \times 2 = 589 \text{ J}$$

Also, since no work is done,

gain in kinetic energy = loss in potential energy

or   kinetic energy = $0 + (883 - 589)$ J

= 294 J

(c) On reaching the ground,

potential energy = 0 (height above ground is now zero)

All the initial potential energy has now been converted to kinetic energy, so that

$$\text{kinetic energy} = \underline{883 \text{ J}}$$

The values of kinetic energy can be checked by calculating the velocity of the body at each instant, as follows:

(a) Before starting to fall, $v = 0$ and K.E. $= 0$

(b) After falling 1 m

$$u = 0, a = g = -9\cdot81 \text{ m/s}^2, s = -1 \text{ m}$$
$$v^2 = u^2 + 2as$$
$$v^2 = 0 + 2 \times (-9\cdot81) \times (-1)$$
$$= 19\cdot62$$
$$v = \pm 4\cdot43 \text{ m/s}$$

(In this case v will be $-4\cdot43$ m/s as it is obviously directed downwards.)

Then   K.E. (J) $= \frac{1}{2} \times$ mass (kg) $\times$ [velocity (m/s)]^2
$$= \frac{1}{2} \times 30 \times (-4\cdot43)^2 \text{ J}$$
$$= \frac{1}{2} \times 30 \times 19\cdot62$$
$$= \underline{294 \text{ J as before}}$$

(Positive since the square of a negative number is a positive number.)

(c) On reaching the ground,

$$(u = 0, a = g = -9\cdot81 \text{ m/s}^2, s = -3 \text{ m})$$
$$v^2 = u^2 + 2as$$
$$v^2 = 0 + 2 \times (-9\cdot81) \times (-3)$$
$$= 58\cdot9$$
$$v = \pm 7\cdot67 \text{ m/s (again negative here)}$$

Then K.E. (J) $= \frac{1}{2} \times$ mass (kg) $\times$ [velocity (m/s)]^2
$$= \frac{1}{2} \times 30 \times 58\cdot9$$
$$= \underline{883 \text{ J as before}}$$

Collecting these answers:

(a) Before starting to fall   P.E. = 883 J

                                 K.E. = 0

(b) After falling by 1 m   P.E. = 589 J

                                 K.E. = 294 J

(c) On reaching the ground P.E. = 0

                                 K.E. = 883 J

Note that in each case the sum of the potential energy and the kinetic energy is the same.

The initial energy was supplied to the body as the work done on it by whatever was responsible for raising it to its height of 3 m above the ground. The kinetic energy of the falling body will be given to the ground on which it falls, and will do work on the opposing resistance forces. Assuming that it does not bounce, all the energy will be given up in this way, and will be used in distorting the surface of the ground, and probably in setting up a sound wave. The energy will then be converted to heat energy in the ground, and to the energy of the sound wave. If the body bounces, some of its kinetic energy is returned to it by the ground, but it will eventually all be converted to heat or sound energy as it does work against the opposing forces.

(ii) What is the kinetic energy of a car having a mass of 1·25 tonne when it is travelling at 25 km/h? What happens to this energy when the brakes are applied to stop the car?

First convert the mass of the car to kg, and the speed to m/s.

$$1\cdot25 \text{ tonne} = 1250 \text{ kg}$$

$$25 \text{ km/h} = 25 \text{ km/h} \times \left(\frac{16\cdot7 \text{ m/s}}{60 \text{ km/h}} \right)$$

$$= \frac{25 \times 16\cdot7}{60} \text{ m/s}$$

$$= 6\cdot94 \text{ m/s}$$

Then   K.E. (J) $= \frac{1}{2} \times$ mass (kg) $\times$ [velocity (m/s)]^2

             $= \frac{1}{2} \times 1250 \times 6\cdot94^2$

             $= 30\ 150$ J or $30\cdot15$ kJ

    Kinetic energy of car $= 30\cdot15$ kJ

This energy will be converted to heat energy as it does work against the opposing forces—mainly in the brakes in this case. The brake drums will get noticeably warm.

CHAPTER SUMMARY

Newton's first law of motion: 'A body remains in a state of rest, or of uniform motion in a straight line, unless it is acted on by some external resultant force.'

Momentum = mass × velocity, and is a vector quantity.

Newton's second law of motion: 'The rate of change of momentum is proportional to the force producing the change, and is in the direction of this force.'

Newton's second law leads to the relationship

$$\text{force} \propto \text{mass} \times \text{acceleration}$$
$$\text{or } F = kma$$
$$\text{The constant } k = 1 \text{ for the SI system of units}$$

The potential energy of a mass m at a height h above a datum is mgh. The kinetic energy of a mass m moving at a velocity v is $\frac{1}{2}mv^2$.

QUESTIONS

1. (a) Define 'acceleration'.
(b) An electric train of mass 300 tonne has a constant retarding force applied to it of 300 kN. Calculate the time, in seconds, for the train to stop if it is moving along a level track at 100 km/h.
Ignore the frictional and windage effects.

2. (a) Define 'force' and state its units.
(b) During part of the initial flight of a rocket it is found that it changes its velocity uniformly from 650 to 800 km/h in 3 s. Assuming that the rocket moves in a straight line during this time, calculate (i) the average acceleration in m/s², and (ii) the distance travelled.

3. A bus having a mass of 10 tonne reaches a speed of 65 km/h in 20 s, starting from rest with uniform acceleration. It travels for a distance at this velocity and is then brought to rest in a distance of 120 m. Determine (a) the momentum at 65 km/h, (b) the accelerating and braking forces required.

4. A lift, together with its load, has a mass of 1·25 tonne, and is raised vertically by a rope. The lift reaches a speed of 7·5 m/s after rising 22 m from rest with uniform acceleration. Neglecting the mass of the rope, determine the tension in the rope during this period.

5. A heavy goods vehicle has a mass when loaded of 15 tonne and is travelling at 50 km/h. Determine its momentum.

If the vehicle is brought to rest in a distance of 36 m by a constant braking force,

    (a) what is the value of that force,

    (b) how much work is done by the force in bringing the vehicle to rest,

    (c) what change occurs in the kinetic energy of the vehicle?

6. A train has a mass of 165 tonne. The tractive resistance on a horizontal track is 75 N per tonne mass of train for speeds up to 50 km/h. What force is required to accelerate the train to 50 km/h in 33 s (a) on a level track, (b) up a gradient of 1 in 200?

7. A loaded truck having a mass of 12 tonne moves at a speed of 75 km/h.

    (a) Calculate its momentum.

    (b) What force is necessary to reduce its speed to 30 km/h in 15 s?

    (c) How far will the truck move whilst this reduction in speed is taking place?

8. Define the terms 'velocity' and 'acceleration'.

A truck having a mass of 2 tonne is travelling at a speed of 50 km/h at a given point on a horizontal road. The total resistance to motion is equivalent to a force of 1 kN. Assuming the road to continue horizontal and power to be shut off completely, calculate:

    (a) the time to come to rest,

    (b) the distance travelled during this time.

9. (a) State Newton's second law of motion.

(b) A body having a mass of 4 kg and moving with a velocity of 9 m/s is acted upon by a force which causes it to change direction so that 10 s later it is moving at 30° to its original path at 12 m/s. Determine (i) the acceleration, (ii) the magnitude and direction of the constant force producing this acceleration.

10. (a) Derive an expression for the kinetic energy of a body of mass m kg moving with a velocity v m/s.

(b) A body of mass m kg is falling freely, from rest, under the action of gravity. After it has fallen through a height h m in a time t s its momentum is 360 kg m/s and its kinetic energy is 2·16 kJ. Determine (i) the velocity after time t s, (ii) the height h m fallen by the body, (iii) the mass of the body, (iv) the time of fall t s.

11. A train which has a mass of 240 tonne starts to climb an incline, which rises 1 m for every 60 m moved along the track, at 25 km/h and reaches a speed of 55 km/h in 30 s. The resistance due to friction is 75 N/tonne. Determine (a) the acceleration in m/s², (b) the average tractive force developed by the engine during the acceleration period.

12. A train having a mass of 300 tonne accelerates up a uniform gradient of 1 in 200 against frictional resistances of 80 N/tonne. If it attains a speed of 50 km/h from rest in 2 min calculate the tractive effort.

13. A train which has a mass of 250 tonne ascends an incline of 1 in 200 and accelerates at 0·3 m/s². If the frictional resistances to motion are 60 N/tonne, calculate the tractive effort supplied by the locomotive. If the tractive effort is limited to this value, what is the maximum gradient which the train can ascend? Assume the frictional resistances to motion remain the same.

14. A railway train which has a mass of 300 tonne is hauled up an incline 6·5 km long having a slope of 1 in 120. The frictional resistance, assumed constant, is 75 N/tonne. If the engine exerts a constant pull and the speed of the train is 80 km/h at the bottom of the incline and 35 km/h at the top, find the magnitude of the pull and the time taken for the climb.

15. A mine locomotive which has a mass of 20 tonne pulls a train of 8 mine cars each of mass 7 tonne at a speed of 25 km/h on a level track against frictional resistances of 100 N/tonne.
(a) Calculate the draw-bar pull on the leading car and the total work done by the locomotive each second.
(b) While running at the above speed, the rear three cars are suddenly released. Assuming frictional resistances per tonne and draw-bar pull remain as in part (a), determine the speed in km/h of the locomotive and remaining five cars after 90 s.
(c) If the resistance per tonne remains unchanged, determine the time it will take for the three released cars to come to rest.

16. A vehicle of mass 4 tonne is moving along a level road at 50 km/h when the pull on it is stopped suddenly. If the resistance to motion of the vehicle is equivalent to a force of 2·5 kN, find:
(a) the distance the vehicle will travel before coming to rest,
(b) the time taken in coming to rest,
(c) the linear retardation of the vehicle in m/s².

17. (a) Define the newton.
(b) A constant force is applied for a period of 10 s to a body of mass 10 kg so that it is accelerated from rest to a speed of 15 m/s, against opposing frictional forces equal to 20 N.
Find (i) the applied force,
(ii) the deceleration after the applied force is removed,
(iii) the total distance travelled before the body again comes to rest,
(iv) the total time for which the body is in motion.

18. A vehicle having a mass of 1 tonne starts from rest and rolls down an incline of 1 in 10. If it travels 10 m down the incline in the first 20 s, find the frictional force opposing motion.

19. A total load of 25 kg is raised vertically from rest by a rope attached to the load. After being raised by 5 m in the first 2 s, the speed of lifting is maintained constant for a further 2 s. The load is then brought to rest in a further 2 s.

Find (a) the tension in the rope, during the first accelerating period,

(b) the tension in the rope, during the period of constant speed,

(c) the tension in the rope during the deceleration period,

(d) the total height through which the load has been raised.

20. A body of mass 2 kg moves at a steady speed of 3 m/s when it is acted on by a constant force of 10 N in a direction inclined at 30° to its direction of motion. Find the magnitude and direction of its velocity 5 s after this force starts to act.

10. Angular Motion. Torque

The equations of motion developed so far apply to motion in a straight line, or 'linear' motion. Another type of motion very important in engineering is that of rotation about a point, or 'angular' motion. This is the way in which the spokes of a wheel move as the wheel rotates, or the way in which a point on the outside of a shaft moves as the shaft rotates. Many engineering devices rely on this type of movement, and the basic ideas involved will be discussed in this chapter.

10.1. Angular measure

There are two main units in common use for the measurement of an angle. The student will probably already know of at least one of these —the DEGREE. This may be defined as one-ninetieth part of a right angle. A spoke of a wheel moves through an angle of 360 degrees (written 360°) as the wheel turns through four right angles to make one complete revolution. Each degree may be divided into 60 minutes of angle, and each minute of angle may be further divided into 60 seconds of angle. An angle of 42 degrees, 15 minutes and 10 seconds would be written 42° 15′ 10″. A second of angle is very small indeed, and angles are very rarely measured to this accuracy in normal engineering applications.

One way to measure an angle is to measure the length of the circular path travelled by the end of a radius whose centre is at the point about which rotation is occurring. This length will be proportional to the length of the radius chosen and the angle turned through. For example, suppose the radius used has a length r m. When the radius turns through a full 360°, the moving end will move through a length equal to the circumference of a circle of radius r m; that is, $2\pi r$ m. If the radius turns through only 180°, the moving end travels through only half the circumference, or πr m. If the radius turns through 90°, the distance travelled by the moving end is a quarter of the circumference, or $\frac{1}{2}\pi r$ m.

A part of the circumference of a circle is called an ARC of the circle, and it follows that the arc length traced out by the moving end of a rotating radius is proportional to the angle turned through by the radius, or that:

arc length traced out ∝ angle turned through by radius

As before (Section 9.4, page 260) the expression 'is proportional to' can be replaced by 'is equal to a constant multiplied by', so that, with k again representing the constant of proportionality:

arc length traced out $= k \times$ (angle turned through by radius)

The value of k in this case can be found by inserting corresponding values of angle turned through and arc length traced out.

For the cases considered, the angles were 360°, 180° and 90°. Substituting the values of arc length corresponding to these,

$$2\pi r = k \times 360° \text{ m}$$
$$\pi r = k \times 180° \text{ m}$$
$$\tfrac{1}{2}\pi r = k \times 90° \text{ m}$$

From each of these relationships it follows that, for angles measured in degrees,

$$k = \frac{\pi r}{180} \text{ metres per degree}$$

Then, for any other angle, represented by $\theta°$ (pronounced 'theta'), the relationship would be given by

$$\text{arc length} = k \times \theta°$$

or, substituting the value of k,

$$\text{arc length} = \frac{\pi r}{180} \times \theta° \text{ m} \quad . \qquad . \qquad . \qquad . \qquad \text{(i)}$$

In many engineering applications this arc length is used very frequently, and the relationship given above is rather awkward and inconvenient. Consequently, a new unit of angular measure is defined which makes the value of $k = r$, so that

$$\text{arc length} = r \times \text{(angle turned through)}$$

(The radius r must be included as the arc length obviously depends on r as well as on the angle turned through.)

This unit of angular measure is called the RADIAN (rad), and the relationship described can be re-written as:

ARC LENGTH = RADIUS × ANGLE TURNED THROUGH (RADIANS)

In symbols,

$$s = r\,\theta \qquad . \qquad . \qquad . \qquad . \qquad . \qquad \text{(ii)}$$

where s = arc length

r = radius

θ = angle turned through (radians)

The units in which s and r are measured are the same for both. For example, if r is in km, s will be in km; if r is in metres, s will be in metres; and so on.

An angle of one radian can be defined from equation (ii) as that angle turned through when the arc length is equal to the radius. This is sometimes expressed as

'that angle "subtended" at the centre of a circle by an arc of length equal to the radius of the circle'.

These points are summarized in diagram 112.

The arc length for one complete revolution is the complete circumference, or $2\pi r$, so that the angle in radians corresponding to one complete revolution is given by:

$$s = r\,\theta$$
$$\text{or } 2\pi r = r\,\theta$$
$$\text{or } \theta = 2\pi \text{ rad}$$

There are 2π rad in one complete revolution.

Since there are 360° in one complete revolution,

$$2\pi \text{ rad} = 360°$$
$$\text{or } \pi \text{ rad} = 180°$$

It follows that 1 rad $= \dfrac{180°}{\pi} \simeq 57°\ 18'$

10.2.   Examples

(i) Express an angle of 87° in radians.

$$87° = 87 \text{ \sout{degrees}} \times \left(\frac{\pi \text{ rad}}{180 \text{ \sout{degrees}}} \right)$$

$$= 87 \times \frac{\pi}{180} \text{ rad}$$

$$\simeq 1{\cdot}52 \text{ radians}$$

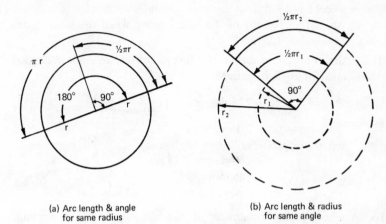

(a) Arc length & angle
for same radius

(b) Arc length & radius
for same angle

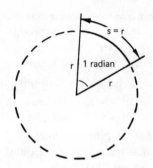

(c) Definition of the radian

112. Arc length used to measure angles

(ii) Express an angle of 1·7 rad in degrees.

$$1.7 \text{ rad} = 1.7 \text{ rad} \times \left(\frac{180 \text{ degrees}}{\pi \text{ rad}} \right)$$

$$= 1.7 \times \frac{180}{\pi} \text{ degrees}$$

$$\simeq 97.3°$$

or about $\underline{\underline{97° 18'}}$

(Note: $0.3° = 0.3 \text{ degrees} \times \left(\frac{60 \text{ min}}{1 \text{ degree}} \right) = 18 \text{ min}$)

(iii) A wheel has a radius of 250 mm. Through what arc length does a point on the circumference of the wheel move when the wheel turns through an angle of 125°?

It is easier in problems such as this first to convert an angle in degrees to the equivalent angle in radians:

$$125° = 125 \text{ degrees} \times \left(\frac{\pi \text{ rad}}{180 \text{ degrees}} \right)$$

$$= 2 \cdot 18 \text{ radians}$$

$$\text{Then arc length} = \text{radius} \times \text{angle (rad)}$$

$$= 250 \text{ mm} \times 2 \cdot 18 \text{ (rad)}$$

$$= 545 \text{ mm}$$

$$\text{Arc length moved through} = \underline{545 \text{ mm}}$$

(iv) A wheel having a diameter of 800 mm rolls, without slipping, along a level floor.

(a) Through what horizontal distance has the centre of the wheel moved when the wheel has turned through an angle of 5 rad?

(b) Through what angle has the wheel turned when its centre moves through a horizontal distance of 1 m?

Note: the *diameter* of the wheel is given in this problem:

$$\text{diameter of wheel} = 800 \text{ mm}$$

$$\text{radius of wheel} = 400 \text{ mm}$$

If the wheel rolls without slipping, the horizontal distance moved will be equal to the arc length traced out by a point originally in contact with the ground (see diagram 113).

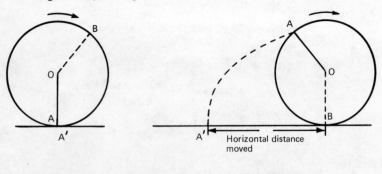

(a) Before rolling   (b) After rolling

113. Horizontal distance moved is equal to arc length AB, since the length A′B would just wrap round arc AB on the wheel

(a) Then horizontal distance moved through
    = arc length moved through
    = (radius) × (angle in radians)
    = 400 mm × 5 (rad)
    = 2000 mm = 2 m

(b) If horizontal distance moved is 1 m, arc length moved through is 1 m.

But

$$\text{arc length} = (\text{radius}) \times (\text{angle in radians})$$
$$\therefore \ 1000 \text{ mm} = 400 \text{ mm} \times \theta \text{ (rad)}$$

$$\theta = \frac{1000}{400} \text{ rad}$$

$$= 2\cdot 5 \text{ rad}$$

Horizontal distance moved for 5 rad = 2 m

Angle turned through for 1 m movement = 2·5 rad

10.3. Angular velocity

If a wheel rotates at a steady number of revolutions every minute, the angle turned through by a radius of the wheel would increase steadily with time. The rate at which the angle increases is known as the ANGULAR VELOCITY of the wheel, the usual symbol for this being the Greek letter ω (pronounced 'omega'). Note that this is a *velocity* and not a speed, since the direction in which the angle increases (clockwise or anti-clockwise) should be known, as well as the actual rate of increase. The angular or rotational speed is just the magnitude or 'number part' of the angular velocity.

The fundamental units used for angular velocity are RADIANS PER SECOND, usually abbreviated to 'rad/s', so that

$$\text{angular velocity} = \frac{\text{angle turned through}}{\text{time taken}}$$

or, in symbols,

$$\omega \text{ (rad/s)} = \frac{\theta \text{ (rad)}}{t \text{ (s)}} \qquad . \qquad . \qquad . \qquad . \qquad \text{(iii)}$$

It follows that the angle θ turned through in t s is

$$\theta = \omega\, t \text{ rad} \qquad . \qquad . \qquad . \qquad \text{(iv)}$$

These equations should be compared with the corresponding equations for linear velocity.

The rather more familiar units 'revolutions per minute' or rev/min are, then, really alternative units in which to express an angular velocity. The actual measurement is easier in terms of rev/min, since it is easier to count the number of times a wheel makes a complete revolution in a minute. Consequently, it is often necessary to convert a speed expressed in rev/min or rev/s to the equivalent value in rad/s.

For each complete revolution, a radius of the wheel will turn through 2π rad, so that

$$n \text{ rev/min} = n\, \frac{\text{rev}}{\text{min}} \times \left(\frac{2\pi \text{ rad}}{1 \text{ rev}}\right)$$

$$= 2\pi\, n\, \frac{\text{rad}}{\text{min}}$$

$$= 2\pi\, n\, \frac{\text{rad}}{\text{min}} \times \left(\frac{1 \text{ min}}{60 \text{ s}}\right)$$

$$= \frac{2\pi\, n}{60} \text{ rad/s}$$

A wheel revolving at n rev/s has an angular velocity ω rad/s where

$$\omega = 2\pi\, n \text{ rad/s} \qquad . \qquad . \qquad . \qquad . \qquad \text{(v)}$$

Alternatively, a wheel revolving at ω rad/s has a speed of n rev/s where

$$n = \frac{\omega}{2\pi} \text{ rev/s} \qquad . \qquad . \qquad . \qquad . \qquad \text{(vi)}$$

10.4. Examples

(i) Express a speed of 100 rev/min in rad/s.

$$\omega = \frac{2\pi\, n}{60} \text{ rad/s}$$

$$= \frac{2\pi \times 100}{60} \text{ rad/s}$$

$$\simeq 10 \cdot 5 \text{ rad/s}$$

(ii) Express a speed of 25 rad/s in rev/s.

$$n = \frac{\omega}{2\pi} \text{ rev/s}$$

$$= \frac{25}{2\pi} \text{ rev/s}$$

$$\simeq 4 \text{ rev/s}$$

(iii) In an experiment, the time for a wheel to make 25 complete revolutions was found to be 14 s. Find the rotational speed of the wheel in rad/s. What will be the angle turned through in 5 s?

$$\text{Rotational speed} = \frac{25 \text{ rev}}{14 \text{ s}}$$

$$= \frac{25 \text{ rev}}{14 \text{ s}} \times \left(\frac{2\pi \text{ rad}}{1 \text{ rev}} \right)$$

or $$\omega = \frac{25 \times 2\pi}{14} \text{ rad/s}$$

$$= 11 \cdot 2 \text{ rad/s}$$

Alternatively,

$$\text{rotational speed} = \frac{25 \text{ rev}}{14 \text{ s}} \times \left(\frac{60 \text{ s}}{1 \text{ min}} \right)$$

$$= 107 \text{ rev/min}$$

or $$\omega = \frac{2\pi \times 107}{60} \text{ rad/s}$$

$$= 11 \cdot 2 \text{ rad/s}$$

Angle turned through in 5 s is

$$\theta = \omega t \text{ rad}$$
$$= 11 \cdot 2 \times 5 \text{ rad}$$
$$= 56 \text{ rad}$$

Rotational speed of wheel is $\omega = 11 \cdot 2 \text{ rad/s}$

Angle turned through in 5 s is $\theta = 56 \text{ radians}$

10.5. Relationship between angular velocity and linear velocity

If a body is whirled round on the end of a piece of string, the body will have an angular velocity about the centre of its circle of rotation. If the string were to break, the body would move off at a tangent to its circle of rotation. This means that at any instant in the circular motion of the body, its velocity is directed along a tangent to the circle. Since the direction of the tangent is constantly changing, the velocity of the body must be constantly changing also. From Section 9.1, page 258, this means that a force must be exerted on the body, and that it is the force of the tension in the string that keeps the body moving in its circular path. This force is removed when the string breaks so that the velocity of the body is no longer changed, and it continues with the same velocity along the tangential path.

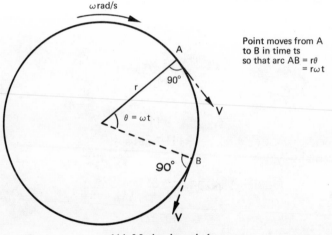

114. Motion in a circle

While moving in a circular path because of the tension in the string, the body will have an acceleration in the direction of the applied force. There is thus an acceleration towards the centre of the circle, known as the 'centripetal' acceleration. The 'centrifugal force' is the outwards reaction to the accelerating force directed towards the centre.

If a point moves in a circular path of radius r at an angular velocity ω rad/s, as shown in diagram 114, the velocity v at any instant, called the 'instantaneous velocity', will always be directed along a tangent at right angles to the radius to the point. In time t s, the radius will have turned through an angle $\theta = \omega t$ rad.

In this time, the point will have moved through an arc of length

$$s = r\,\theta$$
or
$$s = r\,\omega\,t$$

The linear velocity of the moving point will be given by

$$\text{linear velocity} = \frac{\text{distance moved}}{\text{time taken}}$$

or

$$v = \frac{s}{t}$$

$$= \frac{r\,\omega\,t}{t}$$

i.e. $\underline{v = r\,\omega}$ . . . . (vii)

In words,

$$\text{linear velocity} = \text{radius} \times \text{angular velocity}$$

Alternatively,

$$\text{angular velocity} = \frac{\text{linear velocity}}{\text{radius}}$$

or

$$\omega = \frac{v}{r} \quad . \qquad . \qquad . \qquad . \qquad . \qquad . \quad \text{(viii)}$$

Note that compatible units must be used; for example, if ω is in rad/s and r is in m, v will be in m/s.

10.6. Examples

(i) A point moves with a constant angular velocity of 20 rad/s in a circular path of radius 0·25 m. What is its linear velocity in m/s?

$$v = r\,\omega$$
$$= 0\text{·}25\ (\text{m}) \times 20\ (\text{rad/s})$$
$$= 5\ \text{m/s}$$

Linear velocity of point is $\underline{\underline{5\ \text{m/s}}}$

(ii) A car is driven round a corner at 50 km/h. If the radius of the corner is 30 m, what is the angular velocity of the car as it goes round the corner?

First convert the car speed to m/s.

$$50\ \text{km/h} = 50\ \cancel{\text{km/hr}} \times \left(\frac{16\text{·}7\ \text{m/s}}{60\ \cancel{\text{km/h}}}\right)$$

$$= 13\text{·}9\ \text{m/s}$$

Then
$$\omega = \frac{v}{r}$$

$$= \frac{13 \cdot 9 \text{ m/s}}{30 \text{ m}} \text{ rad/s}$$

$$= 0 \cdot 463 \text{ rad/s}$$

Angular velocity of car round corner $= \underline{0 \cdot 463 \text{ rad/s}}$

(iii) The wheels of a car are 0·6 m in diameter. What is the angular velocity of the wheels when the car is travelling at 100 km/h?

The linear velocity of a point on the outside edge of the wheel will be equal to the linear velocity of the car, if it is assumed that there is no slip between tyre and road.

Then linear velocity of point at 0·3 m radius is

$$100 \text{ km/h} = 100 \text{ km/h} \times \left(\frac{16 \cdot 7 \text{ m/s}}{60 \text{ km/h}} \right)$$

$$\text{or } v = 27 \cdot 8 \text{ m/s}$$

Angular velocity $\omega = \dfrac{v}{r}$

$$= \frac{27 \cdot 8}{0 \cdot 3} \text{ rad/s}$$

$$= 92 \cdot 7 \text{ rad/s}$$

Angular velocity of car wheels $= \underline{92 \cdot 7 \text{ rad/s}}$

Note that the speed of rotation of car wheels is then

$$n = \frac{\omega}{2\pi} \text{ rev/s}$$

$$= \frac{92 \cdot 7}{2\pi} \text{ rev/s}$$

$$= 14 \cdot 78 \text{ rev/s}$$

10.7. Angular acceleration

If the angular velocity of a point moving in a circular path changes with time, the point will have an angular acceleration given by

$$\text{angular acceleration} = \frac{\text{change in angular velocity}}{\text{time taken}}$$

The symbol usually used to represent angular acceleration is the Greek letter α (pronounced 'alpha').

If the angular velocity of a point changes from ω_1 rad/s to ω_2 rad/s in time t s, the average angular acceleration is given by

$$\alpha = \frac{\omega_2 - \omega_1}{t} \text{ radians per second per second, or rad/s}^2$$

As with linear acceleration, the value of angular acceleration may be positive or negative, according to whether the angular velocity increases or decreases.

It is possible to build up equations of angular motion with constant angular acceleration which are directly comparable with the equations of motion for constant linear acceleration. These are given below in angular terms:

(a) $\quad \theta = \frac{1}{2}(\omega_1 + \omega_2)t$ . . . . (ix)

(b) $\quad \omega_2 = \omega_1 + \alpha t$ . . . . (x)

(c) $\quad \theta = \omega_1 t + \frac{1}{2}\alpha t^2$ . . . . (xi)

(d) $(\omega_2)^2 = (\omega_1)^2 + 2\alpha\theta$ . . . . (xii)

where

ω_1 = initial angular velocity (rad/s)   (compare with u m/s)

ω_2 = final angular velocity (rad/s)   (compare with v m/s)

θ = angle moved through (rad)   (compare with s m)

α = constant angular acceleration   (compare with a m/s^2)
       (rad/s^2)

t = time taken (s)   (compare with t s)

Note that $s = r\theta$
$\qquad\quad v = r\omega$ where r is radius of circular
$\qquad\quad \alpha = r\alpha$ path of motion

10.8. Turning effect of a force. Torque

In Section 4.1, page 94, it was seen that a force had a moment about any point not in its line of action. The moment of the force about a point is given by the product of the force and the perpendicular distance of the point from the line of action of the force. The name 'torque' was applied in Section 4.10, page 116, to the pure turning moment produced about a point in a plane by a couple; i.e. by two equal forces in opposite directions having parallel lines of action.

It follows that if a torque is applied to a body, the body will tend to turn. For example, torque is applied to tighten up a nut on a screw, or to turn the starting handle of a car, or to turn the wheels of a bicycle, or to cause a shaft to rotate in its bearings.

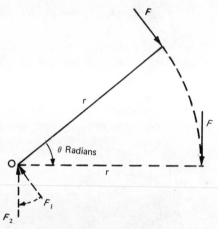

115. Work done by a torque

It was seen in Section 6.1, page 174, that if a force moves through a distance, the force does work on whatever it is moving. In just the same way, a torque will do work if it moves through an angle. Work is done when the key of a clock is turned, as the torque applied to the key is moved through an angle as the key turns.

The relationship between the torque, the angle through which it turns and the work done can be found as follows:

Suppose a force F is applied at right angles to a radius r, centre O, as shown in diagram 115; for example, as when a spanner is used to tighten a nut, when O would represent the centre of the bolt. Then, if the whole system does not move in the line of action of F, an equal and opposite reaction force is set up at O, shown as F_1 in diagram 115. These two forces then set up a couple of turning moment, or torque, equal to $F \times r$.

Suppose the radius turns through an angle θ rad under the action of this torque. The reaction at O will move through the same angle θ, to F_2 as shown.

The force F therefore moves through a total distance equal to the arc length $s = r\,\theta$, so that the work done by the force F is work done = force × distance moved in direction of force

$$= F \times r\,\theta$$

But $\qquad F \times r$ = torque due to couple = T (say)

Then $\qquad$ work done = $T\,\theta$

If the torque is measured in Nm, the work done will be measured in Nm; i.e. joules.

In each case, the angle θ *must* be measured in *radians*.

Summary

Work done (J) = torque (Nm) × angle turned through (rad)

10.9. Examples

(i) Find the work done when a torque of 30 Nm is applied to tighten down a nut by turning it through an angle of 240°.

First convert the angle to radians:

$$240° = 240 \text{ degrees} \times \left(\frac{\pi\,\text{rad}}{180\,\text{degrees}} \right)$$

$$= 240 \times \frac{\pi}{180}\,\text{rad}$$

$$= 4 \cdot 19\,\text{rad}$$

Then

$$\text{work done (J)} = \text{torque (Nm)} \times \text{angle (radians)}$$
$$= 30\,(\text{Nm}) \times 4 \cdot 19\,(\text{rad})$$
$$= 125 \cdot 7\,\text{J}$$
$$\text{Work done in tightening nut} = \underline{125 \cdot 7\,\text{J}}$$

Some of this work will be converted to strain energy in the nut and bolt, and some will be converted to heat energy against the opposing frictional forces.

(ii) A pulley having a diameter of 200 mm is driven by a belt. If the effective belt tension tending to turn the pulley is 250 N, find the work done per revolution.

The torque which turns the pulley is

$$T = \text{force} \times \text{radius}$$
$$= 250\,\text{N} \times 0 \cdot 1\,(\text{m})$$
$$= 25\,\text{Nm}$$

The angle turned through per revolution is 2π rad.

Then

> work done (J) = torque (Nm) $\times$ angle (rad)
> = 25 (Nm) $\times$ 2π (rad)
> = 157·1 J

Work done per revolution in turning the pulley = 157·1 J

Some of this work will be used to turn whatever load the pulley is driving, and some will be used, and converted to heat, in overcoming opposing frictional forces.

(iii) A shaft rotates in a cylindrical bearing. The diameter of the shaft is 40 mm, and the load acting vertically downwards on the shaft at the bearing is 2·5 kN. If the coefficient of friction between shaft and bearing is 0·05, find the work done against friction per revolution.

The tangential frictional force opposing the rotation of the shaft will be

> $F = \mu\, R_n$ (See Section 7.3, page 197)
> = 0·05 $\times$ 2500 N
> = 125 N

This will set up an opposing frictional torque

> T_f = force $\times$ radius
> = 125 (N) $\times$ 20 (mm)
> = 2500 Nmm
> = 2·5 Nm

The angle turned through per revolution is 2π rad. Then,

> work done (J) = torque (Nm) $\times$ angle (rad)
> = 2·5 (Nm) $\times$ 2π (rad)
> = 15·71 J

Work done per revolution against friction = 15·71 J

This work will be converted to heat in the bearing.

(iv) The torque on the coil of an electrical instrument is 0·003 Nm. Find the work done if the coil is deflected through 60°.

First convert the angle to radians.

$$60° = 60 \text{ ~~degrees~~} \left(\frac{\pi \text{ rad}}{180 \text{ ~~degrees~~}} \right)$$

$$= 1\cdot05 \text{ rad}$$

Work done (J) = torque (Nm) × angle (rad)

$$= 0\cdot003 \text{ (Nm)} \times 1\cdot05 \text{ (rad)}$$

$$= 0\cdot003\ 15 \text{ J}$$

Work done in deflecting the coil = $\underline{0\cdot003\ 15 \text{ J}}$

CHAPTER SUMMARY

One radian is that angle subtended at the centre of a circle by an arc equal in length to the radius of the circle.

$$s = r\,\theta$$

where

s = arc length

r = radius

θ = angle subtended, in radians

π rad = 180°

or 1 rad = $\dfrac{180°}{\pi} \simeq 57\cdot3°$

Angular velocity = $\dfrac{\text{angle turned through}}{\text{time taken}}$, or $\omega = \dfrac{\theta}{t}$ rad/s

Angle turned through in t s at ω rad/s is $\theta = \omega t$ rad.

A rotational speed of n rev/min corresponds to an angular velocity ω rad/s where

$$\omega = \frac{2\pi\,n}{60} \text{ rad/s}$$

A point moving in a circular path of radius r at an angular velocity of ω rad/s has a linear velocity v where

$$v = r\omega$$

Angular acceleration = $\dfrac{\text{change in angular velocity}}{\text{time taken}}$

or $\alpha = \dfrac{\omega_2 - \omega_1}{t}$ rad/s^2

Equations of angular motion with uniform angular acceleration are:

$$\theta = \tfrac{1}{2}(\omega_1 + \omega_2)\,t$$
$$\omega_2 = \omega_1 + \alpha t$$
$$\theta = \omega_1 t + \tfrac{1}{2}\alpha t^2$$
$$(\omega_2)^2 = (\omega_1)^2 + 2\,\alpha\theta$$

θ = angle turned through
ω_1 = initial angular velocity
ω_2 = final angular velocity
α = angular acceleration
t = time taken

$$s = r\theta$$
$$v = r\omega$$
$$a = r\alpha$$

r = radius of circular path
s, v, a are linear distance, velocity and acceleration.

Work done when a torque T moves through an angle θ radians is $T\theta$.

If T is in Nm, work done is in J.

QUESTIONS

1. A motor car has wheels of 700 mm effective diameter.
(a) How many rev/min will each wheel make when the car is travelling at 65 km/h?
(b) How many m/s will the car travel when the wheels are rotating at 750 rev/min?

2. If the cutting speed of brass is 60 m/min, determine the spindle speed, in rev/min, of a lathe turning a rod 50 mm diameter.

3. A railway turntable 9 m in diameter is rotated from rest by an accelerating force of 250 N acting tangentially at its edge. This produces a uniform tangential acceleration of $0\cdot03$ m/s² at the periphery, which is maintained until a peripheral velocity of $0\cdot25$ m/s is attained.
(a) Determine (i) the time taken to achieve maximum velocity, (ii) the angle turned through in degrees in this time, (iii) the kinetic energy acquired by the turntable.
(b) The turntable comes to rest from its maximum velocity while turning through 30°. What is its constant angular deceleration in rad/s²?

4. A wheel, of diameter 200 mm, rotates at 2400 rev/min. Calculate:
 (i) the angular velocity of the wheel in rad/s
(ii) the speed of a point on the rim of the wheel in m/s.

5. Establish the relationship between the angular velocity ω of a rotating disc and the linear speed v of a point on the disc distant r m from the centre of rotation. A disc 1 m in diameter rotates at 150 rev/min. What is the angular velocity in rad/s and what is the speed of the rim in m/s?

6. Starting from rest, a vehicle having road wheels of 1 m diameter reaches a speed of 25 km/h after moving a distance of 300 m with uniform acceleration. Find

(a) the time, in seconds, taken to cover this distance,

(b) the angular velocity of the road wheels, in rad/s, at 25 km/h,

(c) the angular acceleration of the road wheels in rad/s².

7. A bicycle with 650 mm diameter wheels starts from rest and attains a speed of 20 km/h in 50 s. Determine (a) the uniform acceleration of the cycle, (b) the distance travelled in the 50 s, (c) the angular velocity of the wheels in rad/s at full speed and (d) the angular acceleration of the wheels.

8. The speed of a motor increases uniformly from zero to 500 rev/min in 10 s. Find (a) the angular acceleration in rad/s², (b) the total number of revolutions in the 10 s.

9. A force of 50 N is applied at right angles to the end of a spanner, 150 mm long, to tighten a nut. Find the work done if the spanner is moved through 150°.

10. A torque of 150 Nm is applied to a motor shaft at standstill so that it is made to rotate. The speed of the shaft increases from zero to 250 rev/min in 15 s. Find

(a) the angular velocity of the shaft, in rad/s, at the end of the 15 s,

(b) the angular acceleration, in rad/s²,

(c) the total angle turned through,

(d) the work done by the torque.

11. A brake drum is rotating at 500 rev/min when the brakes are applied, to give a constant braking torque of 40 Nm. If the brake drum slows down uniformly to a speed of 100 rev/min in 10 s, find the work done by the braking torque in this time.

12. A torque of 10 Nm is applied to the handle of a lifting mechanism. Find the work done in turning the handle through 25 revolutions.

K

11. Power

In the discussions of work and energy in the preceding chapters, attention has been confined entirely to the *amount* of work or energy involved in a particular process. For example, it has been seen that work is done whenever a force moves through a distance along its line of action, or whenever a torque moves through an angle. The amount of work involved is measured as force × distance, or as torque × angle, as already discussed.

However, in most engineering applications the time taken to do the work is also of importance, and this point will now be considered.

11.1. Power

If a car falls into a ditch, a certain amount of work, represented by a product of force and distance, is necessary to lift it out again. It would be quite possible to arrange for a small clockwork motor to perform this work, if suitable equipment in the way of gears and so on were available. It would be a tedious process, however, and would take a very long time indeed. The preferable method would be to use a break-down lorry for the job, which would then be done very much more quickly.

The difference between these two methods is due to the fact that the motor on the breakdown lorry is capable of doing the same amount of work at a faster rate than the clockwork motor. A motor capable of performing work at a faster rate than another motor is said to be more 'powerful'.

In scientific terms, POWER IS THE RATE OF DOING WORK. A powerful motor is not necessarily capable of doing more work than a less powerful motor, but it *will do the work in a shorter time*. Thus

$$\text{power} = \frac{\text{work done}}{\text{time taken}} \qquad . \qquad . \qquad . \qquad . \qquad \text{(i)}$$

Note that for a force moving through a distance along its line of action,

$$\text{work done} = \text{force} \times \text{distance moved}$$

so that

$$\text{power} = \frac{\text{work done}}{\text{time taken}}$$

$$= \frac{\text{force} \times \text{distance moved}}{\text{time taken}}$$

$$= \text{force} \times \text{velocity} \qquad . \qquad . \qquad . \qquad \text{(ii)}$$

The units in which power is measured are those of (work, or energy, units) ÷ (units of time).

The fundamental unit of power is the JOULE PER SECOND, which is given the special name of the WATT (symbol W). Also in common use are the usual metric multiples and sub-multiples, such as the megawatt (MW), the kilowatt (kW), or the milliwatt (mW). The prefixes have their usual meanings. For example:

$$1 \text{ MW} = 1 \times 10^6 \text{ W} \, (= 1\,000\,000 \text{ W})$$
$$1 \text{ kW} = 1 \times 10^3 \text{ W} \, (= 1000 \text{ W})$$

$$1 \text{ mW} = 1 \times 10^{-3} \text{ W} = \left(\frac{1}{1000} \text{ W}\right)$$

Note the very different significance of the large 'M' and the small 'm' when these precede a symbol.

11.2. Power transmitted by a torque

When a torque moves through an angle, work is done whose value is given by the product of the torque and the angle turned through in radians. The power involved is then dependent on the *rate* at which the angle is turned through. In other words,

work done (J) = torque (Nm) × angle (rad)]
power (W) = torque (Nm) × angular velocity (rad/s)

or, in symbols,

$$\text{work} = T\,\theta \text{ J}$$
$$\text{power} = T\,\omega \text{ W} \qquad . \qquad . \qquad . \qquad . \qquad \text{(iii)}$$

where T is in Nm, θ in radians, ω in rad/s.

This may be compared with

$$\text{power} = F \times v$$

for a linear force.

It has been seen in Section 10.3, page 277, that if the speed of rotation is η rev/min, the corresponding angular velocity is given by

$$\omega = \frac{2\pi n}{60} \text{ rad/s}$$

Substituting this value for ω in the above expression for power gives

$$\text{power} = T \times \frac{2\pi\eta}{60} \text{ W} \qquad . \qquad . \qquad . \qquad . \qquad \text{(iv)}$$

Note: T is in Nm

η is in rev/min.

This relationship should also be remembered.

11.3. Examples

(i) A load of 4 tonne is raised through a vertical distance of 15 m in 30 s by a crane motor. Calculate the work done and the average power of the motor.

$$\begin{aligned}
\text{Work done} &= \text{force} \times \text{distance} \\
&= 4000 \times 9{\cdot}81 \text{ (N)} \times 15 \text{ (m)} \\
&= 588\,000 \text{ Nm} \\
&= \underline{588 \text{ kJ}}
\end{aligned}$$

$$\begin{aligned}
\text{Average power} &= \frac{\text{work done}}{\text{time taken}} \\
&= \frac{588 \text{ kJ}}{30 \text{ s}} \\
&= 19{\cdot}62 \text{ kJ/s} \\
&= \underline{19{\cdot}62 \text{ kW}}
\end{aligned}$$

Work done in lifting load $= \underline{588 \text{ kJ}}$

Average power of crane motor $= \underline{19{\cdot}62 \text{ kW}}$

(ii) The output power from a pump is calculated to be 15 kW. If the pump is used to raise water to a height of 30 m, calculate the rate of pumping in cubic metres per second. (1 cubic metre of water has a mass of 1 tonne.)

$$\begin{aligned}
\text{Output power} &= 15 \text{ kW} \\
&= 15\,000 \text{ Nm/s}
\end{aligned}$$

The water is pumped to a height of 30 m above intake,

$$\text{Work done in one second} = 15\,000 \text{ Nm}$$
$$\text{Work done} = \text{force} \times \text{distance}$$
$$15\,000 = F\,(\text{N}) \times 30\,(\text{m})$$
$$\therefore \; F = 500 \,(\text{N})$$

$$\therefore \; \text{mass of water lifted per second} = \frac{500}{9 \cdot 81} \text{ kg}$$

$$= 50 \cdot 9 \text{ kg}$$

$$\text{volume of water lifted per second} = 50 \cdot 9 \text{ kg} \times \left(\frac{1 \text{ m}^3}{1\,000 \text{ kg}} \right)$$

$$= 0 \cdot 050\,9 \text{ m}^3$$
$$\text{volume rate of flow} = 0 \cdot 050\,9 \text{ m}^3/\text{s}$$
$$\text{Rate of pumping} = \underline{\underline{0 \cdot 050\,9 \text{ m}^3/\text{s}}}$$

(iii) A shaft transmits 18 kW when it is rotating at 200 rev/min. What is the torque on the shaft?

$$\text{Power} = \frac{2\pi \, nT}{60}$$

$$\frac{2\pi \times 200 \times T}{60} = 18\,000$$

$$\therefore \; T = \frac{18\,000 \times 60}{2\pi \times 200}$$

$$= 860 \text{ Nm}$$
$$\text{Torque on shaft} = \underline{\underline{860 \text{ Nm}}}$$

(iv) The power of a motor is found by a brake being applied to a pulley on the motor and the torque developed by the brake at a particular motor speed being measured. In such a test, the brake torque requires a mass of 10 kg to be applied to an arm 350 mm long in order to give balanced conditions. If the motor speed is 950 rev/min, what is the output power of the motor?

$$\text{Motor torque} = \text{opposing brake torque at balance}$$
$$\text{or } T = 10 \times 9 \cdot 81 \,(\text{N}) \times 0 \cdot 350 \,(\text{m})$$
$$= 34 \cdot 3 \text{ Nm}$$

Then

$$\text{output power} = \frac{2\pi \, nT}{60}$$

$$= \frac{2\pi \times 950 \times 34\cdot3}{60} \, \text{W}$$

$$= 3410 \, \text{W}$$

Output power of motor $= \underline{3\cdot41 \, \text{kW}}$

(v) A shaft rotates at 250 rev/min in a cylindrical bearing, and is subjected to a vertically downwards load of 20 kN at the bearing. The diameter of the shaft is 75 mm. If the power 'lost' in friction is 1 kW, calculate the frictional torque and the coefficient of friction between the shaft and its bearing.

Power lost in friction $= \dfrac{2\pi \, nT}{60} \, \text{W}$ where $T =$ frictional torque

$$\therefore \frac{2\pi \times 250 \, T}{60} = 1000 \, \text{W}$$

$$T = \frac{1000 \times 60}{2\pi \times 250}$$

$$= \underline{38\cdot2 \, \text{Nm}}$$

This torque is produced by the frictional force F N acting at the shaft radius of 37·5 mm

$$F \times 0\cdot037\,5 = 38\cdot2 \, \text{Nm}$$

$$F = \frac{38\cdot2}{0\cdot037\,5} \, \text{N}$$

$$= 1020 \, \text{N} = 1\cdot02 \, \text{kN}$$

But the load on the bearing, $R = 20$ kN

and $F = \mu R$, where $\mu =$ coefficient of friction

$$\therefore 1\cdot02 = \mu \times 20$$

or $$\mu = \frac{1\cdot02}{20}$$

$$= \underline{0\cdot051}$$

Frictional torque at bearing $= \underline{38\cdot2 \, \text{Nm}}$

Coefficient of friction between shaft and bearing $= \underline{\underline{0\cdot051}}$

(vi) What is the power required to drive a train having a mass of 400 tonne along a level track at 75 km/h if the forces opposing the motion of the train amount to 100 N/tonne?

Force required to drive train at steady speed

$$= \text{opposing forces}$$
$$= 400 \times 100 \text{ N}$$
$$= 40\,000 \text{ N} = 40 \text{ kN}$$

This force must be moved at 75 km/h, or at

$$75 \text{ km/h} \times \left(\frac{16 \cdot 7 \text{ m/s}}{60 \text{ km/hr}} \right) = 20 \cdot 85 \text{ m/s}$$

$$\text{Power} = \frac{\text{work done}}{\text{time taken}}$$

$$= \frac{\text{force} \times \text{distance moved}}{\text{time taken}}$$

$$= \text{force} \times \text{velocity}$$
$$= 40 \text{ (kN)} \times 20 \cdot 85 \text{ (m/s)}$$
$$= 834 \text{ kNm/s}$$
$$= 834 \text{ kW}$$

Power required to drive train $= \underline{\underline{834 \text{ kW}}}$

11.4. Efficiency

It has been seen in Chapter 7, page 195, that frictional forces will always be set up to oppose the motion of a moving body. It follows that work must be done in moving the body against these frictional forces, and it has already been pointed out that this work will be converted to heat energy at the rubbing surfaces. The energy so converted is usually a 'loss' of energy from the system concerned. The term 'loss' must be clearly understood. The energy concerned has not been destroyed, but has been converted into a form other than that for which any energy input to the system may have been intended.

Any practical device will have such energy 'losses', so that the total output of work or energy will be less than the total input of work or energy. Devices for energy conversion are dealt with separately at various points in this book, but the principle of energy conversion and the energy considerations of a particular problem should always be borne in mind.

The EFFICIENCY of any device can be defined as the ratio of 'work output' to 'work input'. In other words,

$$\text{efficiency} = \frac{\text{work output}}{\text{work input}} \qquad . \qquad . \qquad . \qquad \text{(v)}$$

where work output and work input are expressed in the same units. This fraction will *always be less than 1*. It may sometimes be convenient to consider a theoretically ideal device for which the fraction is 1, but the principle of conservation of energy shows that the value *can never be greater than 1*.

If the efficiency is calculated from the fraction shown, it is known as a PER UNIT value (p.u.). It shows then the work output obtained *for each unit* of work input.

It is also common practice to state efficiency as a PERCENTAGE value (%). This value is obtained simply by multiplying the 'per unit' value by 100. This then shows the work output obtained *for each 100 units* of work input. The percentage efficiency can never exceed 100% for the reasons already given.

11.5. Examples

(i) Water is pumped to a height of 15 m at a rate of 8 litres/second. Find the power required. If the pump has an efficiency of 70%, find the input power to the pump.

(1 litre of water has a mass of 1 kg)

Mass of water
$$\begin{aligned}
\text{pumped per minute} &= 8 \times 1 \text{ kg/s} \\
\text{Power required} &= 8 \times 9\cdot81 \text{ (N/s)} \times 15 \text{ (m)} \\
&= 1178 \text{ W} \\
&= \underline{1\cdot178 \text{ kW}}
\end{aligned}$$

$$\begin{aligned}
\% \text{ efficiency} &= \frac{\text{work output}}{\text{work input}} \times 100\% \\
\\
&= \frac{\text{work output per second}}{\text{work input per second}} \times 100\% \\
\\
&= \frac{\text{power output}}{\text{power input}} \times 100\%
\end{aligned}$$

Then, for the pump

$$\frac{\text{power output}}{\text{power input}} \times 100 = 70$$

or $\quad\quad$ power input $= \dfrac{\text{power output}}{70} \times 100$

$$= \frac{\text{power output}}{0.7}$$

$$= \frac{1.178 \text{ kW}}{0.7}$$

$$= 1.68 \text{ kW}$$

Output power required from pump $= \underline{1.178 \text{ kW}}$

Input power required to the pump $= \underline{1.68 \text{ kW}}$

Note that:

$$\text{work output} = \text{work input} \times \text{per-unit efficiency}$$

or

$$\text{work input} = \frac{\text{work output}}{\text{per-unit efficiency}}$$

Similar expressions also apply for power output and input. In each case the values concerned must be expressed in the same units; for example, work output *and* work input must be expressed in Nm, or power output *and* power input in W.

(ii) An electric train starts from rest on a level track and reaches a speed of 75 km/h in 45 s. The train has a mass of 250 tonne and the total opposing forces amount to 70 N/tonne.

Find (a) the average acceleration, (b) the average tractive force required, (c) the power input to the train motors when the speed has just reached 75 km/h, if the motors and gears have a combined efficiency of 70%.

What would be the power input to the motors at a steady speed of 75 km/h, if the overall efficiency is assumed to be the same?

(a) Average acceleration
In this case,

$$u = 0, v = 75 \text{ km/hr} \times \left(\frac{16\cdot7 \text{ m/s}}{60 \text{ km/h}}\right) = 20\cdot85 \text{ m/s}$$

$$t = 45 \text{ s}$$
$$v = u + at$$
$$20\cdot85 = 0 + a \times 45$$
$$a = \frac{20\cdot85}{45} \text{ m/s}^2$$
$$= \underline{0\cdot464 \text{ m/s}^2}$$

(b) Average tractive force.

$$\text{Force (kN)} = \text{mass (tonne)} \times \text{acceleration (m/s}^2)$$
$$= 250 \times 0\cdot464 \text{ kN}$$
$$= 116 \text{ kN}$$

To this accelerating force must be added the force required to overcome the opposing forces of

$$70 \times 250 = 17\,500 \text{ N} = 17\cdot5 \text{ kN}$$

In other words,

$$\text{total tractive force} = 116 + 17\cdot5 \text{ kN}$$
$$= \underline{133\cdot5 \text{ kN}}$$

(c) Power input to motors as 75 km/h is reached

$$\text{Power output} = \text{force} \times \text{velocity}$$
$$= 133\cdot5 \text{ (kN)} \times 20\cdot85 \text{ (m/s)}$$
$$= 2785 \text{ kW} = 2\cdot785 \text{ MW}$$

$$\text{Power input} = \frac{\text{power output}}{\text{per-unit efficiency}}$$
$$= \frac{2\cdot785 \text{ MW}}{0\cdot7}$$
$$= \underline{3\cdot98 \text{ MW}}$$

(d) Power input to motors at a steady 75 km/h. The only force now required is that to overcome the opposing forces of 17·5 kN.

$$\text{Power output}$$
$$\text{of motors} = 17\cdot5 \times 20\cdot85 \text{ kW}$$
$$= 365 \text{ kW}$$

Power input

$$\text{to motors} = \frac{365}{0.7} \text{ kW}$$

$$= \underline{522 \text{ kW or } 0.522 \text{ MW}}$$

Average acceleration of train = $\underline{0.464 \text{ m/s}^2}$
Average tractive force required = $\underline{133.5 \text{ kN}}$
Power input just as 75 km/h is reached = $\underline{3.98 \text{ MW}}$
Power input at a steady 75 km/h = $\underline{0.522 \text{ MW}}$

CHAPTER SUMMARY

Power is the rate of doing work.

$$\text{Power} = \frac{\text{work done}}{\text{time taken}}$$

or   work done = power × time

Units are Nm/s = J/s = W.

$$\begin{aligned} \text{Power} &= \text{force} \times \text{velocity} &&= Fv \\ &= \text{torque} \times \text{angular velocity} &&= T\omega \end{aligned}$$

The power transmitted by a torque T Nm at a rotational speed n rev/min is given by

$$\text{power} = \frac{2\pi \, \eta T}{60} \text{ W}$$

$$\text{Efficiency} = \frac{\text{useful output}}{\text{input}} \text{ per unit}$$

$$= \frac{\text{useful output}}{\text{input}} \times 100\%$$

(Useful output and input expressed in the same units.)

QUESTIONS

1. (a) Explain what is meant by (i) work, (ii) energy, (iii) power.

(b) A train having a mass of 200 tonne is travelling on the level at a steady speed of 45 km/h, the frictional resistances to motion amounting to 75 N/tonne. Determine the power developed by the locomotive. If the train continues at the same speed up an incline of 1 in 100, calculate the additional power required, assuming the frictional resistances remain as before.

2. What is meant by (a) work, (b) power?
How much work is done when 3 tonne of coal are raised 120 m up a pit-shaft? What power would be required to carry out the operation in 100 s?

3. A pump is used to raise 40 litres/s through a height of 6 m. Calculate:
(a) the work done by the pump in 5 min,
(b) the power output of the pump.

4. If 15 kW will propel a car at 100 km/h, calculate the propulsive force.

5. (a) Explain what is meant by the terms 'work' and 'power'. In what units may work be expressed?
(b) The force exerted by a shaping-machine tool is a cutting force of 7·5 kN. If the cutting speed is 300 mm/s, determine the power absorbed in cutting.

6. A winding drum is rotated by means of a radial lever 1·8 m long. If a force of 250 N is applied at right angles to the end of the lever, calculate (a) the moment of this force about the axis of the drum, (b) the power needed to move the end of the lever through 7 m in 5 s.

7. (a) The coefficient of friction between a lathe spindle and its bearings is 0·005 and the vertical load on the spindle is 2 kN. If the diameter of the bearings is 75 mm, calculate the power absorbed in friction when the lathe is running at 600 rev/min.
(b) If the lathe in part (a) is designed to take cuts at 15 m/min, with a tangential force at the tool point of 2·25 kN, calculate the power absorbed in cutting.

8. When a certain lathe is turning a bar to 40 mm diameter at a speed of 200 rev/min the force at the tool point is 3 kN. If one-sixth of the output of the driving motor is required to overcome frictional resistances in the moving parts of the lathe, determine the output power of the motor.

9. A machine spindle runs in two plain bearings, and the coefficient of friction between the spindle and each bearing is 0·02. When operating at 750 rev/min the load on one bearing is 1·25 kN and on the other 2·25 kN. If the spindle is 90 mm diameter, calculate the saving in power which would be obtained by fitting roller bearings in which the frictional resistance may be assumed to be negligible.

10. A machine having a mass of 5 tonne is to be moved a distance of 2 m across a concrete floor.
Calculate the work done. If this movement is made in 10 s, what power is being used?
Coefficient of friction = 0·4.

11. A vehicle having a mass of 3 tonne is moving up an incline of 1 in 40 at a uniform speed of 25 km/h. Calculate:

(a) the kinetic energy of the vehicle at this speed,

(b) the tractive effort required if the tractive resistance is 200 N/tonne,

(c) the power required,

(d) the angular velocity of the road wheels in rad/s, given that their effective diameter is 0·8 m.

12. Distinguish clearly between 'work' and 'power'.

An electric motor supplies power to a haulage gear which has to raise a total load of 10 tonne through 3·3 m in 30 s. If the efficiency of the haulage system is 80%, determine:

(a) the power to be supplied by the motor,

(b) the energy lost or wasted per second when working at this efficiency.

13. (a) Define energy and name two different kinds of energy.

(b) A mass of 160 kg is lifted through a height of 6 m in 6 s. Calculate (i) the energy stored in the mass due to its having been lifted and (ii) the average power required to lift the mass.

14. Define 'coefficient of friction'.

A vertical engine has a stroke of 0·9 m, and the coefficient of friction between the crosshead and guides is 0·06. When the engine runs at 55 rev/min the power lost in friction is 1 kW. Find the average thrust between the crosshead and guides.

15. Define the terms 'work' and 'power'.

A pump delivers 5 m³ of water through a vertical height of 100 m. What is the amount of work done? If this is accomplished in 100 s, what power is developed? If the efficiency of the pump and motor is 75%, what is the motor power required?

16. A conveyor, 200 m long, is inclined to the horizontal at 1 in 25 measured along the slope. The conveyor delivers 3 tonne of coal per minute. If the conveyor has an efficiency of 80% and the driving motor an efficiency of 90%, determine the power supplied to the motor.

17. (a) Define the terms 'power' and 'energy'.

(b) A conveyor is 200 m long and rises uniformly 1 in 12, measured along the slope. What power must be supplied to the driving pulley if 600 tonne of material is delivered from bottom to top of the conveyor at a uniform rate in 8 h, assuming that 20% of the total power supplied is lost?

18. Explain, with the aid of a diagram, the meaning of the term 'torque'.

Develop a formula for the output of a prime mover in terms of the torque and the speed of rotation.

Determine the torque at the output side of a reduction gear driven by an engine developing 90 kW at 1000 rev/min if the efficiency of the gear-box is 90% and the gear ratio is 15 to 1.

19. What is the meaning of the term 'torque'?

Develop a formula for the power output of a prime mover whose output torque is T Nm, and which is running at a speed of n rev/min.

A railway traction motor develops 150 kW when the train moves at 50 km/h. The rail wheel has a diameter of 1·2 m. Neglecting losses in the gearing, calculate:

(a) the torque developed on the driving axle,
(b) the tractive force.

20. A 10-tonne lorry increases its speed from 10 km/h to 35 km/h in 22 s when ascending an incline of 1 in 28. Assuming that the acceleration is uniform and that the road resistance is constant at 75 N/tonne, calculate the maximum power developed by the engine.

21. State the meaning of the term 'power'.

In turning a steel shaft, 225 mm diameter, on a lathe, the force on the lathe tool was found to be 875 N. If the shaft was making 50 rev/min, calculate the power being absorbed in turning.

12. Machines

The maximum force which a man can apply unaided is limited. Even the strongest man will find some weights too heavy for him to lift. Consequently, since very early times man has tried to devise methods by which a large load can be moved by a small effort. There are also occasions when it may be required to apply force to a load at some point remote from where the effort is being made. Any device which fulfils one or both of these objects is called a MACHINE.

The simple lever already discussed in Section 4.5, page 102, is a machine, just as the more complicated mechanisms which make up an aeroplane engine are machines. The 'effort' applied may be the direct pull exerted by a man, or it may be the force developed in, say, an electric motor. The term 'machine' covers them all.

In general, a complicated machine is itself composed of an arrangement of simpler machines. This chapter will introduce the main principles of a machine, and then discuss some particular examples.

12.1. Force ratio or mechanical advantage

In a machine, some load is moved at the output end of the machine through the application of some effort at the input end. The advantage of having the machine is that a large load may be moved by a small effort, and this idea is expressed in what is known as the FORCE RATIO of the machine. This is defined by the ratio

$$\text{force ratio (mechanical advantage)} = \frac{\text{load}}{\text{effort}}. \qquad \text{(i)}$$

The greater the force ratio, the greater will be the load that can be moved for a given effort. Because of the frictional forces opposing motion, and for other reasons to be discussed later, the force ratio of a practical machine will not be a constant. For example, it has been seen that a force equal and opposite to the limiting frictional force is required before any motion can start. Thus some effort will be required to achieve this even if there is no actual load at all. The force ratio at small values of load may, then, be quite small. At higher values of load, the proportion of the effort required to overcome friction will be smaller and the force ratio will increase. It will be seen later that the force ratio of a particular machine has a maximum value determined by the arrangement of the machine. In most cases, this maximum value is approached at the higher values of loads, even though it may never quite be reached.

12.2. Movement ratio or velocity ratio

For an ideal machine, the work input would be equal to the work output. Then if the output force, or load, were greater than the input force, or effort, the distance moved by the effort would have to be greater than the distance moved by the load. This follows from the fact that output force × distance, will, ideally, be equal to input force × distance.

The MOVEMENT RATIO of a machine is defined by the ratio

$$\text{movement ratio} = \frac{\text{distance moved by effort}}{\text{distance moved by load}} . \qquad . \quad \text{(ii)}$$

Unlike the force ratio, the movement ratio will be determined for all loads by the arrangement of the machine.

12.3. Efficiency

The efficiency of a machine has already been defined in Section 11.4, page 295, as the ratio

$$\text{efficiency} = \frac{\text{work output}}{\text{work input}} \text{ per unit}$$

Since

$$\text{work output} = \text{load} \times \text{distance moved by load}$$

and

$$\text{work input} = \text{effort} \times \text{distance moved by effort}$$

then

$$\text{efficiency} = \frac{\text{load}}{\text{effort}} \times \frac{\text{distance moved by load}}{\text{distance moved by effort}} \text{ p.u.}$$

$$= \frac{\dfrac{\text{load}}{\text{effort}}}{\dfrac{\text{distance moved by effort}}{\text{distance moved by load}}} \text{ p.u.}$$

or

$$\text{efficiency} = \frac{\text{force ratio}}{\text{movement ratio}} \text{ p.u.} . \qquad . \quad \text{(iii)}$$

For an ideal machine, the efficiency would be 1 p.u. (or 100%)—it cannot possibly be higher. For such an ideal machine, then,

$$\text{movement ratio} = \text{ideal force ratio}$$

$$\text{or} \qquad \text{movement ratio} = \frac{\text{load}}{\text{'ideal' effort}} \qquad . \qquad . \qquad . \qquad \text{(iv)}$$

where the 'ideal' effort would be that required to move the load in an ideal machine. The actual effort in a practical machine will be greater than this.

This gives an alternative expression for efficiency, since

$$\text{efficiency} = \frac{\text{force ratio}}{\text{movement ratio}}$$

$$= \frac{\text{load}}{\text{actual effort}} \times \frac{\text{'ideal' effort}}{\text{load}}$$

$$\text{or} \qquad \text{efficiency} = \frac{\text{'ideal' effort}}{\text{actual effort}} \text{ p.u.} \qquad . \qquad . \qquad . \qquad \text{(v)}$$

As a result of the effects of friction in a practical machine, and also as a result of other effects in some machines, the efficiency at low values of load is usually small. The efficiency of most machines will, however, rise fairly quickly with increasing loads, and will reach a maximum value at loads near those for which the machine is designed, although the value of the efficiency obtained can vary quite widely for different types of machine.

12.4. Relationship between load and effort

If the values of the required effort are plotted on a graph against the load for a simple machine, the graph is found to be approximately a straight line of the general form shown in diagram 116. The relationship between effort (P) and load (F) then has the general form

$$P = aF + b \qquad . \qquad . \qquad . \qquad \text{(vi)}$$

where a and b are constants whose value depends on the particular machine concerned.

The value of the constant 'b' represents the effort required to overcome any force opposing the motion of the load, and will include the effects of friction. It is given by the value of effort (P) when the load (F) is zero, as shown on the graph.

The value of the constant 'a' will depend on the ideal force ratio of the machine, and would be equal to the reciprocal of the $F.R.$ $\left(= \dfrac{1}{F.R.} \right)$ for an ideal machine having no opposing forces; i.e. for a machine for which the value of b was zero. It is given by the slope of the straight-line graph (see Section 8.4, page 223, where the slope of a straight-line graph is discussed in connection with another type of problem).

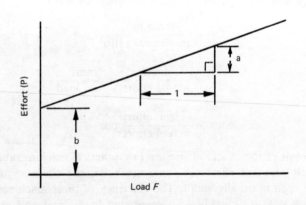

116. Graph of effort against load for a simple machine

If the relationship $P = a F + b$ is found for a given machine, when it is sometimes called the 'law' of the machine, the effort that will be required for a given load can be estimated. An example of this is given a little later, in Section 12.9, page 316.

12.5.   The lever

The lever has already been discussed in Section 4.5, page 102, in connection with the moment of a force about a point. Since it enables a load to be moved by the application of an effort at some other point, the lever is a machine, and is probably one of the earliest to have been used.

Consider the simple lever shown in diagram 117. It is a lever of the first order, with the fulcrum between the load and the effort.

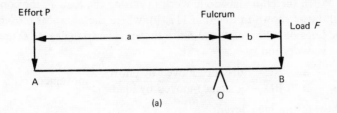

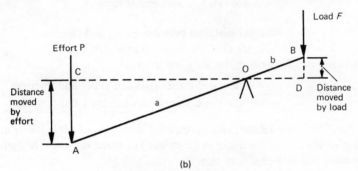

(b)

117. The lever as a machine

(a) Before work is done by effort on load

(b) After work has been done by effort on load

(Distances moved along the lines of action of the forces are as shown)

Before the effort does work in raising the load, the conditions for equilibrium are that

anti-clockwise moment = clockwise moment

From diagram 117 (a), and neglecting any other opposing forces not shown,

$$P \times a = F \times b$$

or

$$\frac{a}{b} = \frac{F}{P} = \frac{\text{load}}{\text{effort}} = \text{force ratio}$$

P will have to be very slightly larger than this value if a resulting acceleration force is to be applied to move F.

This increase in P can be neglected for a 'static' analysis of the problem, since the power, which involves the *rate* at which F is moved, is not considered here. Since other opposing forces have been neglected, this would be the result for an ideal machine.

When the effort has done work in raising the load F, the conditions will be as shown in diagram 117 (b), where the distances moved along the lines of action of P and F are shown. The triangles ACO and BDO are similar, and so

$$\frac{a}{b} = \frac{AC}{BD} = \frac{\text{distance moved by effort}}{\text{distance moved by load}} = \text{movement ratio}$$

Thus, for an ideal lever,

$$\text{ideal force ratio} = \text{movement ratio} = \frac{a}{b}$$

Since a = perpendicular distance between effort and fulcrum
and   b = perpendicular distance between load and fulcrum,
this result can be written, for an ideal lever,

$$F.R. = M.R. = \frac{\text{perpendicular distance between effort and fulcrum}}{\text{perpendicular distance between load and fulcrum}} \text{(vii)}$$

In this form, the relationship is true for any type of ideal lever, and will give the movement ratio in all cases. The force ratio will be rather less than this in a practical case.

Since the lever has been taken to be ideal, $F.R. = M.R.$, and the efficiency is $\dfrac{F.R.}{M.R.} = 1$ p.u., or 100%.

12.6.   The wheel and axle

The wheel and axle can be thought of as being similar in principle to the lever. A wheel and axle is illustrated in diagram 118.

A circular wheel of radius r_1 is fixed firmly to a circular axle of smaller radius r_2, as shown. A string is wound round the wheel, with one end fixed to the wheel and the effort applied to the free end. A similar string is wound in the opposite direction round the axle, with one end fixed to the axle and the free end attached to the load. As the effort is moved downwards, the wheel and axle turns to unwind the string round the wheel. This rotation winds up the string round the axle, and so raises the load. Diagram 118 (a) shows that the axis of rotation acts as the fulcrum of a lever, so that for equilibrium,

$$\text{anti-clockwise moment} = \text{clockwise moment}$$

and, neglecting any forces not shown,

$$P \times r_1 = F \times r_2$$

or
$$\frac{r_1}{r_2} = \frac{F}{P} = \frac{\text{load}}{\text{effort}} = \text{force ratio}$$

Once again, this is an ideal value. The force ratio of a practical wheel and axle will be less than this, because of the presence of other forces opposing the effort.

If the wheel and axle makes one complete revolution, a length of string equal to the circumference of the wheel is unwound by the effort.

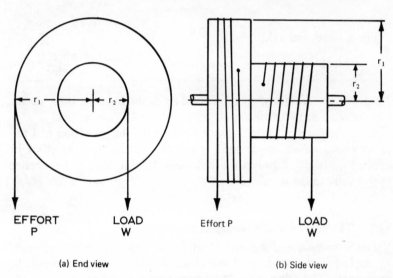

(a) End view   (b) Side view

118. Wheel and axle

At the same time, the load is raised by an amount equal to the circumference of the axle as one more turn of string is added to those on the axle. Thus,

distance moved by effort per complete
revolution of wheel and axle $= 2\pi r_1$

and

distance moved by load per complete
revolution of wheel and axle $= 2\pi r_2$

so that,

$$\text{movement ratio} = \frac{\text{distance moved by effort}}{\text{distance moved by load}}$$

$$= \frac{2\pi r_1}{2\pi r_2}$$

$$= \frac{r_1}{r_2}$$

Once again, for an ideal machine, $F.R. = M.R.$ and efficiency is 1 p.u. or 100%.

Summary

For a wheel and axle,

'ideal' force ratio = movement ratio = $\dfrac{\text{radius of wheel}}{\text{radius of axle}}$ (viii)

Note that, if the axis of rotation is taken as the fulcrum, these results are the same as those for a lever.

Since the perpendicular distance between the line of action and fulcrum would remain unchanged, it is not essential that the effort be applied vertically downwards, but only that it should be applied tangentially to the wheel.

12.7. The wheel and differential axle movement

The force ratio and movement ratio of a wheel and axle are limited by the largest diameter wheel and smallest diameter axle that would be practicable. The axle cannot be made too small in diameter as it would not then be able to support the load, and would bend or even break.

A wheel and axle may be modified to give a 'differential' arrangement which overcomes this difficulty and enables any desired force ratio to be obtained. Diagram 119 shows the general arrangement of a wheel and differential axle.

The effort is applied to a string wrapped round and fastened to the wheel as before. The second string is attached to the axle and is wound round it in the opposite direction to the string on the wheel, also as before. It is then, however, passed round a pulley and brought back to a second part of the axle which has a reduced diameter. It is wound round this second axle-section in the direction opposite to its direction round the first axle-section. The load is then hung from the spindle of the pulley as shown in diagram 119.

Then, when the effort is moved downwards, and the wheel and

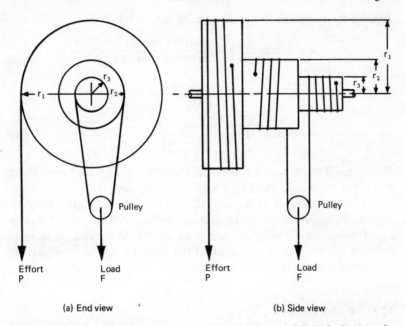

(a) End view   (b) Side view

119. Wheel and differential axle. (The pulley is shown in full in both views for simplicity. It will 'set' itself at some angle to the axis of rotation of the wheel and axle)

axles turn, string is wound up on to the larger-diameter section of the axle, but is unwound from the smaller section. The total length of string between the two axle-sections, which carries the pulley, is then shortened by the difference between the string wound on to the large section and the string unwound from the small section. The load will then be raised by half this amount, since to raise the load by 10 mm *each* supporting string must shorten by 10 mm, so that the total length of string between the axles must shorten by 20 mm. It is this 'difference' arrangement that gives the system its name of the wheel and 'differential' axle.

To calculate the movement ratio, let the wheel and axles make one complete revolution under the action of the effort. Then

distance moved by effort $= 2\pi r_1$
length of string wound on to larger axle $= 2\pi r_2$
length of string unwound from smaller axle $= 2\pi r_3$
string between axles shortens by $2\pi r_2 - 2\pi r_3$ or $2\pi (r_2 - r_3)$

Load is raised by half this length; i.e. by $\pi(r_2 - r_3)$. Then

$$\text{movement ratio} = \frac{\text{distance moved by effort}}{\text{distance moved by load}}$$

$$= \frac{2\pi r_1}{\pi(r_2 - r_3)}$$

or $\qquad$ movement ratio $= \dfrac{2r_1}{(r_2 - r_3)}$ $\qquad . \qquad . \qquad .$ (ix)

For an ideal machine, the force ratio would be equal to this movement ratio. For a practical machine it would be rather less.

Very high values of M.R. and F.R. can be obtained quite simply by making $(r_2 - r_3)$ small; i.e. by making the two axle sections of nearly equal diameters. If they are made equal, the M.R. and ideal F.R. become infinite, but this means that the load will not be raised at all, no matter how far the effort is moved.

12.8. Pulley systems

Various pulley systems of differing complexity are widely used for cranes, lifts and hoists of many different types. The fundamental principles given here govern the general behaviour of these systems.

A single pulley may be used to reverse or otherwise modify the direction of a force. If one end of a string passing over a pulley is pulled downwards, the other end will be pulled upwards with an equal force (if the friction in the pulley is neglected). A single pulley would thus have a movement ratio of 1.

Pulley blocks containing several pulleys may, however, be arranged to give values of movement ratio much higher than this. These pulleys are usually arranged side-by-side on the same shaft, but to simplify the diagrams they will be shown here vertically above one another.

(a) Two-pulley systems

Diagram 120 shows the general arrangement. The two pulleys are arranged in separate frames, and the lower one will move up or down in relation to the upper one, which is fixed to a suitable support.

A continuous string is fastened to the same support as the upper pulley, and passed round the pulleys to the effort as shown.

Suppose the load is raised by 10 mm. Then *each* supporting string

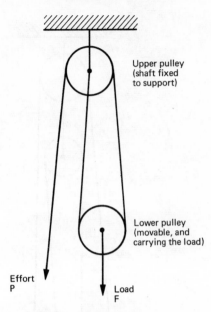

120. Two-pulley system

must shorten by 10 mm, so that a total length of 20 mm must pass over the upper pulley in the direction of the effort. Then

$$\text{movement ratio} = \frac{\text{distance moved by effort}}{\text{distance moved by load}}$$

$$= \frac{20}{10}$$

$$= \underline{2}$$

The ideal force ratio would be equal to this, but the practical force ratio would be a little less.

(b) Three-pulley systems with continuous string

Diagram 121 shows the general arrangement of a three-pulley system. The upper 'fixed' pulley block carries two independently rotating pulleys, while the lower pulley block carries one pulley as before. The arrangement of the continuous string should be clear from the diagram. The pulleys in the upper block will more usually be mounted

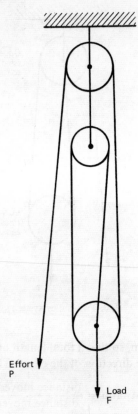

Effort
P

Load
F

121. Three-pulley system

side by side, but are shown above one another in the diagram for simplicity.

If the load is again raised by 10 mm, there will be 10 mm of slack in each of the three supporting strings, so that the effort would need to be moved by 30 mm to take up this slack. This is a convenient method of assessing the final result, although in practice the strings are always tight and the effort would be pulled down by 30 mm to raise the load by 10 mm. Then

$$\text{movement ratio} = \frac{30}{10}$$

$$= 3 \text{ in this case.}$$

(c) Other pulley arrangements

Pulley arrangements are possible using several different strings, and in Diagram 122 one such system is shown. For this arrangement, if the load is raised by 10 mm, each of the two strings supporting the load

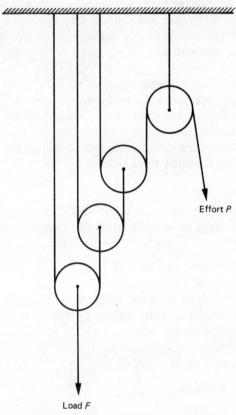

Effort *P*

Load *F*

122. Pulley system using several strings

pulley must shorten by 10 mm, so that the next highest pulley must be raised by 20 mm. From similar reasoning, the next pulley must be raised by 40 mm and the effort string must be moved through 80 mm. For this case, then,

$$\text{movement ratio} = \text{ideal force ratio}$$
$$= 8$$

The method of analysis used here and in the previous examples should be carefully noted. Imagine the load to be raised by 10 mm and then determine how much the string would have to shorten to produce this rise. In general, each string supporting the load must shorten by 10 mm, whether they are parts of the same continuous string or not. In this way the distance moved by the effort and hence the movement ratio and ideal force ratio of the system can be determined. Notice that where the pulleys revolve independently the diameters of the pulleys do not affect the result.

Differential pulley systems are possible with pulleys of different diameters fixed together, and usually with a chain fitted into special grooves in the pulleys. The principle of these is generally similar to that of the wheel and differential axle. Note that the mass of the lower pulley block must be raised in addition to any actual load, and that this effect will reduce the actual force ratio.

12.9. Examples

(i) In a test on a machine, an effort of 20 N was required to raise a load of 200 N. If the effort moves through 125 mm to raise the load by 10 mm, find:

- (a) the force ratio for this load
- (b) the movement ratio
- (c) the work done in raising this load by 30 mm
- (d) the distance moved by the effort in raising this load by 30 mm
- (e) the work done by the effort while the load is raised by 30 mm
- (f) the efficiency of the machine
- (g) the wasted effort.

(a) $\qquad$ Force ratio $= \dfrac{\text{load}}{\text{effort}}$

$$= \frac{200 \text{ N}}{20 \text{ N}}$$

$$= \underline{\underline{10}}$$

(b) $\qquad$ Movement ratio $= \dfrac{\text{distance moved by effort}}{\text{distance moved by load}}$

$$= \frac{125 \text{ mm}}{10 \text{ mm}}$$

$$= \underline{\underline{12 \cdot 5}}$$

(c) Work done on load in raising it by 30 mm
$$= \text{force} \times \text{distance}$$
$$= 200 \, (\text{N}) \times 0 \cdot 030 \, (\text{m})$$
$$= \underline{\underline{6 \, \text{Nm}}} \, (\text{i.e. } \underline{\underline{6 \, \text{J}}})$$

(d) Distance moved by effort in raising load by 30 mm
$$= \text{M.R.} \times \text{distance moved by load}$$
$$= 12 \cdot 5 \times 30 \, \text{mm}$$
$$= \underline{\underline{375 \, \text{mm}}}$$

(e) Work done by effort while load is raised by 30 mm
$$= \text{force} \times \text{distance}$$
$$= 20 \, (\text{N}) \times 0 \cdot 375 \, (\text{m})$$
$$= \underline{\underline{7 \cdot 5 \, \text{Nm}}} \, (\text{i.e. } \underline{\underline{7 \cdot 5 \, \text{J}}})$$

(f) $\text{Efficiency} = \dfrac{\text{work done on load}}{\text{work done by effort}}$

$$= \frac{6 \, \text{J}}{7 \cdot 5 \, \text{J}}$$
$$= \underline{\underline{0 \cdot 8 \, \text{p.u. or } 80\%}}$$

(Alternatively,
$\text{efficiency} = \dfrac{\text{force ratio}}{\text{movement ratio}} = \dfrac{10}{12 \cdot 5} = 0 \cdot 8 \, \text{p.u.})$

(g) $\text{Wasted effort} = \text{actual effort} - \text{ideal effort}$

But
$$\text{movement ratio} = \text{ideal force ratio}$$
$$= \frac{\text{load}}{\text{ideal effort}}$$
$$\therefore \text{ideal effort} = \frac{\text{load}}{\text{M.R.}}$$
$$= \frac{200 \, \text{N}}{12 \cdot 5}$$
$$= 16 \, \text{N}$$
$$\therefore \text{wasted effort} = 20 - 16 \, \text{N}$$
$$= \underline{\underline{4 \, \text{N}}}$$

(ii) A wheel and axle consists of a wheel 300 mm diameter and an axle 75 mm diameter, and its efficiency is 75% at a load of 120 N. Find the movement ratio of this machine and the effort required to raise the 120 N load. What would be the effort required for this load if the machine's efficiency were raised to 85% by lubrication of the bearings? What is the ideal effort for this load for this machine?

$$\text{Movement ratio} = \frac{\text{distance moved by effort}}{\text{distance moved by load}}$$

$$= \frac{\text{circumference of wheel}}{\text{circumference of axle}}$$

$$= \frac{\pi \times \text{wheel diameter}}{\pi \times \text{axle diameter}}$$

$$= \frac{300 \text{ mm}}{75 \text{ mm}}$$

$$= \underline{4}$$

If efficiency at this load is 75% (i.e. 0·75 p.u.), then

$$0·75 = \frac{\text{actual force ratio}}{\text{movement ratio}}$$

or

$$\text{F.R.} = 0·75 \times 4$$
$$= 3$$

then

$$\frac{\text{load}}{\text{effort}} = 3$$

$$\text{Effort} = \frac{\text{load}}{3}$$

$$= \frac{120 \text{ N}}{3}$$

$$= \underline{40 \text{ N}}$$

If efficiency increased to 85% (i.e. 0·85 p.u.),

$$\text{F.R.} = 0·85 \times 4$$
$$= 3·4$$

Then

$$\text{effort} = \frac{120 \text{ N}}{3·4}$$

$$= \underline{35·3 \text{ N}}$$

$$\text{Ideal effort} = \frac{\text{load}}{\text{M.R.}}$$

$$= \frac{120 \text{ N}}{4}$$

$$= \underline{30 \text{ N}}$$

Movement ratio of wheel and axle $= \underline{\underline{4}}$
Effort to raise 120 N at 75% efficiency $= \underline{\underline{40 \text{ N}}}$
Effort to raise 120 N at 85% efficiency $= \underline{\underline{35 \cdot 3 \text{ N}}}$
Effort to raise 120 N at 100% efficiency $= \underline{30 \text{ N}}$

(Note that efficiency $= \dfrac{\text{ideal effort}}{\text{actual effort}}$. This fact can be used to check the results obtained.

Thus

(i) $\dfrac{\text{ideal effort}}{\text{actual effort}} = \dfrac{30 \text{ N}}{40 \text{ N}} = 0 \cdot 75 \text{ p.u.}$

or (ii) $\dfrac{\text{ideal effort}}{\text{actual effort}} = \dfrac{30 \text{ N}}{35 \cdot 3 \text{ N}} = 0 \cdot 85 \text{ p.u.}$

These check with the given values.)

(iii) The following results were obtained in an experiment on a machine, where a load F N was raised by an effort P N.
Plot these results on a graph and deduce the law of the machine.
Draw a graph of force ratio against load (F).

Load F N	20	40	60	80	100
Effort P N	3	4·9	7	9·2	10·8

The graph of P against F is shown in diagram 123.

A straight line graph fits the given points.

(Note that, as in most cases of experimentally-obtained graphs, all the points do not lie exactly on the graph, because of errors of observation. The line should be drawn in so that it passes through, or close to, the greatest number of observed points.)

Since the graph is a straight line, the law of this machine will have a form

$$P = aF + b$$

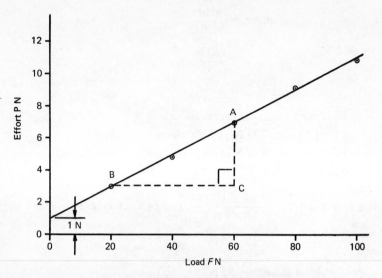

123. Effort/load graph—numerical example

The value of 'b' is given by the value of P when the load F is zero, and this is seen from the graph to be 1 N. The value of 'a' is given by the slope of the graph. Selecting two convenient points on the graph, say A and B as shown, then

$$a = \text{slope of graph} = \frac{AC}{BC}$$

$$= \frac{4 \text{ N}}{40 \text{ N}}$$

$$= \frac{1}{10}$$

Then the law of this machine is

$$\underline{\underline{P = \frac{1}{10} F + 1 \text{ N}}}$$

From the given table of values,

Load F N	20	40	60	80	100
Effort P N	3	4·9	7	9·2	10·8
Force Ratio $= \dfrac{F}{P}$	6·7	8·5	8·6	8·7	9·3

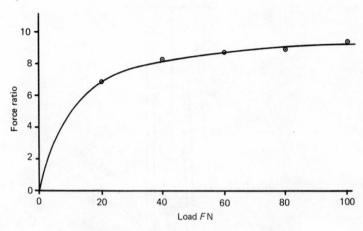

124. Force ratio/load graph—numerical example

These values are plotted in diagram 124, where, since they do not lie on a straight-line graph, a smooth curve is drawn so as to pass through or near the most points possible.

Note that since

$$\text{efficiency} = \frac{\text{force ratio}}{\text{movement ratio}}$$

a graph of efficiency against load would have the same shape as this graph of force ratio against load. (Movement ratio is constant and independent of load.)

(iv) A lifting tackle consists of two pulley blocks, the upper having three sheaves (i.e. pulleys) and the lower one having two. Find the movement ratio.

If an effort of 40 N is required to raise a load of 150 N, find the force ratio and the efficiency at this load.

Since there are 5 pulleys altogether, there will be 5 ropes supporting the load. This is illustrated in diagram 125. Then each of these ropes must be pulled up by 10 mm in order to raise the load by 10 mm, so that the velocity ratio = 5

L

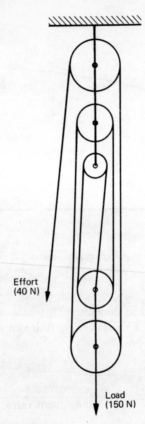

125. Five-pulley system—numerical example

$$\text{Force ratio} = \frac{\text{load}}{\text{effort}}$$

$$= \frac{150 \text{ N}}{40 \text{ N}}$$

$$= \underline{3 \cdot 75}$$

$$\text{Efficiency} = \frac{\text{force ratio}}{\text{movement ratio}}$$

$$= \frac{3 \cdot 75}{5} \text{ p.u.}$$

$$= \underline{0 \cdot 75 \text{ p.u.} \text{ or } 75\%}$$

$$\text{Movement ratio} = \underline{\underline{5}}$$
$$\text{Force ratio} = \underline{\underline{3 \cdot 75}}$$
$$\text{Efficiency} = \underline{\underline{0 \cdot 75}} \text{ p.u. or } \underline{\underline{75\%}}$$

Note that the mass of the lower pulley block will be responsible for some of the effort wasted in this case.

12.10.   The inclined plane

It has been known for a very long time that it is easier to raise a heavy weight to a certain height by pushing it up a slope until the height is reached, than it is to lift it by a direct vertical pull. It is said that the ancient Egyptians used this method to drag the heavy blocks of stone to the required heights when building the Pyramids. The slope, or inclined plane, is thus an elementary form of machine. Equilibrium conditions for the inclined plane have been considered in Section 3.13, page 80, and Section 7.8, page 208.

Consider a load m kg being moved up an inclined plane at angle θ to the horizontal by an effort P applied in a direction parallel to the plane, as shown in diagram 126.

If the load is pushed from A to B, the distance moved by the effort along its line of action is AB. The distance moved by the gravitational force on the load *along its line of action*—i.e., in a vertical direction—is BC.

Then the movement ratio

$$\text{M.R.} = \frac{\text{distance moved by effort}}{\text{distance moved by load}}$$

$$= \frac{AB}{BC}$$

$$= \frac{1}{\sin \theta} \ (= \operatorname{cosec} \theta) \qquad . \qquad . \qquad . \qquad \text{(x)}$$

The movement ratio, and hence the ideal force ratio, is, then, dependent on the angle between the plane and the horizontal. It is given mathematically by $\dfrac{1}{\sin \theta}$, or $\operatorname{cosec} \theta$, where θ is the angle of inclination to the horizontal. The actual force ratio will be less than this because of the effects of friction. The movement ratio will, however, be that given above.

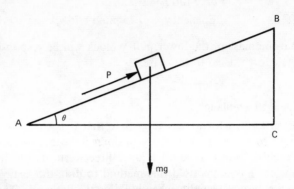

126. Inclined plane

If the effort P is applied horizontally, the distance moved by this effort along its line of action would be AC, and the movement ratio would be

$$\text{M.R.} = \frac{AC}{BC} = \frac{1}{\tan \theta} = \cot \theta \qquad . \qquad . \qquad \text{(xi)}$$

12.11. The screw-jack

A screw thread provides a means of converting a circular motion into a motion along a straight line. It is an adaptation of the basic idea of the inclined plane, as is indicated in diagram 127, which shows that the inclined edge of a triangular piece of paper becomes the line of a screw thread when the triangle is wrapped round a cylinder. This type of path round a cylinder is known as a HELIX, so that a screw thread may be said to form a 'helical' path round a cylindrical bolt.

The distance, measured parallel to the axis of the cylinder, between corresponding points on adjacent threads of a screw is known as the PITCH of the screw.

The distance moved by a nut along the axis of the screw when the screw makes one complete revolution is known as the LEAD of the screw. For a single-start thread of the type indicated in diagram 127 (b), the lead is the same as the pitch. It is possible, however, to arrange for a multi-start thread by forming other screw threads between the first, starting these at different points round the cylinder. As an example,

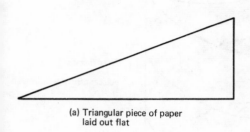

(a) Triangular piece of paper
laid out flat

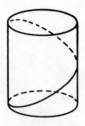

(b) Triangle in (a)
wrapped round a
cylinder.
The spiralling line
round the cylinder is
known as a 'Helix'

127. Formation of a helix

diagram 128 indicates the formation of a double-start thread, by showing two triangles wrapped round a cylinder. For multi-start threads, the
lead is equal to (number of starts) × (pitch).

A screw-jack is a device for lifting heavy loads by using the 'inclined
plane' of a screw thread, which is commonly a single-start thread for
this application. The general arrangement is illustrated in diagram 129,
although many variations are possible.

The main body of the jack is usually of cast iron, and has an internal
thread formed in a central hole into which the screw is screwed. The
effort P is applied to the end of a 'tommy' bar so that the screw is
turned. This raises the load, which is applied to a suitable pad. Arrangements are often made so that the top section of the pad can turn freely
in relation to the screw. This ensures that a lifting force is applied to the
load, without any turning force also being applied.

Let the lead of the screw be L (= pitch for a single-start thread), and
let the effort be applied to the tommy bar at a radius r. Then, since one
revolution of the screw will raise the load through a distance equal to
the lead of the screw,

distance moved by effort for one turn of screw $= 2\pi r$
distance moved by load for one turn of screw $= L$

and   movement ratio $= \dfrac{2\pi r}{L}$ . . . (xii)

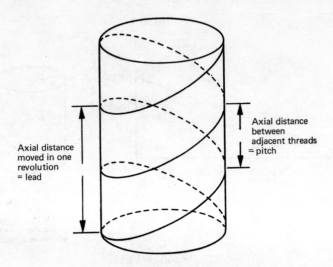

Axial distance moved in one revolution = lead

Axial distance between adjacent threads = pitch

128. Formation of double-start thread

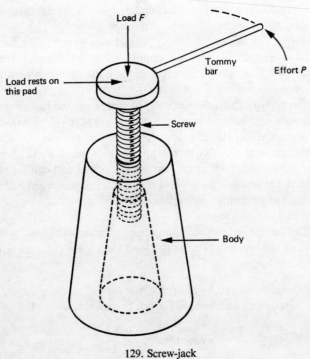

Load F

Tommy bar

Effort P

Load rests on this pad

Screw

Body

129. Screw-jack

This also gives the ideal force ratio. The effect of the mass of the screw itself, together with the effect of friction, which may be quite considerable, will mean that the actual force ratio is less than this value. The 'angle of inclination' of the thread is made less than the angle of friction between the surfaces, so that the application of a load, even in the absence of an effort, will not cause the screw to be screwed down into the body of the jack.

The screw-jack is in very widespread use in one form or another. Examples of it are the small portable jack used to raise a car for wheel changes, and the power-driven screw used on tip-up lorries.

12.12. Examples

(i) The effort is applied at a radius of 250 mm on a certain screw-jack. The screw has a lead of 12 mm. An effort of 100 N is required to raise a load of 6 kN. Find:

(a) the movement ratio
(b) the force ratio
(c) the work done on the load when it is raised by 48 mm
(d) the work done by the effort in raising the load by 48 mm
(e) the efficiency.

(a)   Movement ratio $= \dfrac{\text{distance moved by effort}}{\text{distance moved by load}}$

$$= \frac{2\pi \times 250 \text{ mm per turn of screw}}{12 \text{ mm per turn of screw}}$$

$$= \underline{131}$$

(b)   Force ratio $= \dfrac{\text{load}}{\text{effort}}$

$$= \frac{6000 \text{ N}}{100 \text{ N}}$$

$$= \underline{60}$$

(c) Work done on load in raising it by 48 mm

$$= \text{force} \times \text{distance}$$
$$= 6000 \text{ (N)} \times 0\cdot048 \text{ (m)}$$
$$= \underline{288 \text{ Nm}} \text{ (i.e. } \underline{288 \text{ J}})$$

(d) Work done by effort in raising load by 48 mm (4 turns of screw)

$$= \text{force} \times \text{distance}$$
$$= 100\,(\text{N}) \times 4 \times 2\pi \times 0.250\,(\text{m})$$
$$= 628.4\,\text{Nm (i.e. } 628.4\,\text{J)}$$

(e) $\qquad$ Efficiency $= \dfrac{\text{work done on load}}{\text{work done by effort}}$

$$= \frac{288\,\text{J}}{628.4\,\text{J}}$$

$$= 0.458 \text{ p.u. or } 45.8\,\%$$

Alternatively, efficiency $= \dfrac{\text{force ratio}}{\text{distance ratio}}$

$$= \frac{60}{131}\ \text{p.u.}$$

$$= 0.458 \text{ p.u. or } 45.8\,\%$$

Movement ratio $= \underline{131}$

Force ratio $= \underline{60}$

Work done on load by raising it by 48 mm $= \underline{288\,\text{J}}$

Work done by effort in raising load by 48 mm $= \underline{628.4\,\text{J}}$

Efficiency $= \underline{\underline{0.458 \text{ p.u. or } 45.8\,\%}}$

(ii) A spanner having an effective length of 150 mm is used to tighten a nut having a pitch of 2·5 mm (single start). What is the movement ratio?

If the mechanical efficiency is 25 % when an effort of 200 N is applied at right angles to the spanner, find the force exerted by the nut on the surface against which it is being tightened.

Assuming one complete turn for convenience (the result will be independent of the number of turns considered),

$$\text{movement ratio} = \frac{\text{distance moved by effort}}{\text{distance moved by load}}$$

$$= \frac{2\pi \times 150\,\text{mm per turn}}{2.5\,\text{mm per turn}}$$

$$= \underline{377}$$

$$\text{Efficiency} = \frac{\text{force ratio}}{\text{movement ratio}} \text{ p.u.}$$

$$\therefore \quad \frac{25}{100} \text{ p.u.} = \frac{\text{force ratio}}{377} \text{ p.u.}$$

$$\text{Force ratio} = 0 \cdot 25 \times 377$$
$$= 94 \cdot 25$$

Then, as

$$\frac{\text{load}}{\text{effort}} = \text{force ratio}$$

$$\text{load} = (\text{force ratio}) \times (\text{effort})$$
$$= 94 \cdot 25 \times 200 \text{ N}$$
$$= 18\ 850 \text{ N} = 18 \cdot 85 \text{ kN}$$

$$\text{Movement ratio} = \underline{\underline{377}}$$
$$\text{Force exerted by nut} = \underline{\underline{18 \cdot 85 \text{ kN}}}$$

Note the high movement ratio possible with a screw thread, and, despite the low efficiency in this problem, the large force exerted by the nut. Care should be taken not to over-tighten a nut, particularly one with a fine thread, since this may damage the thread, or even break the bolt.

12.13. Gear drives

A gear wheel has a number of specially-shaped projections or 'teeth' formed on its periphery. The shape of these teeth is arranged so that they may mesh with similar teeth on an adjacent gear wheel. The two wheels may then turn, successive teeth in one wheel engaging in the gaps between the teeth of the other. Ideally, the teeth should roll on each other without slipping, and with a minimum of 'back-lash'; i.e. movement of one wheel when the other wheel is held stationary. Diagram 130 indicates the general arrangement of two gear wheels in mesh.

As is evident from this diagram, the directions of rotation of two adjacent spur gear wheels in mesh must be opposite to one another.

Since the teeth mesh one at a time, the relative speeds of the two wheels will depend on the number of teeth on each wheel, which must be a whole number in each case. Suppose there are N_a teeth on gear wheel A, and N_b teeth on gear wheel B. If a total of T teeth mesh together, then

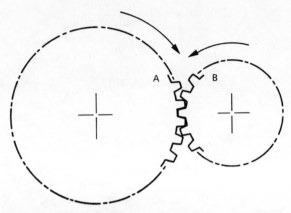

130. Gear wheels in mesh. These are known as 'spur' gears.
Other types are possible for special applications

A will have made $\dfrac{T}{N_a}$ of a revolution

and

B will have made $\dfrac{T}{N_b}$ of a revolution

For example, if $N_a = 40$ and $N_b = 20$, then after 40 teeth have meshed together, A will have made $\dfrac{40}{40}$, or 1 revolution, while B will have made $\dfrac{40}{20}$, or 2 revolutions. The gear having the smaller number of teeth revolves the faster of the two.

It follows that

$$\frac{\text{revolutions of A}}{\text{revolutions of B}} = \frac{\dfrac{T}{N_a}}{\dfrac{T}{N_b}} = \frac{N_b}{N_a}$$

Hence

$$\frac{\text{speed of A in rev/min}}{\text{speed in B in rev/min}} = \frac{\text{number of teeth in B}}{\text{number of teeth in A}} \qquad . \text{(xiii)}$$

If gear wheel A is driven by some turning effort or driving torque, and in turn drives gear wheel B against some load torque, this relationship can be expressed as a movement ratio:

$$\text{movement ratio} = \frac{\text{revolutions of driver wheel}}{\text{revolutions of driven wheel}}$$

$$= \frac{\text{number of teeth in driven wheel}}{\text{number of teeth in driver wheel}} \quad . \quad \text{(xiv)}$$

Remember that the smaller wheel makes the larger number of revolutions—a point easily checked by observation.

12.14. Use of idler gear

It was pointed out in the previous section that if two spur gear wheels are in mesh, their directions of rotation must be in opposition. If it is required that the driver and driven wheels should rotate in the same direction, an 'idler' wheel is placed between them, meshing with each. The function of this wheel is merely to reverse the direction of rotation of the driven wheel, and it does not affect the movement ratio between the driver and driven wheels. The arrangement is sketched in diagram 131. The idler wheel, C, reverses the direction of rotation of the driven wheel B, which now revolves in the same direction as driver wheel A. Suppose there are N_a, N_b, N_c teeth on wheels A, B and C respectively. Then

$$\frac{\text{revolutions of A}}{\text{revolutions of C}} = \frac{N_c}{N_a} \text{ from equation (xiii)}$$

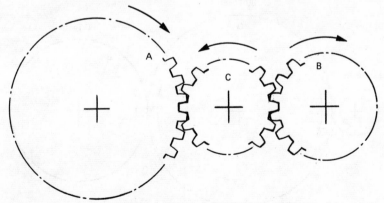

131. Use of idler wheel. The idler wheel, C, reverses the direction of rotation of the driven wheel B, which now revolves in the same direction as driver wheel A

and

$$\frac{\text{revolutions of C}}{\text{revolutions of B}} = \frac{N_b}{N_c}$$

In other words,

$$\frac{\text{revolutions of A}}{\text{revolutions of C}} \times \frac{\text{revolutions of C}}{\text{revolutions of B}} = \frac{N_c}{N_a} \times \frac{N_b}{N_c}$$

or

$$\frac{\text{revolutions of A}}{\text{revolutions of B}} = \frac{N_b}{N_a}$$

This would be the case without the idler wheel being present. The only function of the idler wheel is to reverse the direction of rotation of the driven wheel.

12.15. Examples

(i) Three spur gear wheels P, Q and R are on parallel shafts. P meshes with Q, and Q meshes with R. The number of teeth on the wheels are: P, 20; Q, 80; R, 60. Find the speeds of Q and R when P rotates at 120 rev/min. Show that the speed of gear R is independent of the number of teeth on gear Q. Diagram 132 shows a sketch of the layout of these gears.

$$\frac{\text{Speed of Q}}{\text{Speed of P}} = \frac{\text{teeth on P}}{\text{teeth on Q}}$$

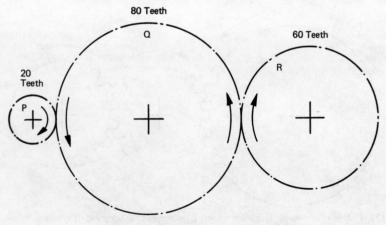

132. Simple gear train—numerical example

$$\therefore \text{ speed of Q } = 120 \times \frac{20}{80} \text{ rev/min}$$

$$= 30 \text{ rev/min}$$

$$\frac{\text{Speed of R}}{\text{Speed of Q}} = \frac{\text{teeth on Q}}{\text{teeth on R}}$$

$$\therefore \text{ speed of R } = 30 \times \frac{80}{60} \text{ rev/min}$$

$$= 40 \text{ rev/min}$$

Suppose there were N teeth on Q. Then

$$\text{speed of Q } = 120 \times \frac{20}{N} \text{ rev/min}$$

$$= \frac{2400}{N} \text{ rev/min}$$

$$\text{speed of R } = \frac{2400}{N} \times \frac{N}{60} \text{ rev/min}$$

$$= 40 \text{ rev/min}$$

so that the result is unaffected by the value of N

$$\text{Speed of Q } = 30 \text{ rev/min}$$

$$\text{Speed of R } = 40 \text{ rev/min}$$

Speed of R is unaffected by number of teeth on Q

(ii) The length of the handle of a single-geared winch is 300 mm, and the diameter of the drum is 150 mm. A spur gear having 25 teeth is fastened to the same spindle as the handle, and meshes with a gear having 100 teeth, which is fastened to the drum. Find the movement ratio of the winch. If the winch has an efficiency of 75% at a load of 3 kN, what effort must be applied at right angles to the handle to lift this load?

The general arrangement of the winch is shown in diagram 133.

Suppose the drum makes one complete revolution, so that the distance moved by the load is $\pi \times 150$ mm.

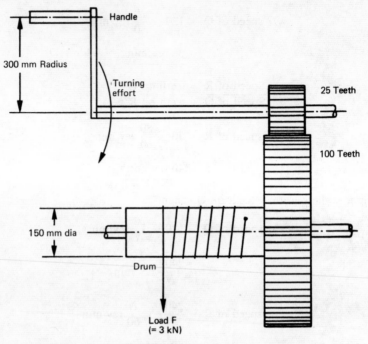

133. Single-geared winch—numerical example

$$\frac{\text{Revolutions of handle}}{\text{Revolutions of drum}} = \frac{\text{teeth on drum gear}}{\text{teeth on handle gear}}$$

$$\therefore \text{ revolutions of handle} = \frac{100}{25} \times 1$$

$$= \underline{4}$$

During each revolution, the handle moves through a circle of circumference $2\pi \times 300$ mm.

$$\therefore \text{ total distance moved}$$
$$\text{by handle (effort)} = 4 \times 2\pi \times 300 \text{ mm}$$
$$= 2400\pi \text{ mm}$$

Then

$$\text{movement ratio} = \frac{\text{distance moved by effort}}{\text{distance moved by load}}$$

$$= \frac{2400\pi \text{ mm}}{150\pi \text{ mm}}$$

$$= \underline{16}$$

$$\frac{\text{Force ratio}}{\text{Movement ratio}} = \text{efficiency p.u.} = 0.75 \text{ p.u.}$$

$$\therefore \text{ force ratio} = 0.75 \times \text{movement ratio}$$
$$= 0.75 \times 16$$
$$= 12$$

$$\therefore \frac{\text{load}}{\text{effort}} = 12$$

$$\text{Effort} = \frac{\text{load}}{12}$$

$$= \frac{3000}{12} \text{ N}$$

$$= \underline{250 \text{ N}}$$

$$\text{Movement ratio of winch} = \underline{\underline{16}}$$
$$\text{Effort required to lift 3 kN load} = \underline{\underline{250 \text{ N}}}$$

(iii) The gearing of a machine tool is shown in diagram 134. The motor shaft is connected to A, and rotates at 975 rev/min. Gear wheels B and C, D and E are fixed to the same parallel shafts, and rotate together. The final gear wheel F is fixed to the output shaft G. Find the speed of the output shaft if the number of teeth on each wheel is as given in the following table:

Gear	A	B	C	D	E	F
No. of teeth	20	50	25	75	26	65

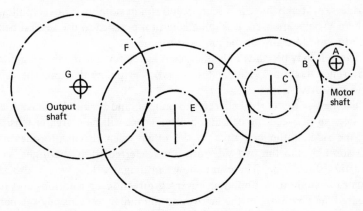

134. Gear train of machine tool—numerical example

$$\frac{\text{Speed of B}}{\text{Speed of A}} = \frac{\text{teeth on A}}{\text{teeth on B}}$$

$$\text{Speed of B} = 975 \times \frac{20}{50} \text{ rev/min} = \text{speed of C}$$

$$\text{Speed of D} = \text{speed of C} \times \frac{\text{teeth on C}}{\text{teeth on D}}$$

$$= 975 \times \frac{20}{50} \times \frac{25}{75} \text{ rev/min} = \text{speed of E}$$

$$\text{Speed of F} = \text{speed of E} \times \frac{\text{teeth on E}}{\text{teeth on F}}$$

$$= 975 \times \frac{20}{50} \times \frac{25}{75} \times \frac{26}{65} \text{ rev/min} = \text{speed of G}$$

$$\text{Speed of G} = 975 \times \frac{20}{50} \times \frac{25}{75} \times \frac{26}{65} \text{ rev/min}$$

$$= 52 \text{ rev/min}$$

$$\text{Speed of output shaft} = 52 \text{ rev/min}$$

12.16   Belt drives

Driving torque may be transmitted between two parallel shafts by means of a belt passed between suitable pulleys fixed to each shaft. The belt may be a simple flat one passing over flat or slightly domed pulley surfaces, or it may have a V-section and run in suitably grooved pulleys. Where V-belts are used, it is quite common practice to use several belts side by side to transmit the required torque.

The belt may be made of leather, canvas-reinforced rubber, or similar material. Diagram 135 indicates the types of pulley that may be used with belt drives.

The belt is tightened between the pulleys, and torque is transmitted by friction between the belt and pulley. There will be a greater tension in one side of the belt than in the other when driving torques are transmitted, and the two sides are often referred to as the 'tight' side and the 'slack' side. These are shown in diagram 136, which also indicates a method of obtaining reversed direction of rotation, and increased 'angle of lap' of the belt round the pulley, by crossing the belt. This method of crossed belts is satisfactory only with flat belts.

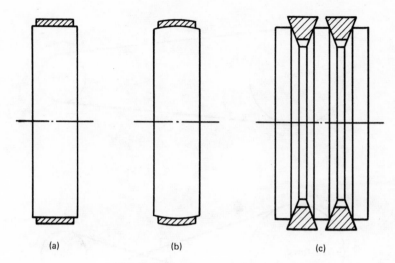

135. Pulley outlines for belt drives

(a) Flat pulley for flat belt drives
(b) Domed pulley for flat belt drives. (Belt tends to 'ride up' to top of dome)
(c) V-pulley for V-belt drives. (Belt should not touch bottom of grooves)

Belts do not give a 'positive' drive in the sense that gears do. There will be some load at which the belts will slip, and in fact some slip is usually present, particularly if the initial belt tension is incorrectly adjusted. A belt drive, however, is the simplest practical way of transmitting torque between parallel shafts some distance away from each other.

Suppose the diameter of the driver pulley A is d_a and the diameter of the driven pulley B is d_b. Then, on the assumption that there is no slip, if the driver pulley makes n_a revolutions, a total length of belt equal to $n_a \times$ (circumference of A), or $n_a \times \pi d_a$, passes round both pulleys. The number of revolutions of B is then given by

$$\text{revolutions of B} = \frac{\text{length of belt passed}}{\text{circumference of B}}$$

or

$$n_b = \frac{n_a \times \pi d_a}{\pi d_b}$$

or

$$\frac{n_b}{n_a} = \frac{d_a}{d_b}$$

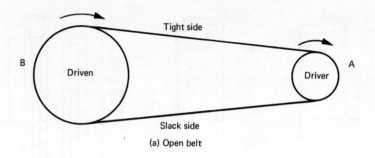

(a) Open belt

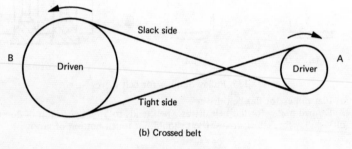

(b) Crossed belt

136. Belt drives

In other words,

$$\frac{\text{revolutions of B}}{\text{revolutions of A}} = \frac{\text{diameter of A}}{\text{diameter of B}}$$

or

$$\frac{\text{speed of B}}{\text{speed of A}} = \frac{\text{diameter of A}}{\text{diameter of B}} \qquad . \qquad . \qquad . \qquad \text{(xv)}$$

This result can be compared with that for a gear drive.

A chain drive is similar to a belt drive, except that the chain passes over suitably-shaped teeth or 'sprockets' on the chain wheels. This ensures that no slip takes place, so that a chain gives a positive drive. A relationship similar to that for belt drives exists between the speeds of the chain wheels. Since the number of sprockets on the wheel is directly proportional to the diameter of the wheel, this relationship can also be written as

$$\frac{\text{speed of B}}{\text{speed of A}} = \frac{\text{number of sprockets on A}}{\text{number of sprockets on B}} \qquad \text{(xvi)}$$

A crossed drive is not practical with a chain. Perhaps the most common examples of chain drives are those used for most pedal- and motor-cycles.

The torque transmitted by a belt or chain drive is determined by the tensions in the tight and slack sides. If the radius of the pulley or chain wheel is r and the tension in the tight side is T_1, while that in the slack side is T_2, the torque transmitted is $(T_1 - T_2)r$. The power transmitted will be given by

power = torque × angular velocity (rad/s) (see Section 11.2, page 291)

If the pulley rotates at n rev/min,

$$\text{angular velocity } \omega = \frac{2\pi n}{60} \text{ rad/s}$$

(see Section 10.3, page 277)

$$\therefore \text{ power (W)} = \text{torque (Nm)} \times \frac{2\pi n}{60} \text{ (rad/s)}$$

$$\text{power transmitted} = (T_1 - T_2)r \cdot \frac{2\pi n}{60} \text{ W} \qquad . \qquad . \qquad \text{(xvii)}$$

where T_1 and T_2 are tensions in N
$\quad r$ is pulley radius in m
$\quad n$ is pulley speed in rev/min

Since $\qquad r \cdot 2\pi = $ circumference of pulley (m)

$$\frac{r \cdot 2\pi n}{60} = \text{linear speed at circumference of pulley (m/s)}$$

$$= \text{belt speed (m/s)}$$

and the above expression can also be written as

$$\text{power transmitted} = (T_1 - T_2) \times \text{belt speed in m/s W} \qquad \text{(xviii)}$$

These expressions assume that there is no belt slip. In practice, the transmitted power would be slightly less than this.

12.17 Speed cones

A belt drive between pulleys of different diameters gives a convenient method of speed changing which is widely used. Stepped pulleys are fixed on to parallel shafts, as shown in diagram 137, so that sections of each pulley have different diameters. These are arranged so that the sum of the diameters of sections that are opposite to each other on the two shafts is constant. This means that the same belt length is required to link each pair of sections, and one belt can be moved to occupy various positions on the pulleys, and can thus give various speed ratios between the shafts. Such an arrangement is often called a pair of 'speed cones'.

Speed cones may be used on machine tools such as lathes or drills in order to give different shaft speeds for a constant motor speed. Although such tools now usually have gear-boxes to provide different speed ratios, the use of speed cones has not been entirely discontinued. The fact that a belt will slip if the driven shaft becomes 'locked' may avoid damage to equipment in some circumstances.

12.18. Examples

(i) Pulley A drives pulley B by means of a belt. The diameter of A is 150 mm and its speed is 200 rev/min. What is the diameter of B if its speed is 50 rev/min? What is the belt speed in m/s?

$$\frac{\text{Speed of A}}{\text{Speed of B}} = \frac{\text{diameter of B}}{\text{diameter of A}}$$

$$\therefore \quad \frac{200}{50} = \frac{\text{diameter of B}}{150 \text{ mm}}$$

$$\therefore \quad \text{diameter of B} = 150 \times \frac{200}{50} \text{ mm}$$

$$= 600 \text{ mm}$$

$$\text{Belt speed} = \text{circumferential speed of pulleys}$$
$$= (\text{circumference}) \times (\text{rotational speed})$$
$$= (\pi \times 150 \text{ mm}) \times (200 \text{ rev/min})$$

$$= \pi \times 150 \text{ mm} \times \left(\frac{1 \text{ m}}{1000 \text{ mm}}\right) \times \left(200 \frac{\text{rev}}{\text{min}}\right)\left(\frac{1 \text{ min}}{60 \text{ s}}\right)$$

$$= \frac{30\ 000\ \pi}{1000 \times 60} \text{ m/s}$$

$$= 1 \cdot 57 \text{ m/s}$$

This result has been calculated for pulley A. As a check, the same result must be obtained for pulley B, since slip is neglected.

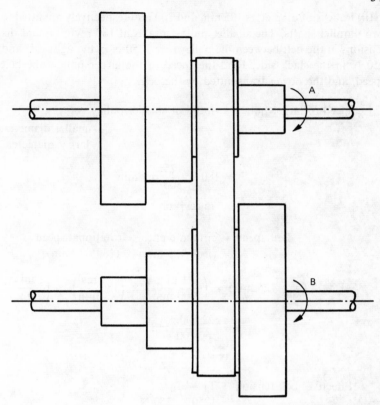

137. Speed cones.

The ratio of the speeds of the shafts A and B may be varied in steps by moving the belt to different pairs of sections of the speed cones.

The sum of the diameters of any pair of sections is constant so that the same belt can be used for any pair

$$\text{Belt speed} = (\pi \times 600 \ \cancel{mm}) \times \left(\frac{1 \ m}{1000 \ \cancel{mm}}\right) \times \left(50 \ \frac{rev}{\cancel{min}}\right) \left(\frac{1 \ \cancel{min}}{60 \ s}\right)$$

$$= \frac{30\,000\pi}{1000 \times 60} \ m/s$$

$$\underline{1 \cdot 57 \ m/s}$$

Diameter of pulley B = $\underline{600 \ mm}$
Belt speed = $\underline{\underline{1 \cdot 57 \ m/s}}$

(ii) Pulleys of diameters 125 mm and 300 mm respectively are fitted to two parallel shafts. The smaller pulley rotates at 180 rev/min, and the tensions in the belt between the pulleys are 1250 N in the tight side and 250 N in the slack side. Find the speed of the larger pulley, the belt speed, and the power transmitted by the belt.

Speed of larger pulley = speed of smaller pulley ×

$$\frac{\text{smaller diameter}}{\text{larger diameter}}$$

$$= 180 \times \frac{125}{300} \text{ rev/min}$$

$$= \underline{75 \text{ rev/min}}$$

Belt speed = circumference × rotational speed
$$= (\pi \times 125 \text{ mm}) \times (180 \text{ rev/min})$$

$$= (\pi \times 125 \text{ mm}) \times \left(\frac{1 \text{ m}}{1000 \text{ mm}}\right) \times \left(180 \frac{\text{rev}}{\text{min}}\right) \times \left(\frac{1 \text{ min}}{60 \text{ s}}\right)$$

$$= \frac{22\ 500\pi}{60\ 000} \text{ m/s}$$

$$= \underline{1 \cdot 18 \text{ m/s}}$$

'Effective' belt tension = $T_1 - T_2$
$$= 1250 - 250 \text{ N}$$
$$= 1000 \text{ N}$$

Effective torque
(smaller pulley) $= 1000 \text{ (N)} \times 62 \cdot 5 \text{ (mm)} \times \left(\frac{1 \text{ m}}{1000 \text{ mm}}\right)$

$$= 62 \cdot 5 \text{ Nm}$$

Power transmitted $= \frac{2\pi \, nT}{60} \text{ W}$

$$= \frac{2\pi \times 180 \times 62 \cdot 5}{60} \text{ W}$$

$$= 1180 \text{ W} = \underline{1 \cdot 18 \text{ kW}}$$

As a check, the same power should be given by the effective torque and speed of the larger pulley.

Effective torque

$$\text{(larger pulley)} = 1000 \times 150 \times \frac{1}{1000} \text{ Nm}$$

$$= 150 \text{ Nm}$$

$$\text{Power transmitted} = \frac{2\pi \times 75 \times 150}{60} \text{ W}$$

$$= 1\cdot18 \text{ kW}$$

The same result is also obtainable from the effective belt tension and speed (equation (xviii)):

$$\text{Power transmitted} = (T_1 - T_2)(N) \times \text{belt speed (m/s) W}$$
$$= 1000 \times 1\cdot18 \text{ W}$$
$$= 1\cdot18 \text{ kW as before}$$
$$\text{Speed of larger pulley} = 75 \text{ rev/min}$$
$$\text{Belt speed} = 1\cdot18 \text{ m/s}$$
$$\text{Power transmitted} = 1\cdot18 \text{ kW}$$

Note: Although calculations have been made to three significant figures, the answers given are likely to be high. This is due to the likely accuracy of the data, and the fact that the calculations have neglected any belt slip.

(iii) Each of a pair of speed cones has four 'steps' of diameters 300 mm, 250 mm, 200 mm and 150 mm. If the driving shaft has a constant speed of 240 rev/min, find all the speeds obtainable at the driven shaft.

Diagram 138 gives a sketch of the arrangement.

Top speed of driven shaft occurs when the belt links the 300 mm diameter pulley on A with the 150 mm diameter pulley on B.

$$\text{Top speed of B} = \text{speed of A} \times \frac{\text{diameter of A}}{\text{diameter of B}}$$

$$= 240 \times \frac{300}{150} \text{ rev/min}$$

$$= 480 \text{ rev/min}$$

Second speed of B (belt round 250 mm on A and 200 mm on B) $= 240 \times \dfrac{250}{200}$ rev/min

$$= 300 \text{ rev/min}$$

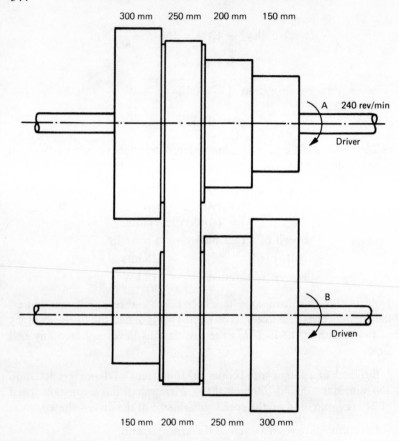

138. Speed cones—numerical example

Third speed of B (belt round 200 mm
  on A and 250 mm on B) $= 240 \times \dfrac{200}{250}$ rev/min

$= \underline{192 \text{ rev/min}}$

Lowest speed of B (belt round 150 mm
  on A and 300 mm on B) $= 240 \times \dfrac{150}{300}$ rev/min

$= \underline{120 \text{ rev/min}}$

Speeds of driven shaft could be <u>480, 300, 192 or 120 rev/min</u>

CHAPTER SUMMARY

$$\text{Force ratio} = \frac{\text{load}}{\text{effort}}$$

$$\text{Movement ratio} = \frac{\text{distance moved by effort}}{\text{distance moved by load}}$$

$$\text{Efficiency} = \frac{\text{useful output}}{\text{input}} \text{ p.u.}$$

$$= \frac{\text{force ratio}}{\text{movement ratio}} \text{ p.u.}$$

$$= \frac{\text{ideal effort}}{\text{actual effort}} \text{ p.u.}$$

The law of a simple machine has the form $P = aF + b$ where P = effort, F = load and a and b are constants.

$$\text{M.R. of lever} = \frac{\text{perpendicular distance between effort and fulcrum}}{\text{perpendicular distance between load and fulcrum}}$$

$$\text{M.R. of wheel and axle} = \frac{\text{radius of wheel}}{\text{radius of axle}}$$

M.R. of wheel and differential axle

$$= \frac{2 \times \text{radius of wheel}}{(\text{radius of larger axle section}) - (\text{radius of smaller axle section})}$$

M.R. of continuous-string
  pulley system = number of strings supporting load (discounting the string leading directly to the effort)
         = number of pulleys

M.R. of inclined plane, at angle θ to horizontal

  (i) with effort parallel to the plane,

$$\text{M.R.} = \operatorname{cosec} \theta \left(= \frac{1}{\sin \theta} \right)$$

  (ii) with effort horizontal

$$\text{M.R.} = \cot \theta \left(= \frac{1}{\tan \theta} \right)$$

$$\text{M.R. of screw-jack} = \frac{2\pi \times (\text{radius at which effort is applied})}{\text{lead of screw}}$$

$$\text{M.R. of gear drive} = \frac{\text{turns of driver wheel}}{\text{turns of driven wheel}}$$

$$= \frac{\text{teeth on driven wheel}}{\text{teeth on driver wheel}}$$

$$\frac{\text{Speed of gear A}}{\text{Speed of gear B}} = \frac{\text{teeth on B}}{\text{teeth on A}}$$

$$\text{M.R. of belt drive} = \frac{\text{diameter of driven pulley}}{\text{diameter of driver pulley}}$$

$$\frac{\text{Speed of pulley A}}{\text{Speed of pulley B}} = \frac{\text{diameter of B}}{\text{diameter of A}}$$

Power transmitted by a belt having tensions T_1 N and T_2 N on tight and slack sides respectively is

$$\text{power} = (T_1 - T_2) \times \text{belt speed in m/s W}$$
$$\text{Belt speed} = \text{circumferential speed of pulley (neglecting slip)}$$

$$= \frac{2\pi n}{60} \times \text{radius of pulley}$$

QUESTIONS

1. A machine is in the form of a wheel, of 1·8 m diameter, and an axle of 150 mm diameter. It is used to haul a grab across a horizontal surface. If the grab and contents have a mass of 1 tonne and the coefficient of fraction between it and the ground is 0·5, find the force necessary to move the grab, applied tangentially at the circumference of the wheel. Assume that the efficiency of the machine is 70%.

2. A machine is driven through a gear train which is shown in the diagram. If the driving and driven spindles are the same size, calculate the movement ratio of the machine.

If the values of effort required to overcome various loads are as shown in the table, plot a graph of efficiency against load.

Load (kN)	1	1·5	2	2·5	3	3·5	4
Effort (N)	155	210	262	312	360	410	465

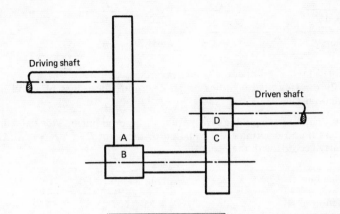

Wheel	No. of teeth
A	80
B	10
C	20
D	16

3. In a test on a screw-jack the following results were obtained:

Load F N	25	50	75	100	125	150
Effort E N	2·25	3·5	4·75	6	7·2	8·5

The diameter of the pulley at which the effort E was applied was 200 mm; the pitch of the screw was 10 mm.

(a) Plot the load-effort graph on a base of load and hence determine the law of the machine.

(b) Determine the load that could be raised by an effort of 12·5 N, and calculate the efficiency of the screw-jack at this load.

4. Explain, clearly, what is meant by the terms 'movement ratio' and 'force ratio'.

A motor running at 1200 rev/min drives a crane through gearing as follows:

On the motor shaft there is a pinion with 30 teeth geared with a wheel having 100 teeth on an intermediate shaft B. A pinion with 20 teeth on shaft B gears with a second wheel having 120 teeth on a shaft C. Shaft C carries a drum 225 mm diameter on which is coiled a rope from which the load hangs.

Sketch the arrangement. Determine the speed in m/s at which the load is rising.

5. The results of a test on a block and tackle are given in the table below:

Load F N	300	750	1000	1500	2000
Effort P N	35	65	85	115	145

Plot values of F horizontally and P vertically.

By drawing a straight-line graph determine the values of a and b in the equation $P = aF + b$.

6. The following table gives results of an experiment. Plot the load/effort diagram and determine the equation of the form $E = mF + c$ which most nearly accords with the results.

F (load in N)	35	70	105	140	175	210	245	280
E (effort in N)	15	32·5	47·5	62·5	80	93·75	110	125

7. The following results were obtained from an experiment on a set of pulley blocks:

Load F N	30	60	125	180	235	275
Effort E N	24	32	48	62	76	86

Show by plotting a graph that these values of F and E obey a law of the form $E = aF + b$.

Use your graph to find the values of a and b.

8. (a) In a single-purchase winch, the handle is 375 mm long, and the pinion has 20 teeth gearing with a wheel of 80 teeth fixed to a drum of 300 mm diameter. Sketch the arrangement and calculate the movement ratio.

(b) If a load of 490 N is slowly raised by an effort of 75 N,

 (i) calculate the force ratio,

(ii) obtain the efficiency of the machine.

9. (a) Define (i) movement ratio, (ii) force ratio, (iii) efficiency, as applied to a lifting machine.

(b) Make either (i) a line diagram of the arrangement of a system of pulley blocks having a movement ratio of 4, or (ii) a sketch of a simple wheel and axle, stating clearly how the movement ratio is obtained.

10. Give reasons why the efficiency of a machine is never 100%.

A screw-jack has a pitch of 12 mm. The load to be lifted is 20 kN. If the efficiency of the machine is 30% and the length of the arm is 450 mm calculate the effort required.

11. Define movement ratio as applied to a machine. A rope pulley system has a block of three pulleys at the top and a block of two pulleys at the bottom. An effort of 82·5 N raises a load of 200 N. Determine the efficiency of the pulley system. Draw a line diagram illustrating how the pulleys would be arranged.

12. A wheel and differential axle has the following dimensions: effort wheel 300 mm diameter, major axle 150 mm diameter, minor axle 70 mm diameter. To raise a load of 450 N an effort of 75 N is required. Calculate the force ratio and efficiency of the machine at this load.

13. The lead of the screw thread in a lifting jack is 10 mm and the effective length of the handle is 250 mm. What force applied at the end of the handle will be required to raise a load of 10 kN if the efficiency of the jack is 25%? How much work is wasted during one revolution of the handle?

14. 4·5 kW is transmitted by means of a belt and pulleys from a shaft A to shaft B. Shaft A runs at 540 rev/min and the pulley on it is 250 mm diameter. The pulley on shaft B is 450 mm diameter. If the tension in the tight side of the belt is 1·5 kN, calculate the tension in the slack side and the speed of shaft B.

15. A water pump is driven by an electric motor through the medium of a belt, the pulley on the pump shaft being 450 mm diameter. The overall efficiency of the pump is 60% at a speed of 600 rev/min when delivering 15 litres of water per second against a head of 36 m. If the ratio of the belt tensions is 2·2 to 1, find the width of the belt required to transmit the power to the pump. Take the allowable belt tension as 14 N/mm width.

16. Describe briefly an experiment to determine the force ratio and movement ratio of a simple winch.

A small winch has a movement ratio of 40, and is capable of raising loads of 7·5 kN and 22·5 kN with efforts of 400 N and 850 N respectively. Determine the relationship of the load, F, to the effort, P, and express it in the form $P = aF + b$. Calculate the effort, the force ratio and efficiency when the load lifted is 17·5 kN.

17. The following figures are extracted from the results of an experiment on a system of pulley blocks. When the load was 100 N, the effort was 23 N; and when the load was 235 N, the effort was 50 N. The movement ratio of the machine was 10.

Determine the efficiency of the machine when raising a load of 500 N.

18. A simple screw-jack has a single-thread screw of 12 mm lead, turned by applying a force tangentially through a bar at a radius of 500 mm. The equation of the machine is $P = 0·005\ 4\ F + 60$, where P is the effort needed to raise a load F, both in newtons. Determine the efficiency of the jack when it is lifting (a) 10 kN, (b) 5 kN.

Account for the difference between the two values.

19. State the meaning of the terms 'force ratio', 'movement ratio' and 'efficiency' as applied to a simple lifting machine.

A small winch has a movement ratio of 50, and is capable of raising loads of 10 kN and 30 kN with efforts of 450 N and 1·05 kN respectively.

(a) Find the relationship between the effort and the load.

(b) Calculate the effort, the force ratio and the efficiency when the load lifted is 22·5 kN.

20. Indicate by sketches how a belt produces:

(a) rotation in the same direction as the driving pulley,

(b) rotation in the opposite direction to the driving pulley.

A belt drive is required to transmit 15 kW from a shaft running at 100 rev/min to one running at 200 rev/min. Find the tensions in the tight and slack sides of the belt assuming the smaller pulley to be 600 mm diameter and the ratio of the tensions is to be $2\frac{1}{2}$ to 1. Also determine the width of the belt required if the allowable working tension is 24 N/mm width.

21. Describe how to carry out an experiment to show how force ratio, effort and efficiency vary with load for a given machine. Assume the machine is a lifting machine with a movement ratio of 50 and that a load of 750 N requires an effort of 35 N to raise it at a steady speed. Sketch a machine to give this movement ratio and give a specimen set of calculations based on these figures in your description.

22. (a) A flat belt drives a pulley 450 mm diameter at 400 rev/min and the maximum tension on the driving side is three times that on the slack side. Calculate the width of belt required if it transmits 15 kW and the belt strength is 10 N/mm of width.

(b) The pulley drives a 50 mm diameter shaft by means of a key, 12 mm wide and 75 mm effective length. Calculate the shear stress in the key.

23. In a wheel and differential axle, the diameter of the effort wheel is 300 mm and the axle diameters are 125 mm and 100 mm. Calculate the movement ratio. For this machine it was found that an effort of 3 N was required to raise a load of 48 N and an effort of 5 N was required to raise a load of 100 N. Determine the effort at a load of 80 N, and the efficiency at this load.

24. During an experiment on a double-purchase winch, the following values of efforts and loads were recorded:

Effort (N)	6·25	9·85	13·4	16·95	20·5
Load (N)	250	500	750	1000	1250

The effort is applied at the end of a handle 375 mm long, the pinions have 15 and 20 teeth, the wheels 75 and 80 teeth. The effective diameter of the barrel is 150 mm. Draw a graph of effort against load and determine (a) the law of the machine, (b) the friction effort at 750 N load, (c) the efficiency at 1000 N load.

25. A wheel and differential axle has an effort wheel of 250 mm diameter and the larger of the load drums is 125 mm diameter. It is required that an effort of 100 N shall raise a load of 900 N with an efficiency of 80%. Calculate the diameter of the smaller load drum.

26. A simple lifting machine has a movement ratio of 40. It is found that an effort of 32·5 N is required to raise a load of 500 N, and an effort of 112·5 N is required to raise a load of 2·5 kN. Determine:

(a) the law of the machine,
(b) the efficiency when the load is 1·25 kN.

13. Atomic Structure

13.1. Atoms

As long ago as 400 B.C., the Greek philosopher Democritus put forward the theory that all substances are built up from a number of basic elements, and that these elements are themselves built up from different kinds of basic units. He called these units 'atoms', from a word meaning something that cannot be divided. Although it was many centuries before this idea was taken up again and developed, it is astonishing how near Democritus was to modern ideas on this subject. Until the late nineteenth century, atoms were considered to be complete units which could not be divided; that is, they were considered to be the fundamental particles of which the various elements are built. The differing properties of the elements were thought to be the result of the different natures of these fundamental particles. Until recently, only 92 different elements had been discovered, and the very large range of substances commonly encountered are built up from these or from combinations of them. More recent work has disclosed the existence of several additional elements, but these are usually found to be unstable, and to change spontaneously into other elements among the 92 already mentioned.

In the light of discoveries made since the late nineteenth century, it is now known that the atom is not a fundamental particle, but that it can be divided, and a simplified outline of present theory is discussed here. This is of importance in that it can be used as a basis for the understanding of the general behaviour of materials. Atoms are now known to be themselves composed of a number of particles, which, in the present state of knowledge, are taken to be fundamental particles. These particles will be discussed in later sections of this chapter, together with a brief outline of the way in which they go together to make up an atom. It must be stated, however, that this represents a theory which has been evolved to fit in with observed experimental results. No one has ever seen, or can ever see, an atom—it is much too small—and on this incredibly small scale many 'natural' laws which are found to be true of the behaviour of materials in bulk can no longer be applied. A tremendous amount of research work has been carried out into the structure of the atom, and such work is continuing. No hard-and-fast statements can be made with confidence, although the present basic theory seems very likely to remain acceptable for a long time. The acid test of any theory is its ability to explain experimentally observed facts, and the simplified theory of atomic structure given here does enable many such facts to be explained.

It has been stated that an atom is extremely small. Any attempt to give an impression of its size usually ends up in unimaginably large numbers or equally unimaginable small ones. For example, it can be said that there are about a million million million atoms in a grain of fine table salt—which has roughly the same significance as saying that an atom is extremely small! On the atomic scale, 'size' in the normally understood sense has no real meaning, and the 'size' of an atom is determined by how close one atom can approach another, and not by the amount of 'stuff' which it contains, or the amount of space which it occupies to the exclusion of something else. In terms of space an atom, small as it is, is thought to be nearly all empty space. The 'limits of approachability' between one atom and another are set by the forces exerted by the particles of which the atoms are composed. These particles will first be considered separately, in the next few sections.

13.2. The electron

The existence of the electron as a fundamental particle was discovered in 1897 by the English physicist J. J. Thomson. Although modern theory tends to show that such a picture is not always correct, it will be sufficient for the present purpose if the electron is visualized as a sort of minute billiard ball, perhaps a little fuzzy round the edges. The electron has a definite mass, although it is so tiny that the figures are difficult to appreciate. The mass of an electron is about 9×10^{-22} g, which is about $\frac{1}{2000}$th of the mass of a complete hydrogen atom (the smallest atom known). These figures are only approximate, and the mass of an electron moving at very high speeds appears to change.

One of the important properties of an electron is that it possesses a negative electric charge. This point is discussed again in Chapter 16, page 437, but it can be said here that it seems at present as if the amount of the electric charge on an electron is the smallest unit of charge obtainable. A value for the electron charge will be given on page 438, when suitable units of measurement have been introduced.

The methods used to measure the values of mass and charge for an

M

electron depend on effects which the student will learn about later, and so it would be pointless to describe these methods here. However, it may be mentioned that a stream of electrons can be obtained fairly readily by heating a suitable type of metal in suitable surroundings. The operation of a television picture tube depends on the production of such an electron beam.

13.3. The proton

The proton was discovered by Rutherford in 1919, and for present purposes it also may be visualized as a sort of extremely small billiard ball. Although it is so small, its mass is still many times that of the electron, being about 1.6×10^{-24} g (roughly 2000 times as heavy as an electron).

The proton is found to possess a positive electric charge, whose value is numerically the same as the negative charge on the electron. A more complete discussion concerning electric charges and their effects is given in Chapter 16, page 436. It will be sufficient for the present to state that there seem to be two different kinds of electric charge, one kind called positive, and the other negative. For some reason not really understood, a positive charge and a negative charge attract one another, or, to put it another way, 'a force of attraction exists between charges of opposite sign'. It is also found that two positive charges repel one another, and so do two negative charges. In other words, 'a force of repulsion exists between charges of the same sign'. These forces were known long before the electron and proton were discovered, and they help to explain many practical effects.

It should be said that a stream of protons is very much more difficult to obtain than the stream of electrons mentioned earlier.

13.4. The neutron

The neutron was discovered by Chadwick in 1932. Its mass is very nearly the same as that of the proton, but it carries no electric charge at all. Its name is derived from the word 'neutral', meaning in this case neither positive nor negative.

It is mentioned here only as a 'building brick' of an atom, although, because of its relatively large mass and lack of electric charge, to the atomic research worker it is an extremely important particle. (The words 'relatively large mass' must be taken as meaning 'relative to the electron or many other particles'. It does, after all, have a mass of less than $1·7 \times 10^{-24}$ g.)

Beams of neutrons are used in atomic research, but can only be produced with expensive and complex equipment.

13.5. Other particles

The idea of atomic structure can be simply expressed in terms of the three particles already mentioned; i.e. the electron, proton and neutron. However, several other particles have been discovered, and there are probably others still to be discovered. The additional particles already detected include for example the 'positron', which is a sort of positive electron; the 'anti-proton', which is a sort of negative proton; and many others. These are all of concern to atomic physicists, but at present they do not really seriously modify the overall picture of the atom given here. Their discovery does show, however, that the present state of knowledge concerning the atom is very far from being complete and final.

13.6. Atomic structure

The general way in which electrons, protons and neutrons are assembled is the same in every atom. There is a central core called the NUCLEUS, which is surrounded by a 'cloud' of electrons. The nucleus contains protons and neutrons (and other particles) which appear to be welded together into a compact mass. Since the nucleus contains positively-charged protons and neutral neutrons, the nucleus as a whole is positively charged. The student may ask how the nucleus keeps together as one compact mass when it contains positive charges which will repel one another. An elaborate theory has been developed to explain this apparently contradictory state of affairs. Stated simply, the nucleus is thought to be held together by binding forces. These are considered to be very powerful short-range forces that are evident only on the atomic scale of dimensions. Such forces diminish very rapidly with increasing distance, and so only act within the confines of the nucleus itself. Once one or more protons are taken away from the nucleus, out of range of these binding forces, they will escape, and the nucleus will divide.

Since a complete atom taken by itself appears to have no electric charge, even though many of the particles involved in its structure are electrically charged, the positive charge on the nucleus must be cancelled as far as outside conditions are concerned by the negative charge on the surrounding electron 'cloud'. This means that there must be as many electrons normally surrounding the nucleus as there are protons inside the nucleus, since the negative electron charge is numerically equal to the positive proton charge. The actual number of protons in the nucleus, and hence the number of electrons surrounding the nucleus in an uncharged atom, depends on the element of which the atom is a part. In other words, it is the build-up of the nucleus that determines the element to which the atom belongs.

The atom of hydrogen is thought to have the simplest structure of all, having one proton for its nucleus and so having one electron in its 'cloud'. It is a bit difficult to imagine a 'cloud' of one electron, but the electron is thought to circle round the proton in an orbit, rather as the earth does round the sun. The electron orbit cannot really be defined quite so exactly as the earth's orbit, but the chances of finding the electron in its orbit are calculated to be much greater than the chances of finding it anywhere else. If this reservation is borne in mind, the idea of an electron circling the proton nucleus of a hydrogen atom at a certain distance from it will be quite satisfactory for a simple understanding of the subject.

The next simplest atom is that of helium. This is thought to have two protons plus two neutrons in its nucleus, so that it will have two circling orbital electrons. The next simplest atom after helium is lithium, which has three protons and four neutrons in its nucleus, with three orbital electrons. This process goes on for all of the elements in order, each one on the list having one more proton in its nucleus and one more orbital electron. The number of neutrons in the nucleus does not follow such a simple arrangement, however, and the ninety-second element on the list, uranium, has 92 protons but 146 neutrons in its nucleus, with 92 orbital electrons.

The electrons surrounding the atomic nucleus circle round it in all directions, so that the original idea of a 'cloud' of electrons gives a reasonably accurate picture. This surrounding cloud shields the nucleus from contact with the nucleus of any other atom which may approach it, and the repulsive forces between the two electron clouds will determine the closeness with which the atoms approach each other. Normal chemical reactions concern only the very outermost electrons in the cloud, and it takes very powerful 'weapons' indeed to get through this surrounding cloud and attack the nucleus. This is why the atoms were for so long thought to be themselves indivisible fundamental particles, when only chemical means of attack were available. It is the composition of the nucleus which fundamentally decides the number of electrons in the cloud, and which also decides the nature of the atom. An atom may sometimes lose or gain electrons from its cloud without its nucleus or its basic properties or identity being changed. A change in the nucleus changes the identity of the atom into that of another element.

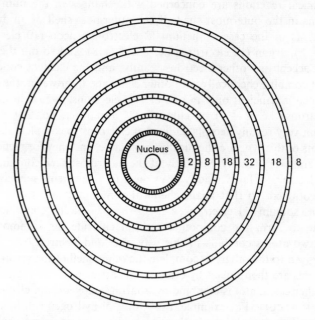

139. Diagram of electron shells surrounding atom nucleus.
(*Not* to scale)

The way in which the electron cloud is made up follows a fairly definite pattern. The electron orbits arrange themselves in definite regions or 'shells' round the nucleus, something like the layers of an onion. The maximum possible number of electrons in any one shell is limited. The innermost shell of all can contain 2 electrons, and the next shell can contain 8. The next shell can also contain 8 electrons if it is the outer shell of the atom, but can accommodate up to 18 electrons if it is covered by a further shell. (It is found that an outer shell will not contain more than 8 electrons).

Each shell can be simply visualized as being spherical, with the electrons following circular orbits in all directions. The maximum number of electrons that can be accommodated in each shell is shown in diagram 139, the radius of the shell being the average distance between electrons and nucleus. These shells normally 'fill up' from the inside, so that an atom of aluminium, which has 13 orbital electrons, will have 2 electrons in the inner shell, 8 electrons in the next shell and 3 electrons in the next shell, which is the outermost shell for this atom.

Chemical reactions are concerned with changes in the number of electrons in the outermost shell. If the outermost shell of an atom is full up, as in the case of helium (2 electrons), neon (10 electrons; i.e. 2 + 8), argon (18 electrons; i.e. 2 + 8 + 8), and so on, the atom cannot accept any other electrons readily, and the element concerned will not combine chemically with other elements. If, however, the outermost shell is deficient only in one or two electrons, as it is in fluorine (9 electrons; i.e. 2 + 7) or chlorine (17 electrons; i.e. 2 + 8 + 7), the atom very readily accepts additional electrons to complete its shell. Elements of this type are chemically very active, and they form chemical compounds very readily. Similarly, if the outermost shell contains only a few electrons, it fairly readily gives these up to elements such as those last mentioned, so that again chemical compounds are formed. For example, sodium (11 electrons; i.e. 2 + 8 + 1) readily combines with chlorine to form the compound sodium chloride, or common salt. When two atoms combine in this way, the 'odd electron over' in the one is given to the other, to complete the outer shell of the second. The two atoms are then linked by electrostatic attraction.

In other cases, atoms combine by 'sharing' outer orbital electrons to form a MOLECULE. For example, two atoms of hydrogen will link up to form a hydrogen molecule. In these molecules the two atoms 'share' the orbital electron belonging to each, so that from this point of view the outer shell of each is full. This bond between the two atoms may be fairly readily broken by chemical means.

A more complete treatment of chemical reactions between atoms would be an unwarranted diversion. The purpose of these examples is to show how the atomic theory put forward can be used to explain observed experimental results.

13.7.   Solids, liquids and gases

The way in which the atoms or molecules are packed together to build up a definite amount of the substance depends on the state of the substance; that is, on whether it is in the form of a solid, a liquid or a gas. In order to simplify matters, only a completely pure element will be considered. In practice, this is an ideal condition which is sometimes difficult to obtain, since atoms of foreign elements, whether chemically combined with the element considered or not, will usually be present unless very careful precautions are taken.

In the solid form, the atoms are packed together fairly closely. (Again, the term 'fairly closely' is a relative one. The distance between nuclei of

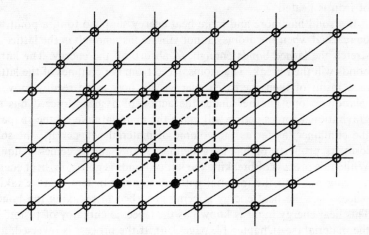

140. Atoms in a cubic lattice.

(The 'bonds' of one of the cubes are shown by the heavier dotted lines. The other cubes will have similar bonds, which are due to attractive forces between the atoms.)

The atoms vibrate around the average positions shown, at a speed dependent on temperature

adjacent atoms will be many atom diameters.) For the crystalline elements, which include metals, the atoms are arranged in an orderly manner, as if strung like beads on a wire framework. The framework may be a simple cube, with an atom at each corner, or it may be much more complicated. A general way of referring to this framework is to call it a crystal 'lattice'. (See diagram 140.)

The position of the atom in the lattice is fixed, but the atom vibrates around this position just as if the bonds of the lattice between them were made of stiff springy wire and were given a sharp tap. Incidentally, the strength of these lattice bonds can be appreciated from the force required to break them apart, as happens when an iron bar is broken. The speed at which the atoms vibrate depends on the temperature of the solid. The higher the temperature, the faster do the atoms vibrate around their average position in the lattice. What happens is that as heat energy is given to the solid to raise its temperature, the atoms store this energy in a sort of kinetic energy of vibration. Some of the heat energy is also absorbed in moving the atoms a little further apart against the forces tending to bind them together to form the lattice of the solid; this accounts for the expansion which takes place when, for example, a bar of iron is heated.

If a solid has more and more heat energy supplied to it, a point will be reached when the atoms cannot vibrate fast enough in the lattice, or stretch the lattice bonds enough, to absorb all the energy. The lattice bonds will then break. The atoms, freed from the confines of the lattice as a result of their increased energy, will now more readily move in relation to one another under the action of a shear force. Thus the gravitational forces acting will make the material take up the shape of the container, as far as the volume of material will permit; the solid loses its property of having a definite shape, and becomes a liquid. While this process of breaking the lattice bonds is going on, heat energy is being put into the material without any rise in temperature taking place, since the heat energy is being absorbed in breaking the bonds. This heat energy input is known as the 'specific enthalpy of fusion' of the material (see Chapter 14, page 386). If the process is reversed, and heat energy is removed, then at the point where solidification takes place heat energy will be released without change in temperature, as the atoms re-form themselves into their lattice structure.

In the solid state, then, the atoms are arranged in an orderly way, while in the liquid state they can more readily move in relation to one another. The speed of vibration of the atoms in the liquid is again dependent on temperature. The higher the temperature of the liquid, the higher will be the speed of vibration. There is still, however, some force of attraction between the atoms, and although any atom in the middle of a volume of liquid will be pulled from all sides so that the resultant force on it is zero and does not affect its movement, this will not be the case near the surface. For atoms near the surface, the force of attraction due to all the other atoms will be one-sided, tending to pull them back into the body of the liquid. This force is responsible for what is known as the 'surface tension' of the liquid. (See diagram 141). If it were possible to see individual atoms, as in the magnified sections of the diagram, the atoms would be found to be vibrating rapidly in all possible directions but still close enough to each other for the attraction forces between them to limit their total movement. The atom at A, near the surface, has a resultant force acting on it tending to retain it in the liquid. There will be some atoms which have sufficient energy to break free from this restraint and leave the liquid surface. These then form a 'vapour about the liquid, and the process is known as 'evaporation'. An increase in liquid temperature will increase the energy of vibration and so increase the number of atoms having sufficient energy to leave the surface.

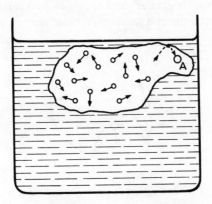

141. Diagram of liquid in a container

As was the case for the solid, a continued supply of heat energy to the liquid is absorbed both in the increased speed of vibration of the atoms and also in the increase of the average distance between atoms. The result is the expansion of the liquid. Again a point is reached where further heat energy is absorbed only by a further breakdown in the bonds between the atoms. The atoms now move very much further apart, and the substance takes up the form of a gas. Once again, as this process takes place heat energy is supplied and absorbed without any increase in temperature, and this heat energy is known as the 'specific enthalpy of evaporation'. (See Chapter 14, page 382.)

This process also is reversible, and at the point where a gas becomes a liquid again, heat energy is released without a change of temperature as the atoms come closer together once more. As a rough analogy, visualize a disorderly crowd of children which is approaching an open playground along a narrow lane. In the lane they tumble and jostle each other, and although they can move about, there will be numerous collisions and their movements will be restricted. Once in the open space they can scatter further apart and, although the chances of collisions are still present, such collisions are likely to be fewer in number. (Because of the very large number of atoms present, there will still be many collisions between the atoms in a gas, even though fewer than for a liquid.)

When the substance takes on the form of a gas, then, the average distance between atoms is much greater than it is in the liquid state, and very much greater again than for the solid state. Similarly, the average speed of the atoms is greater, and they can be visualized as moving rapidly in all directions in a random fashion. Because of the increased

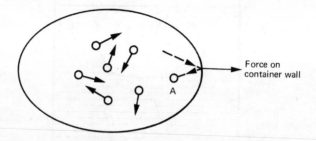

142. Diagram of gas in a container

distance between them, the mutual attractive forces are very greatly reduced, and the atoms can be considered to move about independently of each other. They will, however, collide with one another, and with the walls of any container, and the repeated collisions with the walls are responsible for the outward force exerted by the gas on the container. In other words, the pressure exerted by the gas is due to the fast-moving atoms colliding with the sides of the vessel in which the gas is placed. Since the atoms move in all directions, the resultant force will always be at right angles to the side of the container at any point, whatever shape it may have. In diagram 142 the atoms are moving more quickly and are further apart than in the liquid state. The atom at A has 'rebounded' from the container wall, and a force will have been exerted on the container wall. (Again note that the scale of this diagram differs from that of diagrams 140 and 141, the average distances between atoms in a gas being much greater than in a liquid.)

As in the other cases, the speed of movement of the atoms depends on the temperature of the gas. As the temperature is raised by supplying heat energy to the gas, the added energy is stored in the increased kinetic energy of the atoms. Since the moving atoms then possess greater energy, the force resulting from the collisions with the sides of the container increases, so that the pressure of a given volume of gas will increase with increase of temperature. (See Chapter 14, page 399.)

Summary

The atoms in a solid are tightly packed in an orderly manner, and will vibrate around relatively fixed positions as heat energy is absorbed.

The atoms in a liquid more readily move in relation to one another, and vibrate at a speed dependent on the temperature. The average distance between atoms in a liquid is greater than that between atoms in a solid.

The atoms in a gas move about at random within the gas at a higher speed than they do in a liquid, and this speed is also dependent on temperature. The average distance between atoms in a gas is greater than that between atoms in a liquid.

The transition from solid to liquid to gas is dependent, then, on there being a supply of heat energy to the substance. The temperatures at which these transitions take place are very different for different substances. For example, most metals are in the solid state at normal temperatures (a notable exception being mercury), whilst the lighter elements, such as hydrogen, are in the form of a gas at normal temperatures. Water is not an element, but a chemical compound of hydrogen and oxygen, so that these descriptions should be put in terms of molecules rather than atoms; but it is a substance which is very readily obtained in all three states—ice, water and steam.

The density of a substance (see Chapter 2, page 30) will change as its state changes. In the solid form, it has more atoms tightly packed into a given volume, and so its density is higher. In the liquid form, the atoms are further apart, and so its density is less. In the form of a gas, the atoms are further apart still, and the density is even lower. It should be noted, however, that gas does have mass. It is sometimes overlooked that a rubber balloon, blown up with air, has more mass than it did before it was inflated, since it contains more air.

Because of the expansion that takes place with increase of temperature for each state, the density in each case tends to decrease with rise of temperature. The change in density which takes place at a change of state is, however, very much greater than the density changes with temperature within a given state.

CHAPTER SUMMARY

An atom has a central nucleus containing protons, neutrons and other particles. The nucleus is surrounded by orbital electrons arranged in shells, each shell having a maximum 'permitted' number of electrons. In terms of physically-occupied space, the atomic particles take up an extremely small proportion of the total 'volume' of the atom. The space between the particles is, however, a region in which very large forces are acting.

The nucleus determines the identity of an atom.

The number of electrons in an uncharged atom is equal to the number of protons in the nucleus. Atoms may, however, gain or lose electrons from the outer shell and so become negatively or positively charged, as when chemical reactions take place.

In a solid, atoms are packed together so that their average positions are relatively fixed. They vibrate about these average positions in a manner dependent on temperature.

In a liquid, atoms vibrate at speeds dependent on temperature, but can be more readily moved in relation to each other under the action of a shear force. The average distance between atoms is greater than in a solid, but still small enough for significant attraction forces to exist between them.

In a gas, atoms move in all directions in a random manner at speeds dependent on temperature. The average distance between atoms is, however, much greater than in a liquid, and the atoms can be considered to move about independently of one another.

Transition from the solid state to the liquid state and then to the gaseous state is obtained by continued supply of heat energy to the material.

14. Heat

The sensations produced by heat will be familiar to anyone who has sat by a fire or has been out-of-doors in the sun, although the human body forms a poor scientific instrument with which to measure either the effects of heat, or the degree of hotness of material, with any precision. A simple demonstration will serve to indicate the weakness of the sense of touch as a measuring instrument in this connection. Place one hand in a bowl of cold water and the other hand in a bowl of hot water for a few minutes, and then place both hands in another bowl of lukewarm water. The sensation of heat experienced by each hand will be different, even though both are put into the same surroundings. This shows that the sensations of heat are conditioned by previous experience, and so are unreliable for scientific measurement.

Before the scientific measurement of heat and its effects can be discussed, however, some idea of the nature of heat should be obtained.

14.1. The nature of heat

A clue to the true nature of heat can be found by a few simple experiments. If a bicycle-pump is used to inflate a tyre, vigorous pumping will be found to make the end of the bicycle-pump hot. If a piece of wood is pressed against a rotating shaft, the wood can be made so hot that it will char. If a small piece of metal sheet is vigorously hammered out, the metal will become warm. If a tightly-gripped rope is pulled through the hands, the skin in contact with the rope may be burned.

In each of these cases, heat is produced by the supply of mechanical energy to the system. Mechanical work is done by the force in compressing the air in the pump, by the shaft turning against the frictional forces due to the pressure on the wood, by the hammer in flattening the metal sheet and by the rope being pulled against the frictional forces due to the grip of the hand.

In some cases the process can be reversed, and heat may be made to perform mechanical work. For example, if the air in a can having a tightly-fitting lid is heated, the lid can be blown off against the frictional forces trying to hold it in place. The heated air and steam produced in a kettle of boiling water can lift the lid of the kettle (a fact which is reputed to have led James Watt to the invention of the steam engine).

These experiments lead to the important conclusion that HEAT IS A FORM OF ENERGY. In the first cases mentioned, mechanical energy is converted into the form of heat energy by the processes involved, while in the last cases, heat energy is converted into the form of mechanical energy.

Energy has been defined in Chapter 6, page 188, as 'the capacity to do work', and heat energy possesses this capacity to accomplish work just as does a stretched spring. If two strips of different metals, such as copper and iron, are joined together by rivets and then heated, the mechanical forces exerted by their different expansions will cause the strips to bend. In other words, the heat energy supplied is partly converted to mechanical work in bending the strips.

Energy may be transferred as heat from a hot body to a cold one just as energy can be transferred as work from the wound-up spring of a clockwork motor to a load moving against some restraint. Alternatively, some of the heat energy which is released when a hot body is allowed to cool can be converted to mechanical work. For example, if an iron bar having a hole at one end and fixed at the other end is heated, and a small cast-iron rod is placed through the hole and firmly held, the forces exerted by the bar as it cools can be sufficient to break the cast-iron rod. Some of the heat energy released by the bar is converted to the mechanical energy necessary to break the rod.

The conversion of one form of energy into another is dealt with in more detail in Chapter 22, page 705. The aim here has been to illustrate the fundamental nature of heat as a form of energy. A further discussion of the way in which heat energy transferred to a body increases its internal energy is given in Chapter 13 on page 358.

14.2. The transmission of heat. (1) Conduction

If one end of a copper bar is held in the hand while the other end is heated, say in a flame, the end being held soon becomes warm. This means that the heat energy given to the bar by the flame must have been transmitted along the bar. This method of transmission of heat energy is known as CONDUCTION, and a material such as copper is said to be a good 'conductor' of heat. Although nothing moves along the bar in the sense that it is physically transferred from one end to the other, it is often convenient to refer to the heat 'flow', or the 'flow' of heat energy along the bar. Metals are in general good conductors of heat, although some are better than others. Materials such as wood, glass, wool or paper are poor conductors of heat. For example, it is very possible to hold one end of a piece of wood even while the other end is hot enough to ignite, and this of course is done every time a match is struck.

The heat-conducting property of a material is measured by its 'thermal conductivity'. A good conductor will have a high thermal conductivity.

14.3. The transmission of heat. (2) Convection

Air is not a particularly good conductor of heat (that is, the thermal conductivity of air is not particularly high). However, it is a known fact that a source of heat energy in a room will make even remote parts of the room warm. The mechanism by which this takes place can be described as follows. The air immediately next to the source of heat will become warm by conduction, since it is actually touching the hot surface of the heat source. This mass of warmed air will expand and, because of the increase in its volume, its density will decrease. The higher-density air immediately surrounding the warmed air will then displace it, so that it will rise above the source of heat. The colder air replacing it will then also become warmed by conduction. This process will continue, with the warm air rising and being continually replaced by the colder air. If very fine dust particles are sprinkled above a source of heat, the air movement may be deduced from the movement of the particles. In this way, heat energy given to the air may be transmitted to various parts of the room, and this method of heat transmission is known as CONVECTION.

The air flow which takes place during convection is often referred to as a 'convection current' in the air. Convection currents in liquids are also partly responsible for the transmission of heat energy to various areas of the liquid. A few grains of a water-soluble dye dropped into a beaker of water which is being slowly heated will give a visual indication of the existence of these convection currents.

In these cases, physical transfer of heated particles does occur, although the particles have received, and may release, heat energy by the process of conduction.

14.4. The transmission of heat. (3) Radiation

It is well known that a person sitting in full view of a fire will get warmer than someone who is shielded from it, even if they are both at the same distance from the fire. This means that the first person must be receiving more heat energy than the second. Since neither is touching the fire, and since both are assumed to be in the same position as regards convection currents, this additional heat energy must be transmitted in some other way. The 'extra' heat must be transmitted in the same sort of way as light, since if the light of the fire is shielded, the extra heat is no longer received. This third method of heat transmission is known as RADIATION, and behaves in the same sort of way as the radiation of light. (In fact, both heat radiation and light radiation are examples of the same fundamental type of energy transmission, which is called 'electromagnetic' radiation.) The radiation of heat takes place in straight lines, and may be reflected in the same way as light rays. This fact is used in the construction of the shiny metal reflector placed behind some electric fires.

Heat energy from the sun reaches the earth by means of radiation, since the space between sun and earth is largely devoid of air or other gases, which could set up conduction or convection methods of heat transfer.

Summary

There are three principal methods of heat transmission:

(a) Conduction—by direct contact with a heat source.
(b) Convection—by the physical movement of heated particles.
(c) Radiation—by heat 'rays' which are fundamentally similar to light rays.

In any case of heat transfer, more than one of these methods may be involved. For example, a coal fire will conduct heat to the fire-grate, will set up convection currents in the air and will also radiate heat energy. Conduction or convection, however, can take place only if physical material of some sort is present. Radiation, on the other hand, can take place across an empty space.

It is found that the amount of heat transmitted from a body by radiation, or the heat energy absorbed by a body in the path of radiated heat energy, depends, among other things, on the type of surface rather than on the material concerned. A matt black surface will either radiate more heat energy if heated, or will absorb more heat energy by radiation if placed in the path of heat rays, than a shiny white surface under the same conditions. (This will apply provided neither surface is so hot that it glows.) This means that a silver-painted steam radiator does not in fact radiate very much heat energy, and most of the heat energy will be transmitted from it to its surroundings by conduction and convection. The so-called 'convector heaters' are, however, specially designed to allow air to circulate through them, and so assist in the formation of convection currents in the air. The surface of the reflector of an electric fire is made light in colour, smooth and shiny, in order that it may reflect most of the radiated heat energy it receives from the fire element, and absorb a minimum proportion of it. A simple way of testing this would be to switch on two similar electric fires after having painted the reflector of one of them black. The metal of the painted reflector will be found to get appreciably hotter than that of the shiny reflector, because of the greater amount of the radiated heat energy that it will absorb.

14.5. Temperature

Now that heat has been shown to be a form of energy, the true significance of the TEMPERATURE of a body may be discussed. This term is used to describe the relative degree of hotness of a body, so that, as is probably well known, the hotter a body, the higher its temperature. The temperature does not, however, of itself measure the amount of energy in the body. It takes more time to bring a full kettle of water to boiling point than it does to bring a half-full kettle of water to the same temperature. Different amounts of heat energy are required to cause an equal rise in the temperature of different amounts of the same substance. This point will be considered in more detail later (see Section 14.9, page 371), but it is important to be aware of the fundamental difference between heat, which is a form of energy, and temperature, which is a measure of relative hotness.

14.6. Scales of temperature

The relative hotness, or temperature, of a body may be measured by comparing it with that of other bodies, and any temperatures could be taken as fixed comparison or reference points, from which a scale could be drawn up. For convenience, the fixed points on a scale of temperature are usually taken as the temperature at which ice just begins to melt and the temperature at which pure water will boil under normal conditions of pressure. (The boiling point of water is lowered if the air pressure above it is lowered, or raised if this pressure is increased.)

The customary scale of temperature, known as the CELSIUS (or CENTIGRADE) scale, divides the temperature range between the lower fixed point—the temperature of melting ice—and the upper fixed point —the boiling point of water—into 100 'degrees' of temperature. The lower fixed point is taken as the zero of the scale, so that the upper fixed point is represented by a temperature of 100 Celsius degrees (written as 100°C). (The term 'degrees Centigrade', although still common, is slowly being abandoned in favour of 'degrees Celsius'.)

Summary

> Temperature of melting ice   =   0°C
> Temperature of boiling pure water = 100°C
>   (at normal pressure)

14.7. Methods of measurement of temperature

An instrument used for the measurement of temperature is known as a THERMOMETER, and probably the mercury or alcohol thermometer is already well known to the student. This type of thermometer uses the expansion of a material with increase in temperature for its principle of operation.

A small amount of mercury or alcohol is sealed into a bulb at the end of a glass tube of small, uniform bore, from which air has been excluded. As the temperature of the thermometer is increased, the mercury or alcohol expands and is pushed along the bore of the tube from the bulb at the end. Since this bore is uniform, distances measured along the tube are proportional to the corresponding changes in temperature, and so the side of the tube may be marked off with a scale of temperature. For a given volume of mercury or alcohol, the distance between scale markings will depend on the diameter of the bore, since a given change in volume by expansion will correspond to a greater length for a smaller cross-sectional area. The smaller the bore of the tube, the longer will the thermometer be for a given range of temperature measurement.

The range of temperatures which this type of thermometer may be used to measure depends ultimately on the freezing point and boiling point of the liquid used in it. Mercury freezes at about − 39°C and boils at about 357°C and so these are the extreme limits of temperature at which a mercury thermometer may be used. A practical range of use would be rather within these values. Alcohol may be used down to about − 114°C, but cannot be used to measure high temperatures since it boils at about 78°C. It follows that mercury-in-glass thermometers are the more useful for the range of temperatures usually encountered in simple laboratory work. Because of its lower cost, alcohol is frequently used for the thermometers intended to measure room temperatures.

Outside the ranges of temperature mentioned here, other types of thermometer must be used. Typical among these are 'resistance thermometers', which use the change in the electrical resistance of a conductor brought about by temperature change (Section 16.22, page 481); and 'thermo-couples', which use the electromotive force set up when the junction of two dissimilar materials is heated (Section 21.6, page 700). A third type is the 'optical pyrometer', which compares temperatures in the red-heat and white-heat regions with the previously calibrated temperature of a wire filament, heated by the flow of a measured current whose value can be adjusted (see Chapter 16, page 444).

14.8. Quantity of heat. Units of measurement

Since heat is a form of energy, the units in which a quantity of heat is measured are fundamentally units of energy. There is, then, no real reason why a quantity of heat should not be measured in, say, joules or newton-metres. However, it is more convenient to use joules since heat is a form of energy.

14.9. Specific heat capacity

The quantity of heat energy required to raise the temperature of a body by a given temperature rise depends on the mass of material in the body and the sort of material concerned. This means that if equal masses of two different materials are heated so that their temperature rise is the same, different amounts of heat energy will be required.

The specific heat capacity of a substance can be defined as 'the amount of heat energy required to raise the temperature of unit mass of the substance by unit rise in temperature'.

The units of specific heat capacity are therefore joules per kilogramme °Celsius. Since this unit is small, it is more usually given as kilojoule per kilogramme °Celsius [kJ/kg°C]. For example the specific heat capacity of pure water is 4·186 8 kJ/kg°C, often taken as 4·2 kJ/kg°C. It is often useful to compare the heat capacity of a substance with that of water, giving the expression relative specific heat capacity (formerly called specific heat)

$$\text{relative specific heat capacity} = \frac{\text{specific heat capacity of substance}}{\text{specific heat capacity of water}} \quad \text{(i)}$$

or specific heat capacity of substance = relative specific heat capacity
× specific heat capacity of water

If, for example, the relative specific heat capacity of copper is stated
to be 0·09 then it means that:

specific heat capacity of copper $\simeq$ 0·09 × 4·2 kJ/kg°C
$\simeq$ 0·378 kJ/kg°C

14.10.   Heat energy lost or gained through change in temperature

The terms 'loss' of heat or 'gain' of heat are frequently used in connection with heat energy transfer from and to a body. As pointed out in
Chapter 22, page 706, however, energy cannot be created or destroyed,
and these terms are used in relation to the body considered. The heat
energy 'lost' from a cooling body is transmitted by conduction, convection or radiation, or a combination of these, to other bodies such as
the surrounding air particles. The heat energy 'gained' by a body must
have been delivered to it from something else possessing this energy in
the first place. However, as long as this point is understood, the terms
are very convenient when the conditions for a particular body are being
considered.

The specific heat capacity of a substance has been seen to depend on
the heat energy required to raise the temperature of unit mass by unit
temperature rise. If the specific heat capacity of a substance is c, then c
heat units are required to raise the temperature of 1 kg by 1°C. Then
$2c$ heat units are required to raise the temperature of 2 kg by 1°C.
Similarly, $4c$ heat units would be required to raise the temperature of
2 kg by 2°C. This is expressed mathematically by the statement that the
quantity of heat given out ('lost') or received ('gained') is equal to the
product of the mass of the substance, the specific heat capacity of the
substance, and its change in temperature.

In symbols,

$$Q = m \times c \times (\theta_2 - \theta_1) \qquad . \qquad . \qquad \text{(ii)}$$

where Q = heat 'lost' or 'gained'
m = mass
c = specific heat capacity
$(\theta_2 - \theta_1)$ = change in temperature

Strictly, if θ_1 is always taken as the *initial* temperature and θ_2 as the
final temperature, equation (ii) will always indicate the heat *gained*.

If θ_2 is less than θ_1, then $(\theta_2 - \theta_1)$ is negative, so that Q is negative. A negative heat gain is equivalent to a heat loss.

14.11. Examples

(i) Find the amount of heat energy required to raise the temperature of 7 kg of water by 30°C. Take the specific heat capacity of water as 4·2 kJ/kg°C

$$Q = mc\theta \text{ where } \theta = \text{rise in temperature}$$
$$= 7 \times 4{\cdot}2 \times 30$$
$$= \underline{882 \text{ kJ}}$$

(ii) Water flows through a continuous flow water heater at the rate of 0·75 litre/s. If the water enters the heater at a temperature of 15°C and leaves at a temperature of 82°C, find the rate at which heat energy is being given to the water. Take the specific heat capacity of water as 4·2 kJ/kg°C.

$$\frac{Q}{t} = \frac{mc}{t} (\theta_2 - \theta_1)$$
$$= 0{\cdot}75 \times 4{\cdot}2 \times (82 - 15) \text{ kJ/s}$$
$$= 0{\cdot}75 \times 4{\cdot}2 \times 67 \text{ kJ/s}$$
$$= \underline{211 \text{ kJ/s}}$$

Note: 1 litre of water has a mass of 1 kg.

(iii) How much heat energy is required to raise the temperature of 6 kg of copper from 10°C to 82°C? Take the specific heat capacity of copper as 0·38 kJ/kg°C.

$$Q = mc (\theta_2 - \theta_1)$$
$$= 6 \times 0{\cdot}38 \times (82 - 10) \text{ kJ}$$
$$= 6 \times 0{\cdot}38 \times 72 \text{ kJ}$$
$$= \underline{164 \text{ kJ}}$$

(iv) A block of iron having a mass of 10 kg is allowed to cool from a temperature of 160°C to a temperature of 15°C. How much heat energy is transmitted away from the iron?

Take the relative specific heat capacity of iron as 0·12.

$$Q = mc (\theta_2 - \theta_1)$$
$$= 10 \times 0{\cdot}12 \times 4{\cdot}2 \times (15 - 160) \text{ kJ}$$
$$= -10 \times 0{\cdot}12 \times 4{\cdot}2 \times 145 \text{ kJ}$$
$$= \underline{-730 \text{ kJ}}$$

(v) A piece of copper having a mass of 0·5 kg is heated to a temperature of 100°C and is then dropped into a vessel containing 0·75 litre of water at an initial temperature of 15°C. To what temperature will the water rise?

Neglect heat energy transferred to the vessel or to the surrounding air, and take the relative specific heat capacity of copper as 0·09.

In this case, when the heated copper enters the cold water it will give up heat energy to the water, so that the temperature of the water will rise and the temperature of the copper will fall. Steady conditions will be reached when the temperature of the water is equal to the temperature to which the copper has fallen.

If all other heat transfer (such as to the vessel containing the water or to the surrounding air) is neglected, then the total heat energy 'lost' by the copper will be equal to the total heat energy 'gained' by the water. Then, if the final temperature of the copper and the water is θ_t°C,

$$\text{heat lost by copper}$$
$$= mc\,(\theta_1 - \theta_t)$$
$$= 0\cdot5 \times 0\cdot09 \times 4\cdot2\,(100 - \theta_t)$$
$$= 0\cdot188\,(100 - \theta_t)\ \text{kJ}$$

Heat gained by water

$$= mc\,(\theta_t - \theta_2)$$
$$= 0\cdot75 \times 4\cdot2 \times (\theta_t - 15)$$
$$= 3\cdot15\,(\theta_t - 15)\ \text{kJ}$$

But,

heat lost by copper = heat gained by water

or $\quad\quad 0\cdot188\,(100 - \theta_t) = 3\cdot15\,(\theta_t - 15)$

or $\quad\quad 18\cdot8 - 0\cdot188\theta_t = 3\cdot15\theta_t - 47\cdot2$

or $\quad\quad 3\cdot338\theta_t = 66$

or $\quad\quad \theta_t = 19\cdot8$°C

Final temperature to which the water rises (and to which the copper falls) is 19·8°C

14.12. Thermal capacity

In most practical applications, a definite amount of material will be involved in any particular problem. For example, the cylinder block of any one engine will have a definite amount of iron in it; any one piece of electrical equipment will have a definite amount of conducting material in it, and so on. In almost all cases, several different materials will go together to make up one piece of equipment. For heating problems it is often convenient to consider the whole piece altogether, as a unit, and in these cases use is made of the idea of the THERMAL CAPACITY of the equipment as a whole. The thermal capacity of a mass of material can be defined as the amount of heat energy required to raise the temperature of the whole mass by 1°C. This will depend on the amount of material concerned, and the specific heat capacity of the material itself. If several different materials are concerned, the overall thermal capacity will be the sum of the thermal capacities for the mass of each material. The units in which thermal capacity is measured are 'heat units per degree', i.e. J/°C or kJ/°C.

The thermal capacity of a body also represents the amount of heat energy to be transmitted for each degree change in temperature, and so will determine, for example, the time it will take to cool down under any particular cooling conditions. Thus a large block of iron will have a greater thermal capacity than a small piece of iron because of its greater mass, and if both are heated to the same temperature and then allowed to cool under the same conditions, the large block will take longer to cool down than will the small piece, since it must transmit a greater amount of heat energy to its surroundings. Also, a block of aluminium (relative specific heat capacity $\simeq 0.21$) would have a higher thermal capacity than a block of the same weight of copper (relative specific heat capacity $\simeq 0.09$), because of the higher relative specific heat capacity of aluminium.

An interesting application of the effects of the thermal capacity of a body is the use of a block of concrete for space-heating purposes. The block of concrete may be heated overnight, say, by an electrical heater. The heat energy released by the concrete can then be transmitted to the air in the room during the following day. Because of the relatively high thermal capacity of the concrete block, its temperature rise and fall may only need to be quite small to accept and release enough heat energy to warm the room all day. The advantage is that the electrical energy is taken from the supply at a time when it is cheaper than it would be during the day. An extension of this idea uses the concrete already in the floor of a building as the medium for the transfer of heat energy.

Example

A certain piece of equipment is made up of 1·5 kg of copper, 2·5 kg of iron and 1 kg of aluminium. What is the thermal capacity of the equipment?

How long would it take this equipment to cool down from a temperature of 50°C to 20°C, if it transmits heat energy to its surroundings at an average rate of 1·9 kJ/min?

Take relative specific heat capacities as follows: copper, 0·09; iron, 0·12; aluminium, 0·21.

Thermal capacity of the copper in the equipment
$$= mc\,(\theta_2 - \theta_1)$$
$$= 1\cdot5 \times 0\cdot09 \times 4\cdot2 \times 1 \text{ kJ/°C}$$
$$= 0\cdot567 \text{ kJ/°C}$$

Thermal capacity of the iron in the equipment
$$= 2\cdot5 \times 0\cdot12 \times 4\cdot2 \times 1 \text{ kJ/°C}$$
$$= 1\cdot26 \text{ kJ/°C}$$

Thermal capacity of the aluminium in the equipment
$$= 1 \times 0\cdot21 \times 4\cdot2 \times 1 \text{ kJ/°C}$$
$$= 0\cdot882 \text{ kJ/°C}$$

Total thermal capacity of equipment
$$= 0\cdot567 + 1\cdot260 + 0\cdot882 \text{ kJ/°C}$$
$$= \underline{\underline{2\cdot709 \text{ kJ/°C}}}$$

If the temperature of the equipment falls from 50°C to 20°C,
total heat transmitted to surroundings
$$= \text{thermal capacity (kJ/°C)} \times \text{fall in temperature (°C)}$$
$$= 2\cdot709 \times (50 - 20) \text{ kJ}$$
$$= 2\cdot709 \times 30$$
$$= 81\cdot2 \text{ kJ}$$

If this heat energy is transmitted to the surroundings at an average rate of 1·9 kJ/min, time taken will be

$$\frac{81\cdot2}{1\cdot9} \text{ min} \qquad \left(\frac{\text{kJ}}{\text{kJ/min}} = \text{min}\right)$$

or $\qquad 42\cdot7$ min

The equipment would take about $\underline{\underline{42\frac{1}{2} \text{ min}}}$ to cool down from 50°C to 20°C.

14.13. Water equivalent

The water equivalent of a body is the equivalent mass of water necessary to absorb the same amount of heat energy for the same rise in temperature.

If Q is the amount of heat energy
      m_b is the mass of body
      m_w is the equivalent mass of water
      c_b is the specific heat capacity of the material of the body
      c_w is the specific heat capacity of the water
      $(\theta_2 - \theta_1)$ is the rise in temperature
then $Q = m_b c_b (\theta_2 - \theta_1) = m_w c_w (\theta_2 - \theta_1)$

i.e. water equivalent of body $m_w = m_b \dfrac{c_b}{c_w}$

$\left(\dfrac{c_b}{c_w}\right)$ is the relative specific heat capacity of the material of the body

∴. WATER EQUIVALENT of the body is the mass of the body multiplied by the relative specific heat capacity of the material.

14.14. Calorimetry

The measurement of quantities of heat energy is called CALORIMETRY. For this purpose, use is often made of a containing vessel of known weight and material, so that the thermal capacity of the vessel may be found and allowance made for it in the measurements. Such a vessel is called a CALORIMETER, and the most commonly-used materials for calorimeters are copper and aluminium. They are often simple hollow cylinders with an open top, although they may be enclosed inside another container which is filled with some form of heat 'insulating' material. This material, which may be, for example, wool or asbestos fibre, is chosen because it is a poor conductor of heat, and the heat energy transmitted from the calorimeter to its surroundings is consequently reduced to a minimum. (See diagram 143.)

A calorimeter is used, for example, in the determination of the specific heat capacity of a substance. The following method may be followed for a solid available in a suitable form. The calorimeter is weighed, and from this mass and the specific heat capacity of the material of which it is made, the heat energy associated with any change in its temperature may be calculated.

A measured mass of water at a measured temperature is then placed in the calorimeter. The mass of the water is usually found as the difference between the mass of the calorimeter when it is full and when it is empty. The solid whose specific heat capacity is to be measured is then weighed, and heated to a suitable, measured temperature. The heated solid is then rapidly transferred to the water in the calorimeter, and the maximum temperature reached by the water and solid together is

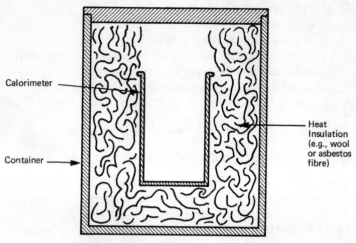

143. Calorimeter in heat-insulated container

measured. The water is stirred to ensure that there is an even temperature distribution throughout. From these results, the required value of specific heat capacity may be calculated.

The following example illustrates these calculations.

Example

A copper calorimeter of mass 120 g is filled with 80 g of water at 15°C. A piece of metal of mass 400 g is heated to 100°C and then transferred rapidly to the water in the calorimeter. If the maximum temperature reached by the water is 24·5°C, find the specific heat capacity of the metal. Assume that 5% of the heat energy originally possessed by the heated metal is transmitted away from the calorimeter through the heat insulation surrounding the calorimeter and to the outside air, and take the relative specific heat capacity of copper as 0·09.

> Water equivalent of calorimeter
> = mass (g) × relative specific heat capacity
> = 120 × 0·09 g
> = 10·8 g
>
> Total equivalent mass of water (water + calorimeter)
> = 80 + 10·8 g
> = 90·8 g = 0·090 8 kg

Total heat gained by water and calorimeter

$$= \text{equivalent mass of water (kg)} \times 4.2 \ (\text{kJ/kg}°\text{C})$$
$$\times \text{rise in temperature } (°\text{C})$$
$$= 0.090 \ 8 \times 4.2 \times (24.5 - 15) \ \text{kJ}$$
$$= 0.090 \ 8 \times 4.2 \times 9.5 \ \text{kJ}$$
$$= 3.62 \ \text{kJ}$$

Total heat lost by metal

$$= mc \ (\theta_2 - \theta_1)$$
$$= 0.400 \times c \times (100 - 24.5) \ \text{kJ}$$
$$= 0.400 \times c \times 75.5 \ \text{kJ}$$
$$= 30.2c \ \text{kJ}$$

Of this heat lost by the metal, only 95% is transmitted to the water and the calorimeter, since 5% is transmitted to the outside air. Heat energy transmitted to water and calorimeter, therefore,

$$= 0.95 \times 30.2c \ \text{kJ}$$
$$= 28.7c \ \text{kJ}$$

Then,

heat lost to water and calorimeter

$$= \text{heat gained by water and calorimeter}$$

or $\quad 28.7c = 3.62$

$$c = 0.126 \ \text{kJ/kg}°\text{C}$$

Specific heat capacity of metal $= \underline{0.126 \ \text{kJ/kg}°\text{C}}$

14.15. Change of state

A material may exist in one of three 'states'—as a solid, liquid or gas. These three states of matter are discussed more fully in Section 13.7, page 358, but a brief summary is as follows.

In the solid state, a material has a definite shape, and a definite volume at a given temperature. It exhibits its greatest mechanical strength in resisting any deformation of this shape or volume.

In the liquid state, the material loses its definite shape but retains its definite volume at a given temperature.

In the gaseous state, the material loses both definite shape and definite volume, and will completely fill any container in which it is placed, although its concentration will decrease as the volume of its container is increased.

Different materials exist naturally in each of the three states. For example, iron is normally in the solid state, water in the liquid state and air in the gaseous state. It is possible, however, to change the state of a material by changing its temperature, and perhaps the easiest example to discuss is water.

If the temperature of water is reduced, it will solidify to form ice, whilst if the temperature of the water is increased it will boil to form steam. The student will already know, from the way in which ice melts, or the way in which steam condenses, that the changes of state mentioned are reversible. This is true in all cases.

The temperatures at which changes of state occur may be vastly different for different materials, but such a change may be considered to be always possible. For example, carbon dioxide, which is a gas at normal temperatures and pressures, may be solidified under suitable conditions of temperature and pressure, and may then be used commercially for keeping foodstuffs etc. cool. Similarly, liquid air and liquid hydrogen are used in industrial processes which require the production of very low temperatures. On the other hand, normally solid materials such as iron do not melt into the liquid form except at very high temperatures.

An input of heat energy is required to change the state from solid to liquid, and further heat energy is required to change the state from liquid to gas. Since energy cannot be destroyed, the heat energy required to change the state from solid to liquid, for example, should be released again when the liquid solidifies. This is discussed in the next section.

14.16. Enthalpy and specific enthalpy

The heat energy required to change the temperature of water by 1°C is approximately constant between freezing point and boiling point, but outside this range of temperature conditions change.

If heat energy is given to ice at standard atmospheric pressure and below 0°C, its temperature will rise until 0°C is reached. Here, its temperature remains constant even though further heat energy is added. This condition will continue until all the ice has melted to form water at 0°C, when further supplies of heat energy will start to raise the temperature of the water. Once again, this rise in temperature with increased heat energy will continue until 100°C is reached (assuming pure water at standard pressure). At this point, the water will begin to boil to form steam, and the temperature remains constant at 100°C while the heat energy supply continues and the water is changed to steam. When all the water has become steam at 100°C, further supplies of heat energy will cause the temperature of the steam to rise above 100°C. Steam at 100°C, with no more water vapour present, is called 'dry' steam. Steam at temperatures above 100°C is called 'super-heated' steam, but steam cannot be super-heated until all the water has been evaporated. These conditions are very dependent on the steam pressure. An increase in pressure will increase the heat energy required to produce the steam, and the temperature at which dry steam is produced (the saturation temperature for the pressure concerned). If all the water has not been turned to steam at the saturation temperature, the steam is said to be 'wet'. If 1 kg of wet steam contains x kg of pure saturated steam, the remainder, $(1 - x)$ g, is water at the saturation temperature. Under these conditions, x is called the 'dryness fraction' of the steam.

Summary

(a) Whilst the material is in any one state, heat energy input will cause a rise in temperature.

(b) Whilst the material is changing state from solid to liquid or liquid to gas, heat energy input does not cause any change in temperature.

Since the whole process is reversible, it follows that if steam at above 100°C is cooled, heat energy is withdrawn from it, with a resulting fall of temperature down to 100°C. At this temperature (assuming normal pressure), further heat energy is withdrawn as the steam condenses to water, with no further fall in temperature until the steam has all condensed. More heat energy is then withdrawn from the water and its temperature falls until 0°C is reached, when the heat energy of the water is released as it turns to ice at 0°C with no change in temperature. When all the water has turned to ice, more heat energy would be withdrawn from the ice if cooling continued, with a further fall in temperature.

There will be a temperature, however, at which no further heat energy could be withdrawn from the ice, so that no further fall in temperature would be possible. This temperature is known as ABSOLUTE ZERO, and is the temperature at which all substances are considered to have zero energy. Absolute zero is about – 273°C.

This discussion of the change of state of water (which assumes that the temperature of the ice, water and steam respectively is uniform at any one instant at all points in the mass, and that the pressure remains constant) can be applied to any substance, although the temperatures at which the change of state occurs will be different. It follows, then, that some heat energy is required to change the state. For example, a gas at the temperature and pressure at which it is converted from the liquid possesses greater energy than the liquid at the same temperature.

A property called ENTHALPY is used in connection with heat transfer to and from a system. It may be defined by the equation

$$H = U + pV$$

where H = enthalpy, U = internal energy of system, p = pressure of system, V = volume of system.

Consistent energy units must be used throughout: e.g. joule, newton metre, etc.

A full discussion of enthalpy is outside the scope of this book, and it is enough to state that the transfer of a quantity of heat to or from the system causes a change in enthalpy:

change in enthalpy = heat energy transferred + work done by system

Again, consistent energy units should be used throughout

Note that in the absence of work done, the heat energy transferred causes an equal change in enthalpy. Their symbols underline this: h denotes enthalpy per unit mass ('specific' enthalpy), where h_f represents specific enthalpy of saturated liquid, in our case water, h_{fg} represents specific enthalpy change due to change of state from water to steam (specific enthalpy of evaporation) and h_g represents enthalpy of dry saturated steam. Note that

$$h_g = h_f + h_{fg} \text{ at a given pressure}$$

Since it is a *change* in enthalpy that is usually important rather than any actual value, relative values are usually measured above some convenient reference point—the enthalpy of water at about 0°C under its own vapour pressure—and this is taken to be zero enthalpy.

Diagram 144 shows a generalized graph of the rise in temperature of a solid as heat energy is given to it, and the 'plateaux' at each change of state. In practice it would not have sharp corners, because temperatures vary from point to point in the mass of the material. As already said, a similar graph is followed in reverse if a gas is cooled.

A simple demonstration of this effect with change of state is given by the 'cooling curve' obtained for paraffin wax. This substance can readily be melted in the laboratory, and solidifies at a convenient temperature.

If a small bath of paraffin wax is heated above its melting point, a thermometer of suitable range inserted in the liquid wax, and the whole then allowed to cool naturally, the loss in heat from the wax will be at a fairly steady rate. A graph of temperature against time will indicate the constant temperature of the mixture of solid and liquid wax at the solidification (or melting) point. This method can be used to determine the melting point of a pure substance with reasonable accuracy.

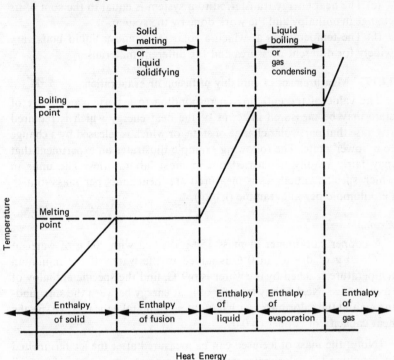

144. Temperature variation with heat energy input. (Not to scale)

A similar temperature/time graph for melting ice will also indicate the acceptance of the enthalpy of fusion of the ice from the surroundings, but it is sometimes difficult in the average laboratory to obtain ice at a temperature very much below 0°C, and so to obtain points on the graph for temperatures below the melting point.

Summary

(a) Supply, or removal, of heat energy to material in any of the three states causes a rise or fall in temperature.

(b) Addition or subtraction of heat energy, with no accompanying change in temperature, is associated with any change of state.

(c) 'Enthalpy of fusion' is heat energy absorbed when a solid melts, and released when a liquid solidifies.

(d) 'Enthalpy of evaporation' is heat energy absorbed when a liquid boils, and released when a gas condenses (or 'liquefies').

(e) The heat energy transferred to a system is equal to the sum of its change in enthalpy and the work done by the system.

(f) The temperatures at which a solid melts and a liquid boils vary widely for different pressures and for different materials.

14.17. Measurement of enthalpy of fusion or evaporation

The value of the enthalpy corresponding to a particular change of state may be measured in terms of the heat energy which is required to cause that particular change of state, or which is released by a change to a 'lower' state. The following example illustrates an experiment that may fairly readily be carried out in most laboratories. The units in which specific enthalpies is measured are 'heat units per mass unit'— i.e. kilojoule per kilogramme (kJ/kg).

Example

A copper calorimeter of mass 150 g is filled with 200 g of water at 15°C. 20 g of dry ice at 0°C is added to the water. If the minimum temperature reached by the water is 6·9°C, find the specific enthalpy of fusion of ice. Neglect any transfer of heat energy between the surrounding air and the calorimeter with its contents, and take the relative specific heat capacity of copper as 0·09.

(Note: the mass of ice used can be measured after the ice has melted by weighing the calorimeter with its contents. A given mass of ice will melt to form the same mass of water, so that the difference between the mass of the calorimeter and water after the experiment, and the mass before the ice is added, is equal to the mass of ice used.)

> Water equivalent of copper calorimeter
> = mass (g) × relative specific heat capacity
> = 150 × 0·09 g
> = 13·5 g

> Total equivalent mass of water before ice is added
> = 200 + 13·5 g
> = 213·5 g = 0·213 5 kg

Heat energy lost by calorimeter and original water content
$$= mc\,(\theta_2 - \theta_1)$$
$$= 0.213\,5 \times 4.2 \times (15 - 6.9)\ \text{kJ}$$
$$= 0.213\,5 \times 4.2 \times 8.1\ \text{kJ}$$
$$= 7.26\ \text{kJ}$$

Heat energy gained by ice at 0°C melting to water at 0°C
$$= \text{specific enthalpy of fusion of ice (kJ/kg)} \times \text{mass of}$$
$$\text{ice (kg)}$$
$$= h_{sf} \times 0.020$$

(where h_{sf} = specific enthalpy of fusion of ice in kJ/kg)

Heat energy gained by water formed from ice at 0°C as a result
of its later rise in temperature to 6.9°C
$$= mc\,(\theta_2 - \theta_1)$$
$$= 0.020 \times 4.2\,(6.9 - 0)\ \text{kJ}$$
$$= 0.58\ \text{kJ}$$

Total heat energy gained by ice after being added to calorimeter
$$= 0.020\,h_{sf} + 0.58\ \text{kJ}$$

Since all other heat transfer is neglected,
heat energy gained by ice = heat energy lost by calorimeter and original
water

or $\qquad 0.020\,h_{sf} + 0.58 = 7.26$

or $\qquad\qquad 0.020\,h_{sf} = 6.68$

or $\qquad\qquad\quad h_{sf} = 334$

This experiment gives a value of the specific enthalpy of fusion of ice
as 334 kJ/kg. (The figure usually accepted is about 335 kJ/kg.)

A basically similar method can be used to measure the specific
enthalpy of evaporation of water. Steam is passed into water in a
calorimeter, and the resulting rise in temperature of the water is
measured.

14.18. Problems on mixtures

The following examples may be taken as a summary of the methods
of dealing with problems concerning the specific heat capacities of
substances, and of heat energy transfers between substances and the
different states of substances. In each case, the way to approach the

N

problem is to obtain values or expressions for the heat energy lost by a cooling substance or gained by a heated substance. Since energy is neither created nor destroyed, the heat energy lost in any exchange must be equal to the heat energy gained in that exchange (assuming that no other energy exchange is involved, such as external work done).

(i) How much heat energy is required to raise the temperature of 250 g of copper from 15°C to 500°C?

If this heated copper is then dropped into 1·5 kg of water at 15°C, what will be the final temperature of the water, if it is assumed that no heat energy is transferred to the vessel containing the water or to the surrounding air? Take the relative specific heat capacity of copper as 0·09.

Heat energy required by copper (kJ)
$$= mc\,(\theta_2 - \theta_1)$$
$$= 0\!\cdot\!25 \times 0\!\cdot\!09 \times 4\!\cdot\!2 \times (500 - 15)\ \text{kJ}$$
$$= 0\!\cdot\!25 \times 0\!\cdot\!09 \times 4\!\cdot\!2 \times 485\ \text{kJ}$$
$$= \underline{\underline{45\!\cdot\!9\ \text{kJ}}}$$

If final temperature of water is θ°C, heat energy gained by water (kJ)
$$= mc\,(\theta - \theta_1)$$
$$= 1\!\cdot\!5 \times 4\!\cdot\!2 \times (\theta - 15)\ \text{kJ}$$
$$= 6\!\cdot\!3\,(\theta - 15)\ \text{kJ}$$

Heat energy lost by copper (kJ)
$$= mc\,(\theta_2 - \theta)$$
$$= 0\!\cdot\!250 \times 0\!\cdot\!09 \times 4\!\cdot\!2 \times (500 - \theta)\ \text{kJ}$$
$$= 0\!\cdot\!094\,5\,(500 - \theta)\ \text{kJ}$$

But since other heat energy transfer is neglected,

heat energy lost by copper = heat energy gained by water

or $0\!\cdot\!094\,5\,(500 - \theta) = 6\!\cdot\!3\,(\theta - 15)$

or $47\!\cdot\!25 - 0\!\cdot\!094\,5\theta = 6\!\cdot\!3\theta - 94\!\cdot\!5$

or $6\!\cdot\!394\,5\theta = 141\!\cdot\!75$

or $\theta = 22\!\cdot\!2$

Final temperature of water $= \underline{\underline{22\!\cdot\!2°\text{C}}}$

(ii) The following table gives values of the enthalpy of dry steam at various pressures. Complete the table, and calculate the enthalpy of 5 kg of dry steam at a pressure of 20 bar. (1 bar $= 10^5\ \text{N/m}^2$.)

Pressure bar	h_f kJ/kg	h_{fg} kJ/kg	h_g kJ/kg
10		2015	2778
15	845		2792
20	909	1890	

Since it is assumed that no work is done by the system,
$$h_g = h_f + h_{fg} \text{ at any one pressure}$$
specific liquid enthalpy at 10 bar $(h_f) = h_g - h_{fg}$ at 10 bar
$$= 2778 - 2015 \text{ kJ/kg}$$
$$= \underline{763 \text{ kJ/kg}}$$

Specific enthalpy of evaporation at 15 bar
$$(h_{fg}) = h_g - h_f \text{ at 15 bar}$$
$$= 2792 - 845 \text{ kJ/kg}$$
$$= \underline{1947 \text{ kJ/kg}}$$

Specific enthalpy of dry steam at 20 bar
$$(h_g) = h_f + h_{fg} \text{ at 20 bar}$$
$$= 909 + 1890 \text{ kJ/kg}$$
$$= \underline{2799 \text{ kJ/kg}}$$

Then at a pressure of 20 bar, enthalpy of
$$5 \text{ kg of dry steam (kJ)} = \text{mass (kg)} \times \text{'specific' enthalpy (kJ/kg)}$$
$$= 5 \times 2799 \text{ kJ}$$
$$= 13\ 980 \text{ kJ} = \underline{\underline{13 \cdot 98 \text{ MJ}}}$$

(iii) A refrigerator produces ice by the evaporation of liquid ammonia. How much liquid ammonia must be evaporated to convert 500 g of water at 15°C to ice at − 5°C if no heat energy is transmitted through the outside walls of the refrigerator?

Take the specific enthalpy of evaporation of ammonia as 1·425 MJ/kg, the specific enthalpy of fusion of ice as 335 kJ/kg, and the relative specific heat capacity of ice as 0·5.

Total heat energy to be extracted from the water
= enthalpy loss of water for temperature fall from 15°C to 0°C
+ enthalpy of fusion of water at 0°C to ice at 0°C
+ enthalpy loss of ice for temperature fall from 0°C to − 5°C

Enthalpy loss from water (kJ)

$= mc\,(\theta_2 - \theta_1)$ kJ

$= 0\cdot5 \times 4\cdot2 \times (15 - 0)$ kJ

$= 31\cdot5$ kJ

Enthalpy of fusion loss as water at 0°C becomes ice at 0°C (kJ)

$= mh_{sf}$ kJ

$= 0\cdot5 \times 335$ kJ

$= 167\cdot5$ kJ

Enthalpy loss from ice (kJ)

$= mc\,(\theta_2 - \theta_1)$ kJ

$= 0\cdot5 \times 0\cdot5 \times 4\cdot2 \times [0 - (-5)]$ kJ

$= 0\cdot5 \times 0\cdot5 \times 4\cdot2 \times 5$ kJ

$= 5\cdot25$ kJ

Total heat energy loss from initial water

$= 31\cdot5 + 167\cdot5 + 5\cdot25$ kJ

$= 204\cdot25$ kJ

This heat energy must be gained by the liquid ammonia as enthalpy of evaporation as ammonia gas is formed.

Heat energy gained by liquid ammonia during evaporation (kJ)

$= mh_{fg}$ kJ

$= m \times 1\cdot425$ MJ

(where m = mass of liquid ammonia which is evaporated, in kg).

Since all other heat transfer is neglected,

heat energy lost by water = heat energy gained by ammonia

or $204\cdot25 = 1425\,m$

or $m = 0\cdot143$ kg

Amount of liquid ammonia evaporated = <u>143 grams</u>

(iv) What mass of ice at -5°C must be mixed with 500 g of water at 18°C, contained in a vessel whose water equivalent is 15 g, to lower its temperature to 8°C?

(Take the specific enthalpy of fusion of ice as 335 kJ/kg, and the relative specific heat capacity of ice as 0·5.)

Neglect heat transfer outside the vessel.

The total equivalent mass of initial water and the vessel = 500×15 $= 515$ g $= 0\cdot515$ kg of water.

Total heat energy lost by initial water and vessel (kJ)

$$= mc\,(\theta_2 - \theta_1)$$
$$= 0{\cdot}515 \times 4{\cdot}2 \times (18 - 8)\ \text{kJ}$$
$$= 0{\cdot}515 \times 4{\cdot}2 \times 10\ \text{kJ}$$
$$= 21{\cdot}6\ \text{kJ}$$

Heat energy gained by ice as its temperature rises from $-5°\text{C}$ to $0°\text{C}$ (kJ)

$$= mc\,(\theta_2 - \theta_1)$$
$$= m \times 0{\cdot}5 \times 4{\cdot}2 \times [0 - (-5)]\ \text{kJ}$$
$$= m \times 0{\cdot}5 \times 4{\cdot}2 \times 5\ \text{kJ}$$
$$= 10{\cdot}5\,m\ \text{kJ}$$

(where m = mass of ice used in kg).

Heat energy gained by ice at $0°\text{C}$ as it melts to water at $0°\text{C}$ (kJ)

$$= mh_{\text{sf}}\ \text{kJ}$$
$$= m \times 335\ \text{kJ}$$

Heat energy gained by water at $0°\text{C}$ as temperature rises to $8°\text{C}$ (kJ)

$$= mc\,(\theta_2 - \theta_1)$$
$$= m \times 4{\cdot}2 \times (8 - 0)\ \text{kJ}$$
$$= 33{\cdot}6\,m\ \text{kJ}$$

Total heat energy gained by ice and the water formed from it

$$= 10{\cdot}5\,m + 335\,m + 33{\cdot}6\,m\ \text{kJ}$$
$$= 379{\cdot}1\,m\ \text{kJ}$$

Since all other heat transfer is neglected,

heat energy gained by ice and water = heat energy lost by initial water and vessel

or $\qquad\qquad\qquad\qquad\qquad 379{\cdot}1\,m = 21{\cdot}6\ \text{kJ}$

or $\qquad\qquad\qquad\qquad\qquad\qquad m = 0{\cdot}057\ \text{kg}$

$\qquad\qquad$ mass of ice required = 57 grams

(v) A boiler burning each hour 1·55 tonne of coal with a calorific value of 31·4 MJ/kg generates 12·5 tonne of steam per hour at a pressure of 20 bar, and dryness fraction 0·8, from feed water at 27°C.

Find (a) the steam raised per kg of fuel burned
$\qquad$ (b) the specific enthalpy of the steam raised
$\qquad$ (c) the efficiency of the boiler.

Pressure bar	Saturation temp. °C	Specific enthalpy h_f (kJ/kg)	Specific enthalpy of evaporation h_{fg} (kJ/kg)
20	212·4	909	1890

(a) 1·55 tonne fuel burned to raise 12·5 tonne steam

$$\therefore \text{ 1 kg fuel would raise } \frac{12\,500}{1550} \text{ kg steam}$$

$$= \underline{8\cdot08 \text{ kg steam}}$$

(b) From given data, each kg of steam at this temperature and pressure will have a specific enthalpy of 909 kJ and a specific enthalpy of evaporation of 1890 kJ. Since the steam is wet, however, of dryness fraction 0·8, only 0·8 kg of each 1 kg of wet steam is actually steam, and so only this amount will have absorbed its specific enthalpy of evaporation. Then, since no work done is considered, specific enthalpy of 1 kg of wet steam $= h_g + x h_{fg}$

$$= 909 + 0\cdot8 \times 1890 \text{ kJ}$$
$$= 909 + 1510 \text{ kJ}$$
$$= \underline{2419 \text{ kJ}}$$

(c) Since the feed water is at 27°C, its specific enthalpy $= c\theta = 4\cdot2 \times 27 = 113$ kJ. The heat energy supplied to this water to convert it to the wet steam is then

$$\text{heat energy supplied} = \text{enthalpy of steam } - \text{ enthalpy of feed water}$$
$$= 2419 - 113 \text{ kJ/kg}$$
$$= 2306 \text{ kJ/kg}$$

Heat energy available from fuel $=$ calorific value of fuel
$$= 31\cdot4 \text{ MJ/kg}$$

But each 1 kg of fuel raises 8·08 kg of steam

$$\therefore \text{ boiler efficiency} = \frac{\text{heat energy supplied to steam}}{\text{heat energy available in fuel}} \times 100\%$$

$$= \frac{8\cdot08 \times 2306}{31\cdot4 \times 1000} \times 100\%$$

$$= \underline{59\cdot4\%}$$

(a) Steam raised per kg of fuel = 8·08 kg
(b) Enthalpy of each kg of steam = 2419 kJ
(c) Efficiency of boiler = 59·4%

Note that at this increased pressure, which is about twenty times normal atmospheric pressure, the steam is not formed until a temperature of 212·4°C is reached. In other words, the water does not boil until this temperature is reached. Compare this with 100°C at normal atmospheric pressure.

14.19. Expansion and contraction

When a material is heated in any one of its three states, it will tend to expand. In the solid and liquid states, this will be evidenced by a direct increase in the volume of the heated material. In the case of a gas, the volume is determined by the container rather than by the gas, but the pressure of a gas will increase if heat energy is given to it at constant volume, or the volume will increase at constant pressure. The case of gases is dealt with in a later section (see Section 14·25, page 399), and attention will now be confined to solids and liquids.

The fact that a heated solid or liquid expands is easily verified in the laboratory. For example, a metal wire between supports, and with a small mass fixed in the centre of the wire, will sag noticeably if the wire is heated. Water completely filling an open vessel will spill over the sides if the water is heated. The measurement of this expansion, and hence its prediction in future cases, is obviously important in any practical use of such materials where they may become hot.

Conversely, if heat energy is removed from a solid or liquid so that it cools, a contraction takes place in the volume. This again can be verified if the materials in the demonstrations just mentioned are allowed to cool. The sagging wire will tighten up again, and the vessel will be less full of water, after each has been allowed to cool.

The two effects of expansion and contraction are linked together, and each depends on the change in temperature of the material. An explanation of this effect of change in volume is given in Section 13·7, page 358.

It is interesting to note that water behaves somewhat unexpectedly at low temperatures. Its volume decreases, or contracts, as the temperature is lowered to about 4°C, and then increases again as the temperature is decreased to 0°C and ice is formed. (It is this expansion which is responsible for the bursting of frozen water-pipes.) Once the ice has been formed, however, further decrease in temperature will again be accompanied by a decrease in volume.

The expansion of solids will be dealt with first, in the next section.

14.20.   Coefficient of linear expansion

Since a solid has a definite shape, it is convenient to consider first the change in linear dimensions which occurs during expansion or contraction. For example, if a retangular block of iron is heated, its volume will be increased, and the length of each of its sides will increase, as shown in diagram 145.

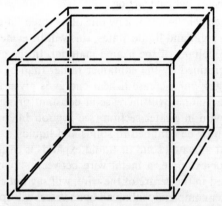

145. Expansion of heated rectangular block

Each of the dimensions of the block will be found to increase by the same fraction of its original length. For example, if the length of the block were originally 250 mm, and the width of the block originally 100 mm, then if the length increased by 2·5 mm (i.e. $\frac{1}{100}$th of original length) the width will increase by 1 mm (i.e. $\frac{1}{100}$th also of original width).

This leads to the idea of a COEFFICIENT OF LINEAR EXPANSION, which measures the linear expansion that takes place in each unit of length for each degree rise in temperature.

The units of the coefficient of linear expansion of a material are 'length units per length unit degree'; for example, 'mm/mm°C'. Since the value of the coefficient of linear expansion will be the same for a particular temperature scale provided that the *same* units are used to measure both the length and the expansion, these coefficients are often quoted just as 'per degree C'. Thus if the coefficient of linear expansion of iron is 0·000 011 per °C (written 0·000 011/°C) an iron bar 100 mm long at, say, 15°C would expand by 0·001 1 mm if its temperature were increased by 1°C to 16°C. From this, the expansion, and the total resulting length of any iron bar, can be worked out for any rise in temperature.

For example, if a 100 mm length expands 0·001 1 mm for 1°C rise,
$\qquad$ a 500 mm length expands 5 × 0·001 1 mm for 1°C rise,
$\qquad$ or a 500 mm length expands 5 × 25 × 0·001 1 mm for 25°C rise

(since each 100 mm of the bar expands 0·001 1 mm for each 1°C rise).

The expansion of the 500 mm iron bar when its temperature is raised from, say, 15°C (at which temperature the 500 mm length is measured) to $(15+25)$°C, or 40°C, would therefore be

$$5 \times 25 \times 0\cdot001\ 1\ \text{mm}$$

or 0·137 5 mm. (Assuming that it could be measured as accurately as that!)

The total length at 40°C would then be 500·14 mm, to the nearest hundredth of a mm.

This may not seem to be much of an expansion, but if long lengths, high temperatures, or 'close' tolerances or dimensions are involved, the actual increase in length can have a considerable effect. The expansion of a heated metal ring may often be used when the ring is to be placed over some other part, since when the ring cools the resulting contraction ensures a tight grip on the part encircled. This is usually known as a 'shrink fit', and is used, for example, for fitting the steel tyres to the rim of a locomotive wheel.

The method of proportion used in the last example to find the expansion of the 500 mm iron bar for a 25°C temperature rise can be used to find a general formula for the expansion in any case where linear expansion is considered.

If the material has a coefficient of linear expansion of α per °C, and a length L_1 'length units' at any reference or 'starting' temperature θ_1, then

$\qquad$ 1 unit of length expands α units for 1° rise in temperature from θ_1

so $\qquad$ L_1 units of length expand $L_1 . \alpha$ units for 1° rise in temperature from θ_1

or $\qquad$ L_1 units of length expand $L_1 . \alpha . \theta$ units for θ° rise in temperature from θ_1.

Suppose this new temperature is θ_2. Since it represents a temperature *rise* of θ above θ_1,

$$\theta = \theta_2 - \theta_1$$

and the expansion $\quad L_1\alpha\theta = L_1\alpha(\theta_2 - \theta_1)$

If the new length at this temperature θ_2 is L_2 then

$$L_2 = L_1 + L_1\,\alpha\,(\theta_2 - \theta_1)$$

or $\qquad \underline{L_2 = L_1\{1 \times \alpha\,(\theta_2 - \theta_1)\}} \qquad\qquad\text{(iii)}$

Note that L_1 is length at θ_1, and L_2 is length at θ_2.)

Examples

(i) The coefficient of linear expansion of lead may be taken as 0·000 028/°C. A length of lead piping is measured at a temperature of 15°C and found to be 30 m. After hot water has been flowing through the pipe for some time, the temperature of the pipe is found to have been raised to 60°C. Find the total length of the hot pipe.

$$L_2 = L_1\{1 + \alpha\,(\theta_2 - \theta_1)\}$$

In this case $L_1 = 30$ m at a temperature $\theta_1 = 15$°C, and the new temperature $\theta_2 = 60$°C, so that

$$
\begin{aligned}
L_2 &= 30\{1 + 0·000\ 028\ (60 - 15)\}\text{ m}\\
&= 30\{1 + 0·000\ 028 \times 45\}\text{ m}\\
&= 30\{1 + 0·001\ 26\}\text{ m}\\
&= 30·037\ 8\text{ m}
\end{aligned}
$$

The total length of the hot pipe is then about $\underline{30·038\text{ m}}$

An expansion in length of 38 mm would need some arrangement to allow for it. This is usually done by including somewhere in the pipe a U-bend that can 'flex' to take up the expansion.

(ii) An overhead electrical conductor made of copper has a length of 50 m between supports. If its temperature then rises by 30°C, find its length at the higher temperature. Take the coefficient of linear expansion of copper as 0·000 017/°C.

$$L_2 = L_1\{1 + \alpha\,(\theta_2 - \theta_1)\}$$

In this case, the individual values of θ_1 and θ_2 are not given, but the temperature *rise* is specified, and from the terms of the question, L_1 is measured at the lower temperature.

If the following values are substituted:

$$L_1 = 50 \text{ m}$$
$$(\theta_2 - \theta_1) = 30°\text{C (temperature rise)}$$

then
$$L_2 = 50 (1 + 0.000\ 017 \times 30) \text{ m}$$
$$= 50 (1 + 0.000\ 51) \text{ m}$$
$$= 50.025\ 5 \text{ m}$$

The total length of the conductor at the higher temperature would be 50·026 m

This expansion of 26 mm would be enough to noticeably increase the sag of the conductor.

(iii) A steel ball is heated to a temperature of 500°C, when it has a diameter of 50·25 mm. It is then placed over a hole having a diameter of 50 mm. At what temperature will the ball just drop through the hole? Take coefficient of linear expansion of steel as 0·000 012/°C.

Using the normal symbol d for diameter, the expansion equation (iii) becomes

$$d_2 = d_1 \{1 + \alpha (\theta_2 - \theta_1)\}$$

In this case $d_2 = 50·25$ mm, $d_1 = 50$ mm, $\theta_2 = 500°\text{C}, \alpha = 0·000\ 012/°\text{C}$, so substituting these values,

$$50·25 = 50 \{ (1 + 0·000\ 012 (500 - \theta_1)\}$$

or
$$50·25 = 50 + 0·000\ 6 (500 - \theta_1)$$

or
$$0·25 = 0·3 - 0·000\ 6\ \theta_1$$

or
$$\theta_1 = \frac{0·05}{0·000\ 6} °\text{C}$$

$$= 83·3°\text{C}$$

Since the ball would probably have to contract to slightly less than 50 mm diameter in order to pass through the hole, say the ball would have to cool down to about 83°C

Notice from these examples that the length units used are the same for L_1 and L_2.

The coefficients of linear expansion for different materials vary quite widely, but they are usually of the same order of magnitude for metals as the values quoted in the examples. Special alloys such as Invar can be made, however, whose coefficient of linear expansion is very small indeed. These are used for special applications requiring minimum change of dimensions with temperature.

14.21. Coefficient of superficial (area) expansion

Since all the dimensions of a block will increase because of the expansion when the block is heated, the area of any face of such a block will also increase. A coefficient of superficial (i.e. area) expansion may be defined in a similar way to the coefficient of linear expansion defined in the previous section.

The COEFFICIENT OF SUPERFICIAL EXPANSION is the increase in area which takes place in each unit of area for each degree rise in temperature.

For all practical purposes, the coefficient of superficial expansion is twice the coefficient of linear expansion, so that with areas represented by A, the equation for superficial expansion may be written:

$$A_2 = A_1 \{1 + 2\alpha (\theta_2 - \theta_1)\} \qquad . \qquad . \qquad \text{(iv)}$$

The explanation of the relationship between the coefficients of linear and superficial expansion is as follows:

Suppose $A_1 = l \times b$ (assuming a rectangular area for simplicity, although the result is true for any area). Then for a temperature rise of $1°$, both l and b will increase so that

$$
\begin{aligned}
A_2 &= l(1 + \alpha.1) \times b(1 + \alpha.1) \\
&= l \times b(1 + \alpha)^2 \\
&= A_1(1 + 2\alpha + \alpha^2)
\end{aligned}
$$

But, as has been seen, a is a very small number of the order of about $0.000\ 01$ or 10^{-5}, so that α^2 will be extremely small, of the order of $0.000\ 000\ 000\ 1$ or 10^{-10}. It may therefore safely be neglected.

Then for $1°$ temperature rise,

$$A_2 = A_1(1 + 2\alpha)$$

and for a temperature rise $(\theta_2 - \theta_1)$,

$$A_2 = A_1 \{1 + 2\alpha (\theta_2 - \theta_1)\}$$

as given in equation (iv).

14.22. Coefficient of cubical (volume) expansion

Again, since all the dimensions of a block increase when the block expands because of a rise in temperature, the volume of the block increases. The COEFFICIENT OF CUBICAL (OR VOLUME) EXPANSION will be the increase in volume which takes place in each unit of volume for each degree rise in temperature.

For all practical purposes, the coefficient of cubical expansion is three times the coefficient of linear expansion, so that with volume represented by V, the equation for cubical expansion may be written:

$$V_2 = V_1 \{1 + 3\alpha (\theta_2 - \theta_1)\} \qquad . \qquad . \qquad \text{(v)}$$

The explanation of the relationship between the coefficients of linear and cubical expansion is similar to that given in the previous section for superficial expansion. Again, assuming a rectangular block for simplicity, although the result is true for any shape,

$$V_1 = l \times b \times h$$

Then for a temperature rise of $1°$,

$$V_2 = l \times b \times h (1 + \alpha)^3$$
$$= V_1 (1 + 3\alpha + 3\alpha^2 + \alpha^3)$$

Again, $3\alpha^2$ and α^3 are both negligible in comparison with 3α so that $V_2 = V_1 (1 + 3\alpha)$ for a $1°$ temperature rise. For a temperature rise of $(\theta_2 - \theta_1)$, the result is

$$V_2 = V_1 \{1 + 3\alpha (\theta_2 - \theta_1)\}$$

as given in equation (v).

14.23. Expansion of liquids

Since a liquid has no definite shape, only its cubical or volume expansion need be considered. A similar relationship to those stated in the previous sections can be written for the cubical expansion of a liquid, although its coefficient of cubical expansion is not constant over a very wide range of temperatures. (The coefficients of expansion of a solid may also vary if the temperature range is wide, but this variation is generally less than that for a liquid. Consequently, when liquids are being dealt with, the range of temperature applicable must be stated for any given value of the coefficient of cubical expansion.)

The special case of water has already been mentioned (Section 14.19, page 391). The coefficient of cubical expansion of water is negative over the range $0°C$ to $4°C$, so that an increase of temperature in this range actually causes a contraction in the volume of the water. This means that water has a maximum density at $4°C$, so that if the surface of a mass of water is steadily cooled from, say, 10°C, the water on the surface contracts, increases in density and sinks to the bottom, until the temperature of the water is 4°C. After this point, a further decrease in the surface temperature causes the water on the surface to expand, and so, being lighter, it stays on top. As is common knowledge, then, water will freeze on top first, and the ice formed, being lighter than the higher-density water beneath, will stay on top.

14.24. Examples

(i) A copper sphere has a diameter of 50 mm at a temperature of 15°C. If the temperature of the sphere is then raised to 500°C, what will be the increase in (a) the diameter, (b) the surface area, (c) the volume of the sphere?

Take the coefficient of linear expansion of copper as 0·000 017/°C.

(a) $$d_2 = d_1 \{1 + \alpha (\theta_2 - \theta_1)\}$$
or $$d_2 = 50 \{1 + 0\cdot000\ 017\ (500 - 17)\} \text{ mm}$$
$$= 50 \{1 + 0\cdot000\ 017 \times 485\} \text{ mm}$$
$$= 50 \{1 + 0\cdot008\ 25\} \text{ mm}$$

Increase in diameter is $50 \times 0\cdot008\ 25$ mm, or about <u>0·41 mm</u>

(b) $$A_2 = A_1 \{1 + 2\alpha (\theta_2 - \theta_1)\}$$
or $$A_2 = 4 . \pi . \left(\frac{50}{2}\right)^2 \{1 + 2 \times 0\cdot000\ 017 \times 485\} \text{ mm}^2$$
$$= 2500\pi \{1 + 0\cdot016\ 5\} \text{ mm}^2$$

Increase in area is $2500\pi \times 0\cdot016\ 5$ mm^2, or about <u>130 mm^2</u>

(c) $$V_2 = V_1 \{1 + 3\alpha (\theta_2 - \theta_1)\}$$
or $$V_2 = \frac{4}{3}\pi \left(\frac{50}{2}\right)^3 \{1 + 3 \times 0\cdot000\ 017 \times 485\} \text{ mm}^3$$
$$= \frac{125\ 000}{6}\pi \{1 + 0\cdot024\ 75\} \text{ mm}^3$$

Increase in volume is $\frac{125\ 000}{6}\pi \times 0\cdot024\ 75$ mm^3, or about <u>1620 mm^3</u>

(ii) A bottle of mass 250 g was completely filled with water at 15°C and re-weighed, when the mass was found to be 650 g. The bottle and water were then heated to a temperature of 50°C, so that some of the water spilled out of the bottle as a result of the expansion which took place. After the bottle and water had cooled down again to 15°C, the outside of the bottle was carefully dried and the bottle and water were re-weighed, when the mass was found to be 645·6 g. Neglecting any expansion in the volume of the bottle, estimate the coefficient of cubical expansion of water for this temperature range.

Since 1 ml of water has a mass of 1 g (very nearly) at 15°C, these results mean that a volume of water of (645·6 − 250) ml, or 395·6 ml at 15°C, just fills the bottle at a temperature of 50°C. But this volume is assumed to have remained constant, and the bottle was just filled at 15°C with (650 − 250) ml, 400 ml of water. That is, a volume of water of 395·6 ml at 15°C expands to a volume of 400 ml at 50°C so that it just fills the bottle. (The extra water originally present at 15°C will have spilled out.)

Then, if the coefficient of cubical expansion of water over this temperature range is $a_w/°C$,

$$V_2 = V_1 \{1 + \alpha_w (\theta_2 - \theta_1)\} \text{ ml}$$

or $\qquad 400 = 395·6 \{1 + \alpha_w (50 - 15)\} \text{ ml}$

or $\qquad 400 = 395·6 + 395·6 \times 35 \times \alpha_w \text{ ml}$

or $\qquad 395·6 \times 35 \times \alpha_w = 4·4$

$$\alpha_w = \frac{4·4}{395·6 \times 35}/°C$$

$$= 0·000\ 318/°C$$

The coefficient of cubical expansion of water between 15°C and 50°C is about 0·000 32/°C

14.25. Expansion of gases

Unlike either a solid or a liquid, a gas has no definite volume at any given temperature, but will completely fill any container in which it is placed. For example, if a given mass of a gas is placed in a cylinder in which a piston can be moved to change the volume, the gas can readily be made to expand or contract in volume by the movement of the piston. If the volume is decreased, the gas is compressed into a smaller space. Its density will be increased, and the pressure it will exert on the sides of the cylinder and the piston will increase, provided no energy is extracted from the gas. If the volume is increased, the gas expands to fill the larger space, its density is decreased, and the pressure on the sides of the cylinder and the piston will be reduced, provided no energy is given to the gas. These conditions are illustrated in diagram 146.

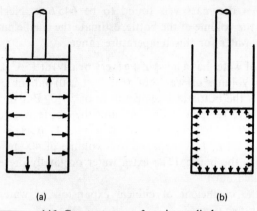

(a)   (b)

146. Constant mass of gas in a cylinder.

(a) Larger volume, lower density, lower pressure
(b) Smaller volume, higher density, higher pressure

Any discussion of the expansion or contraction of a gas must, then, take account of the pressure, the temperature and energy of the gas, as well as its volume. These quantities are not, however, independent of each other. An explanation of the relationship existing between the energy of a gas and the pressure which it exerts on the sides of its container is given in Section 13.7, page 358. In the following sections, the relationships between the pressure, volume and temperature are discussed in more detail. It might be as well to point out, however, that a definite amount of gas contains a definite amount of material and will have a definite mass, although its *density* will be determined by the volume which it occupies. This is why the above statements have been expressed in terms of a given mass of gas. For example, if gas is either added to or taken away from the cylinders in diagram 146, the conditions could be changed.

14.26.   The gas laws

For a given mass of a gas, the pressure, volume and temperature are dependent on one another, and it is helpful to keep one of these three quantities constant in order that the relationship between the other two can be studied. The results of a series of experiments in which different quantities are maintained constant in turn, while the remaining two are allowed to vary, can then be put together to find a general relationship between all three. Another factor, the energy that is possessed by the gas, could also be considered, and a relationship between the pressure and volume of a gas when no heat energy exchange takes place between the gas and its surroundings can be obtained. The temperature of a gas under these conditions will also vary, however, and will be governed by the general relationship suggested here.

Historically, the discoveries of the relationships suggested above were not made at the same time. The first to be investigated was the relationship between the pressure and volume of a given mass of gas at a constant temperature. The results of these experiments were given in 1662 by a scientist named Boyle, and these have been expressed in what is known as Boyle's law.

The next relationship to be investigated was that between the volume and temperature, at constant pressure, and the results of these experiments were given in 1787 by a scientist named Charles. They have been expressed in what is known as Charles' law.

These two laws can be combined to give a general gas law for the behaviour of gases when pressure, volume and temperature are all changed together. These three laws will be discussed in the following sections.

14.27. Boyle's law

It can be shown by experiment that if the pressure of a given mass of a gas is doubled, its volume is halved, or if the pressure is halved, that the volume will be doubled, provided that the temperature of the gas remains constant. This experiment can quite easily be carried out in a laboratory, and the student should investigate this relationship for himself. The results of this experiment are stated in Boyle's law:

'The volume of a given mass of gas, whose temperature is maintained constant, is inversely proportional to the gas pressure.'

This can be expressed in symbols as

$$p \propto \frac{1}{V} \text{ at constant temperature}$$

where p represents the pressure of the given amount of gas

V represents the volume of the given amount of gas.

The relationship is more usually written as

$$p = C \cdot \frac{1}{V}$$

or $\quad\quad\quad\quad pV = C$ at constant temperature . . (vi)

where C is a constant (whose value depends on the amount of gas involved and on the value of the constant temperature).

Alternatively, if a given mass of gas occupies a volume V_1 at a pressure p_1, and a volume V_2 at a pressure p_2 at the same temperature, then

$$p_1 V_1 = C \text{ and } p_2 V_2 = C$$

or $\quad\quad\quad\quad p_1 V_1 = p_2 V_2$ at constant temperature . (vii)

Equations (vi) and (vii) may be used for any units of volume and absolute pressure provided that these are the same throughout the equation at any one time. The term 'absolute' pressure means the pressure above that of an absolute vacuum. The term 'gauge' pressure may be used to measure the pressure above that normally present which is due to atmospheric pressure (about 101 kN/m² or 1 bar). For example, a gauge pressure of 70 kN/m² would be equivalent to an absolute pressure of about 171 kN/m². Absolute pressures *must* be used for equations (vi) and (vii).

For example, if a certain amount of a gas has a volume of 0·1 m³ at a pressure of 150 kN/m² (absolute), then its volume at a pressure of 225

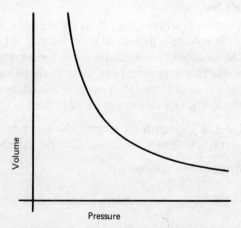

147. Variation of volume with pressure for a given mass of gas at constant temperature

kN/m² (absolute) and at the same temperature, would be given by V, where

$$150 \times 0.1 = 225 \times V$$
$$V = \underline{0.067 \text{ m}^3}$$

Careful experiments show that Boyle's law is really only an approximation of the behaviour of a gas, but the results obtainable with it are usually accurate enough for practical purposes. The law may be said to refer to an ideal gas, although of course the departure of a practical gas from the 'law' is due to the inaccuracy of the 'law', and not to any natural perversity of the gas.

A graph of the variation of volume with pressure has the shape shown in diagram 147. This shape follows from the relationship $pV = C$. If the product of two numbers is a constant, then as one number increases, the other must decrease. (For example,

$$0.1 \times 100 = 1 \times 10 = 10 \times 1 = 100 \times 0.1 = 10.)$$

14.28. Charles' law

If the pressure of a given mass of a gas is maintained constant, it can be shown by experiment that the volume of a gas increases as its temperature is increased.

Although this experiment is a little more complicated than the experiment in connection with Boyle's law, apparatus for it is fairly readily obtainable and the student should carry it out if at all possible.

A graph of the results of such an experiment proves to be a straight line, as shown in diagram 148.

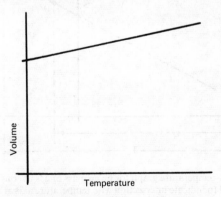

148. Variation of volume with temperature
for a given mass of gas at constant pressure

This form of graph suggests a linear relationship between volume and temperature, so that the equation between volume (V) and temperature (θ) would be expected to have the form

$$V = V_0 (1 + \alpha\theta)$$

in the same way as does linear expansion. Careful experiment shows that, if θ is measured in °C, the value of α (which is the coefficient of cubical expansion of the gas at constant pressure) is very nearly $\dfrac{1}{273}$ for a number of different gases. This means that if the volume–temperature graph for any of these gases is extended or 'extrapolated' until the straight-line graph cuts the temperature-axis, this point would be nearly the same for each; i.e. at -273°C. (For, if $\alpha = \dfrac{1}{273}$ and $\theta = -273$, then $\alpha\theta = -1$, which gives the value of V as zero.)

The results of any extension of a graph beyond the region in which the various experimental points were obtained must be very carefully interpreted. Any relationship derived for the range of values used in an experiment cannot be assumed without further evidence to be true outside this range. For example, it would probably be impossible to reduce the temperature of a gas to very low values without the gas changing its state to a liquid. However, it can be said that, within the range of temperatures used in the experiments, the gas behaves as it would do if the

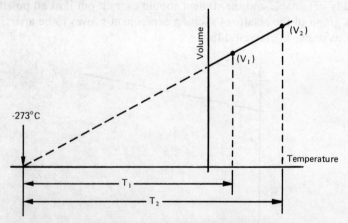

149. Volume–temperature graph for given mass of gas at constant pressure. Extrapolated to indicate intersection with temperature axis at -273°C. The part of the graph shown dotted is not to be taken as representing the behaviour of a gas at low temperatures

volume–temperature graph were to be a straight line which cut the temperature axis (i.e. at zero volume) at − 273°C.

As long as this interpretation is kept clearly in mind, the graph can be extrapolated as shown in diagram 149.

In Section 14.16, page 381, a temperature of − 273°C was stated to be ABSOLUTE ZERO; the temperature at which a body is assumed to have no energy. This temperature is considered as the zero of the ABSOLUTE CELSIUS, or Thermodynamic scale of temperature K (kelvin). When temperatures are measured on this scale, as shown by T_1 and T_2 in diagram 149, it follows from the similar triangles shown on the graph of this diagram that

$$\frac{V_1}{T_1} = \frac{V_2}{T_2} \qquad . \qquad . \qquad . \qquad . \qquad . \quad \text{(viii)}$$

or
$$V \propto T$$

or
$$\frac{V}{T} = \text{a constant} \quad . \qquad . \qquad . \qquad . \quad \text{(ix)}$$

where V = volume of a given mass of gas at constant pressure
T = absolute temperature of the gas.

Charles' law may then be stated as follows:

'The volume of a given mass of gas, whose pressure is maintained constant, is directly proportional to its thermodynamic temperature.'

Once again, Charles' law is only an approximation for the behaviour of a gas, although it gives results which are usually accurate enough for practical purposes.

14.29. Examples

(i) An amount of air of mass 0·05 kg is contained in a cylinder at constant temperature by a piston. At a pressure of 100 kN/m², the density of the air is 1·225 kg/m³. What is the density of the air if the pressure is (a) reduced to 70 kN/m², (b) increased to 300 kN/m², the temperature remaining constant throughout?

Volume of the air at 100 kN/m² and at the constant temperature is given by

$$V_1 = \frac{\text{mass}}{\text{density}}$$

$$= \frac{0\cdot05}{1\cdot225} \text{ m}^3$$

$$= 0\cdot040\ 8 \text{ m}^3$$

Then the volume of the air at 70 kN/m² and the same temperature is given by Boyle's law from the equation $p_1V_1 = p_2V_2$ where $p_1 = 100$ kN/m², $p_2 = 70$ kN/m² and $V_2 = 0\cdot040\ 8$ m³

$$\text{so that } V_2 = \frac{100 \times 0\cdot040\ 8}{70} \text{ m}^3$$

$$= 0\cdot058\ 3 \text{ m}^3$$

The density of the air at this temperature and pressure is then,

$$\text{density} = \frac{\text{mass}}{\text{volume}}$$

$$= \frac{0\cdot05}{0\cdot058\ 3} \text{ kg/m}^3$$

$$= 0\cdot858 \text{ kg/m}^3$$

Similarly, the volume occupied by the air at 300 kN/m² and the same temperature is given by

$$p_1V_1 = p_3V_3$$

or

$$100 \times 0\cdot040\ 8 = 300 \times V_3$$

or

$$V_3 = \frac{100 \times 0\cdot040\ 8}{300}$$

$$= 0\cdot013\ 6 \text{ m}^3$$

so that its density at this temperature and pressure is

$$\text{density} = \frac{\text{mass}}{\text{volume}}$$

$$= \frac{0\cdot05}{0\cdot013\ 6} \text{ kg/m}^3$$

$$= 3\cdot67 \text{ kg/m}^3$$

(ii) A balloon contains 1·2 litre of a gas at a temperature of 15°C. If the temperature of the gas is raised to 60°C, what will be the volume of the gas, on the assumption that the balloon expands so that the gas pressure remains constant?

The initial gas temperature of 15°C corresponds to an absolute or thermodynamic temperature of (15 + 273), or 288 K.

The final gas temperature of 60°C corresponds to an absolute or thermodynamic temperature of (60 + 273), or 333 K.

From Charles' law,

$$\frac{V_1}{T_1} = \frac{V_2}{T_2} \text{ at constant pressure}$$

where, in this case, $V_1 = 1\cdot2$ l, $T_1 = 288$ K, $T_2 = 333$ K.

Then

$$\frac{1\cdot2}{288} = \frac{V_2}{333} \text{ at constant pressure}$$

or

$$V_2 = \frac{333 \times 1\cdot2}{288} \text{ l}$$

$$= 1\cdot390 \text{ l}$$

The volume of the gas would expand to 1·390 l

(iii) A certain mass of gas is contained in a cylinder by a piston. When the temperature of the gas is 15°C and its pressure is 1·3 bar, its volume is 1·6 l. The gas is allowed to expand to a volume of 5·6 l at constant temperature, and then the temperature is raised to 70°C at constant pressure. What is the final pressure and volume of the gas?

For the constant-temperature expansion, Boyle's law may be applied so that

$$p_1 V_1 = p_2 V_2$$

or

$$1\cdot3 \times 1\cdot6 = p_2 \times 5\cdot6$$

or

$$p_2 = \frac{1\cdot3 \times 1\cdot6}{5\cdot6} \text{ bar}$$

or

$$p_2 = 0\cdot372 \text{ bar}$$

For the constant-pressure expansion, Charles' law may be applied, so that

$$\frac{V_2}{T_2} = \frac{V_3}{T_3}$$

or

$$\frac{5\cdot6}{(15 + 273)} = \frac{V_3}{(70 + 273)}$$

or
$$V_3 = \frac{5 \cdot 6 \times 343}{288} \, 1$$

or
$$V_3 = 6 \cdot 67 \, 1$$

Final pressure and volume of the gas are

0·372 bar and 6·67 l

14.30.   Combination of Boyle's law and Charles' law

If the pressure, volume and temperature of a gas all change, Boyle's law and Charles' law may be used together as a combined gas law to determine the result. As in the last example of the previous section, the result can be found if the change is thought of as taking place in two stages; the first stage at constant temperature, and the second stage at constant pressure.

Suppose the pressure, volume and thermodynamic temperature of a given mass of gas change from values p_1, V_1 and T_1 to values p_2, V_2 and T_2.

On the assumption that the first stage takes place at constant temperature (T_1), Boyle's law gives

$$p_1 V_1 = p_2 V_a$$

or
$$V_a = \frac{p_1 V_1}{p_2}$$

where V_2 is an intermediate volume resulting from the first stage of the change.

If the second stage now takes place at constant pressure (i.e. the new pressure p_2 resulting from the first stage), Charles' law gives

$$\frac{V_a}{T_1} = \frac{V_2}{T_2}$$

or
$$V_a = \frac{V_2 T_1}{T_2}$$

The assumed intermediate volume V_2 may now be eliminated by equating the two expressions shown equal to it:

$$V_a = \frac{p_1 V_1}{p_2} = \frac{V_2 T_1}{T_2}$$

Re-arranging this equation gives

$$\frac{p_1 V_1}{T_1} = \frac{p_2 V_2}{T_2} \qquad . \qquad . \qquad . \qquad . \qquad \text{(x)}$$

This general gas law can be seen to combine Boyle's law and Charles' law, since if temperature is constant ($T_1 = T_2$) the equation reduces to that for Boyle's law, and if the pressure is constant ($p_1 = p_2$) the equation reduces to that for Charles' law. It can also be written as

$$\frac{pV}{T} = \text{a constant} \qquad . \qquad . \qquad . \qquad \text{(xi)}$$

For unit mass of gas, the constant is usually written as R, when it is known as the gas constant. Thus, for a mass of gas m,

$$pV = mRT \qquad . \qquad . \qquad . \qquad \text{(xii)}$$

where the gas constant R has a value of about 0·287 kJ/kg K for air, if m is measured in kg, p is measured in kN/m^2, V is measured in m^3, and T is measured in K. Since $R = \dfrac{pV}{mT}$, the units of R may be derived from the other units. For example, $\dfrac{\text{kN/m}^2 \times \text{m}^3}{\text{kg} \times \text{K}}$, or kNm/kg K. Equation (xii) is referred to as the characteristic equation of a gas.

It is sometimes convenient to compare amounts of a gas by their volume at some standard reference temperature and pressure. The reference values usually chosen are 0°C and a normal atmospheric pressure of 101·325 kN/m^2 or 1·013 25 bar. These are called Standard Temperature and Pressure (S.T.P.), although the term Normal Temperature and Pressure (N.T.P.) is also used.

14.31. Examples

(i) If a gas occupies a volume of 400 ml at a pressure of 490 kN/m^2, and a temperature of 30°C, its volume at S.T.P. would be given by V_2, where

$$\frac{p_1 V_1}{T_1} = \frac{p_2 V_2}{T_2}$$

or

$$\frac{490 \times 400}{(30 + 273)} = \frac{101·325 \times V_2}{(0 + 273)}$$

or

$$V_2 = \frac{490 \times 400 \times 273}{101·325 \times 303} \text{ ml}$$

$$= 1742 \text{ ml} = 1·742 \text{ l}$$

Note that any units may be used in the equation $\dfrac{p_1 V_1}{T_1} = \dfrac{p_2 V_2}{T_2}$, pro-

vided they are consistent throughout the equation and that absolute values of temperature and pressure are used. If the characteristic equation $pV = mRT$ is used, however, the units must be those for which the value of the gas constant R is quoted.

(ii) A volume of air of 2·4 l at a pressure of 0·84 bar and a temperature of 27°C is compressed in the cylinder of a diesel engine. If the final pressure is 35 bar and the final temperature is 537°C, find the final volume of air.

Substituting values in equation (x)

$$\frac{p_1 V_1}{T_1} = \frac{p_2 V_2}{T_2}$$

$$\frac{0{\cdot}84 \times 2{\cdot}4}{(27 \times 273)} = \frac{35 \times V_2}{(537 + 273)}$$

or
$$V_2 = \frac{0{\cdot}84 \times 2{\cdot}4 \times 810}{300 \times 35}$$

$$= 0{\cdot}155 \, l$$

Final volume of the air is $\underline{\underline{0{\cdot}155 \, l}}$

(iii) Find the value of the gas constant R for hydrogen given that 1 kg of hydrogen occupies a volume of 11·2 m³ at S.T.P. Units of pressure are to be kN/m², units of volume are to be m³, and units of temperature are to be K.

$$pV = m \cdot R \cdot T$$
In this case
$$m = 1 \text{ kg}$$
$$p = 101{\cdot}325 \text{ kN/m}^2$$
$$V = 11{\cdot}2 \text{ m}^3$$
$$T = 0°C$$
$$= 273 \text{ K}$$

Substituting values,

$$101{\cdot}325 \times 11{\cdot}2 = 1 \times R \times 273$$

or
$$R = \frac{101{\cdot}325 \times 11{\cdot}2}{273}$$

$$= 4{\cdot}16$$

For the given units, the value of the gas constant, R, for hydrogen is about 4·16 kJ/kg K

CHAPTER SUMMARY

Heat is a form of energy.

Transmission of heat may be by conduction, convection or radiation, or by a combination of these.

Temperature is a measure of the relative degree of hotness of a body.

Suitable fixed points for a temperature scale are the melting point of ice (lower fixed point), and the temperature of steam in contact with boiling water at normal atmospheric pressure (upper fixed point).

The temperatures of these fixed points on the common scales of temperature are, respectively, 0°C and 100°C; 273 K and 373 K.

The unit of heat is the joule.

Specific heat
    capacity of a substance = heat energy required to raise the temperature of unit mass of substance by unit temperature rise

Specific heat capacity of water is 4·186 8 kJ/kg°C or $\simeq$ 4·2 kJ/kg°C

$$\text{Relative specific heat capacity} = \frac{\text{specific heat capacity of substance}}{\text{specific heat capacity of water}}$$

Heat lost or gained = mass × specific heat capacity × temperature change

In any transfer of heat energy which does not involve work done,
    heat lost = heat gained

Thermal capacity
    of a body = heat energy required to raise the temperature of the body by 1°C

Water equivalent of a body is numerically equal to the mass of water which would absorb the same heat energy for the same temperature rise.

Enthalpy is that heat energy which causes a change in temperature.

Specific enthalpy of change of phase is that heat energy required by, or released during, a change of phase, and does not correspond to a change in temperature.

Heat energy transfer = change in enthalpy + work done

The temperature of a substance undergoing a change of phase remains constant until the change is complete.

Coefficient of linear expansion (α)

$$= \frac{\text{increase in length for } 1°C \text{ temperature rise}}{\text{original length}}$$

$$L_2 = L_1\{1 + \alpha\,(\theta_2 - \theta_1)\}$$
$$A_2 = A_1\{1 + 2\alpha\,(\theta_2 - \theta_1)\}$$
$$V_2 = V_1\{1 + 3\alpha\,(\theta_2 - \theta_1)\}$$

Boyle's law:

$$pV = C \text{ for a given mass of gas at constant temperature}$$

or, $\quad p_1V_1 = p_2V_2$ for these conditions.

Charles' law: $V \propto T$ for a given mass of gas at constant pressure.

or, $\quad \dfrac{V_1}{T_1} = \dfrac{V_2}{T_2}$ for these conditions.

Combined gas law:

$$pV = mRT$$

or $\quad \dfrac{p_1V_1}{T_1} = \dfrac{p_2V_2}{T_2}$

Note: In the above gas laws,

p = *absolute* pressure
V = volume
T = thermodynamic temperature K = °C + 273
m = mass of gas
R = gas constant.

QUESTIONS

1. Either (a) Distinguish between conduction, convection and radiation of heat, and give an example of each.

or (b) Explain the following:
 (i) Why smoke goes up the chimney.
 (ii) Why wooden handles are often fitted to metal teapots.
 (iii) Why factory roofs are sometimes painted white in summer.

2. (a) State the three ways in which heat may be transferred from one place to another and give an example of each.

(b) Name two liquids used in thermometers, giving their main advantages and disadvantages.

3. What are freezing point and boiling point of water on the Celsius scale? Explain, with the aid of a diagram, how to check the lower fixed point on a thermometer.

4. (a) Heat may cause expansion of solids, liquids and gases. State three other possible general effects of heat and give a practical example of each to illustrate your answer.

(b) A Celsius thermometer is placed (i) in pure melting ice, (ii) in the steam arising from water boiling under normal atmospheric pressure. Give the readings you would expect in each case. With the aid of a neat sketch of a simple mercury barometer, explain what is meant by 'normal atmospheric pressure'.

5. (a) State what is meant by the terms heat and temperature, giving units which may be used for each.

(b) A piece of steel of mass 10 kg is heated from 15°C to 215°C in an oil tank. Calculate the amount of heat gained by the steel given that its relative specific heat capacity is 0·116.

6. A steel component having a mass of 2·5 kg is heated to 750°C and quenched in a tank containing 10 kg of water at 20°C. Calculate the final temperature of the water. Relative specific heat capacity of steel is 0·11. Ignore the heat lost to the atmosphere and tank.

7. (a) State three possible ways in which the addition of heat can affect a substance.

(b) A piece of metal having a temperature of 40°C and a relative specific heat capacity of 0·125 has a mass of 10 kg. It is immersed in water and has its temperature increased to 100°C. Find the heat energy absorbed by the metal.

(c) What is the water equivalent of the metal?

8. (a) Define the joule.

(b) Calculate the number of heat units required to raise the temperature from freezing point of (i) a billet of steel (relative specific heat capacity 0·12), having a mass of 150 kg, to a temperature of 200°C, (ii) 5 litre of water to boiling point.

9. (i) How much heat energy is lost by 30 kg of water in cooling from 100°C to 0°C?

(ii) Calculate the resulting temperature on thoroughly mixing 250 g of water at 20°C with 150 g of water at 100°C. Neglect the effect of the containing vessel.

10. (a) How much heat energy is lost by 150 g of water in cooling from 100°C to 20°C?

(b) Neglecting the effect of the containing vessel, calculate (i) the resulting temperature on thoroughly mixing 50 l of water at 0°C with 100 l of water at 100°C, (ii) the heat energy gained by the cold water.

11. To determine the temperature of a piece of hot metal the following observations were made:

Mass of metal, 225 g; relative specific heat capacity, 0·11
Mass of oil, 800 g; relative specific heat capacity, 0·56
Water equivalent of vessel containing oil, 14 g
Initial temperature of oil and vessel, 16°C.

When the hot metal was immersed in the oil the temperature of the oil rose to 34°C. Calculate the initial temperature of the metal. Heat losses may be neglected.

12. In an experiment to determine the relative specific heat capacity of lead the following observations were made:

Mass of copper calorimeter, empty	95 g
Mass of copper calorimeter and water	152·5 g
Mass of lead	67·5 g
Initial temperature of lead before transfer to the calorimeter	100°C
Initial temperature of water in calorimeter	16°C
Final temperature after transfer of the lead to the calorimeter	18·5°C

If the relative specific heat capacity of copper is 0·1, calculate the relative specific heat capacity of lead from the above data.

13. A steel forging of mass 300 kg is heated to a temperature of 750°C and then quenched in a tank containing 4·5 tonne of oil at 15°C.

Calculate the final temperature of the oil, ignoring the heat losses to tank and atmosphere.

(Take relative specific heat capacity of oil as 0·5, relative specific heat capacity of steel as 0·1.)

14. 100 g of mercury at 100°C is poured into a quantity of water at 16°C, the final temperature of the water being 20°C. Neglecting losses, calculate the mass of water.

(Relative specific heat capacity of mercury = 0·033.)

15. (a) Define specific heat capacity.

(b) The following readings were obtained in a laboratory experiment. Use this information to find the value of the specific heat capacity of the specimen.

Mass of copper calorimeter (rel. sp. ht. cap. = 0·1)	200 g
Mass of the specimen	40 g
Mass of water	100 g
Initial temperature of water and calorimeter	25°C
Initial temperature of specimen	120°C
Final temperature of specimen, calorimeter and water	28°C

What are the most probable errors arising from such an experiment?

16. Describe a method for determination of the specific heat capacity of a liquid by the method of mixtures.

A 10 g mass, of relative specific heat capacity 0·1, is heated to 80°C and transferred to 50 g of liquid at 15°C. If the water equivalent of the calorimeter is 5 g, 60 J are lost in the transfer and the relative specific heat capacity of the liquid is 0·5, calculate the final temperature.

17. A piece of metal of mass 0·75 kg at a temperature of 100°C is lowered into a vessel containing 1 kg of water at a temperature of 15°C. The water equivalent of the vessel is 0·3 kg and the final temperature of the water and the metal is 21°C. Find the relative specific heat capacity of the metal.

18. Given that the specific enthalpy of evaporation of water is 2257 kJ/kg, calculate the amount of heat energy required to convert 5 litre of water, initially at 5°C, into steam at normal atmospheric pressure.

19. Define the term 'specific heat capacity'.

A copper vessel has a mass of 4 kg and contains 5 kg of water at 22°C. The total heat energy required to raise the temperature of the vessel and water to 100°C and then to evaporate 1·5 kg of water at the latter temperature, assuming no losses, is 5·14 MJ. If the specific enthalpy of steam is 2257 kJ/kg, calculate the specific heat capacity of copper.

20. What is meant by the 'water equivalent of a body'?

A vessel has a water equivalent of 1 kg and contains 5 kg of water. The temperature of the vessel and its contents is 15°C. How much heat energy will be required to raise the temperature of the vessel and water to 100°C and evaporate 2·5 kg of water at 100°C, if the specific enthalpy of evaporation is 2257 kJ/kg?

21. Define 'specific enthalpy of fusion'. How much heat energy would be required to convert 20 g of ice at −15°C into water at 40°C? Take the relative specific heat capacity of ice as 0·5 and the specific enthalpy of fusion as 335 kJ/kg.

22. A copper calorimeter has a mass of 48 g and contains 64·2 g of water at 10°C. After passing in 2·5 g of steam at atmospheric pressure, the highest temperature of the calorimeter and contents was observed to be 32°C. Calculate the specific enthalpy of evaporation of the steam. Take the relative specific heat capacity of the copper as 0·1.

23. If 10 g of ice at −15°C are added to 60 g of boiling water contained in a copper calorimeter of water equivalent 7 g, what will be the resulting temperature of the calorimeter and contents, neglecting losses? Take the relative specific heat capacity of ice as 0·5 and the specific enthalpy of fusion of ice as 335 kJ/kg.

24. A calorimeter has a water equivalent of 15 g and contains 90 g of water at 15°C. After adding 5 g of wet ice the final temperature is found to be 12°C. Calculate the percentage of ice present in the original wet ice. Take the specific enthalpy of fusion of ice as 335 kJ/kg.

25. Dry steam at 100°C is passed slowly into a closed vessel of water equivalent 50 g, containing 30 g of water and 10 g of ice. Calculate the total quantity of water in the container when all the ice has just melted.
(Specific enthalpy of fusion of ice = 335 kJ/kg.
Specific enthalpy of evaporation of steam = 2257 kJ/kg.)

26. Define specific enthalpy of evaporation. Calculate the heat energy required to raise 454 g of water from freezing point to boiling point and then to boil away one-ninth of the water, given that the specific enthalpy of evaporation of water is 2257 kJ/kg.

27. (a) Define the terms (i) specific enthalpy of fusion, (ii) specific enthalpy of evaporation.
(b) It is required to convert 10 kg of ice at −9°C to dry saturated steam at atmospheric pressure. The specific enthalpy of fusion of ice is 335 kJ 1 kg, specific enthalpy of evaporation 2257 kJ/kg, relative specific heat capacity of ice = 0·5. How much heat energy is supplied?
(c) If the above heat energy is supplied at a constant rate, sketch a temperature-time graph.

28. 500 kg of steam at a pressure of 0·3 bar enters a surface condenser per hour. The dryness fraction of the incoming steam is 0·9 and the temperature of the condensate is 52°C. If the cooling water enters at a temperature of 15°C, and the quantity is regulated so that its maximum outlet temperature does not exceed 38°C, calculate the quantity of cooling water required per hour.
Steam at 0·3 bar has a temperature of 69·1°C and specific enthalpy of evaporation is 2336 kJ/kg.

29. (a) Explain what is meant by saying that the coefficient of linear expansion of steel is 0·000 01 per degree C.
(b) A length of steel railway line is 15 m long when the temperature is 15°C. What will be the increase in length, in mm, of the line when raised to a temperature of 21°C?
(c) Describe one way in which the expansion of a metal is made use of in industry.

30. Describe an experiment which shows that solids expand when heated. Name three ways in which this effect is allowed for or made use of in daily life.

31. (a) Water at 82°C enters a radiator system and leaves it at a temperature of 60°C. If the rate of flow is 2 litres/min, how much heat energy is given off per hour as the water cools?
(b) In this system a length of iron pipe is 9 m long and contains water initially at a temperature of 10°C. If the final temperature attained by the water is 82°C, find the increase in length of the pipe due to this rise in temperature. (Coefficient of expansion of iron = 0·000 012/°C.)

32. A steel rod is 2·5 m long at 10°C and is raised in temperature to 90°C. If the coefficient of linear expansion of steel is 0·000 012/°C, determine the extension in length.

33. A steel plate has a 50 mm diameter hole. If a 50·100 mm diameter steel shaft is just to enter the hole, find:
(a) The temperature in °C to which the plate will have to be raised if the coefficient of expansion of the steel is 0·000 012/°C.
(b) The amount of heat energy absorbed by the plate in being raised to this temperature, given that the plate has a mass of 4 kg and the relative specific heat capacity of the steel is 0·116.
(Take room temperature to be 15°C.)

34. Explain why it is necessary to provide sleeves and expansion loops in long runs of hot-water pipe. A length of copper tube is 24 m at a temperature of 7°C. Calculate its increase in length, in mm, when water at 93°C is passed through it.
(Coefficient of linear expansion of copper = 0·000 016 5/°C.)

35. A heat exchanger has brass tubes which are 2 m long when fitted at a room temperature of 15°C. What length will the tubes be when
(a) only cooling water at 3°C is passing over the tubes,
(b) only hot oil at 93°C is passing through the tubes?
(Coefficient of linear expansion may be taken as 0·000 020/°C.)

36. (a) Define the 'coefficient of linear expansion'.
(b) A piece of steel rod is 0·75 m long at a temperature of 10°C. What would be the increase in length of the rod when at a temperature of (i) 110°C, (ii) 210°C?
(Assume the coefficient of linear expansion of steel to be 0·000 012/°C.)

37. Define 'coefficient of linear expansion'. If a brass rod is 1 m long at 4°C, what will be its length at 104°C? If a square sheet of brass has an area of 0·040 m² at 4°C, what will be its area at 38°C?
(The coefficient of linear expansion of brass is 0·000 020/°C.)

38. (a) Define 'coefficient of linear expansion'.
(b) A metre rule is pivoted at the 50 mm graduation and is supported by a vertical wire 1 m long fastened at the 100 mm graduation so that at 15°C the rule is horizontal. When the wire is heated to 100°C the end of the rule falls 19·4 mm. Determine the coefficient of linear expansion of the wire material.

39. A boiler supplied with water at a temperature of 18·8°C heats it to 158·8°C and then converts it to steam with a dryness fraction of 0·86. Specific enthalpy of evaporation of the steam under these conditions is 2087 kJ/kg.
(a) Calculate the heat energy supplied by the boiler in producing 1 kg of the wet steam.
(b) The fuel used by the boiler has a calorific value of 33·5 MJ/kg. If 20% of the heat energy in the fuel is lost, calculate the mass of fuel required to produce 900 kg of the wet steam.

o

40. (a) Define the terms as applied to steam: (i) dryness fraction, (ii) specific enthalpy, (iii) total enthalpy.

(b) A mass of 5 kg of dry steam at a pressure of 3·5 bar and a temperature of 138·9°C is blown into a closed tank containing 125 kg of water at a temperature of 5°C. Calculate the final temperature of the water.

(At 3·5 bar, specific enthalpy of evaporation = 2148 kJ/kg.)

Neglect the heat to the tank and treat the question as a simple method of mixtures.

41. A boiler is heated by gas which has a calorific value of 18·75 MJ/m³. If the boiler is in the form of a vertical cylinder 1 m diameter and contains water to a depth of 0·9 m, calculate how many cubic metre of gas would be required to heat the water from 16°C and change half of it into steam.

(Water boils at 100°C. Specific enthalpy of evaporation = 2257 kJ/kg.) Assume no heat losses.

42. A boiler generates 5 tonne of steam per hour at 16 bar from feed water at 49°C. If the dryness fraction of the steam is 0·97, calculate the heat energy supplied by the boiler per kg of steam.

If the boiler fuel has a calorific value of 41·5 MJ/kg and the boiler efficiency is 74%, what mass of fuel will be required per hour?

Pressure bar	Saturation Temp °C	Specific fluid enthalpy (h_f) kJ/kg	Specific enthalpy of evaporation (h_{fg}) kJ/kg
16	201·4	859	1935

43. State Boyle's law. Make a neat sketch of the apparatus you would use to verify this law.

Some hydrogen occupies 1·5 l at 760 mmHg pressure. Calculate the volume of the hydrogen when the pressure is reduced to 570 mmHg, the temperature being kept constant.

44. (a) State Boyle's law.

(b) A volume of 0·084 m³ of gas initially at 14 bar is expanded until the pressure is 2·8 bar. What is the new volume (i) if the temperature remains constant, and (ii) if the temperature subsequently changes from 25°C to 10°C at the constant pressure of 2·8 bar?

45. (a) At the commencement of the compression stroke the cylinder of an air compressor contains 495 ml of air at a pressure of 1 bar and a temperature of 16°C. If this air is compressed so that its volume becomes 55 ml, calculate its pressure assuming that the temperature remains constant.

(b) A volume of 0·1 m³ of air at an initial temperature of 15°C is heated to 115°C, the pressure remaining constant. Calculate the increase in volume.

46. (a) What is meant by the terms 'gauge pressure' and 'absolute pressure'?

(b) State the value of the absolute zero of temperature in (i) °C, (ii) K.

(c) The contents of a cylinder are kept at constant pressure by a gas-tight dead-weight piston. The cylinder is of 600 mm diameter and contains a quantity of gas at 27°C such that the piston is 150 mm from the head of the cylinder. If heat energy is supplied to the gas, increasing the temperature to 54°C, how far will the piston move?

47. Gas at a pressure of 15 bar gauge and a temperature of 227°C occupies a volume of 0·05 m³. It is expanded to a volume of 0·075 m³ at constant temperature, and then heated at constant pressure until the final volume is 0·1 m³.

(a) Sketch the sequence of events on a pressure-volume diagram.

(b) Calculate the final temperature and pressure of the gas.

(Assume atmospheric pressure = 1 bar.)

48. Define 'thermodynamic temperature', and describe an experiment to determine the change of volume of air as the temperature varies from 0°C to 100°C at constant pressure. The volume of a given mass of air is 230 ml at 0°C; calculate its volume at 150°C, assuming the pressure to be unchanged.

49. State the laws of Boyle and Charles in relation to gases. The cylinder of an air compressor is 600 mm diameter and 1·2 m long. Air is drawn in at 0·85 bar and 15°C. When the piston has moved through 600 mm of the compression stroke it is found that the pressure has risen to 5 bar. Find the temperature of the air at this instant.

50. What is meant by 'absolute pressure' and 'thermodynamic temperature'?

An engine cylinder has a compression ratio of 6. At the beginning of the compression stroke, air is drawn in at 13°C and 1 bar, and is compressed to a pressure of 10 bar during the stroke.

Calculate the final temperature of the air.

51. (a) State Boyle's law for a perfect gas.

(b) A compressed air storage vessel has a volume of 1 m³ and the safety valve is set to operate at 6·99 bar gauge. If the gauge reading is 5·99 bar and the temperature of the air in the vessel is 27°C, determine:

(i) the mass of air in the vessel,

(ii) the rise in temperature that must occur to cause the safety valve to blow.

(R for air = 0·287 kJ/kgK

Atmospheric pressure = 1·01 bar

1 bar = 100 kN/m².)

52. A quantity of gas at 2·8 bar and 27°C is contained in a closed vessel of 0·14 m³ capacity. A second quantity of the same gas at 3·5 bar, 27°C and occupying 0·084 m³ is pumped into the container. Determine the final pressure in the container if (a) the action is at constant temperature, (b) the final temperature is 49°C.

53. A compressed-air receiver has a capacity of 0·28 m³. Before charging it is open to atmosphere (pressure 1 bar) and its temperature is 15°C. After charging, the air has a pressure of 20 bar after the temperature has settled again to room temperature. What volume of free air has been pumped into the cylinder?

If $R = 0.287$ kJ/kgK, what mass of air has been handled by the compressor?

54. State clearly what is meant by:
(a) absolute pressure, and
(b) thermodynamic temperature.

The compressed air used for starting an engine is stored in an air bottle of 0.28 m³ capacity. When starting the engine the air pressure was 28 bar and then fell immediately to 25 bar. The initial and final temperatures of the air were 17°C and 7°C respectively. Find the mass of air used in starting the engine. Take R for air as 0.287 kJ/kgK.

55. The pressure of gas in an engine cylinder at the beginning of a compression stroke is 0.84 bar, and the total volume is 0.037 m³.

(a) If the initial gas temperature is 23°C and the compression ratio is 8:1, calculate the gas temperature at the end of compression, assuming the maximum pressure attained is 8.5 bar.

(b) Given that 1 kg of the gas occupies 0.86 m³ under a pressure of 1.01 bar and a temperature of 15°C, determine the mass of gas in the engine cylinder.

(1 bar = 100 kN/m².)

56. A gas cylinder of capacity 0.1 m³ contains oxygen at a pressure of 15 bar at 27°C. Some of the oxygen is used and the pressure in the cylinder is then found to be 12 bar at 0°C. What volume of oxygen at normal pressure and temperature has been consumed?

15. Fluids

15.1. Viscosity

The general name 'fluid' covers the liquid and gaseous states of matter, but this chapter will be concerned mainly with the introduction to the study of the behaviour of liquids.

It has been seen that the particles of which a liquid is composed can be made to move in relation to one another under the action of a shear force much more readily than is the case for a solid. As a result, the gravitational forces acting on these particles ensure that the liquid takes up the shape of its container, so far as the volume of the liquid will permit. The shear force required to move the particles in relation to one another depends on the type of fluid and upon its temperature. It is measured in terms of the VISCOSITY of the fluid. A gas has only a very low viscosity, since the particles move about within the gas very freely, and little resistance is offered to the motion of another body or particle through the gas. The viscosity of liquids is higher than that of gases. Some liquids such as thick lubricating oil possess considerable viscosity, so that they flow less readily than, say, water, whose viscosity is much less. The viscosity of a liquid will increase as its temperature is reduced. As the transition from liquid to solid is approached, the viscosity may become very high indeed, as, for example, in the case of pitch.

15.2. Fluid pressure

A pressure has been defined in Section 2.6, page 27, as the perpendicular force per unit area. The pressure exerted on or by a fluid is thus the force exerted at right angles to a unit area of surface in contact with the fluid. The force exerted by a fluid at any point on a surface will always be at right angles to the surface at that point, and the pressure at any point within the fluid will be the same in all directions. Also, if a pressure is applied to a fluid, this pressure will be transmitted equally in all directions.

For example, if a liquid is contained in a cylinder, and a force is applied to a piston tending to compress the liquid, the pressure at all points in the cylinder will be the same (neglecting the mass of the liquid).

It should be noted that the compression of a liquid which results from such an applied pressure is very small. In many engineering applications this compression may be neglected, although it is strictly inaccurate to consider liquids to be incompressible. This transmission of pressure by a fluid is applied in the hydraulic press, outlined in diagram 150.

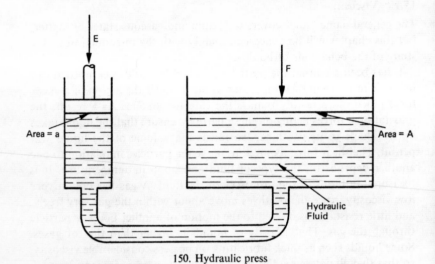

150. Hydraulic press

An effort E is applied to the piston of a cylinder of cross-sectional area a. The resulting pressure in the fluid in the cylinder may be taken as being the same at all points, if the mass of the fluid is neglected, so that this same pressure acts on the larger piston carrying the load F in a cylinder of area A.

Since the pressures on the pistons are the same,

$$\text{pressure} = \frac{\text{force}}{\text{area}}$$

$$= \frac{E}{a} = \frac{F}{A}$$

so that

$$F = \frac{A}{a} \times E \qquad . \qquad . \qquad . \qquad . \qquad \text{(i)}$$

By making the ratio of areas $\dfrac{A}{a}$ very large, a small effort may be made to raise a very much larger load. If the load is raised by a height H, while the effort is moved through a height h, then the volume of fluid displaced in each case must be the same, if it is assumed that the compression of the fluid can be neglected. Then

$$a \times h = A \times H \, (= \text{volume of fluid displaced})$$

or
$$H = \frac{a}{A} \times h \qquad . \qquad . \qquad . \qquad . \qquad . \qquad (ii)$$

In other words, the effort must be moved through a greater distance than the load.

In the terms used in Sections 12.1, 12.2, pages 303–4,

$$\text{force ratio of hydraulic press} = \frac{\text{load}}{\text{effort}}$$

$$= \frac{\text{cross-sectional area of load cylinder}}{\text{cross-sectional area of effort cylinder}}$$

$$= \frac{A}{a}$$

Movement ratio of hydraulic press

$$= \frac{\text{distance moved by effort}}{\text{distance moved by load}}$$

$$\frac{\text{cross-sectional area of load cylinder}}{\text{cross-sectional area of effort cylinder}}$$

$$= \frac{A}{a}$$

Once again, since losses have been neglected,

$$\text{force ratio} = \text{movement ratio}$$

The hydraulic press may be used in industry to exert large forces on large areas, and the same principle is also used in the hydraulic brake systems of cars, etc.

15.3. Effect of the mass of the fluid

Since a fluid will have mass, the gravitational force on this mass will act vertically downwards to produce a force on any surface submerged in the fluid. The pressure at any point within a liquid is dependent only on the vertical depth of that point from the surface of the liquid, together with any pressure that may be acting on the surface. This point may be verified by the pouring of water into a U-tube having sections of differing diameters, as shown in diagram 151.

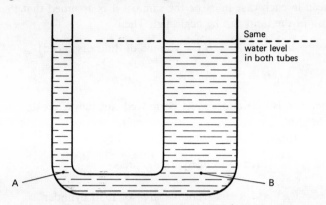

151. Illustration showing that pressure in a fluid depends only on the depth below the surface

The level of the water in each section of the tube will be found to be the same. Since the fluid as a whole is then at rest, the pressure at point A must be the same as that at point B, and the thinner column of water can be thought of as supporting the larger column. The arrangement is similar to that of the hydraulic press already discussed.

The pressure at any point at a given depth below the surface can be calculated from the density of the fluid. Suppose the fluid has a density ρ. Then a point at depth h below the surface can be considered as being on the bottom surface of a tube of fluid having a cross-sectional area of a, so that the volume of the fluid above this point is $a \times h$.

The mass of this tube of fluid is:

$$\text{mass} = \text{density} \times \text{volume}$$
$$= \rho\, ah$$

Force on the bottom surface of the tube = mass × gravitational acceleration

$$= \rho\, ahg$$

$$\text{Then pressure} = \frac{\text{force}}{\text{area}}$$

$$= \frac{\rho\, gah}{a}$$

$$p = \underline{\rho\, gh} \qquad . \qquad . \qquad \text{(iii)}$$

This result neglects any pressure acting on the surface of the fluid, and this should be added to the answer given here.

Since the fluid pressure at a point depends only on the depth of the point below the surface and on the density of the fluid, pressure may be measured in terms of the 'head' of fluid above the point concerned. This is very frequently done in connection with water pressures. For example, the pressure of water at a domestic tap may be measured in terms of the head of water represented by the vertical height of the reservoir above the level of the tap. If the tap is at a height greater than the head of water available, no water will flow when the tap is turned on. The effect is sometimes noticeable in tall buildings, where water from a tap on an upper floor emerges with less force than water from a tap on the ground floor.

15.4. Atmospheric pressure. The barometer

Atmospheric pressure is due to the mass of the air above the ground. The density of air at sea level is about $1·225$ kg/m^3, but as there is an effective height of several kilometres of air above ground level, the resulting pressure is measurable in kN/m^2, a typical value being about $101·3$ kN/m^2 or $1·013$ bar. Atmospheric pressure varies with climatic conditions, but the pressure is usually within about 10% of this value. The pressure of the atmosphere can be made to support a column of liquid in an arrangement known as a barometer. Diagram 152 shows a simple barometer—a tube, closed at one end, filled with liquid and then inverted in a trough of the liquid.

The atmospheric pressure acting on the surface of the liquid in the trough is equal to the pressure due to the column of liquid in the inverted tube, and so can be measured in terms of the height of this column.

If water were used, usual atmospheric pressures would support a column about $10·4$ m high, which would make the instrument rather inconvenient for practical use. Consequently, such barometers usually use mercury for the liquid. Since the relative density of mercury is about $13·6$, the height of the column is only $\frac{1}{13·6} \times$ height of the corresponding column of water.

Atmospheric pressures are often quoted as a head of mercury, and a typical value is about 760 mm. Accurate mercury barometers are available, such as the Fortin barometer, which enable barometric heights to be measured to within, say, a tenth of a millimetre of mercury.

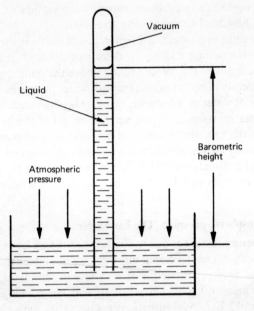

152. Simple barometer

Such barometers are not portable, however, and for applications requiring the measurement of atmospheric pressure by more portable apparatus, the aneroid barometer may be used. This contains a sealed vessel, usually made from thin, flexible metal. The air pressure in the vessel is reduced before the vessel is sealed, so that an increase in atmospheric pressure will distort the shape of the vessel because of the unbalance of pressures outside and within it. This distortion is arranged to move a pointer over a calibrated scale.

15.5.   The siphon

Atmospheric pressure may be used to cause a liquid to flow up a tube and so out of a container in which the tube is placed. This action is known as siphoning, and diagram 153 shows the action of a siphon. The atmospheric pressure acting on the surface of the liquid is sufficient to force the liquid up the siphon tube and out at the other end, provided that the maximum height of the siphon tube above the level of the liquid is less than the barometric height; i.e. less than about 10 m in the case of water. Before the action can start, it is necessary that the tube should

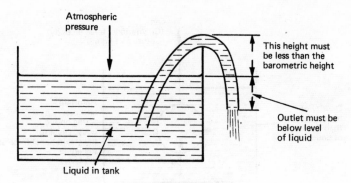

Atmospheric pressure

This height must be less than the barometric height

Outlet must be below level of liquid

Liquid in tank

153. The siphon

first be filled with water. This is because the atmospheric pressure would otherwise also act on the surface of the water inside the tube, and thus give balanced pressures. It is also necessary that the outlet of the siphon should be below the level of the liquid in the container. This is because the liquid at the outlet will also be under atmospheric pressure, so that the resultant pressure forcing the liquid from the tank is due to the head of liquid between the level in the tank and the level of the outlet.

15.6. Archimedes' principle

If a body having a given density is placed in a liquid of greater density, the body will float in the liquid. For example, a wooden block will float in water. It follows that the water must be supporting the gravitational force on the wooden block, and so must be exerting an upthrust on the block. A similar upthrust is exerted even on a body having a greater density than the liquid in which it is placed. In such a case, however, the upthrust is less than the gravitational force on the body, so that the body sinks in the liquid.

Archimedes' principle states that:

'If a body floats, or is submerged, in a liquid, the liquid exerts an upthrust on the body equal to the gravitational force on the liquid displaced by the body.'

This principle should be investigated experimentally by the student. If a body is suspended from a force balance firstly in air and then while submerged in a liquid, the difference between the two readings will be found to be equal to the gravitational force on the volume of liquid displaced by the body.

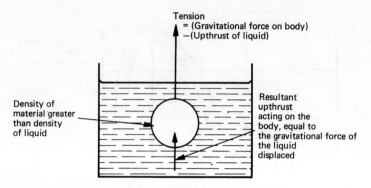

154. Body submerged in a liquid

The conditions may be visualized as being caused by the forces which would be exerted if the volume of the immersed solid were to be replaced —i.e. 'the hole filled up'—by the liquid concerned Equilibrium conditions would then be obtained, so that the liquid would exert an upthrust on the solid's volume equal to the gravitational force on the liquid which it represents. If the density of the body is less than the density of the liquid—i.e. if a given volume of the body has a mass less than the same volume of the liquid—the body will float in the liquid. The body will then displace only enough volume of liquid to equal its own gravitational force, and part of the floating body will be above the surface. If the density of the body is greater than that of the liquid, the same volume of the liquid has a mass less than the body, so that the upthrust is insufficient to support the body even when it is totally submerged, and it sinks.

Note that a hollow steel shell, such as the hull of a ship, will float in water since its *average* density (mass ÷ volume) is less than that of water.

15.7.   The hydrometer

The relative density of a liquid may be measured by means of Archimedes' principle. Diagram 155 shows a simple hydrometer which consists of a loaded tube marked with a scale on the stem.

The hydrometer is placed in the liquid so that it floats in an upright position. The volume immersed in the liquid represents the volume of liquid which has a mass equal to the mass of the hydrometer. If the density of the liquid is high, only a small volume will need to be dis-

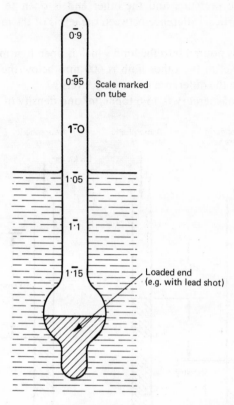

155. Simple hydrometer

placed, and the hydrometer will float high in the liquid. If the density is low, the hydrometer will need to displace a greater volume of the liquid and it will float with a greater length of its body immersed. The scale may, then, be marked off directly in terms of the relative density of the liquid, with the higher values being nearer the loaded lower end.

It is usual to have several such hydrometers, each covering a limited range of relative densities.

15.8. Examples

(i) A U-tube has open ends and is partly filled with mercury. One limb is connected to apparatus such that the pressure is 35 kN/m² above atmospheric pressure, and the other end is open to the atmosphere. Find the vertical difference between the levels of the mercury in the two limbs.

If water is poured into the limb which is open to atmosphere until the mercury level in the other limb is 600 mm below the free water level, what is then the difference in mercury levels?

Density of mercury is 13·6 tonne/m^3 and density of water is 1 tonne/m^3.

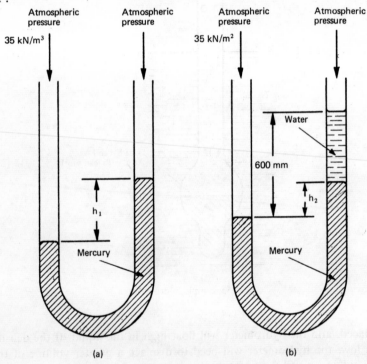

156. Numerical example

(a) Mercury alone

Difference in pressure between the two sides = 35 kN/m^2. This must support a height h_1 m of mercury. Assume a cross-sectional area of tube of a m^2. Then the volume of mercury supported

$$= h_1 \text{ m} \times a \text{ m}^2$$
$$= h_1 \times a \text{ m}^3$$

Then the mass of mercury supported

$$= \text{volume} \times \text{density}$$
$$= h_1 \times a \times 13\,600 \text{ kg}$$
$$= 13\,600\,h_1\,a \text{ kg}$$

Then

$$\text{pressure} = \frac{\text{force}}{\text{area}} = \frac{\text{mass} \times \text{gravitational acceleration}}{\text{area}}$$

$$= \frac{13\,600\,h_1\,a \times 9 \cdot 81}{a} \text{ N/m}^2$$

$$= 13 \cdot 6 \times 9 \cdot 81\,h_1 \text{ kN/m}^2$$

This is equal to the given pressure difference of 35 kN/m²

$$\therefore\ 13 \cdot 6 \times 9 \cdot 81\,h_1 = 35$$

$$h_1 = \frac{35}{13 \cdot 6 \times 9 \cdot 81} \text{ m}$$

$$= 0 \cdot 262 \text{ m}$$
$$= \underline{262 \text{ mm}}$$

(b) Mercury and water

In this case, the same pressure difference supports a column of mercury of height h_2 m together with a column of water of height $(0 \cdot 6 - h_2)$ m.

By reasoning similar to that given in detail for the previous case, the pressure due to these two columns together is given by

$$13 \cdot 6 \times 9 \cdot 81\,h_2 + 1 \times 9 \cdot 81\,(0 \cdot 6 - h_2) \text{ kN/m}^2$$

Again equating this to the pressure difference of 35 kN/m²,

$$13 \cdot 6 \times 9 \cdot 81\,h_2 + 9 \cdot 81\,(0 \cdot 6 - h_2) = 35$$
or
$$133 \cdot 4\,h_2 + 5 \cdot 88 - 9 \cdot 81\,h_2 = 35$$
or
$$123 \cdot 6\,h_2 = 35 - 5 \cdot 9$$

$$h_2 = \frac{29 \cdot 1}{123 \cdot 6}$$

$$h_2 \simeq 0 \cdot 235 \text{ m}$$
$$\simeq \underline{235 \text{ mm}}$$

The difference in mercury levels before the water is added is <u>262 mm</u>
The difference in mercury levels after the water is added is <u>235 mm</u>

(ii) What mass of wire having a relative density of 8 must be wrapped round a cork weighing 10 g in order that the cork shall just sink in water? Take the relative density of cork as 0·25.

In order that the combined cork and wire shall just sink, the average density must be the same as (or very slightly greater than) that of water; i.e. the combined relative density must be 1.

Suppose a mass of m kg of wire is required. Then, since

$$\text{volume (m}^3) = \frac{\text{mass (kg)}}{\text{density (kg/m}^3)}$$

$$\text{volume of wire} = \frac{m}{8 \times 1000} \text{ m}^3$$

$$\text{and volume of cork} = \frac{0 \cdot 010}{0 \cdot 25 \times 1000} \text{ m}^3$$

The total volume is then $\dfrac{m}{8000} + \dfrac{0 \cdot 010}{250} \text{ m}^3$

But the total mass $= m + 0 \cdot 010 \text{ kg}$

$$\therefore \text{ average density} = \frac{\text{total mass}}{\text{total volume}}$$

$$= \frac{m + 0 \cdot 010}{\dfrac{m}{8000} + \dfrac{0 \cdot 010}{250}} \text{ kg/m}^3$$

For the cork and wire just to sink, this average density must be equal to that of water (1000 kg/m³).

$$\therefore \qquad \frac{m + 0 \cdot 010}{\dfrac{m}{8000} + \dfrac{0 \cdot 010}{250}} = 1000$$

$$\therefore \qquad m + 0 \cdot 010 = \left(\frac{m}{8000} + \frac{0 \cdot 010}{250} \right) 1000$$

or $\qquad m + 0 \cdot 010 = 0 \cdot 125 \, m + 0 \cdot 040$

or $\qquad m - 0 \cdot 125 \, m = 0 \cdot 040 - 0 \cdot 010$

$$0 \cdot 875 \, m = 0 \cdot 030$$

$$m = \frac{0 \cdot 030}{0 \cdot 875}$$

$$m = 0 \cdot 034 \, 3 \text{ kg}$$

A mass of 34·3 g of wire must be wound round the cork to make it sink in water.

CHAPTER SUMMARY

Viscosity is a measure of the force required to move a body within a fluid.

Fluid pressure always acts at right angles to any point on a surface in contact with the fluid. Any pressure applied to a fluid will be transmitted equally in all directions.

Movement ratio of hydraulic press

$$= \frac{\text{cross-sectional area of load cylinder}}{\text{cross-sectional area of effort cylinder}}$$

Fluid pressure at a point h vertically below the surface of a fluid of density ρ is $\rho\,gh$ + pressure acting on the surface.

Atmospheric pressure may be measured in terms of the height of a column of liquid which can be supported by the pressure of the atmosphere. This may be referred to as the barometric height.

Archimedes' principle states that:

'If a body floats, or is submerged, in a liquid, the liquid exerts an upthrust on the body equal to the gravitational force on the liquid displaced by the body.'

QUESTIONS

1. Explain the principle of a hydrometer. Give one practical use.

2. Explain either (a) the principle of a simple mercury barometer, or (b) the action of a bicycle pump and the valve attached to the tyre.

3. (a) Describe the construction of a simple mercury barometer and explain any scientific principles involved.

(b) A mercury barometer records a pressure of 760 mm of mercury. Calculate the *total* pressure (in kN/m^2) at a depth of 2 m below the surface of a tank of water. (Relative density of mercury = 13·6.)

4. Show by a small diagram how pressure per square metre due to a given head of fluid is calculated.

If the pressure on a 25 mm diameter circle due to a 1 m head is 7·8 kN/m^2 what would be the total force on the 10 mm diameter aperture of a safety valve due to a head of 11 m?

5. A piece of stone was suspended from a force balance in air and then suspended in water, the respective readings being 0·118 N and 0·073 N. Similar pieces were loosely packed into a container of exactly 1 m³ capacity and the mass of stone required to fill it was 1·55 tonne. Calculate the percentage volume of the container not occupied by the stones.

6. Describe how a simple mercury barometer can be made and calculate a suitable length for the tube assuming an atmospheric pressure of 101 kN/m². (Relative density of mercury = 13·6.)

7. (a) Define 'relative density'.

(b) A piece of cork in the form of a cube is placed in water in a graduated cylinder and causes the level of the water to rise from the 30 ml to the 33·5 ml mark. If the relative density of the cork is 0·25, what is its volume? What mass must be placed on the cube so that it is exactly half immersed?

8. A cylindrical tank, diameter 2·1 m, contains oil of relative density 0·8 to a depth of 1·2 m, and the bottom of the tank is horizontal. Calculate the total force acting on the bottom of the tank.

The tank is emptied by opening a rectangular flap valve in the base which is 300 mm square. If the flap is hinged on one edge and raised by a vertical chain attached to the opposite edge, what force is required in the chain to raise the flap?

9. A U-tube having open arms of equal length is filled with water to such a depth that each arm is filled to within 150 mm from the top. Oil of relative density = 0·75 is then poured into one arm until it is full. What length of tube does the oil occupy? Would a block of wood which floats in water with two-thirds of its volume submerged also float in the above oil?

10. A closed cylindrical oil storage tank is 6 m high and contains oil of relative density = 0·8 to a depth of 5·4 m. If a gauge shows the pressure at the base to be 175 kN/m² absolute, what is the pressure in the tank above oil level? If oil is drawn off until the level falls to 3 m, what pressure will the gauge now read?

11. (a) Describe, with the aid of a sketch, any simple hydrometer, and explain why it may be used to determine the relative density of a solid.

(b) A graduated U-tube contains water and the level is noted and marked as zero. A quantity of oil, which does not mix with the water, is poured into the left-hand limb until the oil level is 29 mm above the original zero and the water in the right-hand limb is seen to rise 22·5 mm. Calculate the relative density of the oil.

12. Define relative density. By means of a force balance and a linen thread, a piece of metal is suspended first in air and then totally immersed and freely suspended in water. The force balance registers first 2·65 N and then 1·665 N. Calculate (a) the mass of water displaced by the metal, (b) the relative density of the metal.

13. A pontoon is 9 m square, 2·5 m deep, and has a mass of 80 tonne. Determine the depth of pontoon below the water line when it floats in sea water of density 1·025 tonne/m³.

14. In a hydraulic press, the ram is 750 mm diameter and the piston of the pump is 100 mm diameter. Calculate the movement ratio of the press.

If a force of 20 kN is applied to the piston, find the load on the ram and the pressure in the hydraulic fluid. Neglect friction.

15. The lower end of a vertical tube stands in a bath of mercury. An air pump connected to the upper end reduces the pressure to 70 kN/m². Find the height of the mercury column in the tube above the free surface of mercury in the bath if the barometric height is 760 mm Hg.

(Relative density of mercury = 13·6.)

16. A U-tube has open ends, the arms have an internal cross-sectional area of 650 mm², and a total height of 840 mm. Mercury is poured into the U-tube until the level is at a height of 173 mm in both arms. Find the greatest amount of water that can be poured into one of the arms.

(Relative density of mercury = 13·6.)

17. Three blocks, A, B and C, are made of gold, silver and an alloy of gold and silver respectively, and have the same mass. When suspended in water, the gold block, A, shows an apparent loss in gravitational force of 0·206 N, the silver block, B, a loss of 0·382 N; and the alloy block, C, a loss of 0·265 N. Find (a) the proportion by mass of gold in the alloy, (b) the density of the alloy.

(Relative density of silver = 10·5.)

16. The Electric Circuit

16.1. Electric charge

It was seen earlier (Chapter 13) that all matter is built up from a small number of fundamental types of particle, of which the most important in a preliminary treatment of scientific theory are the electron, the proton and the neutron. Although all these particles are extremely small, the electron is by far the smallest, and in many (although not all) practical cases the mass of the electron is so small compared with that of other quantities that it is often assumed to have no significant mass at all. However, despite its extremely small mass, the electron possesses a very important fundamental property. It is found experimentally that an electron exerts a force on any other electron, tending to repel it. If it were possible to place two electrons close together, a force would be set up which would tend to push them apart.

The discovery of the electron came at a comparatively late stage in the development of scientific theory. At a much earlier stage, a similar repulsive force had been discovered to exist between materials such as ebony and amber, which had been rubbed with a dry cloth or fur. In order to explain this repulsive force, it had been assumed that the rubbed material acquired what was called a 'charge' of electricity. During these early investigations, it was found that if a material such as amber were to be rubbed with the cloth and then placed near another material such as glass which had been similarly rubbed, an attractive force was set up between them, tending to bring them together. Consequently it was supposed that there were two kinds of electric charge, which were called 'positive' and 'negative'. Since there was no obvious reason to suggest which should be called positive and which negative, an arbitrary decision was made; the glass was said to have acquired a positive charge and the amber to have acquired a negative charge, through being rubbed with the cloth. As will be seen later, the choice made has since proved to have been unfortunate, but by the time later discoveries had shown the desirability of having a particular sign convention, so much fundamental theory had been evolved which was based on the earlier choice that it was decided to retain the 'positive' and 'negative' decision already made. It is important to note that charges of the same sign (i.e. both positive or both negative) mutually repel one another, while charges of opposite sign attract one another (see diagram 157).

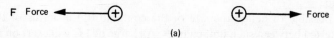

(a)

Repulsion between two positively charged bodies

(b)

Repulsion between two negatively charged bodies

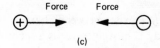

(c)

Attraction between two bodies
having charges of opposite sign

157. Forces between electric charges

A simple test which will illustrate these forces between electric charges is to rub a fountain-pen case (a 'plastic' one will do) on a piece of dry cloth (e.g. a coat sleeve), and then to hold it over some small pieces of paper. The pen will be found to attract the paper, and it should be possible to lift up the paper on the case of the pen. The electric charge produced on the fountain-pen by the rubbing is said to 'induce' an opposite charge on the nearer faces of the pieces of paper. These opposite charges on the pen and the paper then attract one another, and this force of attraction will usually be sufficient to lift the paper towards the pen.

Using the sign convention previously established, scientists found that the electron carried a negative electric charge. As might be supposed, the electron charge is very small, and in many cases it would be very inconvenient to take this as a unit in which to measure electric charges. A more practical unit, many times larger than the charge on an electron, is usually used. This unit is called the COULOMB (named after a French scientist), and the charge on an electron is 1.602×10^{-19} coulomb.

It is possible to define the size of the coulomb (C) in terms of the force exerted between such unit charges. A charge of 1 C will exert on an equal charge, placed 1 m from it in air, a force of 8.988×10^9 N (nearly nine thousand million newtons). This is a very large force, and static charges of the magnitude of 1 C are rarely encountered in practice. For static charges the sub-multiple unit, the MICRO-COULOMB (μC), is more often used. As in other cases, the prefix 'micro' means 'one millionth part', so that one micro-coulomb = 1×10^{-6} coulomb.

The equipment required to measure the force between charges is delicate, and it is difficult to obtain a precise result. It is more convenient in practice to use other methods of measuring charge, which depend on further properties of electric charges which will be discussed later.

16.2. Potential

Since a repulsion force exists between charges of the same sign, if a positively charged body is moved towards a second body also carrying a positive charge, some external force must be applied to bring the two together. Consequently, work will be done by the external force. The amount of work involved in bringing a unit positive charge up to any point near another charge, or system of charges, from a position very far away, is used to measure the 'electric potential' at that point. The units in which potential may be measured are, then, those of 'work per unit charge' or JOULES PER COULOMB. However, as will be seen later, this unit of potential is very important and very frequently used, and a simpler name is given to it. The unit of potential is known as the VOLT (again named after an early scientist). It follows then that

$$1 \text{ VOLT} = 1 \text{ JOULE PER COULOMB}$$

16.3. Potential difference

In the same way that the absolute potential at any point is measured in terms of the work done in moving unit positive charge to that point, so the difference in potential between any two points is measured by the work done in moving unit positive charge from one point to the other.

This potential difference, or p.d., as it is often written, is of course also measured in volts. (See diagram 158.)

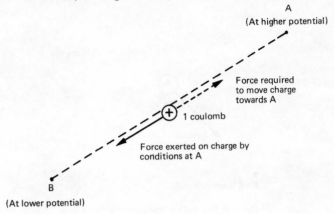

158. Force on charge between points at different potentials

Point A is said to be at a higher potential than point B if work is required to move a positive charge from B to A. This means that a force is exerted by the conditions at A, tending to push the positive charge away from A. If, then, a positive charge were to be released between A and B, it would be pushed from A towards B. In other words, a positive charge free to do so will move from points of higher potential to points of lower potential. If follows that a free negative charge will move from points of lower potential to points of higher potential. (See diagram 159.)

16.4. Conductors and insulators

This discussion of the movement of unit positive charges from point to point near other charges has deliberately been made in general terms, since it is the starting point for many different types of study in electrical theory. However, for present purposes, it will now be possible to confine discussion to particular paths of movement of charge.

First consider the types of material along which movement of electric charge may be made fairly readily. It has been seen that all atoms have a central nucleus. Around this are arranged a number of orbital electrons, these electrons being arranged in a number of shells. Each shell contains a definite number of electrons, although the outermost shell

A (at higher
● potential)

Force on
positive charge

●
B (at lower potential)

(a) Force on 'free' positive charge moves it
from higher potential to lower potential

A (at higher
● potential)

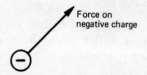

Force on
negative charge

●
B (at lower potential)

(b) Force on free negative charge moves it
from lower potential to higher potential

159. Force on 'free' charges between points at different potentials

of all may not have its full 'complement' of electrons. In some materials, notably the metals, there are one or two electrons in the outer shell which are only very loosely attached to their 'parent' atom. When these atoms are packed closely together, as they are in the solid state of the material, these loosely-bound electrons will move spontaneously from one atom to the next, in a random manner. At any one time there will thus be a large number of electrons in transit from one atom to another. Since the electrons themselves carry a negative electric charge, it follows that it is easy to move charges around in such materials, and, moreover, that there are charges already present that can be moved. Such materials are called CONDUCTORS.

In another important class of materials, however, there are no loosely-bound electrons, and therefore no random interchange of electrons between adjacent atoms. In these materials, the movement of electric charges is difficult, and generally it is possible to assume that no significant movement of charge can take place. These materials are called INSULATORS.

As might be supposed, there are some materials, notably silicon and germanium, which cannot strictly be classed as either conductors or insulators. In these a certain limited movement of charge can be made under certain conditions, and fairly recent developments have made them very important. These materials are called SEMI-CONDUCTORS.

It should be emphasized that there are no really firm divisions between these various classes of materials. All will allow electron movement to a certain extent, and the only difference is one of degree. A conductor will allow an electric charge to move within it fairly readily, a semi-conductor rather less readily and an insulator much less readily. This matter is put on a more scientific basis in the later section on resistivity (see Section 16.20, page 475).

16.5. Electromotive force

It is possible to make electrical equipment, such as an electrical battery, or a generator, which is capable of producing a difference in potential between two points. (The mechanism by which this potential difference is produced is dealt with in later chapters of this book, and need not be considered at present.)

Such equipment is said to produce an 'electromotive force' (usually abbreviated to e.m.f.) and this is measured in terms of the potential difference produced. It follows that the unit in which e.m.f. is measured is the VOLT. The battery or generator terminal at the higher potential is called the 'positive' terminal, while that at the lower potential is called the 'negative' terminal.

16.6. Simple electric circuit. Electric current flow

If the two terminals of a battery are connected to each end of a piece of conducting material, the battery e.m.f. will cause a potential difference to be developed between the ends of the conductor.

It has already been shown that a positive charge free to do so will move from points of higher potential to points of lower potential, while a free negative charge will move in the reverse direction. It follows that the random movement of the negatively-charged electrons between adjacent atoms in the conductor will now have a 'drift' movement superimposed on it by the potential difference across the conductor. The overall result will be a movement of electrons away from the end of the conductor at the lower potential; i.e. the end connected to the negative terminal of the battery. Electrons thus move round the 'circuit' of battery and conductor, leaving the conductor to enter the positive terminal of the battery, and re-entering the conductor from the negative terminal.

It must be emphasized that the speed of movement of any individual electron round this circuit is very slow, being less than 1 millimetre a second. Since, however, an extremely large number of electrons is involved, the total number passing any one point at any instant is very large. Also, there is no loss of electrons from the conductor, because electrons are entering at one end as fast as they are leaving at the other. It is rather like a fairground 'dodgem' car circuit. Each individual car makes a somewhat erratic movement round the circuit, with many collisions on the way, but the overall movement of all the cars is in one general direction. Furthermore, since it can be assumed that they all start at the same time, this 'flow' of cars round the circuit starts immediately the main switch is closed. Similarly, any individual electron makes a slow, erratic movement around the circuit, colliding frequently with the atoms of the conductor, but since the general electron drift starts as soon as the battery is connected, the 'flow' of electrons starts at the instant the connection is made. This electron drift constitutes what is known as an ELECTRIC CURRENT. (Strictly, the electron drift does not start instantaneously at all points. Imagine a line of people standing very close together, shoulder-to-shoulder. If someone gave the person at one end a hard push, the line of people would start to move slowly along, but the 'push' would travel down the line very quickly, with the person at the far end feeling the effects very soon after the first person was pushed. In the case of the electron drift, the 'push' travels very rapidly indeed—at about 3×10^8 m/s—although the average speed of an individual electron is very slow, as has been said.)

Summary

An electric current consists of the steady drift of a very large number of randomly-moving electrons.

As was mentioned earlier, electric currents were known and investigated long before the existence of the electron was discovered. These currents were at that time assumed to consist of the movement of positive charges flowing from the positive battery terminal into the conductor. This is still taken to be the conventional direction of current flow, even though it is now known that in fact the current consists of electrons moving in the opposite direction. It is perhaps unfortunate that the arbitrary positive and negative decision referred to earlier should have been made as it was. However, as long as the fundamental nature of an electric current is appreciated, there is no reason why the conventional direction of current should not be used in the majority of cases.

Summary

The conventional direction of flow of electric current is from high to low potentials, and is in opposition to the direction of electron drift.

16.7. Unit of electric current

A measure of an electric current is a measure of the rate at which electrons pass along a conductor. Since very large numbers of electrons are involved in even a small current flow, it would be impracticable to use the rate of electron flow as a unit of current measurement—rather like measuring a volume of sand by counting grains! It is more convenient to measure a current in terms of the total electric charge which passes a given point in a conductor in unit time. Thus the fundamental unit of electric current is the COULOMB PER SECOND.

Again, since this unit is very important and very frequently used, it is given a special name, the AMPERE (again named after a famous scientist), so that

$$1 \text{ AMPERE} = 1 \text{ COULOMB PER SECOND}$$

Current, in amperes, is equal to the rate of flow of electric charge, in coulombs per second. If a charge of Q C flows along a conductor in t s, the current is I A, where

$$I = \frac{Q}{t} \quad . \quad . \quad . \quad . \quad \text{(i)}$$

The international definition of the ampere is based on other properties of electric currents, which will be discussed later. The definition given here will suffice for the present.

16.8. Effects of electric current

The presence of an electric current was first discovered through the effects it produced in or near the circuit round which it was flowing. These effects can be split up roughly into three groups: the heating effect, the magnetic effect and the chemical effect. Each of these will later be considered in more detail, but a brief description might be of interest here.

(a) Heating effect

When an electric current passes along a conductor, it is found that the conductor gets hot. The more current that flows, the hotter the conductor will become. As is usually the case when practical use is made of a scientific discovery, in some cases this effect is very useful, and in others it is a nuisance. The operation of electric fires, cookers, irons and filament-lamps, for example, depends on this effect, as does the operation of the safety fuse used in circuits to protect them from carrying too much current. The heating effect can also be used to measure the value of current flowing in a circuit.

The heating effect is less welcome, however, to the power-station engineer, for example. The flow of current in the conductors of his generators causes them to get hot, and so limits their output. Some form of cooling is necessary, and very elaborate methods may be used to dissipate the heat energy produced and so increase the possible generator output.

(b) Magnetic effect

The flow of current along a conductor is found to affect a small magnet, such as a compass needle, if it is placed near the conductor. The magnet is swung away from its usual north-south position, and again, the greater the current the greater its effect on the magnet. Considerable practical use has been made of this effect, and the action of electric motors, generators, transformers, bells, relays and so on, all depend on it. It is also used to measure the value of current flowing in a circuit, and the international definition of the ampere is based on this magnetic effect.

(c) Chemical effect

It is possible to pass an electric current through certain chemical solutions—the mechanism of this current flow will be dealt with later. When current passes through such solutions, chemical changes take place. The exact form of these changes depends on the type of solution and the way in which the current is led into and away from it, but they are all due to the movement of electric charges through the solution.

The chemical effect of an electric current is used, for example, in electro-plating, and in the production and refinement of some chemicals. The operation of electrical batteries also depends on this effect, while the corrosion of some metals, such as the rusting of iron, is an instance where the effect is less welcome.

16.9. Resistance

On page 442 it was shown that if a battery is connected across a piece of conducting material, an electric current flows round the circuit thus set up. The conventional direction of this current flow in the conductor is from the positive terminal to the negative terminal of the battery. The value of the current flow will depend on the e.m.f. of the battery, and upon the ease with which the drift of electrons can be superimposed on their normal random movement. This will be seen later to depend on the material and dimensions of the conductor, and on its temperature. However, for a given conductor at a given temperature it is found that the value of the current is directly proportional to the value of the potential difference maintained between the ends of the conductor (e.g. if the p.d. is doubled, the current is also doubled). This important fact is stated in Ohm's law:

'Under constant temperature conditions, the current in a conductor is directly proportional to the potential difference maintained between its ends.'

This simple relationship between current and potential difference enables the current for any value of p.d. to be found once one value of current is known for one value of p.d.

Example

When a potential difference of 10 V exists between the ends of a certain conductor, the current is found to be 2 A.

(i) What current flows for a potential difference of 8 V?

(ii) What potential difference is required to cause a current of 3 A to flow?

Let the current be represented by I A while the potential difference is represented by V V. Then, by Ohm's law, I is proportional to V

or
$$I \propto V$$

or
$$\frac{V_1}{I_1} = \frac{V_2}{I_2}$$

where I_1 is current for potential difference of V_1.

and I_2 is current for potential difference of V_2

Thus (i)
$$\frac{10}{2} = \frac{8}{I_2}$$

giving
$$I_2 = 1 \cdot 6 \text{ A}$$

and (ii)
$$\frac{10}{2} = \frac{V_2}{3}$$

giving
$$V_2 = 15 \text{ V}$$

In the above example, Ohm's law has been expressed in symbols as

$$I \propto V$$

This may also be expressed mathematically as

$$\frac{V}{I} = \text{constant}$$

This constant gives the p.d. required across the conductor to give a current of 1 A along the conductor. It is known as the RESISTANCE of the conductor, and it is measured in VOLTS PER AMPERE. Once again, however, this unit is used so frequently that it is given the simpler name, OHM (Ω) (named after the scientist who put forward the law given above). It follows that

$$1 \text{ OHM} = 1 \text{ VOLT PER AMPERE}$$

For the values used in the previous example, the resistance of the conductor is given by

$$\text{resistance of conductor} = \frac{\text{p.d. between ends of conductor}}{\text{current flowing in conductor}} \tag{ii}$$

or, in symbols,

$$R = \frac{V}{I} \quad . \quad . \quad . \quad . \quad \text{(iii)}$$

$$= \frac{10}{2}\ \Omega$$

$$= \underline{5\ \text{ohms}}$$

Note: A conductor whose most important property is its resistance is usually called a RESISTOR. The term 'resistance' should be confined to the *property* of the conductor as defined above, and not applied to the conductor itself. It should be mentioned that there are some conducting circuits for which Ohm's law does not apply. These are special cases, which have to be dealt with separately, and are not considered here.

16.10. Symbols

Standard symbols are adopted to represent the various quantities and units dealt with in the foregoing sections, and these are given in the following table.

Quantity	Symbol	Unit	Unit Symbol
Electric charge, or Quantity of electricity	Q	COULOMB	C
Electric current	I	AMPERE	A
Potential difference	V	VOLT	V
Electromotive force	E	VOLT	V
Resistance	R	OHM	Ω

16.11. Examples

(i) A p.d. of 20 V is applied across a conductor, and the current flowing in the conductor is 5 A. What is the resistance of the conductor?

$$R = \frac{V}{I}$$

$$= \frac{20}{5}\ \Omega$$

$$= \underline{\underline{4\ \Omega}}$$

(ii) A p.d. of 50 V is applied across a conductor having a resistance of 2 Ω. What current will flow in the conductor?

$$R = \frac{V}{I}$$

$$\therefore I = \frac{V}{R}$$

$$= \frac{50}{2} \text{ A}$$

$$= \underline{\underline{25 \text{ A}}}$$

(iii) A conductor has a resistance of 8 Ω and a current of 3 A flows along it. What is the p.d. between its ends?

$$R = \frac{V}{I}$$

$$\therefore V = IR$$

$$= 3 \times 8 \text{ V}$$

$$= \underline{\underline{24 \text{ V}}}$$

16.12.   Circuit diagrams

Provided that certain easily-recognized and widely-accepted symbols are used, information about many electrical circuits can be presented in a condensed form by means of circuit diagrams. Comparatively few symbols are required for the type of circuit so far discussed, and these are shown in diagram 160.

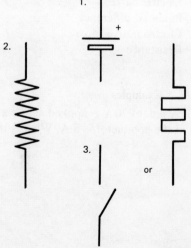

160. Circuit diagram symbols

1. *Battery*

If not marked, the longer line is always taken as the positive terminal.
The e.m.f. is often written by the side of the symbol.

2. *Resistor*

i.e. a conductor having a resistance, the value of which is often written by the side of the symbol.

3. *Switch*

Simple 'single-pole' switch.

When a circuit is drawn in terms of these symbols, it is usual to simplify the diagram by assuming that the resistance of the conductor concerned can be shown by a single 'concentrated' symbol. Any connecting wires required are shown as simple straight lines, and their resistance is accounted for elsewhere (see 'Resistors in Series', Section 16.15, page 452).

Diagram 161 illustrates the circuits dealt with in the preceding examples.

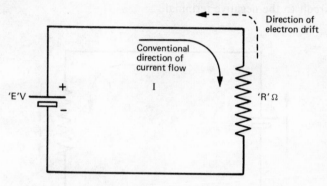

161. Simple electric circuit

16.13. Energy relationships in simple electric circuits

As has already been shown, an electric current consists of a drift of negatively charged electrons from points of low potential to points of higher potential (i.e. away from the negative terminal of the battery towards the positive terminal). However, it will be convenient for most of the following work to consider the theoretical flow of positive charge round the circuit as being in the conventional direction of current flow, as shown in diagram 161.

It was also stated (Section 16.3, page 438) that a free positive charge would experience a force which would tend to move it from a point of higher potential towards a point of lower potential. If the charge were to be moved against this force by some external means, work would have to be done by whatever external agency were responsible. This work is stored as energy by the charge by virtue of its new position at the higher potential. The charge is then said to have an increased POTENTIAL ENERGY. This is comparable with the potential energy stored by a mass which has been lifted vertically against the gravitational

P

force exerted on it. The potential energy stored by the mass is released and converted to other forms of energy if the mass is allowed to fall. In the same way, the potential energy stored by the positive charge will be released and converted to other forms of energy if the charge is allowed to 'fall' in electric potential.

In the simple electric circuit shown in diagram 162 the current flow can be considered as the movement of positive charge in the conventional direction of current from the positive battery terminal round the circuit to the negative terminal.

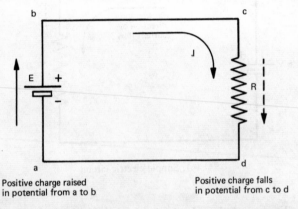

Positive charge raised
in potential from a to b

Positive charge falls
in potential from c to d

162. Energy transfer in simple electric circuit

As it moves through the resistance of the circuit, the charge falls in potential, and so gives up energy to the resistance. This energy will be converted to heat energy in the resistance. As the charge completes the movement round the circuit, it enters the negative terminal of the battery. The battery e.m.f. then raises the potential of the charge again, so that the battery gives up energy to the charge.

The overall result is that the battery 'loses' energy, while the resistance of the circuit 'gains' energy (which is then converted to heat energy). The electric charge acts as a carrier of energy from the battery to the resistance. It is in this way that electrical energy can be 'produced' at one point (say in a generating station) and then carried by electric charges, for very long distances if required, before being converted into some other useful form of energy in some type of electrical apparatus. The heat energy obtained from an electric fire may have originated at a generating station many kilometres away.

It is quite easy to calculate the amount of energy transferred in this way. Each coulomb which is raised in potential by 1 V by the battery must be given 1 J of energy (since $1 \text{ V} = 1 \text{ J/C}$—Section 16.2, page 438). Then, if the battery e.m.f. is E V, each coulomb receives E J of energy. If the potential of Q C is raised in this way, then

energy delivered from the battery $= E.Q$ joules

All this energy is then given up as the charge Q falls back to the potential of the negative battery terminal.

Since current, in amperes, is equal to the rate of flow of electric charge, in coulombs per second (Section 16.7, page 443), the current I A corresponding to the steady flow of Q C round the circuit in time t s is given by

$$I = \frac{Q}{t} \qquad . \qquad . \qquad . \qquad . \qquad \text{(i)}$$

from which

$$Q = I.t \text{ coulombs}$$

Then, if a steady current of I A is drawn from a battery of e.m.f. E V for a time t s, the total energy given up by the battery will be

$$\text{energy} = E.Q \text{ joules} \qquad . \qquad . \qquad \text{(iv)}$$
$$= E.I.t \text{ joules} \qquad . \qquad . \qquad \text{(v)}$$

16.14. Examples

(i) A battery having an e.m.f. of 10 V supplies a steady current of 2 A to a load. How much energy is taken from the battery in 5 min? What total quantity of electricity (charge) will have passed round the circuit in this time?

Energy taken from battery $= E.I.t$ joules

$$= 10 \times 2 \times 5 \text{ min} \times \left(\frac{60 \text{ s}}{1 \text{ min}}\right) \text{ J}$$

$$= 6000 \text{ joules}$$

Total quantity of electricity passed round circuit is

$$Q = I.t \text{ coulombs}$$

$$= 2 \times 5 \text{ min} \times \left(\frac{60 \text{ s}}{1 \text{ min}}\right) \text{ C}$$

$$= \underline{600 \text{ coulombs}}$$

(ii) An electric fire takes a current of 4 A from a supply giving a potential difference of 250 V. How much electrical energy is converted to heat energy every hour?

(Note: In this question the energy concerned is that which has been given up by the electric charge in falling through the p.d. between the supply terminals. The battery or generator which supplies this energy will in practice have to supply rather more than the amount given out as heat by the fire, as there will be other potential differences in other parts of the complete circuit. To distinguish the energy actually converted to heat by the fire from that which may be drawn from the battery or generator, the 'terminal voltage' (V) is used in this calculation instead of the battery e.m.f. (E).)

Energy converted

$$\text{to heat} = V.I.t \text{ joules}$$

$$= 250 \times 4 \times 1\ \cancel{h} \times \left(\frac{60\ \cancel{min}}{1\ \cancel{h}}\right) \times \left(\frac{60\ s}{1\ \cancel{min}}\right)\ \text{J}$$

$$= 3\ 600\ 000\ \text{joules} = 3 \cdot 6\ \text{MJ}$$

It will be seen that the joule is rather a small unit when practical examples of this type are considered. A larger unit is often used in these cases, and this particular point will be considered later.

16.15. Resistors connected in series and in parallel

So far, only simple electrical circuits have been considered, consisting of a source of e.m.f., such as a battery, connected to a conductor having a known resistance. In more complex circuits it may be that several conductors, each having a different resistance, will be connected together to form a circuit which is then connected to the e.m.f. source. Basically, there are two ways in which these resistors may be connected together (neglecting more complex arrangements which need not be considered at present).

(i) Resistors connected in SERIES

In this method the resistors are connected end-to-end as shown in diagram 163. It follows that electric charge leaving the positive terminal of the battery will pass through each resistor in turn, so that the rate of flow of charge through each resistor must be the same; i.e. *the current is the same at all points in a series-connected circuit*.

This is a very important principle, and the student should carry out experiments to investigate it. The current may be measured at various points in a series circuit by means of an AMMETER. (It is not necessary at this stage to understand how and why an ammeter can indicate the value of an electric current—this point will be dealt with later.)

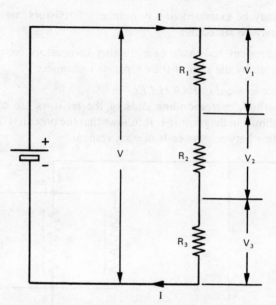

163. Resistors connected in series

For a series circuit as shown in diagram 163 there will be a fall in potential across each resistor in the circuit, since a p.d. must exist between the ends of a conductor if a current is to flow through it. This p.d. across each resistor will be related to the current and resistance by Ohm's law, so that for the case shown,

$$V_1 = IR_1, \qquad V_2 = IR_2, \qquad V_3 = IR_3$$

The total fall in potential for the whole circuit (V) will be the sum of the individual potential differences. (This point may also be checked experimentally, by means of a VOLTMETER which measures the various potential differences, although, for reasons that will be clear later, precise results may not be obtained.) Therefore,

$$V = V_1 + V_2 + V_3$$

or

$$V = IR_1 + IR_2 + IR_3$$
$$= I(R_1 + R_2 + R_3)$$

For the circuit as a whole, a total potential difference of V is associated with a circuit current I. The circuit can be considered as being equivalent to a single resistor whose resistance (R) is such that $V = IR$.

From these two results, it follows that

$$\underline{R = R_1 + R_2 + R_3} \qquad . \qquad . \qquad \text{(vi)}$$

This result may be extended to any number of resistors connected in series, and may be stated as:

'The equivalent resistance of a number of resistors connected in series is given by the sum of their separate resistances.'

(ii) Resistors connected in PARALLEL

In this method, corresponding ends of the resistors are connected together as shown in diagram 164. It follows that the potential difference (V) is the same between the ends of each resistor.

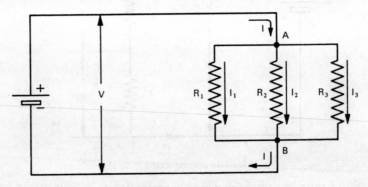

164. Resistors connected in parallel

The total current (I) will, however, divide so that some part of it will flow along each resistor as shown. The current flowing along each resistor will be related to the p.d. between its ends by Ohm's law, so that

$$I_1 = \frac{V}{R_1}, \qquad I_2 = \frac{V}{R_2}, \qquad I_3 = \frac{V}{R_3}$$

However, the *total current will be equal to the sum of the individual branch currents*. This is another very important principle, and follows from the fact that the total charge entering point A in a given time must be equal to the total charge leaving point B in the same time, some of this total having passed along each of the branches. Once again, this fact should be checked experimentally. Thus,

$$I = I_1 + I_2 + I_3$$

or

$$I = \frac{V}{R_1} + \frac{V}{R_2} + \frac{V}{R_3}$$

$$= V \left(\frac{1}{R_1} + \frac{1}{R_2} + \frac{1}{R_3} \right)$$

As before, the circuit as a whole behaves in the same way as a single equivalent resistor whose resistance R is such that

$$I = \frac{V}{R} \left(= V \cdot \frac{1}{R} \right)$$

From these two results, it follows that

$$\frac{1}{R} = \frac{1}{R_1} + \frac{1}{R_2} + \frac{1}{R_3} \qquad . \qquad . \qquad . \qquad . \qquad \text{(vii)}$$

This result may also be extended to any number of resistors connected in parallel, and may be stated as:

'The reciprocal of the equivalent resistance of a number of resistors connected in parallel is given by the sum of the reciprocals of their separate resistances.'

This rather awkward statement may be simplified if the 'reciprocal of a resistance' is given a special name. For the conditions considered here, the reciprocal of the resistance of a conductor is known as the CONDUCTANCE of the conductor. The symbol usually used for conductance is G. Then

$$G = \frac{1}{R} = \frac{I}{V} \qquad . \qquad . \qquad . \qquad . \qquad \text{(viii)}$$

It follows that the units of conductance are equivalent to AMPERES PER VOLT. These units are also known as RECIPROCAL OHMS, or, SIEMENS, so that

1 SIEMEN = 1 AMPERE PER VOLT

The symbol used is S.

In terms of conductance, the above result for resistors connected in parallel becomes:

$$G = G_1 + G_2 + G_3 \qquad . \qquad . \qquad \text{(ix)}$$

or, in words,

'The effective conductance of a number of conductors connected in parallel is given by the sum of their separate conductances.'

16.16. Examples

(i) Three resistors, having resistance of $10\,\Omega$, $25\,\Omega$ and $15\,\Omega$ respectively, are connected in series to a 100-V supply (i.e. a supply providing a total p.d. of 100 V). Find the current taken from the supply and the p.d. developed across the 25-Ω resistor.

Total resistance of the circuit (i.e. the 'equivalent' resistance)

$$R = 10 + 25 + 15\ \Omega$$
$$= 50\ \Omega$$

$$\text{Current } I = \frac{V}{R}$$

$$= \frac{100}{50}\ \text{A}$$

$$= \underline{\underline{2\ \text{A}}}$$

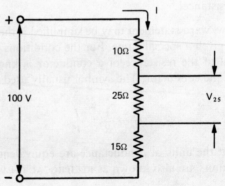

165. Numerical example

P.d. developed across the 25-Ω resistor is

$$V_{25} = I \times R_{25}$$
$$= 2 \times 25\ \text{V}$$
$$= \underline{\underline{50\ \text{V}}}$$

(ii) Four resistors, having resistances of 20 Ω, 40 Ω, 10 Ω and 30 Ω respectively, are connected in series with a switch to a 250-V supply. Assuming the switch to have zero resistance when closed, find the p.d. across each component of the circuit (a) when the switch is closed, (b) when the switch is open.

(a) Switch closed

Total equivalent resistance is

$$R = 20 + 40 + 10 + 30 \ \Omega$$
$$= 100 \ \Omega$$

$$\text{Current } I = \frac{V}{R}$$

$$= \frac{250}{100} \text{ A}$$

$$= \underline{2 \cdot 5 \text{ A}}$$

166. Numerical example

P.d. developed across each resistor is given by $V = IR$

i.e.   P.d. across 20 Ω, $V_{20} = 2 \cdot 5 \times 20 = \underline{50 \text{ V}}$

P.d. across 40 Ω, $V_{40} = 2 \cdot 5 \times 40 = \underline{100 \text{ V}}$

P.d. across 10 Ω, $V_{10} = 2 \cdot 5 \times 10 = \underline{25 \text{ V}}$

P.d. across 30 Ω, $V_{30} = 2 \cdot 5 \times 30 = \underline{75 \text{ V}}$

P.d. across switch $V_s = 2 \cdot 5 \times \ 0 = \underline{0 \text{ V}}$

(Note that these add up to supply p.d. of 250 V)

(b) Switch open

In this case no current can flow, as there is no longer a complete conducting circuit for the circulation of electric charge. The air between the blades of the switch acts as an insulator and prevents movement of charge across it. In other words,

$$\text{Current } I = 0$$

It follows that there will be no p.d. across any of the resistors (e.g. $V_{20} = 0 \times 20 = 0$ V).

The total supply p.d. will then appear across the open switch. In other words,

$$\underline{V_s = 250 \text{ V}}$$

This fact can be checked experimentally, and may be used in practice, for example to locate an 'open-circuit' fault in electrical equipment.

(iii) Four resistors, having resistances of 25 Ω, 40 Ω, 40 Ω and 100 Ω, are connected in parallel to a 10-V supply. Find the total current taken from the supply.

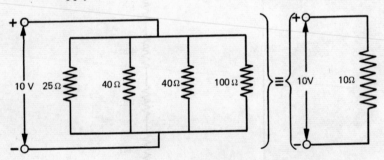

167. Numerical example

The equivalent resistance R of the parallel group is given by

$$\frac{1}{R} = \frac{1}{25} + \frac{1}{40} + \frac{1}{40} + \frac{1}{100} \, S$$
$$= 0.04 + 0.025 + 0.025 + 0.01 \, S$$
$$= 0.1 \, S$$

or

$$R = \frac{1}{0.1} = 10 \, \Omega$$

Then total current taken from the supply is

$$I = \frac{V}{R}$$

$$= \frac{10}{10} \text{ A}$$

$$= \underline{1 \cdot 0 \text{ A}}$$

(iv) A parallel circuit is composed of three branches, having resistances of 50 Ω, 12·5 Ω and 10 Ω respectively. Find the conductance of each branch and of the total circuit.

Label the branches ①, ② and ③ as shown.

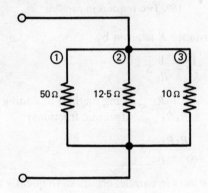

168. Numerical example

Conductance of branch ① is

$$G_1 = \frac{1}{R_1} = \frac{1}{50} = \underline{0 \cdot 02 \ S}$$

Similarly

$$G_2 = \frac{1}{R_2} = \frac{1}{12 \cdot 5} = \underline{0 \cdot 08 \ S}$$

and

$$G_3 = \frac{1}{R_3} = \frac{1}{10} = \underline{0 \cdot 10 \ S}$$

$$\text{Total conductance } G = G_1 + G_2 + G_3$$
$$= 0 \cdot 02 + 0 \cdot 08 + 0 \cdot 10 \ S$$
$$= \underline{0 \cdot 20 \ S}$$

(v) Find a formula for the equivalent resistance of two resistors having resistances $R_1 \ \Omega$ and $R_2 \ \Omega$ connected in parallel.

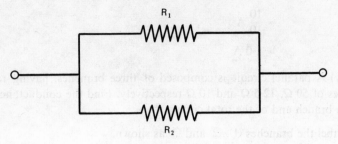

169. Two resistors in parallel

The equivalent resistance R is given by

$$\frac{1}{R} = \frac{1}{R_1} + \frac{1}{R_2} \, S$$

$$= \frac{R_2 + R_1}{R_1 R_2} \, S \quad \text{(using method of adding algebraic fractions)}$$

or $\qquad R = \dfrac{R_1 R_2}{R_1 + R_2} \, S$ $\qquad . \qquad . \qquad . \qquad . \qquad .$ (x)

The case of two resistors in parallel occurs so frequently that it is worth while remembering this formula.

(vi) Show that the equivalent resistance of any two equal resistors connected in parallel is half the resistance of one of them.

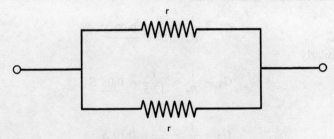

170. Equal resistors in parallel

Let the resistance of each branch be r.

Then, from the previous result, the equivalent resistance of the combination is

$$R = \frac{r \times r}{r + r}$$

$$= \frac{r^2}{2r}$$

$$= \frac{1}{2}\,r$$

This result, also, is worth noting for general use.

(vii) A two-core cable is 500 m long and is fed at one end from a 250-V supply. Load currents are taken at points along the cable as follows: 10 A at point A, 100 m from the supply end; 15 A at point B, 200 m from the supply end; 20 A at point C, 500 m from the supply end.

Draw a diagram of this arrangement and mark on it the current in each section of the cable.

If each conductor of the cable has a resistance of 0·02 Ω per 100 m, find the voltage at each load point.

The arrangement is shown in diagram 171.

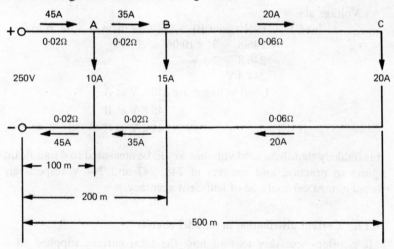

171. Numerical example

The section of cable from B to C must carry the 20-A load current for the load at C, as shown.

The section of cable from A to B must carry this 20 A and in addition must also carry the 15-A load current for the load at B, so that the current in this section is 35 A.

The section of cable between the supply point and A must carry the 35 A for the loads at B and C together with the 10 A for the load at A, so that the current in this section is 45 A.

Each 100 m of each core of the cable has a resistance of 0·02 Ω, so that the resistances of the various sections are as shown on the diagram.

Voltage at
 load A = (supply voltage) − (voltage drop in cable to A)
    = 250 − 2 × (0·02 × 45) V
    = 250 − 1·8 V
    = 248·2 V

Voltage at
 load B = (voltage at A) − (voltage drop in cable A to B)
    = 248·2 − 2 × (0·02 × 35) V
    = 248·2 − 1·4 V
    = 246·8 V

Voltage at
 load C = (voltage at B) − (voltage drop in cable B to C)
    = 246·8 − 2 × (0·06 × 20) V
    = 246·8 − 2·4 V
    = 244·4 V

    Load voltages are 248·2 V at A
         246·8 V at B
         244·4 V at C

It is unlikely that these load voltages would be measured to 4 significant figures in practice, and answers of 248, 247 and 244 V respectively would almost certainly be of sufficient accuracy.

16.17.   Current distribution in parallel circuits

It is often necessary to find how the total current supplied to a number of resistors in parallel will divide between them. In general, the method used is as follows. First, the equivalent resistance of the parallel group is found. Then, from the known value of total current, the voltage developed across this equivalent resistance is calculated. This is also, of course, the voltage across the actual parallel circuit. From the value of this voltage, the individual branch currents can be easily found by applying Ohm's law to each branch in turn. The following example should make the method clear.

Four resistors, having resistance of 10 Ω, 20 Ω, 40 Ω and 40 Ω respectively, are connected in parallel. Find how they will share a total current of 10 A.

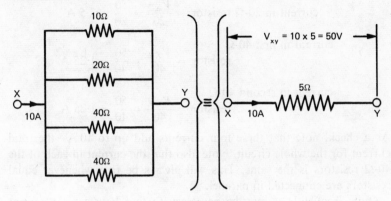

172. Numerical example

Note that the circuit diagram is drawn only for that part of the circuit concerned in this problem. Quite obviously, X and Y will be connected in some way to a source of e.m.f. which sets up the current.

The equivalent resistance R_{XY} of the parallel group is given by

$$\frac{1}{R_{XY}} = \frac{1}{10} + \frac{1}{20} + \frac{1}{40} + \frac{1}{40}\,S$$
$$= 0\cdot1 + 0\cdot05 \times 0\cdot025 \times 0\cdot025\,S$$
$$= 0\cdot2\,S$$

or
$$R_{XY} = \frac{1}{0\cdot2} = 5\,\Omega$$

This means that as far as any external circuit is concerned, the portion between X and Y may be replaced by a single 5-Ω resistor as shown in diagram 172, without any of the external conditions being changed.

Then, since $I_{XY} = 10$ A and $R_{XY} = 5\,\Omega$

$$V_{XY} = I_{XY}.R_{XY}$$
$$= 10 \times 5\,V$$
$$= \underline{50\,V}$$

This means that the parallel group must have a p.d. of 50 V across it. This p.d. will be the same for each of the parallel-connected resistors, so that

$$\text{current in 10-}\Omega\text{ resistor} = \frac{V_{XY}}{10} = \frac{50}{10} = \underline{\underline{5\ A}}$$

$$\text{current in 20-}\Omega\text{ resistor} = \frac{V_{XY}}{20} = \frac{50}{20} = \underline{\underline{2\cdot5\ A}}$$

$$\text{current in first 40-}\Omega\text{ resistor} = \frac{V_{XY}}{40} = \frac{50}{40} = \underline{\underline{1\cdot25\ A}}$$

$$\text{current in second 40-}\Omega\text{ resistor} = \frac{V_{XY}}{40} = \frac{50}{40} = \underline{\underline{1\cdot25\ A}}$$

As a check, note that these four currents add up to 10 A—the total current for the whole circuit. Note also that the current in each of the 40-Ω resistors is the same. This will always be true whenever equal resistors are connected in parallel.

Quite frequently it may be necessary to find how a total current divides between just two resistors connected in parallel. For this special case there is a simple formula which enables the result to be found very quickly.

Suppose the two resistors have resistances $R_1\ \Omega$ and $R_2\ \Omega$ and share a current of I A, as shown in diagram 173.

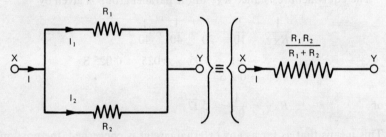

173. Current division between two parallel resistors

From previous results, R_{XY} is such that

$$\frac{1}{R_{XY}} = \frac{1}{R_1} + \frac{1}{R_2}\ S$$

$$= \frac{R_1 + R_2}{R_1 R_2}\ S$$

or $\qquad\qquad R_{XY} = \dfrac{R_1 R_2}{R_1 + R_2}\ S$

Then
$$V_{XY} = I.R_{XY} = I.\frac{R_1R_2}{R_1 + R_2}$$

The current in R_1 is

$$I_1 = \frac{V_{XY}}{R_1}$$

$$= I.\frac{R_1R_2}{R_1 + R_2}.\frac{1}{R_1}$$

or
$$I_1 = I.\frac{R_2}{R_1 + R_2} \qquad . \qquad . \qquad . \qquad . \qquad \text{(xi)}$$

Similarly, current in R_2 is

$$I_2 = I.\frac{R_1}{R_1 + R_2}$$

It would be possible to produce formulae for current division in three or more resistors connected in parallel. However, these formulae would be rather complicated, and it is generally best to use the method shown in the example on page 463.

16.18. Series parallel circuits

By use of these methods of 'combining' resistors connected in series or in parallel to obtain an equivalent resistance value, it is possible to simplify quite complicated circuits. The following examples will illustrate the methods used.

(i) Find the current in each branch of the circuit shown in diagram 174.

First combining the parallel resistors (using the formula derived on page 460 for two parallel resistances)

$$R_{BC} = \frac{2 \times 8}{2 + 8} = \frac{16}{10} = 1.6\ \Omega$$

The circuit is then equivalent to the second circuit shown in diagram 174, having a 0.4-Ω resistance in series with a 1.6-Ω resistance.

The two resistances in series may now be combined so that

total resistance of circuit, $R = 0.4 + 1.6 = 2.0\ \Omega$

Then current taken from the supply is

$$I = \frac{V}{R}$$

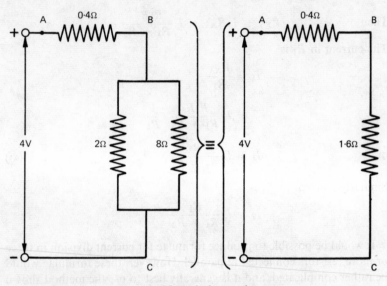

174. Numerical example

$$= \frac{4}{2} \text{ A}$$

$$= 2 \text{ A}$$

The original circuit diagram shows that this current will flow through the 0·4-Ω resistor and then divide between the 2-Ω and 8-Ω resistors. From the formula developed on page 465 for the special case of two parallel resistors,

$$\text{current in 2-}\Omega \text{ resistor} = 2 \times \frac{8}{2 + 8} = \underline{\underline{1 \cdot 6 \text{ A}}}$$

$$\text{current in 8-}\Omega \text{ resistor} = 2 \times \frac{2}{2 + 8} = \underline{\underline{0 \cdot 4 \text{ A}}}$$

$$\text{current in 0·4-}\Omega \text{ resistor} = \underline{\underline{2 \cdot 0 \text{ A}}}$$

(ii) Find the total resistance between terminals A and B of the circuit shown in diagram 175 (a). Hence find the p.d. across the 60-Ω resistor if A and B are connected to the terminals of a 240-V supply.

Successive steps in the combination of the parallel and series group-

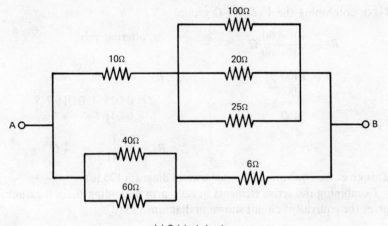

(a) Original circuit

175

ings of resistors are shown in diagrams 175 (b), (c), (d) and (e). The student should follow these through and check each step.

First combining the 100-Ω, 20-Ω, 25-Ω group

$$\frac{1}{R_1} = \frac{1}{100} + \frac{1}{20} + \frac{1}{25} \ S$$

$$= 0{\cdot}01 + 0{\cdot}05 + 0{\cdot}04 \ S$$

$$= 0{\cdot}10 \ S$$

$$R_1 = 10 \ \Omega$$

This gives the equivalent circuit shown in diagram 175 (b).

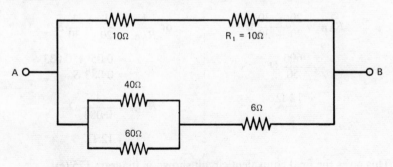

(b) Simplification of circuit—first step

175

Next, combining the 40-Ω, 60-Ω group,

$$R_2 = \frac{40 \times 60}{40 + 60}\ \Omega$$

or, alternatively,

$$= \frac{2400}{100}\ \Omega$$

$$\frac{1}{R_2} = \frac{1}{40} + \frac{1}{60}\ S$$

$$= 24\ \Omega$$

$$= 0 \cdot 025 + 0 \cdot 016\ 7\ S$$

$$= 0 \cdot 041\ 7\ S$$

$$R_2 = \frac{1}{0 \cdot 041\ 7} = 24\ \Omega$$

This gives the equivalent circuit shown in diagram 175 (c).

Combining the series elements in each arm by adding them together gives the equivalent circuit shown in diagram 175 (d).

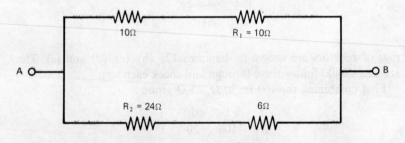

(c) Simplification of circuit—second step

175

Finally, combining these two parallel branches,

$$R_{AB} = \frac{20 \times 30}{20 + 30}\ \Omega$$

or $\dfrac{1}{R_{AB}} = \dfrac{1}{20} + \dfrac{1}{30}\ S$

$$= \frac{600}{50}\ \Omega$$

$$= 0 \cdot 05 + 0 \cdot 033\ S$$

$$= 0 \cdot 083\ S$$

$$= \underline{12\ \Omega}$$

$$R_{AB} = \frac{1}{0 \cdot 083}\ \Omega$$

$$= \underline{\underline{12\ \Omega}}$$

This gives the final equivalent circuit shown in diagram 175 (e).

For the second part of the question, use may be made of the various equivalent circuits derived above.

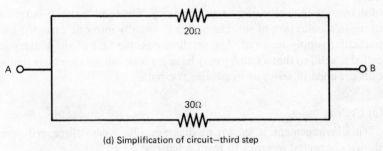

(d) Simplification of circuit—third step

175

First of all, diagram 175 (d) shows that the main branch associated with the required 60-Ω resistance has a total equivalent resistance of 30 Ω. This will be connected across the supply (in parallel, of course, with the 20-Ω equivalent resistance of the other branch). The current taken by this branch (not the *total* current) will therefore be

$$I = \frac{V_T}{R} = \frac{240}{30} = 8 \text{ A}$$

Diagram 175 (c) shows that this current will flow in R_2 ($= 24 \ \Omega$) to give a p.d. across R_2 of

$$V_2 = 8 \times R_2$$
$$= 192 \text{ V}$$

A ○————————————————〰〰〰————————————————○ B

12Ω

(e) Simplification of circuit—final step

176

Since the value R_2 was found by combining the 40-Ω and 60-Ω resistors, it follows that the p.d. across R_2 is also the p.d. across each of these. In other words,

p.f. across the 60-Ω resistor = $\underline{\underline{192 \text{ V}}}$

16.19. Groupings of cells in series and in parallel

Sources of e.m.f. may be grouped together in series, parallel or series-parallel arrangements, in the same way as resistors. The reason for such groupings is that a single source of e.m.f. may be too small for the purpose required, either in that its e.m.f. is too low, or that it is not capable

of delivering the value of current necessary. The term 'battery' is taken
to mean a collection of sources of e.m.f., usually into one case, for the
particular supply required. The smallest possible unit of the battery is
called a 'cell', so that a battery may have just one cell, or may have many
cells grouped in series or in parallel, or both.

(a) Cells in series

This arrangement is shown in diagram 176, where three cells are
shown connected in series to form a battery.

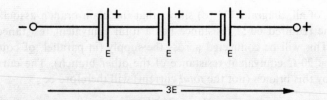

176. Battery having three cells in series

If the e.m.f. of each cell is E V, a positive charge moving from the
negative terminal of the battery, throughough each cell in turn to the
positive terminal of the battery, would be raised in potential by E V by
each cell. It would therefore be raised in potential by a total of $3E$ V.

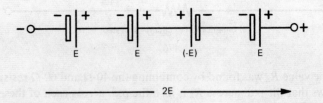

177. Battery having one cell reversed

Thus for a battery having n cells in series, each of e.m.f. E V, the total
battery e.m.f. would be nE V.

In other words, the e.m.f.'s of cells connected in series are added
algebraically to give the total effective e.m.f. The word 'algebraically'
has been used here since the sign of the e.m.f. of the cell must be taken

into account. For example, diagram 177 shows a battery made up of four cells, one of which, however, is reversed in relation to the other three.

In this case, a positive charge moving from the negative battery terminal to the positive battery terminal through each cell in turn would be raised in potential by E V by the first cell, and by another E V by the second cell. The third cell being reversed, however, would lower the potential of the positive charge by E V, while the fourth cell would raise the potential again by E V. The total rise in potential through the whole battery is, then, $E + E - E + E$, or $2E$ V. This result is given by considering the e.m.f. of the reversed cell to be $(-E)$ volts, and applying the previous rule of 'algebraic' addition. In other words,

$$E + E + (-E) + E = 2E \text{ V}$$

Whilst this method of 'opposing' e.m.f.'s is a useful technique for applications where the difference of two e.m.f.'s is required, it would be pointless to use it for building up a battery.

(b) Cells in parallel

This arrangement is shown in diagram 178, where three cells are shown connected in parallel to form a battery.

If each cell has an e.m.f. of E V, a positive charge could be moved from the negative battery terminal to the positive battery terminal through any one of the cells. Any route chosen from $-$ to $+$, however,

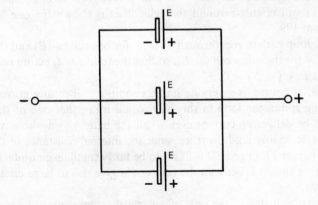

178. Battery having three cells in parallel

will only give a rise in potential of E V. The total e.m.f. of the whole battery is then only the same as that of each cell on its own.

Note that, on the assumption that the cells are identical, each cell of the battery shown would only have to deliver one-third of the total current supplied by the battery to any load resistance. This type of connection would, then, be used if the required load current were more than any one cell could deliver safely, without damage to itself. (See Chapter 18, page 563.)

If a path is traced from the negative terminal of any one cell, round the 'local' circuit through the cells and back to the same point, it will be seen that the e.m.f.'s of the cells oppose each other round this local circuit. Since the e.m.f.'s of the cells are equal, this means that the total

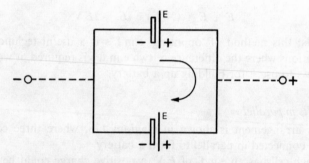

179. Local circuit 'loop' for cells in parallel

e.m.f. acting round any loop of the local circuit is zero, and so no current will circulate round the cells. This is shown for one loop in diagram 179.

The loop path moves through $-$ to $+$ for one cell $(+ E)$ and through $+$ to $-$ for the other cell $(- E)$, so that the total e.m.f. acting *round the loop* is $E + (- E) = 0$.

This, of course, is a very desirable condition, since any current circulating round the loop in this way would mean that one of the cells would be delivering current even when the battery as a whole was not connected to any load. Further, since the internal resistance of the cell (see Chapter 17, page 507) is likely to be fairly small, even quite a small difference in e.m.f. between the cells could give rise to large circulating currents.

Similarly, if one of the cells of a parallel group were to be reversed, the e.m.f.'s would then be additive round the local circuit instead of being in opposition. This would lead to heavy circulating currents and almost certain damage to, or even the destruction of, the cells.

Thus, for cells connected in parallel, the e.m.f.'s of the cells should be equal and should all act in the same direction between the main terminals of the battery. In other words, all the positive terminals of the cells should be connected together and to the positive terminal of the battery. (The negative terminals of the cells would, of course, all be connected to the negative battery terminal.)

As has been mentioned above, and is dealt with more fully in Chapter 17, page 507, a cell will have an internal resistance, which has a p.d. developed across it whenever the cell delivers current. This means that the p.d. between the terminals of a cell supplying load current will be less than the e.m.f. of the cell. For calculations, it is convenient to consider the e.m.f. and the internal resistance of a cell to be separate properties. (Although this is not really true in practice, the overall

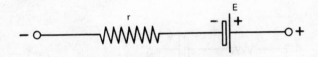

180. Equivalent circuit of a cell

results are the same.) The 'equivalent circuit' of a cell is then drawn as shown in diagram 180, where the internal resistance is drawn separately from the symbol for the e.m.f.

When cells are grouped to form a battery, the resultant e.m.f. of the cell is obtained as explained above, while the equivalent internal resistance of the battery is calculated by the internal resistances of the cells being suitably combined. The following example will indicate the method used.

Example

Find the total e.m.f. and internal resistance of the battery made up from the grouping of cells shown in diagram 181 (a).

Diagrams 181 (b) and (c) show the successive steps in combining the cells of diagram 181 (a) into a single equivalent cell.

First combine the cells in parallel. The effective e.m.f. will be 1·5 V (the e.m.f. of either cell). The effective resistance is given by

$$r_1 = \frac{1 \times 4}{1 + 4}\ \Omega \qquad\qquad \text{or,}\ \frac{1}{r_1} = \frac{1}{1} + \frac{1}{4}\ S$$

$$= \frac{4}{5}\ \Omega \qquad\qquad\qquad = \frac{4 + 1}{4}\ S = \frac{5}{4}\ S$$

$$= 0\cdot8\ \Omega \qquad\qquad\qquad\qquad r_1 = 0\cdot8\ \Omega$$

These values give the equivalent circuit shown in diagram 181 (b). Combining the e.m.f.'s in series gives the total effective e.m.f. as

$$1\cdot5 + 4 = 5\cdot5\ V$$

Combining the resistances in series gives the total effective resistance as

$$0\cdot8 + 0\cdot2 = 1\cdot0\ \Omega$$

This result is shown in diagram 181 (c), from which it can be seen that the battery will have an e.m.f. of 5·5 V and an internal resistance of 1·0 Ω.

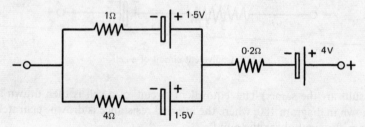

(a) Grouping of cells—numerical example

(b) Simplication of grouping—first step

(c) Equivalent circuit of battery

16.20. Resistivity

The resistance of a conductor (at a given temperature) is dependent on the dimensions of the conductor and the material of which it is made. It is fairly easy to see that conductors of similar shape but made of different materials may have different resistances. The atomic structure of the two materials will be different, the number of loosely-bound electrons per atom available to act as 'current-carriers' may be different, and differences in the atomic lattice-structure (i.e. the way in which the atoms are packed together to build up the material) may give rise to differences in the ease with which electrons can move about in the material.

The effects of variations in the size and shape of the conductor will be dealt with a little later, but in order to compare the resistance effect of different conductor materials, a standard size and shape of conductor may be specified. If this is done, any difference in the resistance of conductors having these standard dimensions must be due to a property of the conductor material alone. The standard shape chosen is a cube, each side of which is of unit length (this is known as a 'unit cube'). Since in the SI system of units lengths are measured in metres, the standard used here is a cube having 1-m sides, or, more simply, a 'metre cube'. This is quite a big cube, and conductors of this size are not really practical, but it will be seen later how the result can be deduced from tests on smaller conductors. The requirement here is only for some method of comparing the resistance-value of different materials, and of calculating the resistance of given conductors.

The resistance of this unit cube of material is known as the RESISTIVITY of the material (an older term which may still be used for this quantity is SPECIFIC RESISTANCE, although this term will not be used further in this book).

'The resistivity of a conducting material is the resistance measured between opposite faces of a unit cube of the material, at a stated, constant, temperature.'

The symbol used to represent the resistivity of a conducting material is ρ. The units in which resistivity is measured will be discussed a little later.

Consider the conductor shown in diagram 182 and consisting of two metre-cubes placed side-by-side. If the resistivity of the conductor material is ρ units, the resistance between opposite faces of each is ρ.

The total resistance between the end faces shown shaded will be the sum of two resistances, each equal to ρ, connected in series. In other words, the resistance between the end faces will be 2ρ.

If there were l such cubes connected in series, the resistance between end faces would be ρl, and this result would be true even if l were not a whole number. (For example, if l is 0·25 m, the resistance would be

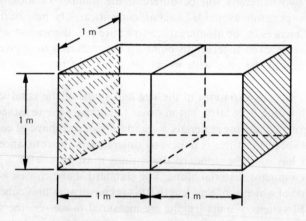

182. Two unit cubes in series

0·25ρ, since it would take four such conductors connected in series to make up a whole cube, of resistance 4 $\times$ 0·25ρ, or ρ.)

It follows that the resistance of any conductor is directly proportional to its length. This is a reasonable result, since a uniform conductor, say 10 m long, could be considered as equivalent to 10 conductors, each 1 m long, connected in series, and so would have 10 times the resistance of each of the 1-m conductors.

The total resistance between the top and bottom faces of the two metre-cubes placed side-by-side (shown shaded in diagram 183) is the result of two resistances, each equal to ρ, connected in parallel. In other words, the resistance between these faces will be $\frac{1}{2}\rho$. Note here that although the total length of the conductor has been kept constant at 1 m, the area available for current flow is now 2 m².

If there were A unit cubes connected in parallel in this way, the resistance between the faces would be $\frac{1}{A} \times \rho$. It will be seen that A represents the area of conductor available for current flow, and again the

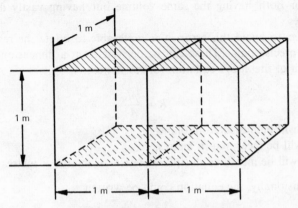

183. Two unit cubes in parallel

result is true even if A is not a whole number. (For example, if A is $\frac{1}{5}$ m², it would need 5 such conductors, each of resistance 5ρ, connected in parallel to make up a cube of resistance $\frac{1}{5} \times 5\rho$, or ρ.)

It follows that the resistance of any conductor is inversely proportional to its cross-sectional area. For example, doubling the cross-sectional area would halve the resistance. Again, this is a reasonable result, since a uniform conductor having a cross-sectional area of, say, 4 m² could be considered as equivalent to 4 conductors, each of cross-sectional area 1 m², connected in parallel, and so would have 0·25 the resistance of each of the thinner conductors.

If these two results are combined, the resistance R, of a conductor having length l m, cross-sectional area A m², and made from a material of resistivity ρ, is seen to be given by

$$R = \frac{\rho l}{A} \qquad . \qquad . \qquad . \qquad . \qquad \text{(xii)}$$

Now to consider the postponed question of the units in which ρ is measured. It may be seen that possible units would be OHM PER METRE-CUBE, and these units are often used. However, it should be noted that this is NOT the same thing as 'ohm per cubic metre'. Equation (xii) shows that the resistance does not depend on the volume of the conductor material, but on the way that material is arranged; i.e. its shape. It would be possible to obtain a short fat conductor and a long thin conductor both having the same volume but having vastly different resistances.

In order to avoid this error, it is preferable to quote the resistivity in more precise units. These can be derived from a dimensional consideration of the above equation for resistance:

$$R = \frac{\rho l}{A}$$

Now R will be measured in ohms,

l will be measured in metres,

A will be measured in square metres, or metres × metres

so, dimensionally, the equation could be written

$$\text{OHMS} = \rho \times \frac{\text{METRES}}{\text{METRES} \times \text{METRES}}$$

or
$$\text{OHMS} = \rho \times \frac{1}{\text{METRES}}$$

In order to make this equation balance, it will be seen that ρ ought to be measured in OHMS × METRES (i.e. ρ has the dimensions of resistance × length). Consequently, suitable units in which to measure resistivity are OHM-METRES, and these avoid the dangers of referring to volume. These units have the added advantage of being shorter and easier to write, and give directly the two important quantities required to interpret the value of resistivity quoted—the unit of resistance used, and the length of side of the unit cube chosen.

It is not always convenient to use the metre as a unit of length when calculating the resistance of a conductor. Consequently, although the ohm-metre is the fundamental unit of resistivity, other units are frequently used. The size of the unit cube may be adjusted to the length unit required for a particular calculation. Further, since the resistivity of conducting materials is very small, the sub-multiple unit 'microhm' ($\mu\Omega$) is frequently used (where $1 \ \mu\Omega = 10^{-6} \ \Omega$).

Thus the value of the resistivity of a material may be quoted in such units as ohm-millimetres (Ω mm), or microhm millimetres ($\mu\Omega$ mm). Provided that due allowance is made for any change of units involved, no difficulties should be experienced. Later examples will illustrate the methods used.

It is now possible to return for a moment to the question of conductors, semi-conductors and insulators already mentioned earlier in

Section 16.4, page 438. In this earlier section materials were seen to be classified in accordance with the ease or difficulty with which electric charges could be moved within them.

The above definition of resistivity now gives a rather more precise way of stating and comparing this particular property of a material. In these terms, a conductor material will have a low resistivity, an insulator material will have a high resistivity and a semi-conductor material will have an intermediate (but still rather high) value of resistivity. The following table gives approximate resistivity values for some materials in each of these classes, as an indication of their relative values.

MATERIAL	RESISTIVITY AT $0°C$ (see later Section 16.22, page 481, for effect of temperature)
CONDUCTORS	
COPPER	$1.56 \times 10^{-8} \ \Omega$ m
ALUMINIUM	$2.45 \times 10^{-8} \ \Omega$ m
IRON	$8.90 \times 10^{-8} \ \Omega$ m
PLATINUM	$9.81 \times 10^{-8} \ \Omega$ m
INSULATORS	
GLASS	Between 10^8 and $10^{12} \ \Omega$ m
PAPER (dry)	$10^{10} \ \Omega$ m
EBONITE	$10^{14} \ \Omega$ m
MICA	Between 10^{11} and $10^{15} \ \Omega$ m
PORCELAIN	Between 10^{10} and $10^{13} \ \Omega$ m
SEMI-CONDUCTORS	
GERMANIUM	About $0.009 \ \Omega$ m
SILICON	Between $0.000\ 01$ and $0.01 \ \Omega$ m

(The uncertainty in the values given for insulators and semi-conductors arises from the quite wide variations that can result from slight changes in purity, surface condition and temperature.)

It is important to note that a 'perfect' insulator; that is, one having infinite resistivity—does not exist. In practice, some 'leakage' current will flow along or through an insulating material, although it will usually be very slight, since the 'insulation resistance' should be high. This, however, may not be the case at higher temperatures, or, for example, for insulators of the type used outside for high-voltage transmission lines, under wet or dirty surface conditions.

16.21. Examples

(i) Find the resistance of a wire having a diameter of 1 mm and a length of 10 m if the conductor material has a resistivity of $2 \times 10^{-8} \ \Omega$ m.

Since ρ has been quoted in Ω m, it will be convenient to express lengths and areas in terms of the metre as length unit.

Conductor
area A $= \dfrac{\pi}{4} \times 1^2$ mm^2

$= \dfrac{\pi}{4} \times 1^2$ ~~mm~~ $\times$ ~~mm~~ $\times \left(\dfrac{1 \text{ m}}{1000 \text{ ~~mm~~}}\right) \times \left(\dfrac{1 \text{ m}}{1000 \text{ ~~mm~~}}\right)$

$= 0.785 \times 10^{-6}$ m^2

Conductor
length $l = 10$ m

Conductor
resistance $R = \dfrac{\rho l}{A}$

$= \dfrac{2 \times 10^{-8} \times 10}{0.785 \times 10^{-6}} \ \Omega$

$= \underline{\underline{0.255 \ \Omega}}$

As shown in this example, it is very important that all quantities should be expressed in similar units.

(ii) A wire has a length of 100 m and a diameter of 1·6 mm. Find its resistance if the conductor material has a resistivity of 0·017 $\mu\Omega$ m.

Conductor
area A $= \dfrac{\pi}{4} \times (1 \cdot 6)^2$ mm^2

$= \dfrac{\pi}{4} \times 2 \cdot 56$ ~~mm²~~ $\times \left(\dfrac{1 \text{ m}}{1000 \text{ ~~mm~~}}\right) \times \left(\dfrac{1 \text{ m}}{1000 \text{ ~~mm~~}}\right)$

$= 2 \cdot 01 \times 10^{-6}$ m^2

Conductor
length $l = 100$ m

Conductor
resistance $R = \dfrac{\rho l}{A}$

$= \dfrac{0 \cdot 017 \times 10^{-6} \times 100}{2 \cdot 01 \times 10^{-6}} \ \Omega$

$= \underline{\underline{0 \cdot 847 \ \Omega}}$

16.22. Variation of resistance with temperature

So far, only passing mention has been made of the fact that the temperature of a conductor may affect its resistance—for example, in the statement of Ohm's law, and again in the discussion of resistivity. This point will now be considered in more detail.

The random movement of the loosely-bound electrons of a conducting material has already been discussed and indicated to be the fundamental reason for the conduction of an electric current. Both this random movement and the vibration of the atoms of the material about their average or 'mean' position in the lattice structure are affected by the temperature of the material. The higher the temperature, the faster the electrons move about between atoms, and the more rapidly do the atoms vibrate. Consequently, the higher the temperature of a conducting material, the more likely it is that collisions will occur between the electrons drifting along the conductor, and the atoms of the material. The increased number of collisions slows down the average drift-rate of the electrons; i.e. it reduces the current flow. It follows that an increase in temperature will (generally) increase the resistance of the conductor.

Two important special cases, the 'resistance alloys' and insulating materials, are considered separately at the end of this section.

If the resistance of a metallic conductor is measured at different conductor temperatures and a graph plotted of the results, a graph similar to that shown in diagram 184 is obtained. Provided the range of temperatures is not too large, this graph is found to be a straight line, so that, fortunately, the relationship between resistance and temperature is a simple one. This relationship can be written as

$$R_\theta = R_0 (1 + \alpha_0\theta) \quad . \qquad . \qquad . \qquad . \qquad \text{(xiii)}$$

where

R_0 = resistance at 0°C
R_θ = resistance at any other temperature θ°C

and α_0 is known as the TEMPERATURE COEFFICIENT OF RESISTANCE (or more simply as the 'resistance-temperature coefficient') of the conductor material.

(For larger temperature ranges, the relationship becomes

$$R_\theta = R_0 (1 + \alpha_0\theta + \beta_0\theta^2)$$

Q

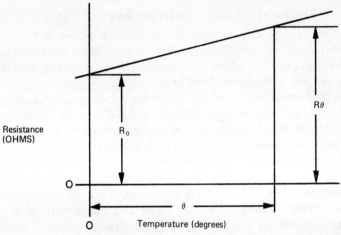

184. Variation of resistance with temperature

but the value of the coefficient β_0 is usually small enough to be neglected except at very high temperatures.)

If the student has dealt with the mathematics of a straight-line (or linear) graph, an equation of the form

$$y = mx + c$$

might be expected for the graph shown, where

$$m = \text{slope of the graph}$$
$$c = \text{intercept on the y-axis.}$$

This is, in fact, the case here, where y is represented by R_θ and x by θ.

The above equation (xiii) may be re-written

$$R_\theta = \alpha_0 R_0 \theta + R_0$$

This indicates that R_0 = intercept on R_θ-axis (as shown in diagram 184) and that $\alpha_0 R_0$ is the slope of the straight-line graph.

It follows that α_0, the resistance-temperature coefficient of the conductor material, is the slope of the resistance/temperature graph obtained for a resistance whose value is 1 Ω at 0°C. This leads to a definition of α_0 as follows:

'The resistance-temperature coefficient of a conducting material is the increase in resistance for each ohm at 0°C for each °C rise in temperature from 0°C.'

α_0 is usually referred to as 'the resistance-temperature coefficient from and at $0°C$', and this explains why the $_0$ suffix is used. As will be seen later, it is possible to define a resistance-temperature coefficient relating to any other starting temperature, although of course its value will be different from α_0.

Note that the units of resistance-temperature coefficient are thus OHMS PER OHM DEGREE TEMPERATURE RISE. Since the temperature rise is usually measured in $°C$, these units may be written $\Omega/\Omega°C$.

Although α_0 can be found for any given conducting material from experimental results, and the results recorded for general use (see table on page 750), it is not always convenient to refer every resistance-temperature calculation to the resistance at $0°C$. This inconvenience may be avoided in the following way. Let

R_0 = resistance at $0°C$
R_1 = resistance at $\theta_1°C$
R_2 = resistance at $\theta_2°C$
a_0 = resistance-temperature coefficient from and at $0°C$.

Then

$$R_1 = R_0 (1 + \alpha_0\theta_1)$$
$$R_2 = R_0 (1 + \alpha_0\theta_2)$$

Dividing these two equations gives

$$\frac{R_1}{R_2} = \frac{1 + \alpha_0\theta_1}{1 + \alpha_0\theta_2} \qquad . \qquad . \qquad . \quad \text{(xiv)}$$

(Note that although R_0, being a common factor of numerator and denominator, has disappeared from this equation, α_0 still refers to a starting temperature of $0°C$ and θ_1 and θ_2 are of course still measured from $0°C$.)

The special case of copper is important, since it is very frequently used as a conducting material. It is interesting that, for copper,

$$\alpha_0 = \frac{1}{234\cdot5} = 0\cdot004\ 26\ \Omega/\Omega°C$$

The easily-remembered number, $234\cdot5$, suggests a useful form of the above equation.

Thus, for copper (but *not* for other materials)

$$\frac{R_1}{R_2} = \frac{1 + \dfrac{\theta_1}{234 \cdot 5}}{1 + \dfrac{\theta_2}{234 \cdot 5}}$$

or

$$\frac{R_1}{R_2} = \frac{234 \cdot 5 + \theta_1}{234 \cdot 5 + \theta_2} \qquad . \qquad . \qquad . \qquad \text{(xv)}$$

The resistance-temperature coefficient of some special materials should be particularly mentioned.

Resistance alloys

There are two basic requirements for the material used to construct standard resistors of known value. The first is a low resistance-temperature coefficient, which would ensure that the value of the resistance remained practically constant over a wide range of temperatures. The second is a high resistivity, which would ensure that a given value of resistance could be obtained from a coil using a shorter length of given-diameter wire.

Such materials have been developed, and are usually alloys of several metallic elements. They are often referred to as 'resistance alloys', and are made under various trade names. They are usually, however, alloys of copper, manganese, nickel, iron and silicon (to mention the more commonly used elements) in various proportions. These materials have values of resistance-temperature coefficient within the range of about $-0 \cdot 000\ 04$ to $+0 \cdot 000\ 05$, which should be compared with the value of $+0 \cdot 004\ 26$ for copper (all values given in $\Omega/\Omega°C$ from and at $0°C$). A negative value of resistance-temperature coefficient means that the value of resistance for that material falls with increasing temperature. Carbon is another material having a negative resistance-temperature coefficient.

Insulators

The effect of temperature on the resistivity of the common insulating materials is very important, since the resistivity of such materials noticeably *decreases* with temperature. This has an obvious bearing on the maximum safe working temperature of electrical equipment since it would be possible for the insulation resistance to be so decreased at the higher temperatures that the leakage current could become excessive.

The decrease in insulation resistance with increase in temperature is not a simple linear relationship, and so a value for insulation-resistance-temperature coefficient is not obtainable in the way described for conducting materials. Broadly speaking, however, the insulation

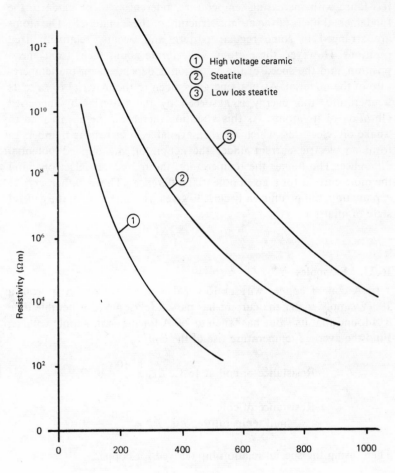

① High voltage ceramic
② Steatite
③ Low loss steatite

185. Variation of resistivity with temperature for typical insulation materials

resistance will decrease quite rapidly as the temperature is increased. Diagram 185 shows the approximate variation of insulation resistance with temperature for three different materials.

As a brief explanation of the reason for this decrease in insulation resistance with increasing temperature, reference can be made to the fundamental ideas of the atomic structure of these materials. The atoms are arranged in some regular pattern and occupy relatively fixed positions. However, these atoms will vibrate about their 'fixed' mean position, and the speed of this vibration is dependent on the temperature of the material. As heat energy is given to the material to raise its temperature, this energy is absorbed by the material by increased vibration of its atoms. As this vibration increases, the atoms tend to 'shake off' electrons, which are then available in increasing numbers to form an electric current under the action of any applied potential difference. The higher the temperature, the more 'free' electrons, and the more current for a given potential difference. (This is rather a crude explanation, but is sufficiently close to give a visual picture of the general state of affairs.)

16.23. Examples

(i) A coil of copper wire at 15°C takes a current of 2·5 A from a 100-V supply. After the current has passed for some considerable time it is found that its value has fallen to 2·0 A for the same supply voltage. Find the average temperature rise of the coil.

$$\text{Resistance of coil at } 15°C, R_{15} = \frac{100}{2\cdot5} \ 40 \ \Omega$$

$$\text{Resistance of coil at} \atop \text{final temperature, } \theta°C, R_\theta = \frac{100}{2\cdot0} = 50 \ \Omega$$

Then, using the special relationship derived for copper,

$$\frac{R_\theta}{R_{15}} = \frac{234\cdot5 + \theta}{234\cdot5 + 15}$$

Substituting values and re-arranging the equation gives

$$(234\cdot5 + \theta) = 249\cdot5 \times \frac{50}{40}$$

or
$$\theta = 312 - 234 \cdot 5°C$$
$$= 77 \cdot 5°C$$

Final temperature of coil $= 77 \cdot 5°C$,

so that average temperature

rise of coil $= 77 \cdot 5 - 15°C$

$$= \underline{\underline{52 \cdot 5°C}}$$

As a result of heat losses from the exposed surfaces of the coil, and the insulation on the wire—which also gives some heat insulation—the coil will be hotter at the inner layers than on the outside. The temperature rise calculated in this example is the average rise in temperature of the whole coil. The temperature rise in the inner layers is likely to be rather more than this.

(ii) The 'hot' resistance of a 240-V tungsten filament lamp at its working temperature of 2000°C is 1000 Ω. Assuming that the resistance/temperature graph is linear for this temperature range, estimate the maximum initial current when the lamp is switched on at a room temperature of 15°C. Take $\alpha_0 = 0 \cdot 005 \ \Omega/\Omega°C$ for tungsten.

Substituting in the general equation,

$$\frac{R_{15}}{R_{2000}} = \frac{1 + 0 \cdot 005 \times 15}{1 + 0 \cdot 005 \times 2000}$$

or
$$R_{15} = 1000 \times \frac{1 \cdot 075}{11} \ \Omega$$

$$= 97 \cdot 8 \ \Omega$$

Initial current $= \dfrac{240}{97 \cdot 8} \simeq \underline{\underline{2\tfrac{1}{2} \ A}}$

This answer can only be taken as approximate, as the assumption made that the resistance/temperature graph is linear over this temperature range is rather a sweeping one and of doubtful validity. It does indicate, however, that a short 'surge' of current is to be expected when a lamp is first switched on. The actual measurement of the resistance of a lamp filament at different lamp currents—and hence filament temperatures—is an interesting experiment.

16.24. Resistance-temperature coefficient at other reference temperatures

It is sometimes convenient to use some other temperature than 0°C as a reference or starting temperature for resistance-temperature calculations. In this case, still assuming a linear resistance/temperature graph, the relationship is written

$$R_1 = R_\theta \{1 + a_\theta (\theta_1 - \theta)\} \qquad . \qquad . \qquad . \quad \text{(xvi)}$$

where

R_θ = resistance at 'reference' temperature $\theta°C$
R_1 = resistance at any other temperature $\theta_1°C$
$(\theta_1 - \theta)$ = temperature rise from reference temperature
α_θ = resistance-temperature coefficient from and at $\theta°C$

The value of α_θ may be derived from the value of α_o as follows:

From above, equation (xvi)

$$\frac{R_1}{R_\theta} = 1 + \alpha_\theta (\theta_1 - \theta)$$

From previous results

$$\frac{R_1}{R_\theta} = \frac{1 + \alpha_o\theta_1}{1 + \alpha_o\theta}$$

Equating the R.H.S. of these two equations,

$$1 + \alpha (\theta_1 - \theta) = \frac{1 + \alpha_o\theta_1}{1 + \alpha_o\theta}$$

$$\therefore \alpha_\theta (\theta_1 - \theta) = \frac{(1 + \alpha_o\theta_1) - (1 + \alpha_o\theta)}{1 + \alpha_o\theta}$$

$$= \frac{\alpha_o(\theta_1 - \theta)}{1 + \alpha_o\theta}$$

whence

$$\alpha_{\theta o} = \frac{\alpha_o}{1 + \alpha_o\theta} \qquad . \qquad . \qquad . \quad \text{(xvii)}$$

Example

Find the resistance-temperature coefficient of copper from and at 50°C. Use this result to find the resistance at 75°C of a conductor whose resistance at 50°C is 10 Ω. Compare this answer with that given by use of the resistance-temperature coefficient of copper from and at 0°C.

From the relationship $\alpha_\theta = \dfrac{\alpha_o}{1 + \alpha_o\theta}$

and substituting $\quad \alpha_0 = \dfrac{1}{234 \cdot 5} \; \Omega/\Omega°\text{C}$ from and at $0°\text{C}$

$$\alpha_\theta = \dfrac{1}{\dfrac{1}{\alpha_0} + \theta}$$

$$= \dfrac{1}{234 \cdot 5 + \theta} \; \Omega/\Omega°\text{C} \text{ from and at } \theta°\text{C}$$

or $\qquad \alpha_{50} = \dfrac{1}{284 \cdot 5} \; \Omega/\Omega°\text{C}$ from and at $50°\text{C}$

From given figures,

$$R_{75} = R_{50}\{1 + \alpha_{50}(75 - 50)\}$$

$$= 10\left\{1 + \dfrac{1}{284 \cdot 5} \times 25\right\}\Omega$$

$$= 10(1 + 0 \cdot 088)\,\Omega$$

$$= \underline{\underline{10 \cdot 88 \; \Omega}}$$

Using previous formula involving α_0,

$$\dfrac{R_{75}}{R_{50}} = \dfrac{234 \cdot 5 + 75}{234 \cdot 5 + 50}$$

$$\text{or } R_{75} = 10 \times \dfrac{309 \cdot 5}{284 \cdot 5} \; \Omega$$

$$= \underline{\underline{10 \cdot 88 \; \Omega}}$$

16.25. Electrical power

It was shown in Section 16.13 (page 449) that if a current I A flows for a time t s as a result of a potential difference V V then an amount of energy is liberated in the circuit, given by

$$\text{energy} = V.I.t \text{ joules}$$

In the circuits so far considered, this energy is converted into heat energy by the resistance of the circuit. Other circuit arrangements are possible, however, by means of which the energy may be converted into forms other than heat energy. In all cases, though, the above equation is true for the total amount of electrical energy supplied to the circuit from the source of e.m.f.

Just as in the case of mechanical forms of energy, the *rate* at which electrical energy is supplied from a source or converted by a 'load' is very important. Once again this rate of energy supplied or converted is known as the POWER.

POWER IS THE RATE OF SUPPLY OR CONVERSION OF ENERGY

The electrical unit of power is then, fundamentally, the JOULE PER SECOND. As in other cases, this unit is given a special name, the WATT (W) (after another scientist, James Watt), so that

$$1 \text{ WATT} = 1 \text{ JOULE PER SECOND}$$

Note that since 1 J is the amount of work expended when a force of 1 N is moved through a distance of 1 m along its line of action,

$$1 \text{ JOULE} = 1 \text{ NEWTON METRE}$$
$$\text{and } 1 \text{ WATT} = 1 \text{ NEWTON METRE PER SECOND}$$

so that the watt can also be used directly as a unit of mechanical power.

Then when a steady current I A flows for t s under the action of a potential difference of V V,

$$\text{power} = \frac{\text{energy supplied (or converted)}}{\text{time taken}}$$

$$= \frac{VIt}{t} \text{ J/s (or W)}$$

or
$$\text{Power} = VI \text{ W}$$

If the current I is set up in a resistance R as a result of the potential difference V across the resistance, this equation for the electrical power can be written in two other ways by being combined with the Ohm's law equation. So, remembering that $I = \dfrac{V}{R}$ or $V = IR$,

$$\text{power } P = VI \text{ W}$$

$$= V \cdot \left(\frac{V}{R}\right) \text{ W}$$

$$= \frac{V^2}{R} \text{ W}$$

or
$$\text{power } P = VI \text{ W}$$
$$= (IR) I \text{ W}$$
$$= I^2R \text{ W}$$

Then for a purely resistive circuit the power equations are

$$\text{power } P = VI = \frac{V_2}{R} = I^2R \text{ W} \qquad . \qquad . \qquad . \text{ (xviii)}$$

16.26. Examples

(i) A generator supplies a load current of 20 A at a p.d. of 200 V. What is the power output of the generator?

$$\text{Power } P = VI$$
$$= 200 \times 20 \text{ watts}$$
$$= 4000 \text{ W}$$

For cases where large powers are involved, the multiple units KILO-WATT (1 kW = 1000 W) or the MEGAWATT (1 MW = 1 000 000 W) are often used. The above answer would most conveniently be stated as

$$\text{Power output of generator} = 4 \text{ kW}$$

(ii) What is the operating resistance of a 250-V, 100-W electric filament lamp?

(By a 100-W lamp is meant a lamp which converts electrical energy into light and heat energy at the rate of 100 joules every second.)

$$\text{Power } P = \frac{V^2}{R}$$
$$\therefore 100 = \frac{(250)^2}{R} \text{ W}$$

or
$$R = \frac{(250)^2}{100} \ \Omega$$
$$= 625 \ \Omega$$

(iii) A steady current of 2 A flows for 1 h in a conductor having a resistance of 5 Ω. How much electrical energy is converted into heat energy?

Power $P = I^2R$

$= (2)^2 \times 5$ W

$= 20$ W

Then total energy converted to heat in 1 h is

energy = power $\times$ time

$= 20 \times (60 \times 60)$ watt-seconds

$= 72\,000$ joules (since 1 W-s $= 1$ J)

$= \underline{72\text{ kJ}}$

16.27.   Cost of electrical energy

Electrical energy is produced by the conversion of other forms of energy. For example, in a power station the chemical energy in the fuel (usually coal or oil) is converted into heat energy when the fuel is burnt. This heat energy is converted into the heat and pressure energy of steam, which is converted into mechanical energy in the turbines, which in turn drive the generators to produce the electrical energy. At each stage of energy conversion, not all the energy of one form is converted into useful energy; some will go to heat up the air in the chimney, or some heat energy will be left in the steam after it leaves the turbine, and so on. In simple terms, the EFFICIENCY of each stage of energy conversion will always be less than 100%. It will be remembered that the efficiency of a machine may be defined by the ratio:

$$\% \text{ EFFICIENCY} = \frac{\text{USEFUL ENERGY OUTPUT}}{\text{TOTAL ENERGY INPUT}} \times 100\ \%$$

It is clearly an advantage to keep the overall efficiency of the system as high as possible, and the various Generating and Supply Authorities and Boards do all they can to maintain and improve this overall efficiency. There are, of course, other costs than those for fuel, and these will be studied in some detail by the power engineer, but, broadly speaking, it should be seen that each unit of electrical energy produced will cost a certain amount.

It has been seen in an earlier example (Section 16.14, page 451) that the joule is a very small amount of electrical energy. Even when a single electric fire is switched on for an hour, the energy converted into heat runs into several million joules. To avoid numbers of astronomical proportions, a unit equivalent to a much larger amount of energy is used in this sort of problem. Use has already been made of the kilowatt as a unit in which to express large powers. The unit of energy often used in cases of this type is the amount of energy supplied at a rate of one kilowatt for one hour, and is known as the KILOWATT-HOUR (kWh).

Thus an energy of 1 kWh = 1000 W for (60 × 60) s
$$= 3\ 600\ 000\ \text{W-s}$$
or 1 kWh = 3·6 × 10⁶ J = 3·6 MJ

The kilowatt-hour is sometimes referred to as the 'Board of Trade Unit', or even more loosely as just the 'unit' of energy. Thus the statement on an electricity bill that 'the price per unit is 0·8 pence' means that the Area Electricity Board charges 0·8 p for each kilowatt-hour of electrical energy taken from the supply by the consumer.

A more complete discussion of the costs of electricity supply and the methods of recovering these costs from the consumer would be out of place here, but some background knowledge is useful.

16.28. Examples

(i) The heating elements of a 250-V electric cooker have an effective resistance between terminals of 10 Ω when the cooker is switched to maximum heat. If electrical energy costs 0·8 p/kWh, how much does it cost to operate the cooker at maximum heat for ½ h?

$$\text{Power} = \frac{V^2}{R}$$

$$= \frac{(250)^2}{10}\ \text{W}$$

$$= 6250\ \text{W}$$

$$= 6·25\ \text{kW}$$

Then electrical energy used in ½ h is

$$\text{energy} = 6·25 \times \tfrac{1}{2}\ \text{kWh}$$
$$= 3·125\ \text{kWh}$$
$$\text{Cost} = 3·125 \times 0·8\ \text{p}$$
$$= \underline{2·5\ \text{p}}$$

(ii) A consumer takes electrical energy from a 240-V supply and is charged 0·8 p/kWh. If an electric fire costs him 1·6 p an hour to use, what is the current taken by the fire?

$$\text{Power 'rating' of fire} = \frac{1·6}{0·8}\ \text{kW}$$

$$= 2\ \text{kW}$$

But $$\text{power } P = V \times I$$

or $$I = \frac{P}{V}$$

$$= \frac{2 \times 1000}{240} \text{ A}$$

$$= \underline{8 \cdot 33 \text{ A}}$$

CHAPTER SUMMARY

Electric charges are of two kinds, known as positive and negative.

Like charges repel, and unlike charges attract, each other.

The unit of electric charge is the coulomb, and an electron carries a negative electric charge of about $1 \cdot 6 \times 10^{-19}$ C.

The electric potential at any point is measured by the work done in bringing a positive charge of one coulomb to that point from a position very far away. The unit of electric potential is the volt.

$$1 \text{ V} = 1 \text{ J/C}$$

The electric potential difference between two points is also measured in volts, and is equal to the work done in taking a positive charge of 1 C between the points.

A free positive charge moves from points of higher potential to points of lower potential.

Conductors readily permit movement of electric charge. Semiconductors less readily permit such movement, and in insulators any movement of electric charge is generally negligible.

An electric current flow along a conductor consists of a slow drift of a large number of electrons along the conductor.

The conventional direction of current flow is from high to low potential (i.e. from positive to negative) although the electron drift is actually in the reverse direction.

The unit of electric current flow is the ampere.

$$1 \text{ A} = 1 \text{ C/s}$$

or $$I = Q/t$$

Electric current flow is accompanied by heating, magnetic and chemical effects.

Ohm's law:

'Under constant temperature conditions, the current in a conductor is directly proportional to the potential difference maintained between its ends.'

The resistance of a conductor is given by

$$R = \frac{V}{I}$$

and is measured in ohms

$$1\,\Omega = 1\ \mathrm{V/A}$$

The energy given up by a charge of Q C falling through a potential difference of V V is $V.Q$ joules. The energy released when a current of I A flows for t s between points having a potential difference of V V is then VIt joules (since $Q = I.t$).

The equivalent resistance, R, of a number of resistances R_1, R_2, R_3, etc., connected in series, is

$$R = R_1 + R_2 + R_3 + \ldots$$

The equivalent resistance, R, of a number of resistances R_1, R_2, R_3, etc., connected in parallel, is given by

$$\frac{1}{R} = \frac{1}{R_1} + \frac{1}{R_2} + \frac{1}{R_3} + \ldots$$

For two resistors connected in parallel, the equivalent resistance is

$$R = \frac{R_1 R_2}{R_1 + R_2}$$

If a total current I flows in two resistors R_1 and R_2 connected in parallel, the current I_1 flowing in resistance R_1 is

$$I_1 = I\frac{R_2}{R_1 + R_2}$$

The total e.m.f. of a battery having a number of cells in series is equal to the sum of the e.m.f.'s of the cells.

The total e.m.f. of a battery having a number of cells of equal e.m.f.'s in parallel is equal to the e.m.f. of any one cell.

The resistivity of a conducting material is the resistance measured between opposite faces of a unit cube of the material, at a stated, constant, temperature.

The resistance R of a conductor of length l and cross-sectional area A, of a material having resistivity ρ, is

$$R = \frac{\rho l}{A}$$

The units of resistivity are (resistance units) × (length units), e.g. Ω m.

The resistance, R_θ, of a conductor at temperature θ is given by

$$R_\theta = R_0 (1 + \alpha_0\theta)$$

where R_0 is the resistance at $0°$ and α_0 is the resistance-temperature coefficient from and at $0°$.

The resistance-temperature coefficient of a material is the increase in resistance per unit resistance at the reference temperature for each degree rise in temperature above the reference.

The resistances, R_1 at θ_1, and R_2 at θ_2, are related by

$$R_1 = R_2 \frac{1 + \alpha_0\theta_1}{1 + \alpha_0\theta_2}$$

The resistance-temperature coefficient, a_θ, from and at $\theta°$, is related to α_0 by the equation

$$\alpha_\theta = \frac{\alpha_0}{1 + \alpha_0\theta}$$

The electrical power associated with a current I A flowing under the action of a potential difference V V is

$$\text{Power} = VI \text{ W}$$
$$1 \text{ W} = 1 \text{ J/s}$$

For a circuit of resistance R, the power supplied to the resistor is

$$VI = I^2R = \frac{V^2}{R} \text{ W}$$

Where large amounts of electrical energy are involved, the unit in which the energy is measured is the kilowatt-hour (kWh)—often referred to as the 'Board of Trade Unit'.

$$1 \text{ kWh} = 3\cdot6 \text{ MJ}$$

QUESTIONS

1. Each of the following substances is either a good conductor of electricity or an insulator. State which is which, and give a use for each: copper, rubber, cotton, mica, tungsten, carbon, porcelain, bakelite.

2. What are the three main effects of an electric current? Describe briefly with suitable sketches how these effects may be utilized in practice.

3. Explain the purpose of a fuse in an electric circuit. State the electrical effect involved when a fuse blows and name the unit of electricity it controls.

4. Name the units of electric current, pressure and resistance. Explain why insulation must have high resistance and conductors low resistance.

5. (a) Explain the difference between negatively and positively charged bodies.

(b) Describe, with diagrams, two methods of determining the nature of a charge.

6. Define the unit 'coulomb'.
A 100-W lamp is used on a 240-V supply. Determine (a) the quantity of electricity, and (b) the electrical energy, taken by the lamp in 3 min.

7. (a) What are the units used for current, electromotive force and resistance? State the relationship between these quantities.

(b) Three resistances are connected in series, their values being 1, 2, 3 Ω respectively. If they carry a current of 5 A, what will be the p.d. (i) across each resistance, (ii) across all three?

8. A coil of wire of 1 Ω resistance is connected in series with two other coils of 2 Ω and 3 Ω resistance which are joined together in parallel. What voltage across the coils will maintain a current of 5 A through the 1-Ω coil?

9. (a) State Ohm's law and give the formula.

(b) The diagram shows three resistors connected to a 6-V supply. Determine the equivalent resistance of the circuit and the total current flowing.

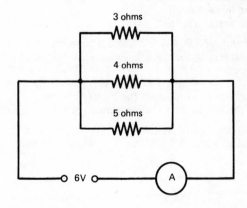

10. What is meant by the internal resistance of a cell? An electric torch battery is made up of three cells in series, each having an e.m.f. of 1·45 V and an internal resistance of 1·2 Ω. If the torch lamp takes a current of 0·3 A, what is the resistance of the lamp filament?

11. An arc lamp takes a current of 10 A at 48 V. Draw a circuit diagram showing how a resistor may be connected to the lamp so that the lamp may be used from a supply of 240 V. Calculate the value of the resistor.

12. Three resistances of 6, 9 and 18 Ω respectively are connected in parallel and this group is placed in series with a single resistance of 2 Ω across the terminals of a 12-V battery.
Sketch the circuit diagram. Calculate the total current in the circuit.

13. Two identical 200-V, 100-W lamps (A and B) are connected in series across a 250-V supply.
Calculate the number of similar lamps which, when connected in parallel across lamp A, will enable lamp B to operate under its rated conditions. Assume that the resistance of each of the various lamps remains constant throughout.

14. A circuit has three resistors connected in series across a 200-V supply. The current flowing through the circuit is 4 A. If two of the resistors are 10 Ω and 15 Ω respectively, calculate the resistance of the third resistor.
Find also the current through, and voltage drop across, each resistor.

15. Two resistors A and B are connected in parallel. The resistance of A is 10 Ω, and the current through the circuit is 6 A when connected to a 12-V supply.
Calculate the resistance of B.
If these two resistors are now connected in series with a third resistor C, calculate its resistance if the current for this circuit is 4 A.

16. Six cells are connected (a) in series, (b) in parallel. Each cell has an e.m.f. of 1·5 V and an internal resistance of 0·4 Ω. Current is supplied to a coil of resistance 10 Ω.
For each arrangement of the cells, calculate:
 (i) the current in the circuit,
 (ii) the voltage across the coil.

17. Three resistors, of 3 Ω, 4 Ω and 6 Ω, are connected in parallel. They are supplied from a battery of four cells in series, each having an e.m.f. of 1·5 V and internal resistance of 0·2 Ω.
Draw the circuit, showing a voltmeter to measure the battery terminal voltage and an ammeter to measure the battery current.
What will be the readings on the instruments when the circuit is closed?

18. Show from first principles that the total resistance of two resistors r_1 and r_2 connected in series is $(r_1 + r_2)$, and when connected in parallel is $\left(\dfrac{r_1 r_2}{r_1 + r_2} \right)$.

A battery consists of four cells connected in series, each having an e.m.f. of 1·5 V and an internal resistance of 1·0 Ω. Across the terminals of the battery are two parallel-connected resistors of 30 Ω and 60 Ω respectively. Calculate the total current taken by the resistors and the total energy dissipated, in joules, if the current flows for 4 min.

19. You are provided with several 5-Ω resistors. How would you connect them to give a resistance of (a) 20 Ω, (b) 1 Ω, (c) 12·5 Ω, (d) 7·5 Ω? Give a diagram of the arrangement in each case.

20. Three resistors of 4 Ω, 6 Ω and 12 Ω are connected in parallel to a supply, and the total current is 66 A. Find the current through each resistor.
What would be the value of current if these three resistors were connected in series to the same supply?

21. Three coils of resistance 4, 6, 12 Ω respectively are connected in parallel and this group is connected in series with a further single coil of 6 Ω resistance. Calculate the total current taken by the coils when connected to a 48-V d.c. supply.
Calculate the current in the 4-Ω coil.

22. Give the units and symbols for (a) current, (b) power, (c) resistance, (d) quantity of electricity.
In the following diagram is shown a portion of an electric circuit. Find the value of R, the voltage drop across AB and the current in the 4-Ω coil.

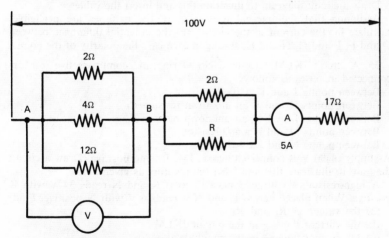

23. For the circuit shown in the diagram, calculate:
(a) the current in branch ABD,
(b) the current in branch ACD,
(c) the reading of the voltmeter V,
(d) which of the two points B and C is positive with respect to the other,
(e) the value of X.

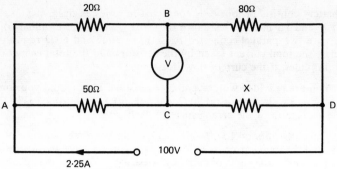

2·25A

The current through the voltmeter may be neglected.

24. D, E, F, G, H and J are points in a complete series circuit consisting of three batteries and three resistors connected as follows. Between points D and E, a battery of e.m.f. = 24 V with its positive terminal at E,
Between points E and F, a resistor of 15 Ω,
Between points F and G, a battery of e.m.f. = 10 V with its positive terminal at F
Between points G and H, a resistor of 45 Ω
Between points H and J, a battery of e.m.f. = 6 V with its positive terminal at J
Between points J and D, a resistor of 20 Ω.
Draw a circuit diagram to illustrate this and insert the values.
Assuming that the internal resistances of the batteries are negligible, calculate (a) the current in the circuit, (b) the potential difference between D and F, F and H, H and D, stating in each case the polarity of the points.

25. A circuit JKLMN forms a closed ring and comprises five resistors connected in series as follows:
Between points J and K a 10-Ω resistor
Between points K and L an unknown resistor R_1
Between points L and M an unknown resistor R_2
Between points M and N a 6-Ω resistor
Between points N and J a 9-Ω resistor.
A supply of 90 V is connected across JM, J being positive. Draw a circuit diagram to illustrate this and label the resistors as given above.
A high-resistance voltmeter placed across K and N reads 34 V with K positive. When placed across L and N it reads 6 V with N positive. Find:
(a) the values of R_1 and R_2
(b) the current flowing in the circuit JKLM
(c) the current flowing in the supply leads.

26. How is the resistance of (a) a conductor, (b) the insulation of a conductor, affected by length and cross-sectional area?
If the resistance of 1 km of copper conductor of cross-sectional area 1·22 mm² is 12·4 Ω, calculate the resistance of 2·5 km of similar material 2·01 mm² cross-sectional area.

27. Upon what factors does the resistance of a conductor depend? What length of resistance wire would be required to wind a coil which would take 4 A at 200 V if the diameter of the conductor is 0·5 mm and the resistivity of the material is 250×10^{-8} Ωm?

28. Define resistivity.
A wire 37 m long has a diameter of 2·5 mm and a resistance of 0·13 Ω. Calculate the resistivity of the material in ohmmetre.

29. Define resistivity and state a unit in which it can be expressed.
The resistance of a 100 m length of copper conductor, diameter 0·9 mm, is 2·47 Ω. Calculate the resistance of a cable 800 m in length composed of 19 strands of similar copper conductor but each strand being 1·32 mm diameter. Allow 5 % increase in length for the lay (twist) of each strand in the completed cable.

30. Define resistivity.
Find the resistance of 4·5 m of Eureka wire of diameter 0·375 mm.
Resistivity for Eureka = 48×10^{-8} Ωm.

31. (a) The voltage at the receiving end of a d.c. feeder 1 km long is 540 V. What cross-section must each copper conductor have so that the voltage drop will not exceed 10 % of the sending-end voltage when 100 A is flowing?
(b) Determine the relative mass and the relative cross-section if aluminium be used instead of copper.
Resistivity of copper = $1·67 \times 10^{-8}$ Ωm
Relative density = 8·9
Resistivity of aluminium = $2·82 \times 10^{-8}$ Ωm
Relative density = 2·7.

32. A factory installation takes 200 A at 240 V. It is fed from a sub-station by a twin cable 80 m long. If the cross-sectional area of the conductor is 130 mm², what voltage is maintained at the sub-station?
Assume the resistivity of the conductor material to be $1·8 \times 10^{-8}$ Ωm.

33. A two-core distribution cable has a load of 40 A at a point X, 200 m from the feeding end, and another load of 60 A at a point Y, 400 m beyond X.
(a) Draw a diagram of this and show the current values which exist in the various parts of the cable.
(b) If the 60-A load is switched off, find the voltages at points X and Y if the supply at the feeding end is 240 V and the resistance of the cable is 0·025 Ω per 100 m of single conductor.

34. Three trolley-buses A, B and C are 0·5, 1 and 2 km respectively from the 600-V power station. A and B are taking 50 A each and C, which is starting, 200 A. Each of the overhead trolley wires has a resistance of 0·25 Ω/km. Draw a circuit diagram to illustrate this and show the current values in the various parts of the system.
Calculate the voltage at each of the trolley-buses.

35. A two-wire cable 1 km long is fed at one end at 250 V and supplies four loads, each of 50 A, at distances of 250, 500, 750 and 1000 m from the feeding point. Calculate the current in each section of the cable and the potential difference across each load. Each conductor in the cable has a resistance of 0·08 Ω/km.

36. An electric generator has an e.m.f. of 250 V and lights 14 incandescent lamps which are connected in parallel. The resistance of each lamp is 84 Ω. Find the total current and the power required to drive the generator. Neglect any losses in the generator.

37. (a) Define the unit of potential difference.

(b) A 240-V electric iron, with no thermostat control, has a rating of 500 W. Assuming no change of resistance to occur, calculate the power consumption when the iron is used on a 200-V supply.

38. Name and define a unit of (a) electrical energy, (b) electrical power.

The heating element of an electric cooker consists of two resistors each of 50 Ω. By means of a three-heat switch they can be grouped as follows:

  (i) two in series,

 (ii) one only in circuit,

(iii) two in parallel.

If the heater is connected to a 240-V supply, calculate the total power consumption for each grouping.

39. (a) Distinguish between power and energy and give the unit used in electrical engineering.

(b) Calculate the values of resistances which, when separately connected to a 200-V supply, will dissipate the following: 2, 10, 50, 500 W.

State, with a reason, which resistor would be the largest in size.

40. (a) An industrial heating element consists of four resistors each of 50 Ω, and is used on a 250-V supply. A switch connects them in series, or in parallel. Calculate (i) the total current taken from the supply in each position, (ii) the power consumption of the heater in each position.

(b) If an open circuit should develop in one resistor, what would be the effect on the value of the supply current in both switch positions?

41. The consumption of a 300-V heating element is 900 kJ in 4 min. Calculate:

(a) the kW rating of the element

(b) the current consumption

(c) the resistance of the element

(d) the cost over a period of 12 h at 0·8 p/kWh.

42. The diagram shows an electric circuit connected to a 230-V supply. Determine:

(a) the reading on the voltmeter V and each of the ammeters A_1 and A_2

(b) the power in the 30-Ω coil.

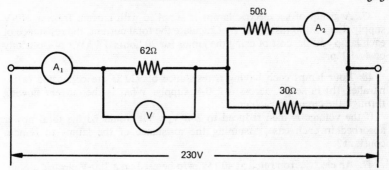

43. A 2-V battery is connected between the terminals A and B in the circuit shown in the diagram. Find the current taken from the battery and the p.d. across EF.

If the terminals E and F are now closed by another 20-Ω resistor, find the current flowing in each 20-Ω resistor and the power dissipated in the 40-Ω resistor.

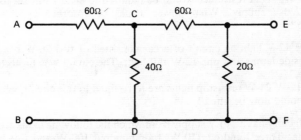

44. It is required to reduce the heating effect of a 3-kW 200-V d.c. element by 20% by the inclusion of a series resistor. Calculate (a) the value of the resistor, (b) the power dissipated in the resistor and the total power dissipated in the circuit when the resistor is included. Neglect the effect of temperature coefficient of resistance.

45. An electric motor develops 7·5 kW and is 80% efficient. The motor has 93·8 V at its terminals in this condition. Determine the cross-sectional area of the copper conductor if a total of 150 m of conductor is used to connect the motor to a 100-V supply.

ρ for copper may be taken as $1\cdot78 \times 10^{-8}$ Ωm.

46. What is understood by (a) resistance, (b) resistivity?

Explain how you would determine the resistivity of a given metal wire.

An electric motor develops 7·5 kW and its efficiency is 82%. If it is situated 50 m from a supply point and fed with a cable of 20 mm² cross-sectional area so that the voltage at the motor terminals is 230 V, find the voltage drop in the cable.

Resistivity of copper = $1\cdot78 \times 10^{-8}$ Ωm.

47. A group of six electric lamps is supplied with current from a 240-V supply. Each lamp takes 100 W. Calculate the total current, the resistance of each lamp and the cost of using the lamps for 20 hours if 1 kWh of electricity costs 1·1 p.

48. Four lamps each having a resistance of 920 Ω are connected (a) in parallel, (b) in series, across a 230-V supply. What is the current flowing through the circuit in each case?

If the voltage is then reduced to 200 V, what would be the total power absorbed in each case, assuming the resistance of the lamps to remain constant?

49. An electric iron rated at 400 W is to be used on a 200-V electric circuit. Calculate the working resistance of the element.

How much would it cost to run this iron for a year of 52 weeks if its average use is 3 h per week at a cost of 2·5 p per unit?

50. State Ohm's law.

An American radio set is designed to operate from a 110-V supply and takes 100 W. What resistance would be required to enable this set to be run from a 230-V supply? What power would be absorbed by this added resistance?

51. The 12-V lighting circuit of a car consisted of two 36-W headlamps, two 6-W side lamps and one 12-W tail light. The circuit was protected by a 10-A fuse.

If two 12-W/24-W rear/stop lights are to be fitted to this circuit, what value of fuse should now be fitted?

52. A factory has a 240-V supply from which the following loads are taken:
Lighting: Three hundred 150-W, four hundred 100-W and five hundred 60-W lamps
Heating: 100 kW
Motors: A total of 45 kW with an average efficiency of 75%
Miscellaneous: Various loads taking a total current of 40 A.
Assuming that the lighting load is on for a period of 4 h per day, the heating for 10 h per day and the remainder for 2 h per day, calculate the weekly consumption of the factory in kWh when working on a five-day week.

What current is taken when the lighting load only is switched on?

53. A small electrically driven battery vehicle, having a mass of 800 kg, runs at 8 km/h along a level stretch of road. If the tractive resistance to motion is equivalent to a force of 0·25 N/kg, calculate the required output of the battery (in watts).

54. An electric heater has a rating of 1 kW at 200 V. If the wire of the element is 0·2 mm² cross-sectional area, find the required length in metres.

Take the working temperature as 120°C, the resistivity at 0°C as 0·5 × 10⁻⁸ Ωm and the temperature coefficient of resistance at 0°C as 0·005/°C.

55. In the circuit shown in the diagram, the ammeters A_1 and A_2 give readings of 3 A and 2 A respectively. Calculate (a) the power in the 5-Ω coil, (b) the p.d. across AB, (c) the value of the resistor R, (d) the total resistance of the circuit.

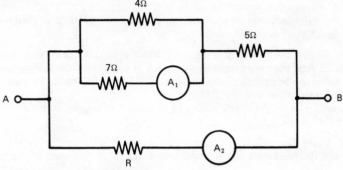

56. An installation consists of:
(a) Several motors taking a total of 80 kW
(b) Six ovens taking 3000 W each
(c) Various small accessories taking a total of 6 A at 240 V.
Find: (i) the total power in kW
(ii) the energy used in 8 h
(iii) the cost for 8 h at 0·5 p/kWh.

57. What is the difference between energy and power?
Name and define the units of electrical energy and power. An installation consists of the following: (a) two motors, each having an input of 7·5 kW, (b) one 3-kW heater, (c) ten 100-W lamps. If the full load is on for 5 h calculate the cost of energy if 1 kWh costs 0·8 p.

58. A 500-V d.c. motor has an output of 15 kW at an efficiency of 80%. It is supplied from a generator through a two-core cable 300 m long. If the maximum voltage drop between the generator and the motor is limited to 20 V, calculate (a) the minimum cross-sectional area of the cable required, (b) the actual voltage drop using a cable selected from the table below.
The resistivity of the copper conductor is $1·78 \times 10^{-8}$ Ωm.

Size of cable	7/1·32	7/1·60	19/1·12	19/1·32
Area in mm²	9·35	14·0	18·7	25·5

59. Define temperature coefficient of resistance.
A constant p.d. of 100 V was applied to the field winding of a d.c. machine. The current was initially 1·25 A but after 45 min it had fallen to 1·1 A. If the winding was at room temperature of 18°C at the start of the test, what was the average temperature rise of the winding, assuming that the resistance-temperature coefficient of the winding conductor material at 0°C is 0·004 3/°C?

60. What do you understand by the term 'temperature coefficient of resistance' of a conductive material?

The field coil of a generator takes a current of 4 A when the temperature of the coil is 16°C. After a period of time the current has fallen to a value of 3·5 A and the temperature of the coil has risen to 51·5°C. Calculate the temperature coefficient of resistance of the material of the coil. Assume the voltage remains constant.

61. During the period of a test on a 400-V field coil, the current dropped from 5·5 A at the commencement to 4·3 A at the end. If the temperature of the coil at the beginning of the test was 15°C, calculate the final temperature at the finish of the test.

Take the temperature coefficient of resistance of copper to be 0·004 3/°C from and at 0°C.

62. Using the following values, plot a graph showing the relationship between the resistance and temperature of the given specimen of copper.

Resistance (Ω)	2·66	2·75	2·93	3·16	3·34	3·56
Temperature (°C)	15	25	40	60	80	100

From the graph find the temperature coefficient of resistance at 0°C.

Describe how a knowledge of the temperature coefficient is of value in calculating the temperature rise of the windings of an electrical machine after operation on load.

63. Define resistance-temperature coefficient at (i) 0°C, (ii) 20°C.

If the resistance-temperature coefficient of a certain material is 0·000 25 at 0°C, what would be its value at 20°C?

Calculate the length of wire of 0·56 mm diameter required for a resistance of 1000 Ω at 15°C if the material of the wire has a resistivity of $41\cdot7 \times 10^{-8}$ Ωm at 15°C. What will be the resistance at 100°C if the resistance-temperature coefficient is 0·000 3 at 20°C?

17. Electrical Measurements

17.1. Internal resistance of a source

The measurement of the e.m.f. of a source of electricity presents special problems. Most voltmeters work on the principle of measuring a current through a known resistance inside the meter. A good voltmeter giving a maximum indication of, say, 10 V will have a resistance of the order of a few thousand ohms, so that it requires a current to operate it, even if this current is only about one milliampere.

Now all sources of electricity have some 'internal' resistance; due, among other causes, to the conductors used in their construction. This means that, as current is drawn from the source, a potential difference will be set up across this resistance. The 'terminal' p.d. of the source will then be less than the e.m.f., because of this internal 'volt-drop'.

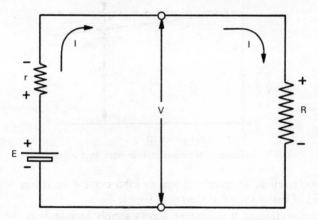

186. Battery connected across a load resistance R

In diagram 186 a battery is represented as having an e.m.f. E V and an internal resistance r Ω,* and is shown connected to a load resistance of R Ω. The terminal voltage of the battery is V V and the load current flowing is I A.

* Although it may not be possible in practice to separate the e.m.f. of the battery from its internal resistance, it is convenient to show them as separate in the circuit diagram.

The load current I flows through the internal resistance r and sets up a p.d. across it (often referred to as a 'voltage drop' across it) of Ir V. The polarities of the e.m.f. and this voltage drop across the internal resistance are shown in the diagram, and it follows that the terminal voltage V is given by

$$V = E - Ir \qquad . \qquad . \qquad . \qquad \text{(i)}$$

This simple equation is very important, as it will apply to all forms of generators as well as to batteries. Re-arranging this equation gives

$$r = \frac{E - V}{I}$$

If a test is taken to measure different values of V for different values of I, a value for r may be found from the results. A graph drawn of V against I will be a straight line, as shown in diagram 187, always provided that E and r remain constant during the test, which unfortunately is sometimes not the case.

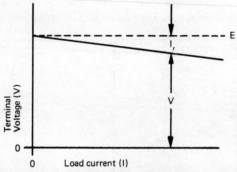

187. Variation of terminal voltage with load current

This steady fall in terminal voltage as load current increases is characteristic of many forms of electrical supply.

The connection of a voltmeter across supply terminals is merely a special case of the connection of a load resistance across the supply, so that the voltmeter will measure the terminal voltage V rather than the e.m.f. E. In some practical cases where the internal resistance (r) is very small, and the voltmeter resistance (R) is very large, there is not much error in assuming that the voltmeter reading is equal to the e.m.f. This is by no means true in all cases, however, and a special method of measuring the e.m.f. of a source having a fairly high value of internal resistance is considered in the next section.

17.2.   Measurement of e.m.f. The slide-wire potentiometer

In Section 16.20, page 475, it was shown that the resistance of a conductor of uniform cross-sectional area is directly proportional to its
length. Then, if the resistance of a length l of a uniform wire is $R\ \Omega$,

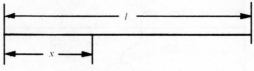

188. Section of uniform wire

the resistance of a portion of the wire of length x will be $\frac{x}{l} \times R\ \Omega$.

(This is only a general way of saying that, for example, the resistance of
a quarter of the length of the wire is a quarter of the total resistance.)

If a potential difference of V V is applied across the whole wire, then
a current I will flow along the wire, where $I = \dfrac{V}{R}$. The potential difference developed across the length x will then be

$$\text{p.d. across length x} = (\text{current}) \times (\text{resistance of length x})$$

$$= I \times \frac{x}{l} \times R \text{ volts}$$

$$= \frac{x}{l} \times IR \text{ volts}$$

But $IR = V$, the total p.d. across the wire, so that

$$\text{p.d. across length x} = \frac{x}{l} \times (\text{p.d. across length } l)$$

This is the principle used in the SLIDE-WIRE POTENTIOMETER.

The circuit diagram of a slide-wire potentiometer is shown in diagram 189. A potential difference is maintained between the ends of a
uniform wire of length l by means of a supply battery B. This potential
difference must be greater than the largest e.m.f. it is intended to
measure. A battery, whose e.m.f. E_s is already known, is connected as
shown between one end of the wire and a variable 'tapping' point. A
sensitive current-measuring instrument, known as a GALVANOMETER
(G), is also included in this part of the circuit. The tapping point along
the wire is made by means of a knife-edged conductor which may be

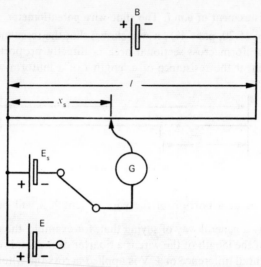

189. Circuit diagram of a slide-wire potentiometer

made to slide along the wire (hence the name 'slide-wire'). It is worth pointing out here that this knife-edged conductor or 'jockey' should be pressed only lightly against the wire—if heavy pressure is used the wire will become grooved and will no longer be of uniform cross-section along its length.

The tapping point is moved along the wire until the p.d. between the 'common' end of the wire and the tapping point, due to the supply battery B, is equal to the e.m.f. E_s of the 'standard' battery. This condition will be indicated by a zero or 'null' reading on the galvanometer. This will perhaps be made clearer by the re-drawn circuit shown in diagram 190.

Terminal A of the galvanometer is held at a potential of $-E_s$ V relative to point C by means of the battery e.m.f.

Terminal B of the galvanometer is held at a potential of $-I.\dfrac{x_s}{l}.R$ volts relative to point C by means of the p.d. developed in the length x_s of the slide-wire by the current I along it.

When $I.\dfrac{x_s}{l}.R = E_s$, it follows that both terminals of the galvanometer are at the same potential, so that no current will flow through the galvanometer. This also means that no current will flow through the

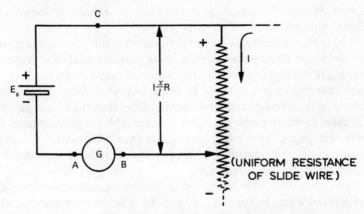

190. Re-drawn section of slide-wire potentiometer circuit

battery, and there can be no voltage drop across its internal resistance.

The same procedure is then carried out for the battery whose e.m.f. E is to be found. Suppose that 'balance' is found when the tapping point is at a distance x from the common end. Then

$$(1) \quad E = I . \frac{x}{l} . R$$

$$(2) \quad E_s = I . \frac{x_s}{l} . R$$

Since I (the current along the slide-wire due to battery B), l (the length of the slide-wire) and R (the resistance of the slide-wire) are all the same in each case, division of equation (1) by equation (2) gives the result

$$\frac{E}{E_s} = \frac{x}{x_s}$$

or $$E = \frac{x}{x_s} . E_s \qquad . \qquad . \qquad . \qquad (ii)$$

This enables the unknown e.m.f. to be calculated from the known, standard, e.m.f. Since no current is taken from the unknown e.m.f. source at the point of balance, the result is independent of the internal resistance of the source and is equal to its true e.m.f.

The commonly used source of known e.m.f. is the Weston Standard Cell. The e.m.f. of this cell is very accurately known, and is 1·018 3 V at 20°C. Care should be taken when such a cell is used, and as little current as possible should be drawn from it. Details concerning its construction will be found on page 558.

During the initial stages of carrying out an e.m.f. measurement with the slide-wire potentiometer, it is quite possible that the first trial position of the tapping-point on the slide-wire may be very far from the point required to give balance. In order to protect both the galvanometer and the standard cell from carrying more than their 'safe' current, it is usual to insert a high resistance in series with the galvanometer for these first stages. As the balance-point is then approached, this resistance may be short-circuited by closing the contacts of some form of switch across the series resistance.

As an alternative, if it is required to protect the galvanometer only, a low resistance may be connected in parallel with the galvanometer. This resistance is usually referred to as a 'shunt', and will carry some of the current that would otherwise pass through the meter. Further consideration of the use of shunts will be found on page 536.

Note that the polarity of the measured e.m.f. *must* be the same as that of the supply to the slide-wire if balance is to be obtained. (The positive terminals must be connected to the same end of the slide-wire.

17.3. Measurement of resistance. Voltmeter-ammeter method

Since the resistance of a conductor is defined by the relationship

$$\text{resistance of conductor} = \frac{\text{p.d. across conductor}}{\text{current through conductor}}$$

it might seem reasonable to measure an unknown resistance by measuring the current flowing through it when a measured p.d. is applied across it. This is a practicable method of resistance measurement, although difficulties can arise.

Consider first the circuit shown in diagram 191 (a). If the voltmeter reading is V V and the ammeter reading is I A, then an approximate value of the resistance R is

$$R \simeq \frac{V}{I} \, \Omega \qquad . \qquad . \qquad . \qquad . \qquad \text{(iii)}$$

This answer is only approximate because the ammeter reading will also include the current taken by the voltmeter. Reference to the diagram shows that

$$I = I_1 + i$$

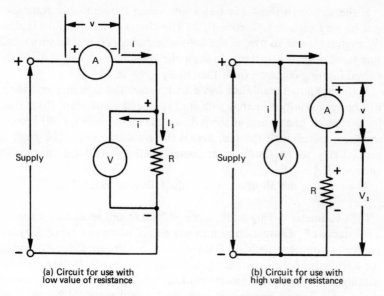

(a) Circuit for use with
low value of resistance

(b) Circuit for use with
high value of resistance

191. Voltmeter-ammeter method of resistance measurement

In other words, the ammeter reading will be more than the current taken by the resistance R when a p.d. of V is applied across it, and the result given by equation (iii) will be rather less than the true value of R. Now consider the circuit shown in diagram 191 (b).

Again, for readings of V V and I A, the resistance R is given approximately by

$$R \simeq \frac{V}{I}\,\Omega \qquad . \qquad . \qquad . \qquad . \qquad \text{(iv)}$$

This time the answer is approximate because the voltmeter indicates the p.d. across the ammeter (v) in addition to the p.d. across the resistance R. The result given by equation (iv) will thus be rather more than the true value of R.

It follows that when the voltmeter-ammeter method of resistance measurement is used, a choice must be made between the two possible arrangements of the circuit and the two resulting kinds of error in the answer. Although these errors can be allowed for in calculations if the meter resistances are known (see following examples), a result of reasonable accuracy can be obtained direct from the meter readings in certain cases.

R

If the unknown resistance has a low value, the voltmeter resistance will be very high compared with it. The circuit of diagram (a) is then the preferable one to use, as the voltmeter current (i) will be very small compared with the current through the resistance (I_1). The error involved in using equation (ii) is then likely to be small.

If the unknown resistance has a high value, the ammeter resistance will be very small compared with it. The circuit of diagram (b) is then the preferable one to use, as the p.d. across the ammeter (v) will be very small compared with the p.d. across the resistance (V_1). The error is again likely to be small if the meter readings are used directly in equation (iv).

These points are all illustrated in the following examples.

(i) A voltmeter having a resistance of 2000 Ω and an ammeter having a resistance of 1 Ω are used to measure an unknown resistance R by the voltmeter-ammeter method. The voltmeter is connected directly across the terminals of the resistance (i.e. circuit (a) is used). If the voltmeter reading is 2 V and the ammeter reading is 0·5 A, find the true value of the resistance, and compare it with the value that would be obtained from the meter readings given.

What would be the meter readings if the same supply were used, and the voltmeter were connected across the ammeter and resistor together (i.e. if circuit (b) were used)? What would be the apparent value of the resistance obtained from these readings?

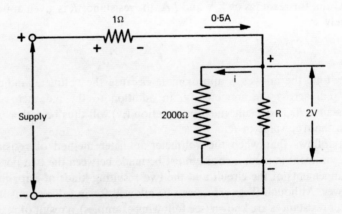

192. Voltmeter-ammeter method of resistance measurement.
Equivalent circuit—numerical example

Circuit (a) may be redrawn for this case, as in diagram 192, to show the meter resistances.

The current taken by the voltmeter (2 V across 2000 Ω) is

$$i = \frac{2}{2000} \text{ A}$$
$$= 0 \cdot 001 \text{ A}$$

Then the true current in the resistor is

$$I_1 = I - i$$
$$= 0 \cdot 5 - 0 \cdot 001 \text{ A}$$
$$= 0 \cdot 499 \text{ A}$$

The true value of the resistance is then

$$R = \frac{2}{0 \cdot 499} \, \Omega$$
$$= \underline{\underline{4 \cdot 01 \, \Omega}}$$

This compares very well with the value obtained direct from the meter readings

$$R \simeq \frac{2}{0 \cdot 5} \, \Omega$$
$$= \underline{\underline{4 \cdot 0 \, \Omega}}$$

(the error is only about 0·25%)

In any case, it is doubtful whether the difference between an ammeter reading of 0·5 A and 0·499 A would be discernible with any accuracy in practice.

Note that there would be a p.d. of 0·5 V (a current of 0·5 A through a resistance of 1 Ω) across the ammeter. This p.d. is of course excluded from these calculations since it is not included in the voltmeter reading. It means, however, that the supply voltage is (0·5 + 2·0), or 2·5 V.

If circuit (b) were now to be used with the same supply, meters and measured resistance, the circuit could be represented as shown in diagram 193.

The voltmeter would now indicate the full supply voltage of 2·5 V (it would take a slightly higher current, but this would not be included in the ammeter reading in this arrangement of the circuit). The total resistance in the branch containing R and the ammeter would be $1 \times 4 \cdot 01 = 5 \cdot 01 \, \Omega$.

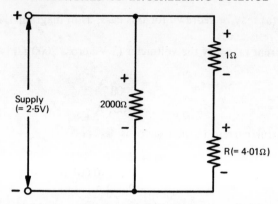

193. Voltmeter-ammeter method of resistance measurement.
Equivalent circuit—numerical example

The ammeter reading would now be

$$I = \frac{2 \cdot 5}{5 \cdot 01} \text{ A}$$

$$= 0 \cdot 499 \text{ A (if it could be read as such!)}$$

(This is, of course, the reading that would also be obtained for circuit (a) if the voltmeter were to be disconnected.)

The apparent value of R obtained from the meter readings would now be

$$R \simeq \frac{2 \cdot 5}{0 \cdot 499} \text{ }\Omega$$

$$= \underline{5 \cdot 01 \text{ }\Omega}$$

This is very far from the actual value, being about 25% more than the right answer. Circuit (a) should therefore be used to measure low values of resistance.

(ii) A voltmeter having a resistance of 10 000 Ω and a milliammeter having a resistance of 50 Ω are used to measure an unknown resistance by the voltmeter-ammeter method. The voltmeter is connected directly across the supply terminals (i.e. circuit (b) is used). If the voltmeter reading is 100 V and the milliammeter reading is 10 mA, find the true value of the resistance and compare it with the value obtained directly from the meter readings alone.

What would be the meter readings if the same supply were used, and the voltmeter were connected directly across the terminals of the resistance (i.e. if circuit (a) were used)? What would be the apparent value of the resistance obtained from these readings?

Diagram 194 shows circuit (b) with the resistances given.

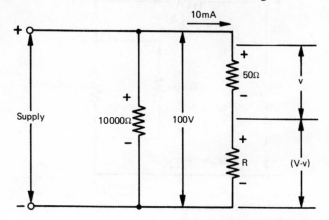

194. Voltmeter-ammeter method of resistance measurement.
Equivalent circuit—numerical example

$$P.d. \text{ across ammeter } v = 50 \times 10 \times 10^{-3} \text{ V}$$
$$= 0 \cdot 5 \text{ V}$$

Thus actual p.d. across R is

$$V_1 = V - v$$
$$= 100 - 0 \cdot 5 \text{ V}$$
$$= 99 \cdot 5 \text{ V}$$

$$\text{True value of resistance } R = \frac{99 \cdot 5}{10 \times 10^{-3}} \ \Omega$$
$$= 9950 \ \Omega$$

This compares quite favourably with the value given direct from meter readings,

$$R \simeq \frac{100}{10 \times 10^{-3}} = 10\ 000 \ \Omega$$

(The error is only about $0 \cdot 5\%$)

Again it is doubtful whether a voltmeter reading of 99·5 V could be very accurately distinguished from a reading of 100 V.

If now circuit (a) were to be used with the same supply, meters and measured resistance, the circuit could be represented as shown in diagram 195.

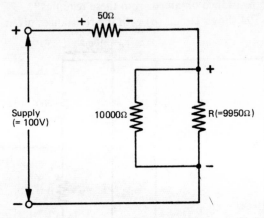

195. Voltmeter-ammeter method of resistance measurement. Equivalent circuit—numerical example

The effective resistance (R') of the voltmeter in parallel with R would be

$$R' = \frac{10\,000 \times 9950}{19\,950}\,\Omega$$

$$= 4990\,\Omega$$

and the total circuit resistance, including the ammeter, would be ($R' + 50$) Ω or 5040 Ω.

The ammeter reading would then be

$$I = \frac{100}{5040}\,\text{A}$$

$$= 19\cdot85\,\text{mA (on the assumption that it could read as accurately as this, which is extremely doubtful)}$$

This current, flowing through the effective 4990-Ω resistance of the parallel circuit, would give a p.d., which would be indicated by the voltmeter, of

$$V = 19\cdot85 \times 10^{-3} \times 4990\,\text{V}$$
$$= 99\,\text{V}$$

The apparent value of the resistance R would then be

$$R \simeq \frac{99}{19 \cdot 85 \times 10^{-3}} \; \Omega$$
$$= \underline{4990 \; \Omega}$$

This is very far from the actual value, being about 50% of the right answer. Circuit (b) should therefore be used to measure high values of resistance.

Summary

If the limits of accuracy in the reading of the meters, and the possible calibration errors in the meters themselves, are borne in mind, the volt-meter-ammeter method of measuring an unknown resistance is capable of giving reasonably accurate results as long as a suitable method of connection of the meters is used. The method is not, however, capable of great precision, even though some correction can be applied if the meter resistances are known.

It might be asked how it is possible to decide which method of connection should be used if the value of the resistance is unknown. Usually, of course, some idea of the approximate value of the resistance is known beforehand. If not, the ammeter, in series with the unknown resistance, should first of all be connected to the supply (preferably a low-voltage supply in case the resulting current were very large). If the voltmeter connection is then tapped across the resistance as in circuit (a), a significant change in the ammeter reading would indicate that circuit (b) might be preferable.

17.4. Measurement of resistance. Potentiometer method

The disadvantage, discussed in the previous section, of the effect of the current taken by the voltmeter when connected directly across the unknown resistance, can be removed if the p.d. across the resistor is measured by a potentiometer method. As seen in Section 17.2, the slide-wire potentiometer does not take any current (at the point of balance) from the source being measured. Consequently the ammeter reading is not affected by this method of measuring the p.d. across the resistor, and a more precise result is obtainable. (Of course, the result is still dependent on the accuracy of the ammeter reading.)

The circuit used is similar to that shown in diagram 189 on page 510, except that connections from each end of the unknown resistance in the circuit under test replace the connections from the battery of unknown e.m.f. Note that, as before, care must be taken that the polarity of these connections matches the polarity of the slide-wire, or it will be impossible to find a point of balance.

Another possible method of using the potentiometer to find the value of an unknown resistance is discussed in Section 17.6, page 521.

17.5.   Measurement of resistance. Substitution

This method assumes that a standard resistance is available, whose value can be adjusted as required. Such standard resistors are usually made up into what are known as 'Resistance Decade Boxes'. Such a box may contain, say, 10 1-Ω resistors, 10 10-Ω resistors, 10 100-Ω resistors and 10 1000-Ω resistors. An arrangement of switches on the box enables any required number of resistors to be selected and connected in series, so that a box such as that described would be capable of a total resistance of any value between 1 Ω and 11 110 Ω in 1-Ω steps. (Some boxes have 9 resistors of each value so that a range of 1 Ω to 9999 Ω would be available.) The name 'decade box' is derived from the fact that such a box covers a number of 'decades' of resistance value, the ranges 1–10, 10–100, 100–1000, 1000–10 000 each being known as a decade.

A resistance decade box may be used to determine the value of an unknown resistance by the method of substitution, as follows.

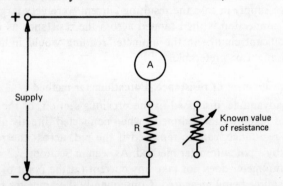

196. Resistance measurement by the method of substitution

The unknown resistance is connected in series with a suitable ammeter to a suitable supply voltage. If possible, the supply voltage may be adjusted until a convenient indication is given on the ammeter. The unknown resistor is then removed from the circuit and replaced by the resistance decade box. The value of the resistance of the box is then adjusted until the same ammeter reading is obtained as before. Since the conditions in the two circuits are then the same, it follows that the resistance value of the box, which can be read off directly from the scales, is equal to the value of the unknown resistance.

Quite good accuracy can be obtained by this method, provided that the resistance decade box has small enough steps in relation to the value of the resistance to be measured. For example, it would hardly be satisfactory to measure a resistance of about 2·5 Ω by means of a box having only 1-Ω steps!

The resistance of a milliammeter may be measured by an interesting extension of this method. The maximum safe current through such a meter is limited to the value for full-scale deflection, and other methods may therefore be difficult to apply. The resistance box should be connected in series with the milliammeter to a suitable low-voltage supply (starting with a high value of resistance in the box for safety's sake). The resistance box is then adjusted until the meter reads full-scale deflection, and this value of resistance is noted. The box is then adjusted until the meter reads half full-scale deflection, and this new value of resistance is noted.

Then, if the meter resistance is r Ω, the resistance-box value for full-scale deflection is R_1 Ω and the resistance-box value for half full-scale deflection is R_2 Ω, it follows that

total circuit resistance for full-scale deflection = $R_1 + r$ Ω
total circuit resistance for half full-scale deflection = $R_2 + r$ θ

But, since the supply voltage is the same for each,

$$R_2 + r = 2 (R_2 + r)$$

(i.e. if the current is halved, the circuit resistance must have been doubled).

Re-arranging the equation gives meter resistance $\underline{r = R_2 - 2 \times R_1}$

The same method could be used for an ammeter of higher current range. However, since the resistance of such a meter is likely to be very small, the result given by this method, depending as it would on the difference of two fairly large and nearly equal numbers, could not be expected to be very accurate.

17.6.   Measurement of resistance. Alternative potentiometer method

The potentiometer method of resistance measurement discussed in Section 17.4, page 519, relies on the accuracy of calibration and reading of the ammeter used. This disadvantage may be overcome by an adaptation of the substitution method discussed in the previous section.

For this method, the unknown resistance is connected in series with a known standard resistance of roughly the same value. (A resistance decade box set to a suitable value might be appropriate in some cases where the maximum safe current that can be carried by the resistance box—which might be quite small, possibly a few milliamperes—is sufficient for the purpose.) The two series-connected resistances are then connected to a suitable supply. An ammeter may be included in the circuit to ensure that a particular current value is not exceeded, but its reading is not used in the calculation of results.

The p.d. across the unknown resistance (V_1) is measured by means of the potentiometer, as before, and the corresponding p.d. across the known resistance (V_s) is measured in the same way. Since the current is the same in each resistance (because they are connected in series), it follows that

$$\frac{V_1}{R} = \frac{V_s}{R_s} (= I, \text{ the common current})$$

So that the value of the unknown resistance R is given by

$$R = R_s . \frac{V_1}{V_s} \Omega \qquad . \qquad . \qquad . \qquad . \qquad (v)$$

This method is capable of giving very accurate results, since it depends only on the accuracy of the potentiometer measurement of p.d. (which is high, if good equipment is used), and on the accuracy of calibration of the resistance decade box (which can be obtained to better than 0·1% accuracy).

17.7. Measurement of resistance. Bridge method

This is perhaps the most widely-used and most acceptable method of measurement of resistance. It is based on a fundamental circuit known as the WHEATSTONE BRIDGE circuit, which is named after its originator. The basic circuit is shown in diagram 197.

The circuit is an extremely important one in the field of electrical measurements and has, in fact, been adapted for application in other fields too. A complete method of analysis of this circuit will not be given at this stage, but the important 'balance conditions' are easily arrived at as follows.

The four resistors R_1, R_2, R_3 and R_4 comprise the 'arms' or 'elements'

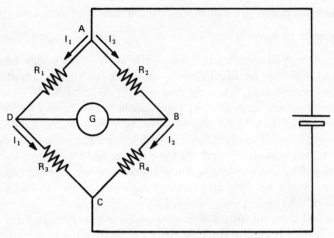

197. Basic circuit of the Wheatstone bridge

of the bridge. If R_1 is the unknown resistance to be measured, R_2, R_3 and R_4 will be standard resistors of known value.

The values of R_2, R_3 and R_4 are adjusted until the galvanometer shows a 'null' reading; that is, until there is no current in the galvanometer branch. If this is the case, then, as shown on the diagram, the current in R_1 and R_3 must be the same (I_1), and the current in R_2 and R_4 must also be the same (I_2). Of course, there is no necessity for I_1 and I_2 to be equal.

Since there is no current in the galvanometer branch, the two terminals of the galvanometer, points B and D in the circuit, must be at the same potential. The p.d. between A and B must therefore be the same as the p.d. between A and D. Similarly, the p.d. between B and C must be the same as the p.d. between D and C. These conditions give the following equations:

(1) $(V_{AB} =) I_2R_2 = I_1R_1 (= V_{AD})$
(2) $(V_{BC} =) I_2R_4 = I_1R_3 (= V_{DC})$

Dividing equation (1) by equation (2),

$$\frac{I_2R_2}{I_2R_4} = \frac{I_1R_1}{I_1R_3}$$

from which the unknown resistance (R_1) is given by

$$R_1 = R_3 \times \frac{R_2}{R_4} \, \Omega \, . \qquad . \qquad . \qquad . \qquad \text{(vi)}$$

From this equation it can be seen that, although the actual resistance of R_3 must be known, only the ratio of $\dfrac{R_2}{R_4}$ need be known. For this reason R_2 and R_4 are often called the 'ratio arms' of the bridge, and for ease of calculation are often made so that their ratio can be adjusted to be, for example, 0·01, 0·1, 1, 10, 100.

An elementary form of this bridge circuit is the SLIDE-WIRE bridge (sometimes called a METRE-BRIDGE since the slide-wire, as in the slide-wire potentiometer, is often made 1 metre long). The slide-wire bridge is very similar in construction to the slide-wire potentiometer (see Section 17.2, page 509) and the same equipment is often used for both functions. Their purposes are different, however, and the student should avoid confusing the two.

A circuit diagram for the slide-wire bridge is shown in diagram 198. The slide wire is used to form the two ratio arms of the bridge (R_2 and R_4 in diagram 197). The variable tapping point made by the slider or 'jockey' will enable the ratio $\dfrac{R_2}{R_4}$ to be varied even though the sum $(R_2 + R_4)$ will, of course, always be equal to the total resistance of the slide-wire. Corresponding points on the circuit diagrams 197 and 198 are labelled in the same way.

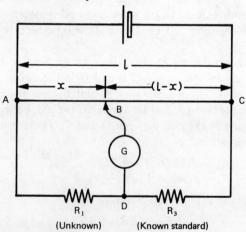

198. Circuit diagram of slide-wire bridge

In operation, the tapping point B is adjusted until no reading is observed on the galvanometer, when the bridge is said to be 'balanced'.

In practice, switches operated by press-buttons may be included in the battery circuit—to prevent any over-heating of the slide wire; and in the galvanometer circuit—to enable a slight deflection to be seen more readily. If these are included, the battery switch should always be closed first.

As seen earlier (Section 17.2, page 509), the resistance of a portion of a uniform wire is proportional to the length considered, so that

$$\frac{R_2}{R_4} = \frac{x}{(l - x)}$$

At balance

$$R_1 = R_3 \times \frac{R_2}{R_4} \text{ (equation (vi))}$$

Then

$$R_1 = R_3 \times \frac{x}{(l - x)} \, \Omega \qquad . \qquad . \qquad \text{(vii)}$$

Wherever possible, the value of the standard resistor R_3 should be chosen so that the balance point is obtained somewhere within about the middle third of the wire. The reason for this is that small errors in reading the values of x and $(l - x)$ from the scale near the wire are then less likely to give disproportionate errors in the result.

For example, suppose $l = 1$ m and x = 450 mm so that the true ratio

$$\frac{x}{(l - x)} = \frac{450}{550} = 0.818$$

If x were to be misread as 451 mm, the apparent ratio would be

$$\frac{x}{(l - x)} = \frac{451}{549} = 0.822$$

which gives an error of about 0.5%.

If, however, $l = 1$ m and x = 50 mm, the true ratio

$$\frac{x}{(l - x)} = \frac{50}{950} = 0.052\,6$$

If x were now to be misread by the same amount as before, giving 51 mm, the apparent ratio would be

$$\frac{x}{(l - x)} = \frac{51}{949} = 0.053\,8$$

which gives an error of about $2\frac{1}{4}$%.

Other forms of the Wheatstone bridge circuit may be briefly mentioned here. For accurate measurements, the bridge arms are usually made up from resistance decade boxes or some similar arrangement. With high-grade components, very accurate results can be expected.

Perhaps passing mention should also be made of the so-called 'Post Office Box'. This is a Wheatstone bridge circuit in which standard resistance coils are arranged in a decade form for the 'R_3' standard arm. These resistance coils are usually brought into circuit by removal of a tapered short-circuiting plug from a split brass connector, and a common arrangement of values is 1 Ω, 2 Ω, 2 Ω, 5 Ω and so on through the various decades available. The ratio arms are built from resistance coils having a similar short-circuiting plug arrangement, and values of 10 Ω, 100 Ω, 1000 Ω and 10 000 Ω are typical for each arm. The resistance coils are interconnected internally to build up the Wheatstone bridge circuit, with connection terminals provided for the battery, galvanometer and unknown resistance. The box usually also contains tapping keys to act as battery and glavanometer switches.

As far as the author is aware, the majority of such boxes are now manufactured for sale to educational establishments, where they tend to give students an unnecessarily complicated impression of the fundamental Wheatstone bridge circuit.

17.8. Measurement of resistivity

The resistance R of a conductor of length l and cross-sectional area A made from a material having resistivity ρ is given by $R = \dfrac{\rho l}{A}$ (see Section 16.20, page 475) where all quantities are in compatible units.

Re-arranging this equation gives

$$\rho = R \cdot \frac{A}{l}$$

The resistivity of a conducting material can, then, be measured in terms of the resistance of a uniform conductor made from the material. If the cross-sectional area and length of the conductor are measured, the material's resistivity can be calculated from the above formula.

It is usual to select a fairly long piece of wire (say about 1 m long) of fairly small diameter (say about 0·45 mm) for this test. The length should be measured as accurately as possible right up to the terminals used, and the diameter of the wire should be measured at various points along its length by means of a micrometer. All other leads used in the test should be made as large in diameter as possible in order to minimize errors due to their resistance. It may be possible to correct for this lead resistance by means of a balance obtained for the condition when the two ends of the test wire are brought together in a short circuit.

Any of the methods of resistance measurement given earlier may be used, although a bridge method is usually preferred.

17.9. Measurement of resistance-temperature coefficient

It has been seen (Section 16.22, page 481) that a graph of the resistance of a conductor against its temperature can be used to evaluate the resistance-temperature coefficient of the conductor material. For this test it is usual to wind the conductor on to a small 'coil-former' or bobbin so that it may be placed inside a test-tube, with leads to the coil brought out and connected to the measuring circuit. The test-tube should also have provision made for the insertion of a stirrer and a thermometer. The test-tube may then be filled with oil and the whole placed in a beaker of water. Resistance measurements are made at various temperatures as the water is heated, and from a graph of the results the value of the resistance-temperature coefficient may be found. Any of the previously-mentioned methods of resistance measurement may be used, although again a bridge method is the most usual.

For temperature ranges outside those given by these arrangements, modifications are required. For example, oil may be substituted for the water in the beaker to enable temperatures above 100°C to be obtained. However, as most conductors are used at temperatures within the 0 – 100°C range, these complications can be left to specialists in electrical measurements.

17.10. Calibration of meters. Voltmeters

Any chapter on electrical measurements would hardly be complete without some mention of the common measuring instruments. Although the principle of action of these meters will be discussed later (see page 687), it is not necessary for this principle to be understood before any use can be made of the meters themselves. It is sufficient for the moment to say that a voltmeter is a device which will give an indication, usually by the movement of a pointer over a scale, of the potential difference applied between its terminals. The fact that a voltmeter will usually require a current to flow in it in order that it may give this indication has already been mentioned (Section 17.3, page 512).

If a voltmeter is to be used with confidence, some check on its accuracy should be available. In other words, it should be possible to calibrate it. There are several ways in which a voltmeter may be calibrated, depending on the equipment available. Two methods are given here.

(a) By comparison with a standard instrument

It is possible, by careful design and manufacture, to make an instrument of very high precision, whose indications are guaranteed by the manufacturers to be within, say, 0·01 % of the actual potential difference between its terminals. Such instruments are very expensive and are not usually suitable for normal day-to-day use in a laboratory, but are kept as 'standard' instruments to check other, cheaper instruments in normal use.

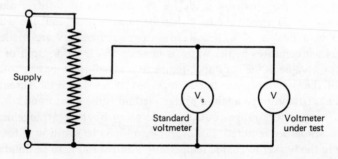

199. Calibration of a voltmeter by comparison with a standard instrument

The circuit shown in diagram 199 could be used for this test, in which the standard voltmeter and the voltmeter under test are connected in parallel to an arrangement giving a variable voltage. In the circuit shown, a resistor is seen to be connected across a supply, and a tapping point on this resistor, together with one end-connection of the resistor, become the supply leads for the voltmeters.

A resistor connected in this way is said to be a 'potential divider', and if the tapping point is variable, it becomes a source of variable voltage. Resistors made for this type of use often consist of a spiral of resistance wire wound on a long straight former, with a suitable bracket arrangement to carry a sliding contact along the spiral. Since the wire is uniform, the p.d. between one end of the spiral and the sliding contact is proportional to the distance between that end and the slider (the value of the voltage will in practice also depend on the resistance of the load circuit, but this point will be considered later).

In the test, [the indication on the voltmeter being calibrated is adjusted to convenient points on its scale by means of the potential divider slider. The indication on the standard voltmeter is compared with these readings at each point, and a calibration chart drawn up. In industrial laboratories, this often takes the form of a ticket attached to the voltmeter, which indicates the 'true' voltage corresponding to each of the major scale divisions. For indications between these points, it is usually assumed that any error is linear. For example, if the following were an extract from the calibration ticket of a voltmeter,

Meter reading (volts)	Standard meter reading (volts)
20	19·8
30	30·1

it can be seen that the meter error ranges from + 0·2 V at a reading of 20 V (that is, the meter reads 0·2 V high) to − 0·1 V at a reading of 30 V (that is, the meter reads 0·1 V low).

On the assumption that the error change is linear between these points, a graph of meter error over this range would be as shown in diagram 200.

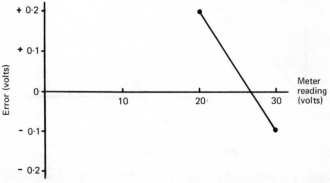

200. Assumed linear variation in meter error between calibration points

The error at any intermediate reading can then be obtained from this graph (or by means of a simple calculation, since in this case, for example, the error changes by $-\dfrac{0\cdot3}{10}$ V for each volt increase from 20 V).

If the meter reading were to be 23 V, the error would be $+ 0 \cdot 2 - 3 \times \dfrac{0 \cdot 3}{10}$ V, or $+0 \cdot 11$ V (that is, the meter would be reading $0 \cdot 11$ V high). Then the true voltage would be $22 \cdot 89$ V, an answer which would probably be taken to 3 significant figures as $22 \cdot 9$ V.

Instead of drawing a graph of meter error against meter reading, it is possible to draw a graph of standard meter reading ('true voltage') against tested meter reading, as shown in diagram 201.

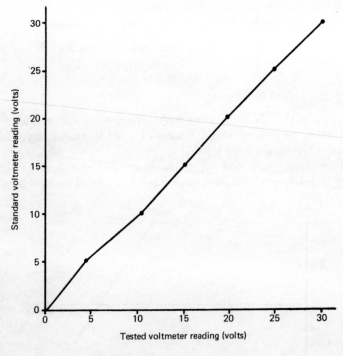

201. Meter calibration graph

Once again the observed points are joined by straight lines as shown, and the true value for any intermediate reading can be read off direct from the graph.

(b) By use of potentiometer

(This is the standard method adopted under the Electricity Supply (Meters) Act of 1936.) The voltmeter to be calibrated is again supplied by a variable potential divider from a suitable source, but this time the 'standard' voltage measurement is carried out by means of a potentiometer, in a way similar to that already described in Sections 17·2 and 17.4, pages 509 and 519. Since the maximum voltage that can conveniently be measured by means of a potentiometer is limited to a few volts, however, it may be necessary to make special arrangements. These are indicated in diagram 202.

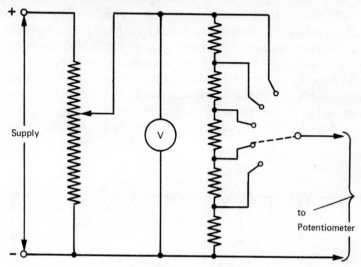

202. Use of a volt-box in the calibration of a voltmeter

The voltage across the voltmeter is also connected across a second potential divider as shown. This usually consists of a number of accurate resistors in series, with tapping points connected to a selector switch. Various positions of the switch select accurately-known fractions of the total voltage (such as $\frac{1}{10}$, $\frac{1}{100}$, $\frac{1}{1000}$ etc.), which may then be measured by the potentiometer. This switched potential divider is sometimes known, rather incorrectly, as a VOLT-BOX. Note that, since the potentiometer does not take any current from the potential divider at the point of balance, no inaccuracies result from any change in the current-distribution along the chain of resistors. It would, however, be incorrect and inaccurate to substitute even a standard voltmeter for the potentiometer connections shown, since the current taken by such a meter would change these currents and hence would change the proportion of the total voltage applied to the standard meter.

17.11.   Calibration of meters. Ammeters

Similar methods are used for the calibration of ammeters.

(a) By comparison with a standard instrument

The ammeter to be calibrated is connected in series with a standard ammeter of similar range, and a current is passed through them both. Although it would be possible to use a single variable resistance in series with both instruments across a suitable supply, it might be difficult in practice to obtain sufficiently close control over the value of the current at both the lower and higher ends of the meter range. Whilst several methods are available to overcome this difficulty, the circuit shown in diagram 203 could be used, and would give reasonable control. Resistor R_1 is a variable resistor of fairly high value—sufficiently high to enable the lowest current required to be obtained—while resistor R_2 has a lower value for the higher current readings. Resistor R_3 is a 'safety' resistor in case both R_1 and R_2 are reduced to zero together.

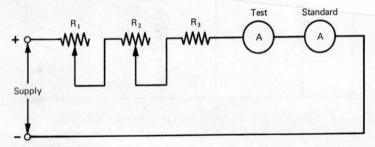

203. Calibration of an ammeter by comparison with a standard instrument

Graded variable resistors are obtainable which consist of several sections of wire of different diameters, and so combine the functions of R_1 and R_2 in this circuit. With these, as with the circuit shown, it is important that the maximum safe current that can be carried by the resistors or sections used should not be exceeded. The higher-value resistance R_1 will be likely to have the smaller current rating, and if the ammeter range is such that it is required to exceed this current, R_1 should be taken out of circuit completely (movement of the slider right up to the connected end will usually be satisfactory for this purpose) before R_2 is adjusted. Similarly, graded resistors should be connected so that movement of the slider takes the smaller-diameter sections out of circuit first.

Calibration graphs may be drawn in the same way as for voltmeters.

(*b*) *By use of potentiometer*

(Also adopted as the standard method under the Electricity Supply (Meters) Act of 1936.) The ammeter to be calibrated is again connected in series with suitable control resistors to a suitable supply. In this case, however, a standard resistance of known value, which is usually very low, but which depends on the ammeter range, is included in this series circuit. The potential difference developed across this standard resistor is then measured by use of a potentiometer as described in Sections 17.2 and 17.4, pages 509 and 519.

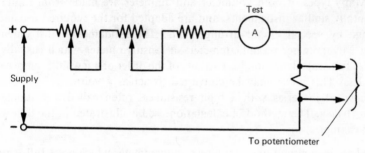

204. Calibration of an ammeter, using a potentiometer method

The standard resistors, or shunts, used for this purpose are usually fitted with four terminals, two at each end. One terminal at each end is made of ample cross-section to carry the required current through the resistor, whilst the second terminal at each end is often smaller and is used for the connection to the potentiometer. This arrangement ensures that any voltage drop occurring at the main current-carrying terminals of the shunt, due to any contact-resistance, is excluded from the voltage drop across the resistance of the shunt which is being measured by the potentiometer.

The value of shunt resistance chosen will depend on the range of the ammeter to be calibrated. For example, an ammeter having a range of 0–10 A would probably be tested with a 0·1-Ω shunt, so that the maximum voltage to be measured by the potentiometer would be 10 × 0·1, or 1·0 V. Then if, for an ammeter reading of 5·0 A, a voltage of 0·512 V were to be measured on the potentiometer, the actual current would be $\frac{0·512}{0·1}$, or 5·12 A, so that the ammeter would be reading 0·12 A low.

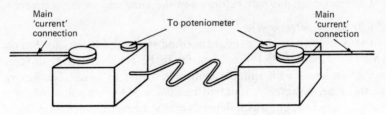

205. Four-terminal shunt

17.12.   Adjustment of meter range. Voltmeters

Many types of both voltmeter and ammeter are made from fundamentally similar instruments, and are adapted for the required use and range by special circuit arrangements. The fundamental instrument is a galvanometer or milliammeter—a sensitive meter which (usually) gives full-scale deflection for currents of the order of a few milli-amperes or less. This meter may be converted to act as a voltmeter by being connected in series with a high resistance, often called a voltmeter MULTIPLIER. The method of calculation used is illustrated in the following example.

Show by a circuit diagram how a milliammeter which gives full-scale deflection for a current of 1·0 mA, and which has a resistance of 75 Ω, may be used as a voltmeter having a range of 0–100 V. Find the value of any additional circuit element required.

The additional circuit element required is a resistor, R, which is connected in series with the milliammeter as shown in diagram 206.

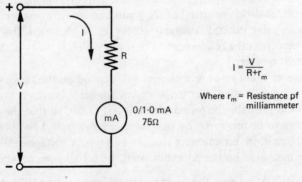

$$I = \frac{V}{R + r_m}$$

Where r_m = Resistance pf milliammeter

206. Basic circuit of a voltmeter

The total current through the meter will depend on the total voltage applied across the series circuit of meter and resistor R and, for a constant value of R, will be directly proportional to this voltage. It follows that the current indicated by the milliammeter is a direct measure of the applied voltage, so that the meter may be scaled directly in volts.

For the given values, the value of R must be chosen so that when the applied voltage is at its maximum value of 100 V, the meter will indicate its full-scale deflection; that is, the meter current will be 1·0 mA.

$$\therefore \text{ Total resistance of voltmeter circuit } = \frac{100}{1 \times 10^{-3}} \ \Omega$$

$$= 100\ 000 \ \Omega$$

But the meter itself has a resistance of 75 Ω, so that the required value of R is

$$R = 100\ 000 - 75 \ \Omega$$
$$= 99\ 925 \ \Omega$$

In practice, unless very high accuracy were required, R would not be measured and adjusted to the 5 significant figures quoted here, and little error would be involved in using a nominal 100-kΩ resistor for R.

The 'sensitivity' of a voltmeter is a measure of the current required to give a particular reading. It is usually quoted in OHMS PER VOLT, and is simply obtained by dividing the total resistance of the voltmeter by the voltage required to give full-scale deflection. Thus, the sensitivity of the voltmeter in the above example is

$$\frac{100\ 000}{100} = 1000 \ \Omega/\text{V}$$

The reciprocal of the sensitivity (the 'volts per ohm') is the current required by the meter for full-scale deflection. Thus a voltmeter which uses a milliammeter requiring 2 mA for full-scale deflection would have a sensitivity of $\frac{1}{0\cdot002}$ or 500 Ω/V, whatever the voltage range for which it was designed.

The sensitivities of typical commercial voltmeters vary from about 2000 Ω/V to about 60 Ω/V (although special types of voltmeter are available with very much higher sensitivities than these).

As an example, a voltmeter having a range of 0–50 V and a sensitivity of 400 Ω/V would

(i) have a total resistance of 50 × 400 Ω, or 20 000 Ω

(ii) have a full-scale deflection current of $\frac{1}{400}$ A, or 2·5 mA

(iii) for a reading of 15 V, take a current of $\frac{15}{50}$ × 2·5 mA, or 0·75 mA.

(The same answer would be given by $\frac{\text{deflection voltage}}{\text{meter resistance}}$

or $\frac{15}{20\ 000}$ A = 0·75 mA.)

17.13. Adjustment of meter range. Ammeters

Again, the fundamental instrument usually used for ammeters of any range is a milliammeter, the range of which is adjusted by connecting it in parallel with a resistor, or shunt. This shunt will share the total current between the terminals of the complete ammeter with the milliammeter, and so change the value of total ammeter current required to give full-scale deflection.

It should be mentioned that certain types of ammeter can be made directly for quite large current ranges, and also that other methods of adjusting range are possible. For the type of circuits dealt with so far, however, shunts are almost invariably used.

The calculations involved in determining the resistance of the shunt are illustrated in the following example.

Show by a circuit diagram how a milliammeter which gives full-scale deflection for a current of 1·0 mA, and which has a resistance of 75 Ω, may be used as an ammeter having a range of 0–1 A. Find the value of any additional circuit element required.

The additional circuit element required is a resistor, S, which is connected in parallel with the milliammeter as shown in diagram 207.

The total current (I) through the circuit will divide between the shunt and the milliammeter as shown. For a constant value of shunt resistance (S), the current through the milliammeter will be a constant fraction of this total current. It follows that the current indicated by the milliammeter is a direct measure of the total current, so that the meter may be scaled directly in terms of this total current.

For the given values, the value of S must be chosen so that when the

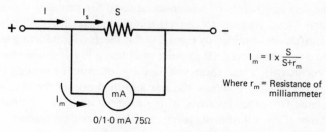

$$I_m = I \times \frac{S}{S+r_m}$$

Where r_m = Resistance of milliammeter

207. Basic circuit of an ammeter

total current is at its maximum value of 1·0 A the meter will indicate its full-scale deflection; that is, the meter current will be 1·0 mA. Then

if I = 1·0 A and I_m = 1 mA (= 0·001 A)
$$I_s = I - I_m$$
$$= 1·0 - 0·001 \text{ A}$$
$$= 0·999 \text{ A}$$

But the p.d. across S is the same as the p.d. across the milliammeter, so that

p.d. across S = 1·0 × 10^{-3} × 75 V
$$= 0·075 \text{ V}$$

Then the required resistance of the shunt S is

$$S = \frac{0·075}{0·999}\ \Omega$$

$$= \underline{0·075\ 1\ \Omega}$$

This is a very small resistance, and indicates the importance of excluding any contact resistance from its value. Once again a four-terminal shunt would be used (see diagram 205, page 534), with the milliammeter connected to the smaller potential terminals while the main current terminals were used as the main terminals of the complete ammeter.

It will be seen that the p.d. across the shunt, and hence its resistance, depends on the milliammeter for which it is designed. A 10-A shunt designed for use with a particular milliammeter will not necessarily be suitable for any other milliammeter. Certain values of potential difference across a shunt have been standardized, however, and a 75 mV, 10 A shunt could be used, with very little error, with either a 1 mA, 75 Ω milliammeter or with a 2·5 mA, 30 Ω milliammeter.

The very low values of resistance required for ammeter shunts, particularly those designed to convert a milliammeter for the higher current ranges, are obtained by the use of flat sheets of conducting material (often a resistance material in order to obtain a low resistance-temperature coefficient). These sheets are fixed by soldering or brazing to solid end-pieces, usually of brass, the size and thickness of the sheets being calculated from the resistivity of the material and the required shunt resistance. Fine adjustments of this resistance are then made by means of saw-slots cut at one or more points in the sheets as required.

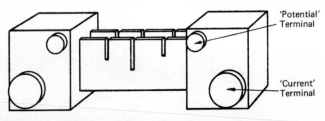

'Potential' Terminal

'Current' Terminal

208. Slotted shunt for higher current-ranges

For precision measurements, allowance is made in the calculations, and eventually in the final calibration and adjustment, for the resistance of the leads to the milliammeter. In this case, the special leads supplied by the manufacturer with the meter and its shunt, or shunts, should always be used for the purpose.

For normal laboratory use, if shunts external to the meter are used (quite often an ammeter will have its own self-contained shunt within its case) undue error will be avoided as long as the leads to the milliammeter are kept reasonably short. The milliammeter itself is likely to have a resistance of between 5 Ω and 75 Ω, which is often enough to 'swamp' small changes in the resistance of the leads.

17.14. Multi-range meters

Many laboratory instruments have several ranges available, a particular range being selected either by the use of separate terminals or by a selector-switch.

(I) *Multi-range voltmeters*

Several voltmeter multipliers can quite readily be contained within the case of an average-sized portable laboratory voltmeter (except perhaps those for very high voltage ranges where the power dissipated in the resistor is such that it must have a large physical size and suitable cooling arrangements).

There are two main ways in which these multipliers can be arranged in the meter circuit, and these are shown in circuits (a) and (b) in diagram 209.

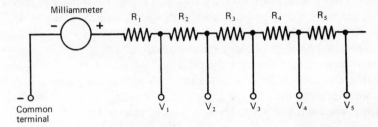

(a) Series—connected voltmeter multipliers

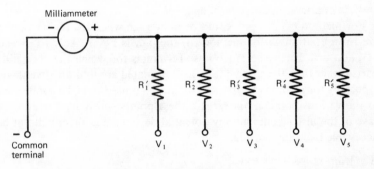

(b) Individual voltmeter multipliers

209

In method (a) the required value of resistance for a given voltage range is obtained by the resistance being added in series with the multipliers used for lower voltage ranges. For example, if the calculated value of the series resistance for range V_1 were 925 Ω, while that for range V_2 were 4925 Ω, and for range V_3 were 9925 Ω, then the resistances in the 'chain' would have values $R_1 = 925\ \Omega$, $R_2 = 4000\ \Omega$, $R_3 = 5000\ \Omega$.

This method has the disadvantage that any error in the resistors is cumulative, so that it is possible that the highest range may have a lower accuracy than the lowest range. Of course, any fault such as an open circuit or short circuit at a point in the chain may affect several of the ranges. Nevertheless, the total resistance required to be accommodated within the case is brought to a minimum with this method, and it is often used.

In method (b) the individual series resistances are connected separately, and of course each must have the full value of resistance required. For example, with the figures quoted above, $R'_1 = 925\ \Omega$, $R'_2 = 4925\ \Omega$, $R'_3 = 9925\ \Omega$.

This method does not suffer from the disadvantages of the series-chain method (a), although the total resistance that must be housed within the instrument case is higher. This makes the method rather more expensive than the first, especially if precision wire-wound resistors are used, and where higher values of voltage are included in the ranges available.

It should be noted for each circuit that, while the instrument is being used on one range, a p.d. will exist between each of the other terminals and the common negative terminal.

For method (a) this p.d. could be quite high when the higher ranges are in use, although for method (b) the p.d. is never likely to exceed 1 V and will usually be much less. Terminals for which the accessible parts (other than the contact faces) are insulated are thus an advantage, especially for method (a). If a selector switch is used to make connection to the various points in the circuit, these points will remain within the case of the instrument and any potential developed at them will not be accessible from the outside.

(II) *Multi-range ammeters*

Once again, there are two possible methods of arranging for several current ranges on the same ammeter, one way using separate individual shunts and the other way using a 'combined' shunt.

(a) Circuit using separate shunts

In this method it is necessary to use some form of switch in order to connect each shunt in turn in parallel with the milliammeter. A possible circuit arrangement is shown in diagram 210.

To obtain a given current range for the circuit shown, connection would be made between the common terminal and the appropriate shunt terminal, with the selector switch moved to the corresponding position. It would be possible for a second selector switch to be 'ganged' with the one shown, in order that the appropriate shunt terminal should be connected to a 'common' positive terminal, when the range would be

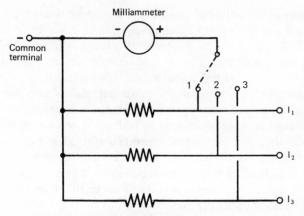

210. Possible circuit arrangement for multi-range ammeter
using separate shunts

selected just by moving the switch. It should be noted that the circuit
given ensures that any contact resistance in the selector switch is included in the meter circuit, where, because of the relatively high resistance of the milliammeter itself, it will have less effect on the accuracy
than if it were to be included in the shunt circuit. This arrangement,
however, is not very frequently used in commercial instruments.

(b) Circuit using 'universal shunt'

This circuit is very commonly used in commercial multi-range
ammeters and uses a tapped shunt to obtain the appropriate current
ranges, as shown in diagram 211.

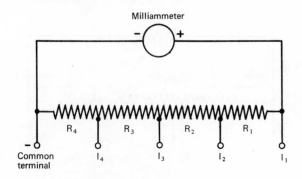

211. Multi-range ammeter using universal shunt

The theory of the universal shunt is given in more detail below, but the principle can be seen to be relatively simple. As already seen in Section 17.13, page 536, the resistance of a shunt is likely to be very much less than the resistance of the milliammeter, certainly for current ranges above about 50 times the normal full-scale deflection of the milliammeter. In the universal shunt, several such shunts are connected in series, and, to a first approximation, the resistance of the shunt for a given current range is obtained by adding the necessary resistance in series with the shunt for the next highest current range. For example, the shunt for range I_3, in the circuit shown, is made up of R_4, the shunt for the range I_4, in series with R_3, the required additional resistance.

When the meter is in use on, say, the I_3 range, the shunt resistances composed of R_2 and R_1 are connected in series in the milliammeter circuit. Provided the milliammeter resistance is relatively high (say 25–75 Ω), and the lowest current range is about 50 times the full-scale deflection current of the milliammeter, the error involved in neglecting this in calculations is likely to be small. This error is sometimes even further reduced by the deliberate addition of a resistance, known as a 'swamp' resistance, into the meter circuit.

This effect can, however, be allowed for as shown below.

Universal shunt calculations

Re-draw the circuit to include the milliammeter resistance as shown in diagram 212, and let it be required that the milliammeter shall take $\frac{1}{n}$th of the total current. Let the total resistance of the whole shunt be $S\,\Omega$, and the portion included between the main terminals be x Ω.

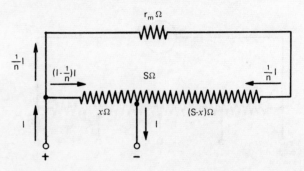

212. Equivalent circuit of meter with universal shunt

Then, equating the voltage drops round the two branches of the parallel circuit,

$$\frac{1}{n} I (r_m + S - x) = \left(1 - \frac{1}{n}\right) I x$$

or

$$\frac{1}{n} r_m + \frac{1}{n} S - \frac{1}{n} x = x - \frac{1}{n} x$$

or

$$x = \frac{1}{n} (S + r_m) \qquad . \qquad . \qquad \text{(viii)}$$

The value of S is chosen to be the required shunt for the smallest current range, and the value(s) of x for higher current ranges calculated from the relationship given.

Example

A milliammeter has a resistance of 75 Ω and gives full-scale deflection for a current of 1·0 mA. Design a suitable universal shunt to convert this meter into a 3-range ammeter having ranges 0–10 mA, 0–100 mA, and 0–1 A.

First consider the lowest current range required, and note that the milliammeter has a p.d. of 75 mV for full-scale deflection. The total shunt resistance S is given by

$$S = \frac{0·075}{0·010 - 0·001} = \frac{0·075}{0·009} = 8·333 \ \Omega$$

For the next highest current range, the meter is required to carry $\frac{0·001}{0·100}$ or $\frac{1}{100}$th of the total current, so that in this case, $n = \frac{1}{100}$.

Substituting in equation (viii),

$$x_1 = \frac{1}{100} (8·333 + 75) \ \Omega$$

$$= 0·833 \ \Omega$$

For the highest current range, the meter is required to carry $\frac{0·001}{1·000}$ or $\frac{1}{1000}$th of the total current, so that in this case, $n = \frac{1}{1000}$.

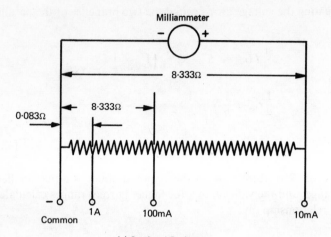

(a) Sectional Resistances

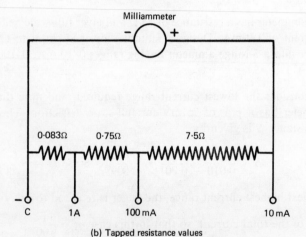

(b) Tapped resistance values

213. Universal shunt—numerical example

Substituting in equation (viii),

$$x_2 = \frac{1}{1000}(8\cdot333 + 75)\,\Omega$$

$$= 0\cdot083\,\Omega$$

Assuming an accuracy of resistance measurement to the nearest $\frac{1}{1000}$th part of an ohm in about 10 ohms (which is a high order of accuracy), a suitable universal shunt for this application would be as shown in diagram 213 (a).

The 100-mA and 1-A connections would be tappings on the 10-mA shunt, so that the universal shunt would be made with sections as shown in diagram 213 (b).

(The student should check for himself that if the current ranges required with this milliammeter had been 0–1 A, 0–5 A, 0–10 A, the universal shunt values would be indistinguishable—within a practical number of significant figures—from the values calculated for the individual shunts.)

(III) *Combined multi-range ammeter and voltmeter*

The methods described in the two preceding sections may be combined to give an instrument having several voltage and several current ranges. Although minor variations are possible, a typical circuit diagram for such an instrument is given in diagram 214.

Note that the use of the universal shunt across the milliammeter must be taken into account when the values of the voltmeter multipliers are calculated. This will mean that the 'sensitivity' of the instrument as a voltmeter will be reduced accordingly. That is, the instrument will take more current when operating as a voltmeter than would have been necessary had the universal shunt not been connected across the milliammeter. (The current required for full-scale deflection as a voltmeter will, of course, be the full-scale deflection current for the lowest current range for which the universal shunt is designed.)

It would be a useful and worth-while project for the student to obtain

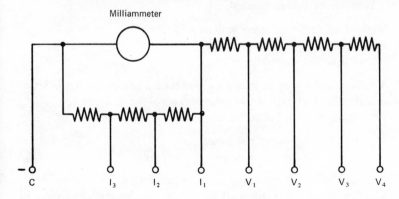

214. General multi-range instrument

S

a small milliammeter (which is quite cheap, even these days) and to design and make the necessary universal shunt and the multipliers required for a multi-range instrument. The measurement of the resistances, and the eventual calibration of the meter on its various ranges, would be good experience; and the useful meter that resulted would be a spur to accurate work.

CHAPTER SUMMARY

A source of e.m.f. will have an internal resistance. If the e.m.f. is E V and the internal resistance is r Ω, the terminal voltage V V for a load current I A is

$$V = E - Ir$$

A potentiometer may be used to measure an e.m.f. by balancing it against a known e.m.f. At balance, no current is drawn from the source being measured, so that there is no p.d. across its internal resistance.

If a resistance is measured by a voltmeter-ammeter method, the effect of the meter resistances should be considered.

Methods of resistance-measurement dealt with here are:
Voltmeter-ammeter methods
Potentiometer method, with an ammeter in circuit
Substitution method
Potentiometer method, with a standard resistor in circuit
Wheatstone bridge method.

Methods of meter-calibration dealt with here are:
Comparison with standard meter
Use of potentiometer.

A milliammeter may be used as a voltmeter when connected in series with a suitable high resistance, known as a voltmeter multiplier.

The sensitivity of a voltmeter is given by

$$\frac{\text{total meter resistance}}{\text{full-scale voltage}} = \frac{1}{\text{current for f.s.d.}}$$

The sensitivity is usually stated in ohms per volt.

A milliammeter may be used as an ammeter when connected in parallel with a suitable low resistance, known as an ammeter shunt.

QUESTIONS

1. What is meant by 'electromotive force' and 'terminal voltage' of an accumulator?

A battery comprising six lead-acid cells is connected across a variable load. The following output values were noted as the load was varied.

Terminal p.d. (volts)	12·0	11·5	11·0	10·5	10
Current (amperes)	2	4	6	8	10

Plot a graph showing this relationship and estimate the value of the terminal voltage when on open circuit, and the value of the internal resistance of the battery. Why does the terminal voltage drop as the load current increases?

2. (a) Draw circuit diagrams with explanatory notes to illustrate how a d.c. potentiometer may be used to determine the internal resistance of a dry cell. Assume the potentiometer has been calibrated to read directly in volts. Give the reason why a potentiometer would be preferable to a voltmeter for this purpose.

(b) The open-circuit e.m.f. of a dry cell was found to be 1·505 V, and the terminal voltage with the cell supplying a load of 0·8 A was 1·425 V.

Calculate the internal resistance of the cell.

3. Describe with the aid of a wiring diagram how you would measure the e.m.f. of a primary cell using a simple potentiometer.

In order to measure the e.m.f. of a given cell, a standard cell of e.m.f. 1·018 6 V was used, and when this was in circuit, a balance was obtained at a distance of 2·043 m. When the given cell was in circuit, a balance was obtained at 3·080 m. Calculate the e.m.f. of the given cell.

4. Describe briefly a simple slide-wire potentiometer and explain, with circuit diagram, how it can be used to measure a small unknown p.d. What advantage has the potentiometer over the ordinary voltmeter for the measurement of p.d.? How may such a device be used to calibrate an ammeter?

5. State Ohm's law.

Draw a circuit diagram showing a battery, switch and resistance.

Show the method of measuring the value of this resistance by inserting a voltmeter and an ammeter correctly into your circuit diagram and give details of the calculation which would have to be made using the readings from the instruments.

State any inaccuracy that would be incorporated in your reading and indicate how it could be corrected.

6. Describe an experiment in which the value of a resistor may be calculated by the ammeter-voltmeter method. Draw a circuit diagram of the connections of all the necessary apparatus, and discuss the reasons for any possible error in the result.

7. Given an ammeter, a voltmeter, a variable resistance, a battery, connecting leads and a switch, explain clearly how you would find the value of an unknown resistance using this equipment. Give a neat diagram of connections and state how several readings may be obtained.

8. An ammeter having a resistance of 0·05 Ω and a voltmeter having a resistance of 2000 Ω were used to measure the resistance of a coil.

With the ammeter connected in series with the coil and the voltmeter across the ends of the coil, the readings were 0·5 A and 210 V respectively.

The voltmeter was then disconnected and reconnected across the combined circuit of ammeter and coil. What would be the new readings of the two instruments?

What is the true resistance of the coil?

9. Explain why the resistance of a moving-coil instrument must be very small when used as an ammeter and very high when used as a voltmeter, and by means of diagrams show how resistors are used in each of these two cases.

10. (a) State and prove the usual formula giving the relationship between the resistances of the arms of a Wheatstone bridge at balance.

(b) A Wheatstone bridge network ABCD was used to measure the resistance of a switch contact of nominal rating 1 A. Balance was obtained with the bridge arms set as follows:

AB = 100 Ω, BC = 10 Ω, AD = 12·5 Ω

The switch was connected in the arm CD.

Calculate the resistance of the switch, and the current flowing through it at balance if the network is supplied from a 2-V accumulator.

11. (a) Describe the principle of the Wheatstone bridge and the method of determining the value of the unknown resistor.

(b) During a test, using a Wheatstone bridge to determine the value of a resistor, the following figures were obtained:

Ratio arms (R_1 and R_2) 1000 Ω and 10 Ω respectively.

Plugs removed from a plug-type resistance box in the third arm: 300 Ω, 300 Ω, 100 Ω, 30 Ω, 1 Ω.

Determine the value of the unknown resistor.

(R_2 and the unknown were connected to the same battery terminal.)

12. A Wheatstone bridge has ratio arms P and Q whose elements are engraved 100, 10, 1 and 1, 10, 100 and a variable arm S whose elements are 1, 2, 2, 5, 10, 20, 20, 50 and 100 Ω. One end of S is connected to one end of P. What range of unknown resistance can be measured on:

(a) the highest setting of the ratio arms

(P = 100, Q = 1), and

(b) the lowest setting (P = 1, Q = 100).

Why is the balance obtained with such a bridge independent of small fluctuations in voltage of the supply battery?

13. The coil of a moving-coil instrument has a resistance of 30 Ω and is fully deflected when a current of 2·5 mA flows through it. Calculate the values of resistors required to enable the instrument to be used (i) as a 0 – 1 A ammeter, (ii) as a 0 – 100 V voltmeter. In each case show by a diagram how the resistor would be connected.

14. A permanent-magnet moving-coil instrument has a full-scale deflection of 15 mA and a full-scale voltage drop across its terminals of 75 mV.

Show, with the aid of circuit diagrams, how this instrument may be used (a) as a voltmeter with a full-scale deflection of 300 V, (b) as an ammeter with a full-scale deflection of 1·0 A. In each case calculate the value of any additional component required.

15. (a) Explain what is meant by a 'universal shunt'.

(b) A milliammeter has a resistance of 50 Ω and gives a full-scale deflection for a current of 1·5 mA. Calculate the value of a shunt resistance so that the meter may be used as a milliammeter having a range of 0/50 mA. At what point should a tapping be made on this shunt if the meter is to have an additional range of 0/500 mA provided? Sketch a circuit diagram of the arrangement.

16. Sketch a circuit diagram for a multi-range voltmeter and ammeter using series-connected voltmeter multipliers and a universal shunt.

If the milliammeter used has a resistance of 30 Ω and gives full-scale deflection for a current of 2·5 mA, calculate the resistance of the various sections of the multipliers and shunt for a meter having 3 voltage ranges and 3 ammeter ranges of 0/10/50/100 V and 0/5/50/500 mA respectively.

17. A milliammeter has a resistance of 50 Ω and gives full-scale deflection for a current of 2 mA. A resistance of 100 Ω is connected across its terminals. What is now the total current for full-scale deflection?

At what point should the 100-Ω resistor be tapped to give a current range of 0/150 mA?

18. Electro-chemistry

The chemical effect of an electric current has been briefly discussed in Chapter 16 on page 445. In the present chapter the discussion will first be centred on the production of an electromotive force by chemical means, and then the chemical effects of an electric current will be dealt with in a little more detail.

The existence of an e.m.f. between plates of two dissimilar metals (such as copper and zinc) separated by a cloth dampened with sulphuric acid in contact with both plates was discovered in 1799 by an Italian scientist named Volta, after whom the unit of e.m.f. and potential difference (the volt) is named. It is this effect which is applied in the electric 'dry' battery so commonly used nowadays for portable electrical equipment. Before these modern batteries are discussed, however, a refined version of Volta's original 'voltaic cell' will be described in more detail, since from this a theory of the action of cells in general may be developed.

18.1. The simple voltaic cell

If a strip of copper and a strip of zinc are placed in dilute sulphuric acid and then connected together by means of wires, bubbles will be seen to form at the surface of the copper plate and the zinc plate will be found slowly to dissolve. If a galvanometer is connected between the plates, it will indicate the flow of a current between them. This shows several things:

(a) A potential difference must exist between the plates in order that the current shall pass through the resistance of the circuit.

(b) The electric circuit must be 'completed' in some way through the dilute sulphuric acid, in order that current may flow round the circuit (i.e. in order that electric charge may drift round the circuit).

(c) This passage of electric current through the dilute sulphuric acid accompanies some chemical changes, as is evidenced by the formation of the bubbles at the surfaces of the copper plate, and by the slow dissolution of the zinc.

(d) The direction of the current flow *in the external circuit* is from copper to zinc.

(If two other materials are used for the plates, for example carbon and iron, similar effects are observed, although the value of the current may be different. This shows that the effect is dependent in degree, but not in principle, on the materials used.)

The dilute sulphuric acid is called an ELECTROLYTE and the two plates are referred to as the ELECTRODES. The copper plate is the external positive electrode, and may be called the ANODE, while the zinc plate is

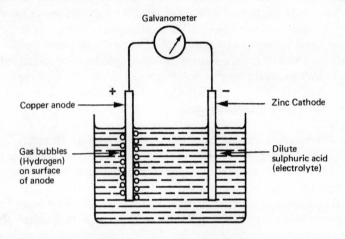

215. Arrangement of simple voltaic cell

the external negative electrode, and may be called the CATHODE. The arrangement of this simple cell is shown in diagram 215.

18.2. Theory of action of simple cell

The potential difference available from a copper-zinc voltaic cell is about 0·75 V. If different materials are used for the electrodes, different values of potential difference are obtained. This potential difference is also dependent on temperature.

The second point (b) made concerning the completion of the electric circuit through the electrolyte will be briefly discussed before a theory of the action of the simple cell is explained.

It is known that an electric current consists of the steady drift of electric charge round a circuit (see Chapter 16, page 442). It follows that some mechanism of transfer of electric charge must exist in the electrolyte. Sulphuric acid consists of a chemical combination of hydrogen, sulphur and oxygen. It is found that metals form 'sulphate' compounds in which the metal takes the place of the hydrogen in this arrangement. The sulphur and oxygen atoms must therefore form a 'sulphate unit' to which either hydrogen atoms or metallic atoms attach themselves to form either sulphuric acid or the sulphate of the metal.

When sulphuric acid is diluted with even quite small amounts of water, the hydrogen atoms become separated from the sulphate units but leave their electrons behind. The resulting particles are called IONS. The hydrogen ion, having lost an electron (negative charge), is positively charged and is known as a positive ion, while the sulphate ion, having excess electrons (there are actually two hydrogen ions for each sulphate ion in sulphuric acid), forms a negative ion. The electrolyte of the simple cell is thus 'ionized', and it is the migration of these ions between the plates which provides the transfer of electric charge through the electrolyte.

If the external circuit between the electrodes is completed, the potential difference between them will act to move the positive hydrogen ions towards the copper electrode and the negative sulphate ions towards the zinc. As the positive hydrogen ions arrive at the copper anode, they accept electrons from it and form hydrogen atoms. These combine to form hydrogen molecules and appear at the surface of the copper as bubbles of hydrogen gas. Simultaneously with the discharge of the hydrogen ions at the anode, zinc atoms from the cathode enter the electrolyte as positive ions, thus releasing electrons at the cathode which start to drift round the external circuit to replace those accepted by the hydrogen ions. The total number of electrons in the external circuit is thus constant, and electrons can be thought of as being 'fed into' one end of the circuit and 'pushed out' at the other. (This point is discussed again a little later.) The electrolyte loses positive hydrogen ions, which are replaced by positive zinc ions as the zinc cathode dissolves, so that the total positive ion content remains constant.

18.3. Local action

If commercial zinc is put into dilute sulphuric acid, hydrogen gas bubbles are seen to rise from it and the zinc will dissolve. This is because of the presence of impurities in the zinc which in effect set up many little primary cells with the zinc when in contact with the electrolyte. These small cells are short-circuited by the direct contact between the impurities forming one electrode of the cell and the zinc forming the other; the resulting current flow is accompanied by the chemical changes already mentioned. This local action is also the reason why metals corrode; for example, why iron rusts. If the iron is in contact with water containing dissolved impurities (such as rain-water or sea-water) the water acts as a weak electrolyte, and impurities in the iron set up local cells. The action of these causes the chemical changes which result in the formation of iron rust. It is possible to slow down local action if the material can be covered up in some way so that contact with the electrolyte is less effective. For example, the iron can be covered with a good coat of paint, although as the paint weathers it usually becomes porous enough to enable sufficient moisture to penetrate to the surface of the iron to speed up the local action and the resulting corrosion.

In the case of zinc, it is found that if a small amount of mercury is rubbed on to it, preferably while it is wet with dilute sulphuric acid, the mercury sinks into the surface without chemically combining with the zinc. The zinc is said to amalgamate with the mercury and the result is called 'amalgamated zinc'. The mercury present on the surface of amalgamated zinc prevents the formation of active local cells. Thus a piece of amalgamated zinc will not dissolve if placed by itself into dilute sulphuric acid. It is usual for the cathode of a simple voltaic cell to be made of amalgamated zinc to prevent local action from causing the fairly rapid dissolving of the zinc when the cell is not in use. When the cell is connected to an external circuit so that current flows, the zinc is dissolved as before, the zinc ions passing through the mercury film on the cathode.

18.4. Polarization

If the simple cell is left connected to the galvanometer for a little while, it is found that the current decreases fairly rapidly. This decrease is due to the formation of a film of hydrogen bubbles on the surface of the copper anode, as can be shown if the copper is removed, rubbed to remove the hydrogen bubbles and replaced. The current will then return to its original value for a short time before steadily decreasing again as the hydrogen bubbles re-form. This effect is known as the POLARIZATION of the cell. The hydrogen 'masks' the surface of the copper from the electrolyte, and thus increases the effective internal resistance of the cell (see page 507). This effect can be overcome by the use of a DEPOLARIZING AGENT, whose function is to remove the hydrogen bubbles as they form. Since mechanical removal of the bubbles is hardly practicable, chemical means are used. If a strong oxidizing agent such as potassium dichromate is added to the electrolyte, the hydrogen is oxidized to form water and the cell will deliver a steady current.

18.5. The Daniell cell

The Daniell cell is now more of historical and theoretical interest than a type of cell in current widespread use. However, its e.m.f. is very nearly constant at 1·09 V, and it may be used in the laboratory with fair accuracy as a standard source of e.m.f.

This cell also uses copper and zinc for the two electrodes, but has an ingenious 'depolarizing' arrangement which itself makes use of electrochemical effects. The general construction of the cell is indicated in diagram 216.

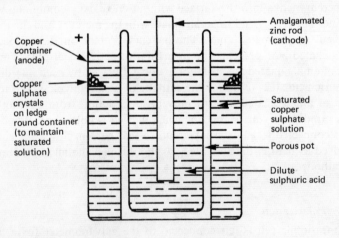

216. Diagram of construction of Daniell cell

The amalgamated zinc cathode stands in a porous pot, which is made of a coarse-textured, unglazed crockery. Liquids can only very slowly seep through the sides of this pot, but ions can pass through rather more readily. The porous pot is filled with dilute sulphuric acid (or zinc sulphate solution may be used instead) and stands inside an outer container which is filled with a concentrated solution of copper sulphate. The outer container may be of copper, and itself act as the anode of the cell, or a copper sheet may be placed in the copper sulphate for this purpose.

The action of the cell can be described as follows. Both the dilute sulphuric acid and the copper sulphate solutions will be ionized, so that within the porous pot positive hydrogen ions and negative sulphate ions will be present, whilst in the outer container positive copper ions and negative sulphate ions will be present. When the external circuit between the copper anode and the zinc cathode is completed, the positive hydrogen ions will move through the porous pot towards the copper anode. As these hydrogen ions enter the copper sulphate solution, there is an excess of positive ions in this electrolyte. Since copper ions are more readily 'discharged' than hydrogen ions, it is the copper ions which accept electrons from the anode and are deposited as metallic copper. In other words, the incoming hydrogen ions displace the copper ions, which, after accepting electrons from the anode, are deposited on the anode with no polarization effect. At the same time as this positive hydrogen ion migration, zinc enters the dilute sulphuric acid in the form of positive zinc ions from the cathode, as before, liberating electrons to the cathode and hence to the external circuit. These electrons drift slowly round the external circuit to constitute the load current of the cell, and arrive eventually at the anode, where they combine with the copper ions as they arrive. The actual electron which combines with a copper ion will not be the same one as is released by a zinc ion going into solution. The overall result can be visualized in the following way.

The external conductors may be compared with hollow tubes crammed with small steel balls representing the 'free' electrons in the conducting material. As an additional steel ball is pushed in at one end of the tube, the other balls in the tube will be jostled along to see that one ball will be pushed out at the other end of the tube. The original 'push' is supplied for the circuit by the e.m.f. of the cell. Note that the injection of an electron into the external circuit at the cathode by the departing zinc ion is accompanied by the simultaneous acceptance of an electron (not the same one) by the copper ion at the anode.

The advantages of the Daniell cell lie in its nearly constant e.m.f., the absence of polarizing effects even for prolonged currents of the order of 2 or 3 A, and cheap running costs. Its disadvantages are that it cannot be left standing idle for long periods because the electrolytes diffuse through the porous pot, so that the cell must be thoroughly cleaned after each period of use.

18.6. The Leclanché cell

The Leclanché cell is important in that it is the one at present in common use for many types of portable battery. For example, a flash-lamp battery is almost always made up of Leclanché cells. The now largely-outdated 'wet' type of Leclanché cell will be described first, since the basic principle of action can be understood better from this than from the so-called 'dry' battery which has been evolved from it.

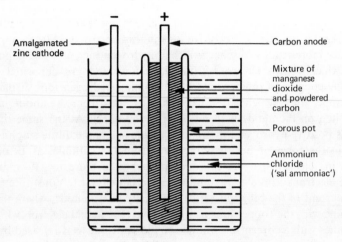

217. Diagram of construction of Leclanché cell ('wet' type)

The e.m.f. of the Leclanché cell is about 1·4–1·6 V; i.e. a 'nominal' 1·5 V. The cell uses zinc for the cathode, carbon for the anode, ammonium chloride for the electrolyte and solid manganese dioxide (a powerful oxidizing agent) for the depolarizing agent.

The general construction of the wet form of the cell is shown in diagram 217. The carbon anode is placed in a porous pot and is packed round with a mixture of solid manganese dioxide and powdered carbon. The powdered carbon effectively disperses the anode throughout the porous pot, mingling it closely with the manganese dioxide. This increases the rate of depolarization and reduces the internal resistance of the cell. The porous pot stands in an outer container filled with the electrolyte—ammonium chloride—and also containing the zinc cathode. The liquid ammonium chloride slowly seeps through the porous pot to dampen its contents and provide for the mobility of ions in this region.

The action of the cell can be described as follows.

The ammonium chloride electrolyte will be ionized so that positive ammonium ions and negative chloride ions will be present. When the external circuit is completed, zinc enters the solution as positive zinc ions, releasing electrons to the external circuit at the cathode as in the previous cases. Simultaneously with the entry of positive zinc ions into solution, the positive ammonium ions accept electrons from the carbon anode and hence from the external circuit. The neutralized ammonium ions decompose to form ammonia, which is very soluble in water, and hydrogen, which is oxidized by the manganese dioxide depolarizing agent to form water.

The depolarizing action of the cell is slow, and the cell will polarize if it is required to supply a large current, although it will recover if allowed to 'rest' for a time on open-circuit. Against this, the Leclanché cell in this form has the advantage that it has a very long life with minimum need for attention. This type of cell was in widespread use as a supply for such devices as electric bells, where the intermittent duty was admirably suited to its slow depolarizing action. Although Le-clanché cells have now largely been displaced for this type of duty, the dry form is still in current use for many applications.

Diagram 218 indicates the general construction of a dry Leclanché

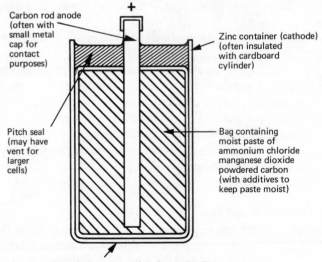

Carbon rod anode
(often with
small metal
cap for
contact
purposes)

Zinc container (cathode)
(often insulated
with cardboard
cylinder)

Pitch seal
(may have
vent for
larger
cells)

Bag containing
moist paste of
ammonium chloride
manganese dioxide
powdered carbon
(with additives to
keep paste moist)

'Negative' contact surface for small cells

218. Diagram of construction of Leclanché cell ('dry' type)

cell, although details differ between cells made by different manufacturers. The zinc cathode is used as the container for the whole cell. A moist paste of ammonium chloride, manganese dioxide, powdered carbon and other additives which are hygroscopic (i.e. which tend to absorb water from the atmosphere and so keep the paste moist) is placed in a cloth bag which also contains the carbon-rod anode, and this bag is placed in the zinc container. The whole is then sealed with pitch to prevent the escape of the paste. Larger sizes of Leclanché dry cells may have a small vent to allow for the escape of any ammonia and hydrogen which may accumulate if the current taken from the cell is fairly high.

(The bag containing the active paste is shown separate from the container for clarity. These will, of course, be in contact in the cell.)

The action of the dry cell is similar to that of the wet type. It is seen that the term 'dry' is really incorrect, since the paste must be moist for the ions to travel between electrodes. As with the wet type, the e.m.f. of this cell is a nominal 1·5 V. This cell also will polarize if called upon to supply a prolonged heavy current, but will recover after a period on open circuit. There will come a point, however, when the action will become increasingly less effective, as more and more of the electrolyte becomes chemically changed by the action of the cell. This means that, as with any primary cell (see Section 18.8, page 560), a point is reached where the cell can no longer act without a fresh charge of chemicals. For a dry cell, re-charging with chemicals would usually be uneconomical, and the complete cell is then discarded.

Since some slow local action may take place in a dry cell, even when the chemicals are exhausted for practical use, a dry cell has a limited storage life, and should never be left unattended for prolonged periods inside equipment with which it is used. If this is done, some of the material inside will almost certainly escape, and can cause extensive corrosion damage inside such equipment. Recent developments in the sealing of dry batteries have overcome this particular problem, but at present by no means all dry batteries are sealed in this way. Provided the batteries can be examined regularly, however, no serious trouble should be experienced.

18.7. The Weston standard cell

Although it is dependent on temperature, the e.m.f. of the Weston 'standard' cell is known very accurately. It has a value of 1·018 6 V at 10°C, 1·018 3 V at 20°C and 1·017 8 V at 30°C, and will not vary from one cell to another, provided the cells are not called upon to supply any significant amount of current. It is very widely used as a standard source of e.m.f. in laboratories, and an example of this use is given in Chapter 17, page 509.

The general construction of the cell is shown in diagram 219. The cell uses very pure mercury as the anode, cadmium sulphate as the electrolyte and an amalgam of cadmium and mercury as the cathode.

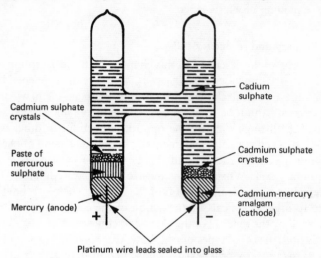

Cadium sulphate

Cadmium sulphate crystals

Cadmium sulphate crystals

Paste of mercurous sulphate

Cadmium-mercury amalgam (cathode)

Mercury (anode)

+   −

Platinum wire leads sealed into glass

219. Diagram of construction of Weston 'standard' cell

The mercurous sulphate is added to provide a supply of positive mercury ions in the electrolyte. The electrolyte is maintained in a saturated condition by the presence of excess cadmium sulphate in the form of crystals within the solution. The action of the cell depends on the formation of positive cadmium ions at the cathode, with the release of electrons to the external circuit. Positive mercury ions accept electrons at the anode and are neutralized to form mercury atoms.

The Weston cell should always be considered to be a piece of precise laboratory equipment, and treated and handled as such. Care should be taken to ensure that it is never called upon to supply a significant current. For example, a high resistance in series with one of the leads will not change the terminal potential difference on open circuit, but will protect the cell in the event of an accidental short-circuit. Since any voltmeter of a suitable range would take appreciable current from the cell, no attempt should be made to try to measure its terminal p.d. by this means. (In any case, the result would differ from the true e.m.f. of the cell because of the cell's internal resistance, as discussed in general in Chapter 17, page 507.)

Where frequent measurements are required, with not too great precision, a good method is to use the Weston cell to measure the e.m.f. of a dry Leclanché cell, and then to use the Leclanché cell as a standard for the remaining measurements.

18.8. Primary and secondary cells

All the cells so far described in this chapter (with the exception of the Daniell cell) are known as PRIMARY cells. They are distinguished by the fact that the chemical changes which take place in them when they supply current cannot be reversed by a current from an external source being passed through them in the opposite direction. In other words, the action of a cell consists fundamentally in the conversion of chemical energy into electrical energy, and this conversion cannot be reversed for a primary cell. When the chemical changes are complete (or, in practice, when a significant amount of the original chemicals have been changed to other chemicals by the action of the cell), the cell can only be 'renewed' by the renewal of the chemicals concerned.

This is not true of all types of cell, however. A second group of cells, known as SECONDARY cells, exists, whose action is reversible. That is, electrical energy may be supplied to these cells from an external source and converted into the form of chemical energy by the action of the cell. This chemical energy is then stored in the cell by virtue of the chemical changes which take place, and can be released and reconverted to electrical energy as required. The name 'accumulator' is often used in connection with secondary cells.

18.9. The lead-acid secondary cell

If two lead plates are dipped into dilute sulphuric acid and a direct current from an external source passed for a short time between them, chemical changes take place. These chemical changes are apparent from the changed appearance of the plate connected to the positive terminal of the supply. This positive plate will be seen to have turned a reddish-brown in colour where it has been in contact with the electrolyte. If the external supply is now switched off and the plates connected through an external circuit which includes an ammeter, it will be seen that current flows in the external circuit from the positive plate (the brown one) to the negative plate. This external load current will be maintained for a short time, but will then decrease to zero, and if the plates are now closely examined, a whitish colour may be visible on each. The further passage of current from an external source in the same direction as the first time will be found to produce the brown colour again on the positive plate and to remove the whitish colour from the negative plate, which becomes a 'clean' lead colour.

The lead plates in the dilute sulphuric acid form a simple lead-acid secondary cell (or lead-acid accumulator). The first process of passing current through the cell is known as 'charging' the cell, whilst the supply of load current from the cell is referred to as the 'discharge' of the cell.

If the charge/discharge cycle described above is repeated several times, the cell will be found to deliver load-current on discharge for longer and longer periods. This process is known as the Planté process of 'forming' the plates, and the chemical reactions take place with deeper and deeper penetration of the lead plates. Originally, the plates of practical lead-acid cells were made in this manner, but the process is lengthy and expensive, and unless special applications are involved, such as heavy-duty cells, formed plates are rarely used now. Where they are used, they are made with a deeply-ribbed cross-section in order to give the maximum surface area for a given weight of plate.

Most plates for this type of cell are of the Faure or 'pasted' type, in which a paste of the active material is pressed into recesses in a grid of lead-antimony alloy. The active material in the paste is usually red lead for positive plates and litharge for negative plates. Both these substances are fairly cheap oxides of lead, the litharge containing rather less oxygen. These plates are then assembled, and a single 'forming' charge is usually sufficient to make the necessary chemical changes. The positive plate material is chemically changed to another oxide of lead which is rich in oxygen and has the reddish-brown colour mentioned (lead dioxide), while the negative plate material is changed into lead, usually in a porous or spongy form.

On discharge, some of the active material on both plates is changed to lead sulphate, which has the whitish colour mentioned. During this change, the volume of active material in the plates tends to increase. If the cell is discharged with an unduly heavy current, the plates may be found to buckle, and heavy-duty cells must be designed to overcome this buckling effect. Heavy charging or discharging current may also cause loosening of the active material in the grids of pasted plates due to the violence of the resulting chemical action, and it is not uncommon to find a 'sediment' of material at the bottom of a lead-acid cell. The plates are usually supported clear of the bottom of the acid container to allow for this, since if the sediment became deep enough to touch the bottoms of the plates it would cause an internal short-circuit, resulting in even more damage to the cell.

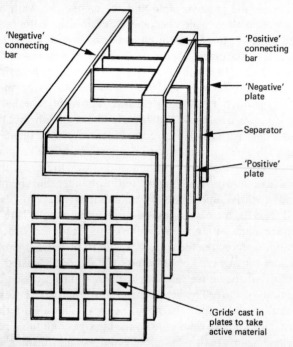

'Negative' connecting bar

'Positive' connecting bar

'Negative' plate

Separator

'Positive' plate

'Grids' cast in plates to take active material

220. Sketch of arrangement of plates for lead-acid cell. (There is usually an odd number of plates, the outer plates being 'negatives', as this is found to reduce the tendency to buckle)

Except for very small cells, each cell usually contains a number of plates connected in parallel so as to give an effective increase in active plate area. This increases the permissible current through the cell and reduces its internal resistance. The internal resistance of a lead-acid cell is usually very low indeed, being of the order of $0 \cdot 1 \ \Omega$ or less for quite a small cell, and even less than this for the larger cells. This means that a lead-acid cell should never be short-circuited, as very heavy currents can flow and cause serious damage to the cell. (The practice of 'flicking' a short-circuit across the terminals of a lead-acid cell to find out whether it is charged or not is very strongly to be deprecated.)

The plates are assembled in groups, with insulating separators between them as indicated in diagram 220. The material of the separators, which must be made porous, varies with the manufacturer, but wood, ebonite, woven glass fibre and some plastic materials have been used. The assembled plates are connected in groups according to polarity, usually by a lead 'burning' (melting) process which welds the connecting 'riser' from each plate to a common connection strip which is then taken to the cell terminal. A battery may be made up of a number of cells connected in series or parallel, usually by means of suitable lead straps between cell terminals.

18.10. Characteristics of the lead-acid secondary cell

Immediately after charge, the terminal p.d. of a lead-acid cell is about 2·1 V or even higher, but this soon falls to about 2 V on load. Provided that it is then discharged at no more than the rated current, the terminal p.d. remains very nearly constant at 2 V for the greater portion of the discharge. Towards the end of the period, the terminal p.d. decreases more rapidly until, at 1·8 V or so, the cell is considered to be fully discharged. If load current is taken from the cell after this point, or if it is left in this discharged state for a long period, there is a tendency for the lead sulphate formed on the plates to harden. It is then much more difficult to re-convert to the required lead dioxide and lead on re-charging, and the life and capacity on the cell may be severely reduced. (This is known as 'sulphating'.)

The 'capacity' of the cell is a measure of the total quantity of electricity which it can cause to be displaced around a load circuit after being fully charged. It could be measured in coulombs (ampere-seconds), but this would be a rather small unit, and so the capacity is usually measured in AMPERE-HOURS (Ah), (1 Ah = 3600 coulombs). The 'rated' or maximum discharge current is usually calculated as the steady load current that would completely discharge the cell in 10 h. It may sometimes be permissible to discharge the cell in a slightly shorter time, but a rather lower ampere-hour capacity would be obtained. In general, the higher the discharge current, the lower the effective capacity of the cell.

Thus a 50-Ah battery (rated for 10-h discharge) could be discharged at a steady current of 5 A for 10 h (the '10-h rate') but would be discharged in about 3–4 h if the load current taken were 10 A. For a reasonable cell life, the 10-h discharge rate should not be exceeded.

Diagram 221 shows typical discharge characteristics for a lead-acid cell.

Note that it is difficult to tell the difference between a recently-charged and a nearly-discharged cell from a measurement of the terminal voltage. A more accurate check is given by the specific gravity of the dilute sulphuric acid electrolyte. This falls fairly steadily throughout the discharge period as a result of the chemical changes taking place. The specific gravity of the electrolyte of a fully-charged cell will

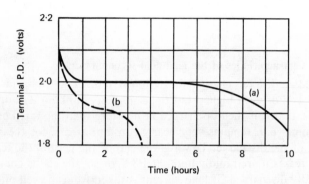

221. Typical discharge characteristics of a lead-acid cell.
  (a) Discharge at 10-h rate
  (b) Discharge at about twice 10-h rate

differ slightly for different types and makes of cell, but a value of about 1·25 is typical. The specific gravity of the electrolyte of a discharged cell will be of the order of 1·18.

When a lead-acid cell is charged from an external supply, the positive terminal of the cell must be connected to the positive terminal of the supply. The e.m.f. of the charging supply then acts in opposition to the e.m.f. of the cell. Since the charging supply e.m.f. should exceed that of the cell, current is passed through the cell in the opposite direction to the load current supplied by the cell. Diagrams 222 (a) and (b) should make this clear. It is very important that the charging supply should be correctly connected to the cell, since if the connections are reversed, the charging e.m.f. and the cell e.m.f. will be additive round the circuit. Since the internal resistance of the cell is so low, a very heavy discharge current could flow, probably causing severe damage to the cell. This is the reason why suitable fuses should always be inserted in a charging circuit to protect the cell in case of error.

Various arrangements of charging circuit are possible, but they should all include some means of controlling the charging current, and preferably also of measuring it, since damage may be caused by charging at too high a rate. Because of energy losses in the internal resistance of the cell, and the chemical changes taking place, the cell will become

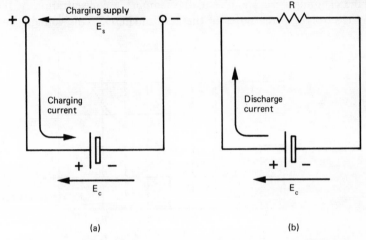

(a)   (b)

222. Charging and discharging circuit conditions for a secondary cell.

(a) Charging connections for a secondary cell. The total e.m.f. acting *round the circuit* is $E_s - E_c$, and since E_s is greater than E_c, charging current flows *into* the positive terminal of the battery. Compare this with (b).
(b) Discharge of cell into load resistance. Here E_c is the only e.m.f. round the circuit, and discharge current flows *out of* the positive terminal of the battery

warm during the charging period. It must not be allowed to get too hot (not more than about 40°C). Gas is liberated towards the end of the charging period, and the gas bubbles rising freely from the plates are an indication that the cell is charged. Since this gas may be released quite vigorously, the screwed vent plugs in the cells should be removed before charging starts, to enable the gases to escape freely. If charging is continued for too long a period, or particularly if the charging current is too high, the gas bubbles may be released very vigorously indeed. Considerable splashing of the dilute acid electrolyte will occur, and severe cases of rapid gas formation can cause some of the paste in the plates to be pushed out of the grids, with a consequent shortening of the useful life of the cell. The gases given off at the end of the charging period are hydrogen and oxygen (see Section 18.13, page 569). This is an explosive mixture, and the room used for the purpose of battery charging should be well ventilated.

A typical charging characteristic of a lead-acid cell is shown in diagram 223. The terminal p.d. must exceed 2 V in order to pass charging current through the cell. The rise in terminal p.d. towards the end of the charging period is due to the temporary concentration of the acid electrolyte in the pores of the active material. This voltage soon

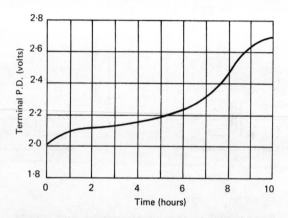

223. Typical charging characteristics of a lead-acid cell

falls to about 2·1 V if the cell is left idle for a short period after charge, as the concentrated acid disperses again in the main body of the electrolyte.

Summary

(a) Cells should not be left for prolonged periods in the discharged state. (Danger of 'sulphating'.)

(b) Specified rates of charge and discharge should not be exceeded.

(c) Level of electrolyte should be kept above the plates by topping up with distilled water (*not* tap-water unless free from injurious chemicals). Addition of acid should very rarely be required, except to make up for losses due to spilling. (Check specific gravity when fully charged.)

(d) Occasional periods of prolonged charge at reduced rate will tend to remove initial formations of hard lead sulphate.

(e) Cells on light or intermittent load should occasionally be fully discharged at normal rate, and re-charged. 'Trickle' charging, a continuous *small* charging-current flow, helps to keep idle cells in good condition.

18.11. Other types of secondary cell

Other forms of secondary cell are available which use an alkaline electrolyte such as potassium hydroxide. The active elements are usually nickel and iron, or compounds of these elements. The specific gravity of the electrolyte in these cells does not change with the state of charge, but remains constant throughout, a typical value being about 1·17.

Topping up is rarely necessary. These cells usually have a terminal voltage of the order of 1·2 V, and so more cells are required to give a battery of a given e.m.f. than would be the case for a lead-acid battery. For example, a 12-V car battery requires 6 lead-acid cells in series, but 10 nickel-alkaline cells in series.

However, the alkaline cells have many advantages over the lead-acid type, and these may be summarized as follows:

(a) Stronger mechanical construction.
(b) Can be left indefinitely in any state of charge or discharge without damage.
(c) Can be discharged at heavy load currents without damage and with less loss of ampere-hour capacity.
(d) Lighter in weight.

The disadvantages of these cells compared with the lead-acid type can be summarized as follows:

(a) Relatively more expensive.
(b) More cells required for given e.m.f.
(c) Higher internal resistance, giving greater variation of terminal voltage with changes in load current.
(d) Rather lower efficiencies.

Note:

$$\text{Ampere-hour efficiency} = \frac{\text{Ah obtained on discharge}}{\text{Ah required on charge}} \times 100\%$$

$$\text{Watt-hour efficiency} = \frac{\text{useful energy released on discharge}}{\text{energy input on charge}} \times 100\%.$$

At present, the alkaline cells are mainly used where the duties require long idle periods or heavy discharge currents. Their field of application seems to be increasing, however.

18.12. Electrolysis

When an electrical current passes through an electrolyte, chemical changes take place. In the earlier sections of this chapter, it has been shown that these changes occur because of the migration of the ions in the electrolyte. These take part in chemical reactions after giving up or receiving electrons at the electrodes. This effect is summarized in diagram 224, which shows two electrodes dipped into an electrolyte

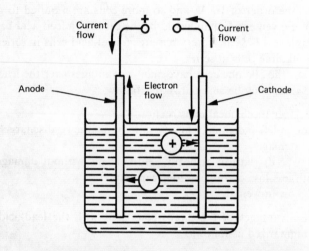

224. Current flow through an electrolyte. (General directions of drift of positive and negative ions are as shown, and are superimposed on random 'thermal' movements)

and connected to an electrical supply. Current flows into the electrode connected to the positive terminal of the supply (the anode) and out of the electrode connected to the negative terminal (the cathode). For this purpose, it is not necessary for the electrodes to be of different materials, and in what follows the electrodes will be considered to be of the same material, unless it is specifically stated otherwise. The general directions of movement of the ions are indicated in the diagram, although these will be 'drift' directions superimposed on the normal rapid random movement of the ions in all directions, due to their thermal energy (see Section 13.7, page 358).

The conditions in diagram 128 are similar to the conditions during the *charging* of a secondary cell, in that current flows *into* the anode. The directions of the ionic drift will be seen to follow from this, since the conventional current direction is the direction of movement of an assumed *positive* charge (see page 443).

As the negative ions reach the anode they give up their excess electrons to it, and these electrons drift round the external circuit, constituting the current flow. At the same instant as electrons from the negative ions enter the external circuit at the anode, other electrons will be leaving this circuit at the cathode to 'neutralize' a positive ion arriving there. Again, as in Section 18.5, page 555, the idea of a hollow tube, crammed with steel balls representing free electrons in the conductors, is useful for visualizing these conditions. (The force 'pushing' the electrons round is this time derived from the e.m.f. of the external source.)

Thus, as long as the current flows, negative ions must be arriving at the anode, and positive ions arriving simultaneously at the cathode. The same number of electrons are given up at the anode by negative ions as are accepted at the cathode by positive ions.

The actual mechanism of the electron transfer to and from the ions in the electrolyte is fairly complex, and depends on the relative ease with which any ions present may be discharged (i.e. gain or lose electrons so as to neutralize their 'ionic charge'). This in turn may be affected by the concentration of the ions, the temperature, and the nature of the electrode. Simplified details will be given for the special cases considered. However, the overall result of the passage of electric current through an electrolyte is that chemical changes take place at the electrodes. The general name given to this effect is ELECTROLYSIS. Apparatus arranged specially for this purpose is called a VOLTAMETER. (This name should not be confused with 'voltmeter'.)

18.13. Electrolysis of water

If slightly acidulated water is used for the electrolyte, and platinum or carbon used as electrodes, the water is decomposed into its constituents of hydrogen and oxygen. (Absolutely pure water is not a very good electrolyte. The presence of a small amount of acid introduces many more ions, which carry the current through the solution. The chemical action accompanying this flow of current results in the decomposition of the water.) A piece of equipment suitable for demonstrating this effect is known as the 'Hoffman water voltameter', and is illustrated in diagram 225. The platinum electrodes are fixed in vertical tubes with taps at the top, and the tubes are connected by a horizontal tube as shown. A 'reservoir' is connected to this junction and enables

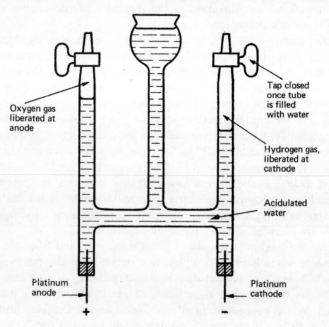

Oxygen gas
liberated at
anode

Tap closed
once tube
is filled
with water

Hydrogen gas,
liberated at
cathode

Acidulated
water

Platinum
anode

Platinum
cathode

+

−

225. Diagram of Hoffman water voltameter

both vertical tubes to be filled with water when the taps are open. Once the vertical tubes are full, the taps are closed.

As electric current is passed between the platinum electrodes, bubbles of gas appear at each electrode. This gas rises, and is collected at the top of each vertical tube as shown. The gas in the tube above the anode can be identified as oxygen, and the gas above the cathode is found to be hydrogen. If the volumes of gas liberated after any given time are measured, it is found that the volume of hydrogen is always twice the volume of oxygen.

(It is the decomposition by electrolysis of water in the electrolyte that causes the 'gassing' at the plates of a lead-acid cell at the end of the charging period. At earlier times during charging, other chemical reactions take place in the active material of the plates.)

18.14. Faraday's laws of electrolysis. Electro-chemical equivalent

Each ion arriving at, or leaving, an electrode gives up or receives a definite number of electrons, representing a definite amount of electric charge. The total charge passed round the circuit of a voltameter by the external supply must, then, determine the total number of ions involved.

These ions become 'liberated' at the electrodes as atoms or molecules, and so it follows that the total amount of any substance liberated in this way must be proportional to the total quantity of electric charge passed. Suppose 1 g of negative ions becomes 1 g of atoms of a substance through giving up a total negative charge of Q coulombs, which is passed round the circuit by the supply e.m.f. Then, if a total charge of $2 \times Q$ coulombs has passed round the circuit, it means that 2 g of negative ions must have become 2 g of atoms of the substance, since twice the total number of electrons must have been given up. This fact was stated by Faraday in 1833 at his first law of electrolysis, which says:

'The mass of any substance liberated at an electrode by electrolytic action is proportional to the total quantity of electricity passed through the electrolyte.'

Faraday also stated a second law of electrolysis, which may be expressed as follows:

'The mass of any substance liberated at an electrode by electrolytic action is proportional to the ELECTRO-CHEMICAL EQUIVALENT of the substance.'

(The actual statement of this second law was in terms of certain chemical properties of the substance, but the statement of the law given here is satisfactory for practical use.)

The electro-chemical equivalent (e.c.e.) of a substance can be defined as that mass of the substance which is liberated at an electrode by electrolytic action caused by the passage of an electric charge of 1 C. The units in which the electro-chemical equivalent of a substance is usually measured are GRAMS PER COULOMB (g/C).

A table of values of the electro-chemical equivalent of some common substances is given on page 750.

Faraday's two laws of electrolysis may, then, be combined into a single equation. If a mass of m g of a substance having an electro-chemical equivalent of z grams per coulomb is liberated by a current of I amperes flowing for a time t seconds, then

$$m = z.I.t \qquad . \qquad . \qquad . \qquad \text{(i)}$$

This equation uses the fact that a current of I A flowing for a time t s is equivalent to a total charge displacement $Q = I.t$ coulombs round the circuit (see page 444).

Note that if $I \times t = 1$ coulomb, this equation gives the mass liberated as z grams, which agrees with the previous definition of the electro-chemical equivalent.

Electrolytic effects have been used to define a value for the ampere. The ampere can be defined as that unvarying current which liberates $0.001\ 118$ g of silver per second by electrolytic action from a silver nitrate electrolyte. (The e.c.e. of silver is, then, $0.001\ 118$ g/C). The electro-magnetic definition given on page 621 is, however, to be preferred.

18.15. Examples

(i) What mass of hydrogen gas is liberated during the electrolysis of water if a current of 0.2 A is passed through the acidulated water electrolyte for a period of half an hour?

The e.c.e. of hydrogen can be taken as 1.05×10^{-5} g/C.

Mass liberated is, by equation (i),
$$m = z.I.t \text{ grams}$$
where z = electro-chemical equivalent in gram/coulomb
        I = current in amperes
        t = time in seconds.
Then in this case,

$$m = 1.05 \times 10^{-5} \times 0.2 \times \left\{ 30 \ \cancel{\text{min}} \times \left(\frac{60 \text{ s}}{1 \ \cancel{\text{min}}} \right) \right\} \text{ g}$$

$$= 1.05 \times 10^{-5} \times 0.2 \times 30 \times 60 \text{ g}$$
$$= 3.78 \times 10^{-3} \text{ g}$$
(or 3.78 milligrams).

Mass of hydrogen liberated is 3.78 mg

(ii) If a current of 0·05 A is passed through a water voltameter for an hour, the mass of oxygen liberated is found to be 14·9 mg.

Estimate the electro-chemical equivalent of oxygen from these results.

From equation (i)
$$m = z.I.t \text{ grams}$$
or, in this case,

$$14.9 \; \text{mg} \times \frac{1 \; \text{g}}{1000 \; \text{mg}} = z \times 0.05 \times 1 \; \text{h} \times \left(\frac{60 \; \text{min}}{1 \; \text{h}}\right) \times \left(\frac{60 \; \text{s}}{1 \; \text{min}}\right)$$

or
$$\frac{14.9}{1000} = z \times 0.05 \times 60 \times 60 \; \text{g}$$

or
$$z = \frac{14.9}{1000 \times 0.05 \times 60 \times 60} \; \text{g/C}$$

$$= 8.28 \times 10^{-5} \; \text{g/C}$$

Electro-chemical equivalent of oxygen

$$\simeq 8.28 \times 10^{-5} \; \text{g/C}$$

The accuracy of this result depends on the precision with which the given measurements were made.

18.16. Electroplating

A very important practical application of the effects of electrolysis is electroplating. Here, a 'plating' of a substance (usually a metal) is deposited on to the surface of an article. Examples of chromium plating, nickel plating or silver plating are very common. The plating may be added for decorative purposes, to give protection against corrosion or for other more specialized purposes. As an example, the copper-plating of a metal object will be described.

The metal object to be plated is dipped into a copper-sulphate solution (which is the electrolyte). A copper plate is then also dipped into the solution. The object to be plated is made the CATHODE, and the copper plate is made the anode of the 'voltameter' so formed (usually called a plating bath in this case). As current is passed through the plating bath, a film of metallic copper is deposited on the metal object. The amount of copper deposited, and hence the thickness of the plating, will depend on the current, the time for which the current flows and the electro-chemical equivalent of copper, as explained in Section 18.14. Diagram 226 shows the general arrangement.

The theory of the action may be explained as follows. The copper sulphate electrolyte will be ionized, giving positive copper ions and negative sulphate ions. The water present in the solution will also ionize to a limited extent, giving positive hydrogen ions and negative hydroxide ions. Under the action of the applied potential difference, the positive copper ions will drift towards the cathode, where they will accept electrons from the external circuit and be deposited as metallic copper atoms on the surface of the cathode. The negative sulphate ions

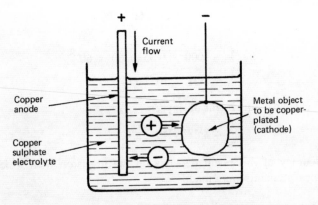

226. Diagram of copper-plating bath. (General directions of ionic drift as shown)

are, however, much less readily discharged than the copper ions, and therefore the copper will enter the solution from the anode as positive copper ions, which have given up electrons to the anode. These electrons are passed round the external circuit by the e.m.f. of the electrical supply as before. The overall result will be that copper is dissolved from the anode and deposited on the cathode, and the total loss of copper from the anode will be equal to the total gain of copper by the cathode.

A plating bath of this type with two copper electrodes and copper sulphate as the electrolyte can be used for a simple laboratory experiment to find the e.c.e. of copper. The electrodes are carefully dried and weighed, and then assembled in the plating bath. A measured current is then passed for a measured length of time, after which the plates are again carefully dried and weighed. The gain in weight of the cathode represents the mass of copper deposited by the measured quantity of electricity, and from these results the e.c.e. of copper can be calculated. In a practical experiment, the loss in weight of the anode may be found to be slightly greater than the gain in weight by the cathode. On the assumption that none of the deposit has been wiped off from the cathode during drying, this difference will be due to the loss of impurities from the anode, released when the copper is dissolved.

If some material other than copper, such as carbon, is used for the anode, copper will still be deposited on the cathode. However, as the supply of copper ions in solution is decreased (they cannot be replaced from the carbon anode) the resistance of the electrolyte increases, and it becomes more and more difficult to maintain the current flow. (In such a case, the negative sulphate ions prove to be less readily discharged than the negative hydroxide ions present because of the partial ionization of the water in the solution. It is then the hydroxide ions which give up their electrons, to form water and oxygen. The oxygen would be released as bubbles of gas at the anode.) A fresh supply of copper ions could be obtained from the addition of further copper sulphate crystals to the electrolyte, and this would decrease the electrolyte resistance again. The normal practice, however, is to use the copper anode as already described.

A similar process using low-purity copper for the anode and a small stick of high-purity copper for the cathode gives a method of producing refined copper at the cathode.

For the electroplating of objects with materials other than copper, methods are used similar to that given. The anode is usually made of the material required for the plating, and the electrolyte is made from a solution of one of its compounds. For example, a silver anode with silver nitrate solution as electrolyte could be used for silver-plating an object (which would be made the cathode). The materials used in practical plating baths are chosen as the result of practical experience, and several additives which have been found to give improved results may be used. The basic theory of the process is, however, as outlined.

An extension of electroplating application is the plating of non-conducting surfaces. These are first sprayed or painted with some form of conducting paint, which contains, for example, fine particles of metal or carbon. This conducting layer can then be used as the cathode in a plating bath, and a metal deposit built up on it. The 'bonding' of the plating deposit can be quite good, especially for porous materials. A similar process can be used to produce a metallic copy of the surface of an object such as a gramophone record, although here, of course, the sprayed-on conducting surface must be capable of being freely lifted, together with the 'plating', from the original.

As stated in Faraday's first law of electrolysis, the amount of material deposited in a plating bath depends on the total quantity of electric charge passed through the bath. This means that the *rate* at which material is deposited depends on the *rate* of flow of charge; i.e. on the current. It is found that if the current is too high, the material is deposited too quickly. As a result it does not adhere well to the surface of the cathode, but tends to flake off.

It follows that the rate at which material can be deposited safely on a given surface area of the cathode is limited. This is measured in terms of the 'current density' for the cathode surface, where cathode current density (here assumed uniform over the cathode surface) is given by

$$\text{cathode current density} = \frac{\text{total current}}{\text{surface area of cathode}}$$

The limiting values of cathode current density are determined by practical experience with the type of plating bath concerned.

18.17.   Example on Faraday's laws of electrolysis

A metal cylinder, 50 mm diameter and 100 mm long, is to be copper-plated over its curved surface (the ends being 'blanked-off' by insulating paint). The required thickness of the copper plating is 0·1 mm, and the current through the plating bath is kept constant at 50 A. Find the time required, assuming the plating to be uniform. E.c.e. of copper can be taken as 0·000 33 g/C and density of copper as 8900 kg/m³.

(A plating bath for this type of application would preferably have the anode in the form of a hollow copper cylinder, with the cylindrical object being plated at its centre and forming a 'co-axial' cathode. This would give a more even thickness of deposit.)

The 'active' surface area of the cathode (A) is in this case cylindrical so that

$$A = \pi . d . h \text{ mm}^2$$

where d = diameter of cylinder in mm
    h = height of cylinder in mm

In this case,

$$A = \pi \times 50 \times 100 \text{ mm}^2$$
$$= 15\ 700 \text{ mm}^2$$

Then, since the thickness is relatively small, volume of copper to be deposited (V) is

$$V = \text{area} \times \text{thickness}$$
$$= 15\,700 \text{ mm}^2 \times 0 \cdot 1 \text{ mm}$$
$$= 1570 \text{ mm}^3$$

Then the mass of copper to be deposited (m) is

$$m = \text{volume} \times \text{density}$$
$$= 1570 \text{ mm}^3 \times \left(\frac{1 \text{ m}}{1000 \text{ mm}}\right)^3 \times 8900 \text{ kg/m}^3$$
$$= 0 \cdot 014 \text{ kg}$$
$$= 14 \text{ g}$$

From equation (i), mass deposited is

$$m = z.I.t$$

In this case,

$$14 = 0 \cdot 000\,33 \times 50 \times t \text{ where } t = \text{time in seconds}$$

or

$$t = \frac{14}{0 \cdot 000\,33 \times 50} \text{ s}$$
$$= 850 \text{ s}$$

or   14·2 min

or   14·2 min

The plating current must flow for <u>14·2 min</u>

18.18. Energy considerations in electro-chemical reactions

The chemical reactions taking place in any electro-chemical cell are governed by Faraday's laws of electrolysis. This means that the total amount of chemicals used or converted in, say, a primary cell is proportional to the total electric charge passed round the circuit by the action of the e.m.f. of the cell. The problem is really one of energy conversion. Chemical energy in the materials of the primary cell is released as electrical energy as a result of the chemical reactions taking place. This energy is given to the electric charge by raising its electric potential. The amount of electrical energy for any one cell, and also the amount of the chemicals converted by the reactions, depends on the total charge displaced. Each coulomb displaced round the circuit will be given one joule of electrical energy for each volt of the cell e.m.f., and this will require an equivalent release of chemical energy by the chemical reactions taking place. (See Section 16.2, page 438.)

T

Similarly, the electrical energy supplied to a voltameter or a plating bath is converted to chemical energy in the chemical reactions which occur. In the special case of secondary cells, these electro-chemical energy conversions are reversible.

Example

A Daniell cell has an internal resistance of $0.5\ \Omega$ and an e.m.f. of 1.1 V. This cell is connected across a resistance of $1.7\ \Omega$. How much zinc is dissolved in an hour? How much chemical energy is converted into electrical energy in this time? The e.c.e. of zinc may be taken as $0.000\ 34$ g/C.

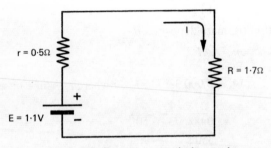

227. Circuit diagram—numerical example

It will be remembered that the Daniell cell uses zinc for the cathode of the cell, and that during the action of the cell when it supplies current to a load, the zinc is slowly dissolved in the dilute sulphuric acid electrolyte. In other words, the zinc is 'liberated' from the cell cathode into solution. (See page 554.) Faraday's laws of electrolysis still apply to this case. Notice that metallic or *positive* ions flow *away from* the cathode when electrical energy is delivered *from* a cell, while these ions flow *towards* the cathode when electrical energy is supplied *to* the cell, even though subsequent chemical reactions may not be reversible.

A circuit diagram for this example is shown in diagram 227.

The total resistance in the circuit is

$$r + R = 0.5 + 1.7\ \Omega$$
$$= 2.2\ \Omega$$

Then current supplied by the Daniell cell is

$$I = \frac{1.1}{2.2}\ A$$
$$= 0.5\ A$$

In a time of 1 h, the total mass of zinc (m) liberated by a current of 0·5 A is given, from equation (i) as,

$$m = z \times I \times t$$
$$= 0\cdot000\ 34 \times 0\cdot5 \times 1\ \cancel{h} \times \left(\frac{60\ \cancel{min}}{1\ \cancel{h}}\right) \times \left(\frac{60\ s}{1\ \cancel{min}}\right)\ g$$
$$= 0\cdot000\ 34 \times 0\cdot5 \times 60 \times 60\ g$$
$$= 0\cdot61\ g$$

In one hour, 0·61 g of zinc will be dissolved.

The total electrical energy supplied by the cell (some of which is converted to heat in its own internal resistance) is given by:

$$\text{electrical energy} = E \times I \times t \text{ joules (see page 451)}$$
$$= 1\cdot1 \times 0\cdot5 \times 3600\ J$$
$$= 1980\ J$$

This answer is also obtained by the reasoning that each coulomb which is raised in potential by each volt of the cell e.m.f. is given one joule of energy (see page 438.)

Thus, for Q C passing through a cell of e.m.f. E V, a total energy of $E \times Q$ joules is given to the electric charge. In other words,

$$\text{energy} = E \times Q \text{ joules}$$
$$= 1\cdot1 \times 1800\ J \text{ for above case}$$
$$= 1980\ J$$

This electrical energy supplied by the cell is obtained by its action in converting chemical energy, so that the total amount of chemical energy converted to electrical energy in this case in 1980 joules.

CHAPTER SUMMARY

A simple voltaic cell uses copper and zinc as the electrodes, and dilute sulphuric acid as the electrolyte.

The copper forms the positive electrode (anode), and the zinc the negative electrode (cathode).

Polarization occurs as a result of formation of hydrogen gas bubbles at the surface of the anode.

Depolarizers act by removing this hydrogen, generally by oxidizing it to form water.

An ion is a charged particle formed when an atom, or group of atoms, gains or loses electrons. Electrolytes are ionized, with free positive and negative ions present in them.

The Daniell cell has an e.m.f. of about 1·09 V, and uses a copper anode and zinc cathode, with dilute sulphuric acid (or zinc sulphate) and copper sulphate electrolytes, separated by a porous pot. The zinc stands in the acid and the copper in the copper sulphate. The Daniell cell does not suffer from polarization.

The Leclanché cell has an e.m.f. of about 1·5 V, and uses a carbon anode and zinc cathode, with ammonium chloride as electrolyte. It uses manganese dioxide as depolarizer, but the depolarizing action is relatively slow.

So-called 'dry' batteries are usually forms of Leclanché cell.

The Weston standard cell has an e.m.f. of 1·018 3 V at 20°C. It uses a pure mercury anode, an amalgam of cadmium and mercury as cathode and cadmium sulphate as electrolyte. This cell is frequently used as a standard source of e.m.f. in the laboratory.

A primary cell is one in which the chemical changes are not reversible.

A secondary cell is one in which the chemical changes can be reversed by a flow of current through it in the reverse direction to that of its normal load current.

The lead-acid secondary cell (or 'accumulator') uses lead dioxide as anode, and lead as cathode, with dilute sulphuric acid as electrolyte.

The chemical changes during charge and discharge may be summarized as

	Charged		Discharged
Anode:	Lead dioxide	$\rightleftharpoons$	Lead sulphate
Cathode:	Lead	$\rightleftharpoons$	Lead sulphate
Electrolyte:	Higher specific gravity	$\rightleftharpoons$	Lower specific gravity

The capacity of a cell is stated in Ah, and is the total quantity of electricity available from a fully-charged cell at the 10-h rate.

When a secondary cell is charged, connect the positive cell terminal to the positive terminal of the charging supply.

See page 566 for a summary of the points concerning the care of lead-acid cells.

Another type of secondary cell in common use is the nickel-iron alkaline cell. See page 567 for a summary of the relative advantages and disadvantages of these cells.

When an electric current flows through an electrolyte, chemical changes take place at the electrodes. This effect is known as electrolysis.

The electrolysis of slightly acidulated water results in the decomposition of the water, oxygen gas being liberated at the anode, and hydrogen gas at the cathode.

The electro-chemical equivalent of a substance is that mass of the substance liberated at an electrode by electrolytic action by the passage of an electric charge of one coulomb.

Then a current I A flowing for a time t s liberates a mass m g of a substance having an e.c.e. of z g/C,

where $m = z.I.t.$

QUESTIONS

1. With the aid of a sketch, describe the construction and operation of any type of primary cell.

Explain briefly the process of 'polarization' in a primary cell.

2. Explain what is meant by 'polarization' and 'local action' with reference to a simple primary cell. Describe, with the aid of a sketch, how these effects are overcome in a dry cell.

3. (a) Describe, with the aid of a diagram, the construction of a wet-type Leclanché cell.

(b) Explain why it is detrimental or even dangerous for a lead-acid accumulator to be short-circuited.

4. With the aid of a sketch give a description of either (a) a wet-type Leclanché cell, or (b) a dry-type Leclanché cell.

The terminal voltage of a battery was 13·3 V when connected in series with a 95-Ω resistor, and 13·5 V when connected in series with a 135-Ω resistor. Determine the internal e.m.f. and internal resistance of the battery.

5. Describe the construction of a lead accumulator. What distinguishes a secondary from a primary cell?

6. (a) State the precautions to be observed in the use of lead-acid accumulators to avoid damage to the cells. How would the state of charge be tested?

(b) Describe briefly, with circuit diagram, an experiment to show the variation of terminal voltage of a cell with load current. Show how the internal resistance of the cell could be found from the results.

7. Draw diagrams to show the construction of either a lead-acid cell or a nickel-iron cell and state the materials of which it is composed.

What is meant by the ampere-hour capacity of such a cell? A battery of 80 cells in series is to be charged at 4 A from a d.c. supply of 240 V. If each cell voltage is 1·8 V, calculate the value of the series resistance required.

8. (a) Explain the statement that the capacity of a lead-acid cell is '100 ampere-hours at a 10-hour rate'.

(b) Calculate the time of charge of a cell having a capacity of 100 Ah if the charging current is 12 A and the ampere-hour efficiency is 80%.

(c) Draw graphs to show the variation of voltage with time during charge and discharge of an accumulator, at the normal rated current.

(d) Describe briefly two methods of determining the condition of a lead-acid cell.

9. Describe, with the aid of a diagram, the construction of a multi-plate lead-acid cell and give briefly the changes which take place whilst the cell is being discharged.

10. (a) Sketch typical charge and discharge curves for a lead-acid cell, and explain the terms 'ampere-hour efficiency' and 'watt-hour efficiency'.

(b) A bank of 35 lead-acid cells, each of 100 Ah capacity, are to be charged at a constant current of 8 A. If the d.c. supply is at 100 V, calculate the maximum and minimum values of the control resistance given that the e.m.f. of each cell varies from 1·8 to 2·4 V over the charging period. Ignore the internal resistance of the cell.

What should be the approximate charging time for these cells?

11. (a) Compare the performance and maintenance of a lead-acid cell with that of an alkaline cell.

(b) A battery of 80 lead-acid cells in series is to be charged at a constant rate of 5 A from a 230-V d.c. supply. If the voltage per cell varies from 1·8 to 2·4 during the charge, calculate the maximum and minimum values of the required control resistance. If the ampere-hour capacity of the cells is 60, state, with reasons, the probable charging time required, assuming that the cells were in a completely discharged condition at the commencement of the charge.

12. What is understood by (a) electro-chemical equivalent, (b) coulomb, (c) cathods, (d) electrolyte? With the aid of a diagram showing the apparatus and electrical connections, explain how you would determine the electro-chemical equivalent for silver. How long will it take to deposit 2 g of silver using a current of 0·5 A?

(Electro-chemical equivalent for silver is 0·001 118 g/C.)

13. A copper voltameter, an accumulator and an ammeter are connected in series. For 55 min the ammeter reading remains constant at 1·85 A, during which time 2·04 g of copper are deposited. Determine the error at this reading of the ammeter, stating whether it is high or low. By diagram, show the way in which the apparatus in question was connected. The following points must be shown clearly:

(a) The direction of conventional current flow
(b) The polarity of the accumulator
(c) The anode of the voltameter.
The e.c.e. of copper may be taken as 0·000 329 g/C.

14. Explain the meaning of the terms 'electro-chemical equivalent', 'coulomb', 'cathode' and 'electrolyte'. A steady current of 3 A is passed for 15 min through a silver nitrate voltameter. Determine the weight of silver deposited on the cathode in this time and also the quantity of electricity circulated, in coulombs.
(Electro-chemical equivalent for silver is 0·001 118 g/C.)

15. On what does the amount of metal deposited during electrolysis depend?
Calculate the current that flows through a copper sulphate voltameter if 0·475 g of copper are deposited in 20 min. The electro-chemical equivalent of copper is 0·000 33 g/C.

16. Define the term 'Electro-chemical equivalent of a substance'. The total surface area of a knife blade is 5000 mm². If it is electroplated with silver to a thickness of 0·05 mm in a process which takes 20 min, what is the value of the current used?
Electro-chemical equivalent of silver = 0·001 12 g/C.
Density of silver = 10 500 kg/m³.

17. A metal plate has a surface area of 15 000 mm², and is silver-plated, using a current of 0·8 A for a period of ½ h. What is the thickness of the silver plating? Take the electro-chemical equivalent of silver as 0·001 12 g/C and its density as 10 500 kg/m³.

19. Electromagnetism

19.1. Magnetic fields

The phenomenon called 'magnetism' has been known and investigated for a very long period of time. It is thought that at some time in the sixth century B.C. it was discovered that a lodestone would point itself in a particular direction if it were freely suspended, say on the end of a piece of thread. (Incidentally, this lodestone was found to exist in a place called Magnesia, in Asia Minor, and the name 'magnet' was derived from this.)

If a lodestone is put into a heap of iron filings, the filings will tend to move so that they are concentrated around two regions on the stone. These regions are called the 'poles' of the stone and when the stone is suspended, a line drawn through the poles is found to point roughly north and south. The pole pointing towards the north is called the 'north pole' of the stone (perhaps 'north-seeking pole' would be a better term), whilst that pointing to the south is called the 'south pole' of the stone.

Later on, this magnetic effect was found to be caused by the presence of iron in the stone, and more recent discoveries have shown that the property is shared by a group of materials known as FERRO-MAGNETIC materials. These include iron, cobalt and nickel, and certain alloys. Modern magnets made of these materials can exhibit the effect to a much greater degree than the original lodestone.

If a magnet is freely suspended it will, as has been said, swing so that a line drawn through its poles will point roughly north and south. (The so-called 'magnetic' north differs slightly from the 'geographical' or 'true' north, and moves slightly in relation to it. This variation must be allowed for in compasses used for long-distance navigation.) If a second magnet is then brought up close to the suspended magnet, the direction in which the suspended magnet points may be changed. A force is found to exist between the magnet poles, which causes 'like' poles (i.e. both north or both south) to repel one another, and 'unlike' poles (one north and one south) to attract one another. This effect is very similar to that already mentioned for electric charges (Section 16.1, page 436) and can be summarized as:

584

'Like magnetic poles repel each other; unlike magnetic poles attract each other.'

As in the case of the electric charges, this force between magnetic poles is a fundamental fact, and may be taken as the basis on which a theory of magnetism can be built. Indeed, the early development of magnetic theory was entirely based on this force between magnetic poles, and it was only later that discoveries indicated that magnetism might be caused by an underlying electrical principle. For the moment this treatment of magnetic theory will follow the lines taken by the earlier scientists, until a few of the basic ideas are established. These will then be viewed in the light of the more modern theory.

If a magnet is placed on a card and iron filings are sprinkled over the card, the filings will be seen to set themselves into a definite pattern when they are moved by a slight tap on the card. This pattern may be thought of as a map of the conditions surrounding the magnet, which are said to be due to the *field* of the magnet. A magnetic field thus has the property of exerting a force on iron filings which tends to set them into a particular pattern. It can also exert a force on another magnet, as explained more fully in the next section. It follows that the earth must possess its own magnetic field, since it exerts a force on a suspended magnet to turn it to a north-south direction.

19.2. Magnetic field of a bar magnet. Lines of force

The magnetic field surrounding a bar magnet may be investigated more accurately than with iron filings. If a small magnetic compass is placed near one end of a bar magnet, the force between the poles of the magnet and the poles of the compass-needle magnet will move the compass needle away from its usual north-south direction. As long as the compass magnet is small in comparison with the bar magnet, the compass will point in the direction of the force exerted by the bar magnet on the poles of the compass. Or, more strictly, the compass will point in *the direction of the magnetic field* surrounding the bar magnet. Since the north pole of the compass will be repelled by the north pole of the bar magnet, it follows that the compass will point away from the north pole of the bar magnet. Thus, THE DIRECTION OF A MAGNETIC FIELD AT ANY POINT IS THE DIRECTION OF THE FORCE EXERTED ON THE NORTH POLE OF A MAGNET PLACED AT THAT POINT. It is assumed that the presence of the 'exploring' magnet does not affect the magnetic field being investigated. Strictly, this cannot be true in practice, but provided the exploring magnet is small, its effect on the main field will also be small. The combination of two magnetic fields and the idea of the strength of a magnet will be considered later.

If the plotting compass is moved steadily in the direction in which it points at any instant, it will be found to follow a continuous path from the north pole to the south pole of the magnet. Any number of these paths can be traced out, depending on the starting point chosen for the plotting compass. The resulting pattern, which is a replica of the pattern taken up by the iron filings, represents a map of the magnetic field of the magnet. Since the lines on this map represent the direction of the force exerted on the north pole of the plotting compass, they are called LINES OF FORCE. Note that THE DIRECTION OF A MAGNETIC LINE OF FORCE IS THE DIRECTION OF THE FORCE EXERTED ON THE NORTH POLE OF A MAGNET.

At one point in the development of magnetic theory, the line of force was used as a unit of measurement. Although the term is still to be found in use for this purpose, it is obsolescent, if not obsolete, and in this book the term 'line of force' will be used in the sense defined above.

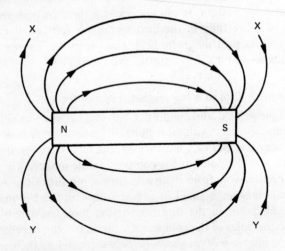

228. Approximate sketch of lines of force around a bar magnet, in the absence of any other magnetic field

Diagram 228 shows the kind of map that would be obtained from the experiment described (an experiment which the student should carry out for himself). Some important properties of the lines of force can be deduced from this map. The lines are seen to emerge from the north pole of the magnet and to re-enter it at the south pole. They are continuous in the sense that every line leaving the north pole will eventually arrive at the south pole. The points marked X in the diagram belong to the same line of force, as do the points Y. The space available for the map prevents the intervening parts from being shown. There is strong evidence to suggest that the lines of force continue within the magnet, with a south-to-north direction *inside* the magnet. For example, if a bar magnet is cut into two, the result is two shorter magnets each with its own north and south pole, and *not*, as might be supposed at first, a

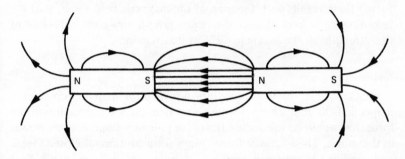

229. Approximate sketch of lines of force between two short magnets

separate north pole and a separate south pole. In fact, it is impossible to have a north pole, or a south pole, on its own; the two always go together. Therefore, if a gap is made in a bar magnet, the sort of field map obtained would be as indicated in diagram 229.

Although the map is complicated by the 'direct' north-south lines of force for each part of the magnet, the general direction of the lines of force in the gap agrees with the direction assumed for the lines of force inside the original single magnet. On this and other evidence, lines of force are said to form continuous closed loops.

Another interesting fact that can be observed from a map of a magnetic field is that, however many lines of force are drawn on the map for a given magnetic field, the lines are always closest together in regions where the magnetic effect is strongest. This point can be checked experimentally in the following way.

If a magnetic compass is placed close to one of the poles of a bar magnet it will very soon take up its new direction. It will generally vibrate very quickly for a few seconds, since the inertia of the needle will cause it to 'overshoot' the required direction. The force acting on it is strong enough, however, to make these vibrations very rapid, with the result that it soon settles into the required position. If the same compass is now placed, say, half-way between the poles and some little distance away from the magnet, it will take up its new position in a much more leisurely manner. Once again it will vibrate because of the inertia of the needle, but this time the vibrations will be slower and of greater amplitude, and will take longer to die away. This time the force tending to make the needle take up its new position is much less than that which was produced when the compass was placed near a pole. Comparing these results with the map of the magnetic field shows that the crowding of the lines of force in a region gives a very good indication of the 'strength' of the magnetic field in that region.

Summary

Magnetic lines of force are lines drawn on a map to represent a magnetic field, and whose direction at any point is the direction of the force that would be exerted on the north pole of a small magnet placed at that point. These lines of force always form continuous closed loops, and tend to be crowded together at points of high magnetic field strength.

The student should not get the impression that, if only he could get a powerful enough magnifying glass, he could see lines of force sprouting out of the ends of a bar magnet like hairs. They are merely lines drawn on a map to help give a visual image of a magnetic field, in much the same way that lines may be drawn on a map to give a visual image of the route taken by an aeroplane.

19.3.   Magnetic effect of an electric current. Magnetic field due to current in a straight wire

In another chapter (Section 16.8, page 444), brief mention was made of the magnetic effect of an electric current. This effect was discovered by Oersted in 1820 and is of fundamental importance in electrical theory. It can be demonstrated in the following way.

A straight piece of wire is held vertical by means of insulated clamps, and a flat piece of cardboard with a central hole is threaded on to it. If a fairly heavy current, say of the order of 10 A or so, is then passed along the wire, a magnetic compass needle placed on the cardboard near the wire will be deflected. If the direction of the current is reversed, the direction of the compass needle will also be reversed. If the current is switched off, the compass needle will return to its normal north-south direction. There is thus a magnetic field surrounding the wire as a result of the current flowing along the wire, and the direction of this magnetic field depends on the direction of the current flow.

If the compass needle is moved steadily in the direction in which it points at any instant, it will trace out a circular path round the current, with the current axis at the centre of the circle. Any number of such

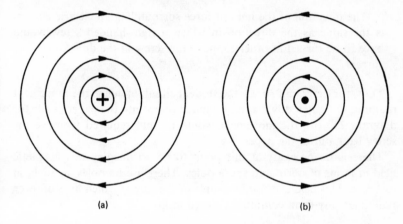

(a)   (b)

230. Maps of magnetic field surrounding electric current in a straight conductor

(a) for current direction into the paper
(b) for current direction out of the paper

circles can be traced out, depending upon the starting 'radius' of the plotting compass. Similar circles can be obtained for any position of the sheet of cardboard along the axis of the wire, provided that the wire, and hence the current, always remains perpendicular to the cardboard. It follows that the magnetic field surrounding the current along a straight wire is cylindrical in form, with the current along the axis of the cylinder. There is strictly no 'outside edge' to this cylinder, although the strength of the field decreases rapidly at points further away from the wire. If a section is taken through the wire perpendicular to its axis, a map of the magnetic field is represented by a number of concentric circles, with the current at their centre. The direction of the field is related to the direction of the current as shown in diagram 230, but this point should be checked by the student from his own observations. Notice the convention used in these diagrams to show the direction of the current flow. It is imagined that an arrow is placed in the conductor, pointing in the direction of the current flow. In diagram 230 (a), the arrow is pointing away from the reader, and the cross represents its tail-feathers. In diagram 230 (b), the arrow points towards the reader, and the dot represents the point of the arrow.

The relation between the direction of the current and the direction of the magnetic field is stated in the *corkscrew rule*:

'The direction of the lines of force surrounding an electric current is the same as the direction in which a right-handed screw would have to be turned in order to move the screw in the direction of the current.'

Thus, for diagram 230 (a), the student should imagine the movement required to tighten down a right-handed screw into the paper, while for diagram 230 (b), the movement would be that required to move the screw back out of the paper.

There is no necessity at this point to try to imagine this magnetic field in terms of north and south poles. There are no poles, as such, in this case. This field is a good example of the way in which lines of force fundamentally form continuous closed loops.

19.4. Magnetic field due to current in a single-turn loop

If the wire considered in the previous section is now bent to form a single-turn loop, the magnetic field due to current flowing along the wire will also be 'bent', rather as if it were a kind of cylindrical coating around the current axis. This is indicated approximately in diagram 231, where a few lines of force are sketched in as typical of those it would be possible to trace.

For any one little piece of the loop, the surrounding magnetic field is much the same as it is for the straight wire. This point can be checked experimentally. Arrange a flat piece of card across a diameter of a vertical loop, and use a plotting compass as before. The resulting map of this cross-section of the magnetic field will be similar to that shown in diagram 232.

Close to the wires, the lines of force are still approximately circles, but further away from the wires these circles become a little distorted, as

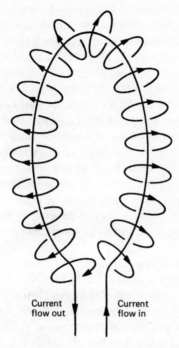

Current
flow out

Current
flow in

231. Approximate map of magnetic field surrounding an electric current in a single-turn loop. The break in the lines of force indicates where they pass behind the wire in this view

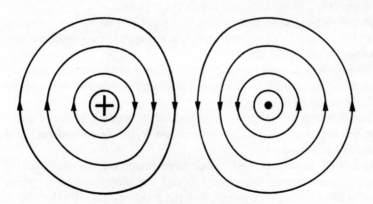

232. Approximate cross-sectional map of magnetic field surrounding current in a single-turn loop

shown. The resulting magnetic field gives the impression that the lines of force repel each other sideways. As stated earlier, magnetic lines of force have no real physical existence, and are merely used to enable the magnetic field to be visualized. However, it is convenient to consider that they have certain physical properties, of which this—that they have a natural repulsive force between them—is an example. This would 'explain' the way in which the circular paths of the lines round a single current become squashed or elongated into a more elliptical form when the two sets of lines of force are made to pass inside the loop. (As a practical point, if a fairly large-diameter loop is used for this experiment, it may be difficult to get an accurate picture of the magnetic field set up by the current in the loop. This is because of the effect of the earth's magnetic field, which, of course, is present as well. As large a current as possible should be used in the loop so that its magnetic field may be as strong as possible compared with the earth's magnetic field.)

From either of the diagrams 231 or 232, it will be seen that the lines of force representing the magnetic field of the current in the loop leave the loop on one side and enter it at the other. If the loop is viewed from one side, lines of force would be coming towards the observer (when the current direction was anti-clockwise round the loop), while if it is viewed from the other side (when the current direction would be clockwise round the loop), lines of force would be going away from the observer. This means that the current-loop behaves as a sort of magnet, and can be considered as having one face which acts as a 'north pole' and the other which acts as a south pole. In fact, if a loop of wire is suitably suspended so that it can swing freely, and current is passed round the loop, it will move in the earth's magnetic field until its axis is pointing north and south.

An easy way of remembering which current-direction round the loop makes the face of the loop a north pole, and which makes it a south pole, is shown in diagram 233.

The fact that the arrows on the ends of the printed letters N and S give the required direction of current is a fortunate coincidence. It is not a law of nature.

It is also interesting, and rather more important, to note that the relative directions of the current round the loop and the magnetic lines of force through the loop follow the corkscrew rule if it is stated in another form, which can be taken as a complementary form to that already given in the previous section. It is as follows:

'The direction of the current flow round a loop is the same as the direction in which a right-handed screw would have to be turned in order to move the screw in the direction of the lines of force through the loop.'

The similarity between the magnetic field of a current flowing round a loop and the magnetic field of a magnet is of fundamental importance in the modern theory of magnetism. It is now thought that all magnetic effects are the result of circulating electric currents. These circulating currents are on a subatomic scale in the case of a bar magnet, and are

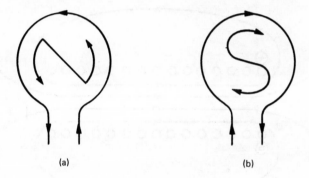

(a)   (b)

233. Relationship between current-direction and direction of
magnetic field for a current loop

In (a) the direction of the lines of force is out of the paper
towards the reader
In (b) the direction of the lines of force is into the paper away
from the reader

due to the way in which the electrons move in certain shells of the atoms of the ferromagnetic materials. In other words, the link between magnetism and electricity is fundamentally a very close one indeed, and neither an electric current nor a magnetic field can exist without the other. A full discussion of the modern theory of magnetism is outside the scope of this book, but it is important to realize just how close is the relationship between magnetic effects and electric currents.

19.5.   Magnetic field due to current in a solenoid

If a length of wire is closely wound in a single layer round a long straight former of circular cross-section—for example, a straight length of glass tube—the resulting coil is known as a SOLENOID. Strictly speaking, the true solenoid is so closely wound that there is no space between the turns at all, but if this were tried in practice there could be no insulation between adjacent turns, so that the current would not flow round, but would flow along, the solenoid so produced. There is very little difference in behaviour between the practical solenoid and the theoretically ideal solenoid, provided the turns are closely wound.

If an electric current is passed through a solenoid, the effect is the same as it would be for a closely-packed series of current loops. Since

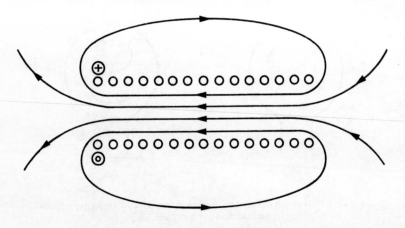

234. Map of magnetic field due to current in solenoid.

(Current flowing into the paper in the conductors shown along the top of the section, and returning round each turn to flow out of the paper in the conductors along the bottom of the section)

the direction of current flow round adjacent turns is the same, the magnetic axes of the turns all point in the same direction along the axis of the solenoid. If a section is taken along the axis of a solenoid, a map of the magnetic field would be similar to that shown in diagram 234.

Note that the direction of the current round the solenoid is related to the direction of the lines of force by the corkscrew rule, so that the rules given earlier for the north and south faces of a single-turn current loop (see diagram 233) apply equally well to the ends of a solenoid.

The similarity between the magnetic field of a solenoid and the magnetic field of a bar magnet is striking. Notice that the lines of force form closed continuous loops which pass through the solenoid in the same way as it was suggested that they might pass through a bar magnet. As would be expected from this, a current-carrying solenoid will behave in the same way as a bar magnet. It will attract pieces of iron; it will exert a force on other magnets or other current-carrying solenoids placed near it; and, if it were freely suspended, it would react with the earth's magnetic field so that its axis pointed north and south. Of course, if the current were to be switched off, it would do none of these things.

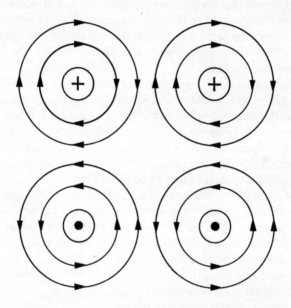

235. Simplified and enlarged diagram of the separate magnetic fields due to adjacent turns of a solenoid

The effects are entirely the result of the electric current flowing round its turns.

The reason for the shape of the magnetic field shown in diagram 234 may be seen a little more clearly from the enlarged view of part of the solenoid shown in diagram 235, when the distance between adjacent turns is exaggerated to simplify the diagram.

This diagram shows that the magnetic fields of adjacent conductors are in opposition in the space between the conductors. That is, the magnetic field due to one conductor would try to push the north pole of a magnet away from the centre of the solenoid, while the magnetic field due to the next conductor would try to push the same north pole towards the centre of the solenoid. Provided the conductors are very close together, the result is that these two fields cancel one another, so that there is no magnetic field between the conductors. Strictly, as long as some gap exists, some magnetic field will be present in the gap, and this is why the 'ideal' solenoid mentioned earlier is often used in theoretical studies. However, as was also mentioned, there is not much practical difference between a closely-wound coil and an ideal solenoid.

Diagram 235 also shows that the magnetic fields of adjacent conductors point in the same direction along the axis of the solenoid, so that their effects add together here. The overall result is the magnetic field pictured in diagram 234.

The solenoid is very important in the development of electromagnetic theory. One of the main reasons for this is that the magnetic field inside the solenoid is uniform. That is, the magnetic field has the same 'strength' at all points inside the solenoid (except very near the ends). At this stage, this can only be inferred from the fact that all the lines of force inside the solenoid are straight lines parallel to the axis. A formal proof is too complicated to be given here.

Most of these points can be (and should be) checked experimentally by the student. A suitable arrangement would be a helical coil wound through a series of holes made in two parallel lines in a sheet of cardboard. If an electric current is then passed along this coil, the resulting magnetic field can be investigated either by the use of iron filings sprinkled on the cardboard, or by the use of a plotting compass. Once again, the highest value of current possible should be used in order to give the greatest possible magnetic effects.

19.6. Magnetic field due to current in a toroid

If a piece of glass tube were to be heated and bent so that its ends could be joined, with the axis of the tube bent to form a circle, the resulting shape would be a circular ring. This shape is often referred to as an 'anchor ring'. If a length of wire is now closely wound round the ring, the coil so formed is known as a TOROID. It is rather as if a long straight solenoid had been bent until the two ends met. Once again, strictly speaking a toroid would have no space at all between adjacent turns of the coil, but there is little practical difference between the coil described and a theoretically ideal toroid. The winding of a toroidal coil can be a tedious business since for every turn of the coil the wire must be

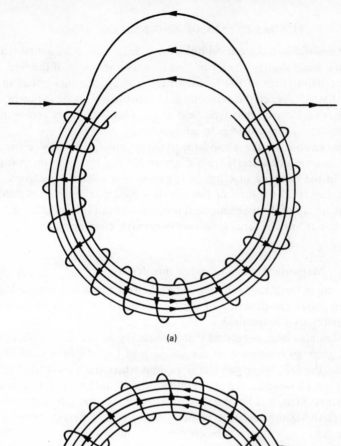

(a)

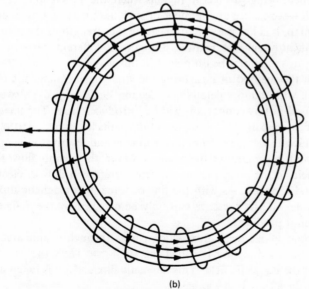

(b)

236. Magnetic field due to current in a toroid

(a) Intermediate step in formation of a toroid from a solenoid
(b) Total enclosure of magnetic field inside toroid
(In both cases, the turns of the coil must be much closer than
shown in the diagram)

threaded through the central hole. It is a help if the wire is first wound on to a small shuttle which can pass through the centre of the ring.

The importance of the toroid in electromagnetic theory lies in the fact that, ideally, *all* the magnetic field exists solely inside the turns, and there is no external magnetic field at all. This is the only arrangement where the magnetic field is so confined.

The reason for the enclosure of the magnetic field inside the coil may be seen more clearly from diagram 236 (a), where an intermediate step in the bringing together of the ends of a solenoid is shown. The enclosing of all the lines of force is then indicated in diagram 236 (b), where a map of the magnetic field inside the toroid is seen to consist of a number of lines of force following concentric circular paths.

19.7. Magnetic flux and magnetic flux density

A line of force has been seen to be a line on a map of a magnetic field which shows the direction of the force exerted on the north pole of a magnet placed in the field.

It has also been suggested that the spacing of the lines of force in a field gives an indication of the strength of the magnetic field in any region, the field being stronger in regions where the lines tend to crowd together. However, since any number of such lines may be drawn on a particular map, it is not possible to measure the strength of the field by this method, although the relative strengths in different parts of the same field can sometimes be estimated in this way.

Although the method of measuring the strength of a magnetic field will be dealt with in more detail later (Section 19.13, page 611), two of the terms used in this connection will be introduced here. The lines of force on a field map are said to represent the paths taken by a MAGNETIC FLUX which leaves a magnet from its north pole and returns to the magnet at its south pole. Despite the name, however, there is no 'flow' in a magnetic field in the sense that an electric current is a flow of electric charge round a circuit. As with the line of force, this magnetic flux is quite invisible, and its presence can only be detected by the magnetic effects which it produces.

The amount of magnetic flux which passes through a unit area at right angles to its direction is called the MAGNETIC FLUX DENSITY for that part of the magnetic field. This magnetic flux density is taken as a measure of the strength of the field.

The unit of magnetic flux is called the WEBER (Wb), and the unit of

magnetic flux density is the TESLA (T) where 1 Tesla = 1 WEBER PER
SQUARE METRE (Wb/m²). The size and precise meanings given to these
units will be discussed in Section 19.13, page 611.

19.8.   Effect of iron in a magnetic field

It is well known that if a piece of iron or other ferromagnetic material
is placed near the pole of a bar magnet, the iron will be attracted to the
magnet. This effect may be investigated by means of the following
experiment.

First plot the magnetic field surrounding a bar magnet, using a plotting compass as already described (Section 19.2, page 586). Then place

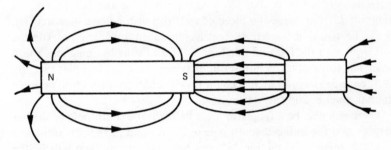

237. Distortion of magnetic field of bar magnet due to presence of iron close
to the magnet

a piece of unmagnetized soft iron near one of the poles of the magnet,
and again plot the magnetic field. (If nothing else is available, a bundle
of nails could be used in place of the piece of soft iron. In either case, it
may be necessary to fix the magnet and the iron to prevent them from
moving together.) It will be found from this second field-plot that the
original magnetic field of the bar magnet has become distorted by the
presence of the iron. Diagram 237 represents the sort of result to be
expected.

Compare the map of the magnetic field of the bar magnet alone with
that of the magnetic field when the piece of iron is near the magnet.
It appears that the lines of force (and hence the magnetic flux) are
pulled towards the piece of iron. A line of force 'returning' to the south
pole of the bar magnet seems to prefer to travel through the piece of iron
rather than through the air, almost as if the iron sucked in the magnetic
flux towards itself. This preference of magnetic flux for iron rather than

for air—or, more generally, for a ferromagnetic material rather than for a non-ferromagnetic material—is important. The iron is said to be more PERMEABLE to the magnetic flux, and the term RELATIVE PERMEABILITY is used to describe and measure this effect for different materials. A more precise definition of these terms will be given later (page 724).

In the meantime, the term as used here can be compared with the same word as used in other connections; for example when a gas is said to 'permeate', or pass through, some form of barrier.

If the map in diagram 237 is now compared with the map given in diagram 229, page 587, for the magnetic field between two magnets placed end-on, they will be found to be very similar indeed. In each case the magnetic flux passes through the metal in the same way. The obvious conclusion is that the magnetic field of the bar magnet in diagram 237 has made the piece of soft iron also behave as a magnet. It can be said that the bar magnet has 'induced' magnetic poles in the soft iron, with the induced north pole closest to the bar magnet's south pole. The force of attraction set up between these unlike poles (Section 19.1, page 584) would then account for the observed attraction between the bar magnet and the soft iron.

There will also be a repulsive force between the south pole of the bar magnet and the induced south pole at the far end of the soft iron. The resulting force of attraction between bar magnet and iron will be the difference between the attractive force existing between the unlike poles and the repulsive force existing between the like poles. It is only because the unlike poles are nearer together that the force of attraction between them is the greater of the two forces. This result can also be expressed in another way. The strength of the magnetic field of a bar magnet has been seen to vary from point to point (Section 19.2, page 585), being strongest near to the poles. The nearer of the poles induced in the soft iron lies in a stronger magnetic field than does the more remote induced pole, and the force on it is consequently greater. If the magnetic field were completely uniform, so that all the lines of force were parallel, the force on the two poles would be equal and the soft iron would not tend to move bodily. If it were inclined to the direction of the lines of force, a turning moment or torque would be set up, which would tend to align it with the direction of the magnetic field. This result may be expressed in yet another way: an unmagnetized piece of ferromagnetic material will tend to move towards the region of the strongest magnetic field, so that the maximum amount of magnetic flux can pass through it. It will be seen later that the presence of iron in a magnetic field has another profound effect, since it also increases the strength of the field.

The magnetizing effect of the magnetic field of a bar magnet can be verified in another way. If a piece of soft iron is placed close to one end of a powerful magnet and is then taken away again, it will be found that some of the induced magnetic effect will remain, and that the soft iron has itself become a magnet. This will be even more pronounced if the soft iron is stroked from end to end with one end of a bar magnet. It is as if the soft iron contained inside it a large number of tiny magnets which tended to align themselves with the magnetic field of the bar magnet in the same way as the magnet of a compass aligns itself with the earth's magnetic field. In the unmagnetized state, these tiny internal magnets in the soft iron would form themselves into closed rings so that no external magnetic field could be detected. An idea of these conditions can be obtained from a simple experiment. If a number of plotting compasses are placed close together, their needles will tend to line up, head to tail, in a closed ring. If a powerful magnet is then placed near to the group, its field will cause all the needles to swing to more-or-less parallel positions. Diagram 238 indicates the results that might be expected.

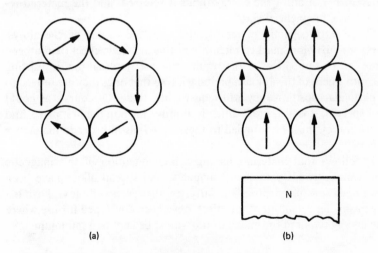

(a)   (b)

238. Behaviour of a number of magnetic compasses placed close together

(a) No external magnetic field (other than earth's field, which is not strong enough to greatly influence this result)
(b) Strong external magnetic field due to bar magnet placed near the compasses

In the case of the plotting compasses used in this experiment, removal of the strong external magnetic field will result in the re-formation of the closed loops. In the case of the soft iron, a sort of 'friction' can be thought of as preventing the tiny internal magnets from returning completely to their original closed loops. Some magnetic effect therefore remains even after the external magnetizing field has been removed. This idea led to the formation of the so-called molecular theory of magnetism, in which molecules, or groups of atoms, were thought to be arranged to form the internal magnets mentioned. A more modern theory has since been evolved. The atoms of the ferromagnetic materials are magnetized because of the way in which the electrons move in these atoms. Groups known as 'domains' are formed of atoms having similar directions of magnetization, and in the unmagnetized state of the material the domains form themselves into closed rings. When a magnetizing force is applied, the boundaries between adjacent domains move so as to enlarge those domains whose direction of magnetization more nearly coincides with the direction of the magnetizing force, and to diminish the others. This movement of the domain boundaries requires an energy input. When the magnetizing force is removed, the domain boundaries do not return completely to their original positions. Therefore, not all of the energy input is released, and the material remains in a magnetized state.

Some ferromagnetic materials, and especially some of the alloys, show a much more marked retention of this magnetic effect than others. This can be thought of as the result of greater internal forces resisting the movement of the domain boundaries, so that once they are moved to a particular position they will tend to stay there. Of course, as could be expected, it is also more difficult to move them in the first place, and more energy must be supplied to these materials in order to magnetize them.

It follows that materials having a high retention of this magnetic effect make good 'permanent' magnets, and special alloys have been developed for this purpose. Similarly, another group of alloys, having a much smaller retention of the effect, have been developed for use where the energy required for magnetization must be kept to a minimum.

19.9. Effect of an iron core inside a solenoid

In the previous section, it was shown that magnetic flux seems to prefer to travel through a ferromagnetic material rather than through a non-ferromagnetic material. This effect is very pronounced. If an iron core is placed inside a solenoid, the core becomes magnetized because of the current in the solenoid, and nearly all the magnetic flux is found to emerge from the end of the iron core. What is even more important, however, is that with the same current in the solenoid, the resulting magnetic field is found to be many times stronger when the iron core is present than when it is not. This effect can be judged from the behaviour of a small magnetic compass placed near the end of a solenoid. The compass will be found to vibrate very rapidly indeed, and to settle very quickly to its final position along the direction of the magnetic field when the solenoid has an iron core. If the solenoid has no ferromagnetic material in its core, the movement of the compass needle will be slower.

The increase in the strength of the magnetic field, which is entirely because of the presence of the iron core, may be by a factor of several hundred times, and it is extremely important in electromagnetic applications. For example, the same current in the same coil can have a very much greater magnetic effect if an iron core is present in the coil. This increase can be thought of as being the result of the growth of the domains whose direction is more nearly aligned with the magnetic field set up by the current in the coil. The strength of all these domains is then added to the strength of the coil's magnetic field.

19.10. Electromagnets

The increased magnetic field obtained when an iron core is used in a coil is applied, for example, in the electromagnet. This can take many forms, and one of them is shown in diagram 239—a simplified arrangement of the electromagnet used in a relay.

When an electric current is passed through the 'energizing' coil, the resulting magnetic field, increased because of the presence of the iron core, causes the movable relay 'armature' to be attracted towards the core against the action of a return spring (not shown in the diagram). As the armature moves towards the core, a flexible conducting bar is pushed against two fixed contacts so that they are connected together, and thus close some other electrical circuit. If the current in the energizing coil is switched off, the magnetic field 'collapses', apart from a small retention in the core, so that the attraction force is reduced to nearly zero. The armature will then be moved back again by the control spring, and the connection between the fixed contacts will be

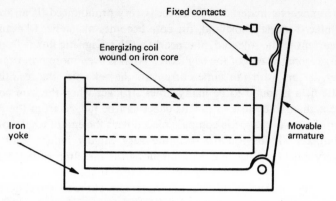

239. Simplified diagram of an electromagnetic relay

removed. Such a device enables one or more electrical circuits to be controlled by the current in the energizing coil of the relay, which may be positioned some distance away from the circuits being controlled.

The iron 'yoke' of the relay is provided as any easy path for the

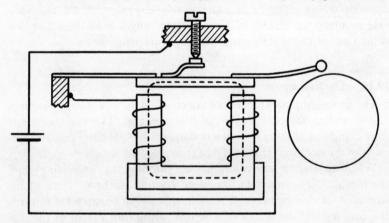

240. Simplified diagram of electric bell

magnetic field. The magnetic flux will be concentrated almost entirely along the yoke before crossing the small air gap back to the iron core.

Another application of the same principle is found in the electric bell, a simplified diagram of which is given in diagram 240.

Electric current in a coil or coils wound on an iron core sets up a magnetic field around the core, across the air gap and in the armature (the average path of the magnetic flux is shown by a dotted line of force in the diagram). The armature is supported on a length of spring-steel strip, and carries a contact which presses against an adjusting screw as indicated. It is arranged that the current in the coil has to flow through this contact and the adjusting screw. When the armature is attracted towards the magnetized core, the contact moves away from the screw and so breaks the coil circuit. The magnetic field will collapse as the current in the coil falls, the force of attraction between core and armature will decrease and the armature will return towards its original position under the action of the spring support. As the armature returns, the contact will be closed again, the magnetic field will start to build up, and the cycle will be repeated. A striker attached to the armature will thus be moved up and down against the gong of the bell. The operation depends rather critically on the position of the adjusting screw, which adjusts the point at which the coil circuit is broken. Perhaps it should be mentioned that a full explanation of the operation of the bell is rather complicated, and that this is only a simplified explanation, which, however, is quite adequate for the present.

One other example of the application of the electromagnetic effect will be given here. Large electromagnets are used in iron and steel works for lifting steel plates, scrap iron, etc. These have to be robust, and capable of exerting a large attractive force in order to lift the very heavy weights involved. They are usually made in a circular form as shown in diagram 241, and the two pole faces of the magnet are formed by the central core and the outer circular ring.

For the current direction shown in the diagram, the magnetic flux leaves the central pole face, crosses whatever air-gap may be present, passes through the steel plate or other ferromagnetic material being lifted, and returns across the air-gap to re-enter the outer pole-face ring. Typical flux paths are shown dotted in the cross-sectional view, but it should be remembered that similar paths will be followed in any other vertical cross-section.

19.11. Force on a current at right angles to a magnetic field

If a flexible wire is suspended in a magnetic field—say between the poles of a suitable electromagnet—and an electric current is passed along the wire, a force will be set up which will act on the wire and tend

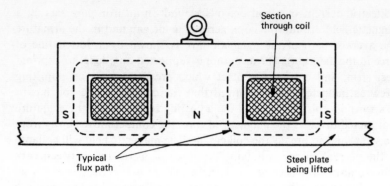

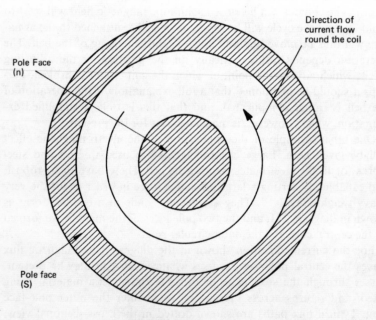

241. Simplified diagram of lifting magnet

(a) Sectional view through a diameter

(b) View looking at under-side, showing pole faces

to push it out of the magnetic field. The direction of this force depends on the direction of the current and on the direction of the magnetic field. The arrangement is indicated in diagram 242, where details of the connections to the flexible wire and of the electrical supply to the electromagnet have been omitted to simplify the diagram. (It is hoped that the student will at least be able to see this effect demonstrated.)

For the arrangement sketched in diagram 242, the force on the conductor will be either vertically upwards or vertically downwards, depending on the relative directions of current in the wire and magnetic field between the poles.

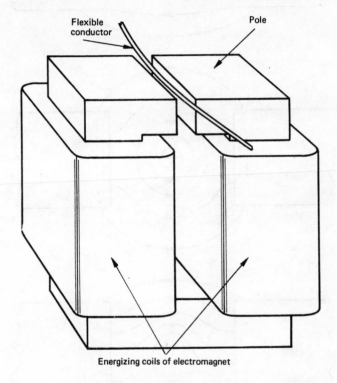

242. Conductor suspended between the poles of an electromagnet

The existence of this force is an experimental fact, and it can be taken as the starting point in the development of a system of measurement of electromagnetic quantities. Incidentally, the force is really exerted on the *current*, and the wire experiences the force only because it happens to be carrying the current. Although in very many practical applications a wire is needed to carry the current and so to transmit the force, it is not fundamentally necessary for there to be a wire before there can be a force. In some circumstances it is possible to obtain a current (which it

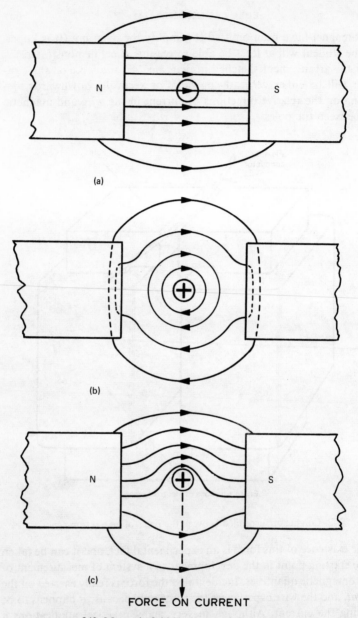

FORCE ON CURRENT

243. Magnetic field in air-gap of electromagnet

(a) No current in wire
(b) Current in wire, assumed direction being into the paper, but
    electromagnet switched off. (Dotted lines indicate continuation
    of magnetic flux in pole face)
(c) Effect of combining magnetic fields shown in (a) and (b)

will be remembered is a flow of electric charge) without there being a wire to carry it. For example, current can flow as an arc in the air between the contacts of a switch. If an arc is so formed that it is at right angles to the direction of a magnetic field, the current in the arc experiences a force in the way already described for the current in the wire. This effect is used in practice to help extinguish the arc drawn out between the contacts of large circuit-breakers when they separate.

It is interesting to compare the maps of the magnetic fields due to the electromagnet alone, the current in the wire alone and the combined magnetic field due to both. These three maps are shown in diagram 243.

From diagram 243 (c), which shows the combined magnetic fields, it is seen that the magnetic field of the electromagnet is distorted by the presence of the magnetic field surrounding the current. The lines of force are bent round the current because on one side of the current the two magnetic fields are in the same direction, while on the other side they are in opposition. The result is that the field is strengthened on one side of the current and weakened on the other.

From the observed direction of the force, it follows that the current tends to move away from a region of a strong magnetic field to a region of a weaker magnetic field. The pattern taken by the lines of force surrounding the conductor gives the impression of a catapult pulled back ready to 'shoot' the current-carrying conductor sideways out of the magnetic field, rather as if the lines of force were made of stretched rubber bands. Whilst this can hardly be put forward as an explanation of why the force is produced, it is useful to note that on the grounds of this experimental evidence, lines of force can be said to act as if they were in a state of tension, so that they will try to straighten out wherever possible. This 'physical' property of lines of force can be remembered and used in future cases to try to forecast the likely behaviour of a magnetic field. In Section 19.4, page 590, it was noted that lines of force behaved as if they repelled one another sideways. These two apparent properties of lines of force—tension along their length and mutual sideways repulsion—are very helpful when a magnetic field is to be visualized. It is also worth noting that this property of tension along a line of force agrees with the known force of attraction between a magnet pole and a piece of ferromagnetic material.

19.12. Fleming's left-hand rule

The direction of the force on a current flowing at right angles to the direction of a magnetic field is perhaps best worked out from the

U

principle stated earlier: that the current will tend to move away from a strong magnetic field towards a weaker magnetic field. However, a rule giving the direction of this force has been stated by Fleming, and may be found helpful. Fleming's 'left-hand' rule states that:

> 'If the thumb and first two fingers of the left hand are held at right angles to each other, and the first finger is pointed in the direction of the magnetic field, with the second finger pointing in the direction of the current, then the thumb will point in the direction of the force on the current.'

This arrangement of the directions is also shown in diagram 244. It should be remembered that Fleming's left-hand rule is only a rule made up to fit the observed facts, and is not a law of nature. Care should be exercised in its use—students sometimes get mixed up between their left and right hands, especially since a little later on a similar rule using the right hand will be stated in another connection. It may be helpful to

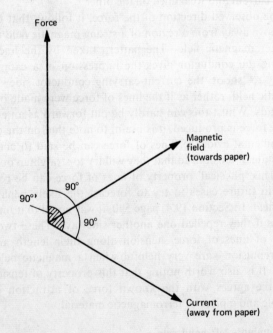

244. Relative directions of magnetic field, current and force on current. (Note: this diagram is intended to represent directions in three dimensions)

remember that it is the leFt-hand rule which gives the direction of the Force on a current at right angles to a magnetic field.

19.13. Units of measurement of strength of magnetic field

The magnitude of the force on a current flowing at right angles to a magnetic field is found to be proportional to three things:

(a) the value of the current, represented by I
(b) the 'active' length of the current flow; for example, the length of the wire carrying the current that actually lies in the magnetic field (usually the electrical circuit will be completed outside the range of the magnetic field). This active length is represented by l
(c) the 'strength' of the magnetic field, represented by B.

With these symbols, the above statements can be summarized as

$$\text{Force } F \propto B.l.I \qquad . \qquad . \qquad . \qquad \text{(i)}$$

where
F is measured in NEWTONS
l is measured in METRES
I is measured in AMPERES

The units of magnetic field strength, B, are such that a current of 1 A flowing for an active length of 1 m at right angles to a magnetic field having a strength of 1 unit will experience a force of 1 N.

The name given to the unit of magnetic field strength is the TESLA, as already stated in Section 19.7, page 599. It is expressed in this form in order to agree with the fact, already noted on several earlier occasions, that a magnetic field is strongest where the lines of force representing the field on a map tend to crowd together most. The result of multiplying a value of magnetic field strength by an area which is at right angles to the direction of the field, and over which the magnetic field strength is constant, is known as the total MAGNETIC FLUX through the area. Therefore the strength of a magnetic field is equal to the flux 'density' in the field at the point considered. The term FLUX DENSITY is often used to mean the strength of a magnetic field.

The symbol usually used for magnetic flux is the Greek letter φ (pronounced 'fie', although written as 'phi'.) With this symbol used for magnetic flux, the symbol B used for magnetic field strength, or flux density, and the symbol A used for area at right angles to the direction of the flux,

$$\text{flux density} = \frac{\text{flux}}{\text{area perpendicular to flux}}$$

$$B = \frac{\varphi}{A}$$

or $\varphi = B . A$.   .   .   .   (ii)

where B is constant over the area A.

It should be noted that the tesla (T) is rather a large unit. Values of flux density usually encountered very rarely exceed 2 T. Similarly, the weber is a very large magnetic flux, and values of flux usually encountered are more conveniently measured in milliwebers (1 mWb = $\frac{1}{1000}$ Wb, or 10^{-3} Wb) or even in microwebers (1 μWb = $\frac{1}{1\,000\,000}$ Wb, or 10^{-6} Wb).

19.14. Examples

(i) A conductor having an active length of 100 mm lies at right angles to a magnetic field having a uniform flux density of 0·1 T. Find the force exerted on the conductor when it carries a current of 2 A.

$$F = B . l . I \text{ newtons}$$

$$= 0 \cdot 1 \times \frac{100}{1000} \times 2 \text{ N}$$

$$= \underline{0 \cdot 02 \text{ N}}$$

(ii) A straight conductor carries a current of 2000 A at right angles to a uniform magnetic field having a flux density of 80 mT. Calculate the force exerted on the conductor in newtons/metre.

$$F = B . l . I \text{ newtons}$$

$$\frac{F}{l} = \frac{80}{1000} \times 2000 \text{ N/m}$$

$$= \underline{160 \text{ N/m}}$$

(iii) The active length of a conductor carrying a current of 50 A at right angles to a magnetic field is 600 mm. If the force on the conductor is 20 N, find the strength of the magnetic field.

$$F = B.l.I \text{ newtons}$$

$$20 = B \times 50 \times \frac{600}{1000} \text{ N}$$

$$B = \frac{20}{50 \times 0.6} \text{ T}$$

$$= \underline{\underline{0.67 \text{ T}}}$$

(iv) A uniform iron bar has a rectangular cross-section measuring 50 mm × 25 mm. If the bar carries a magnetic flux of 1·0 mWb, calculate the value of the flux density in the iron.

$$\text{Magnetic flux density } B = \frac{\varphi \text{ (Wb)}}{A \text{ (m}^2)}$$

$$= \frac{1 \times 10^{-3}}{50 \times 25 \times 10^{-6}} \text{ Wb/m}^2$$

$$= \underline{\underline{0.8 \text{ T}}}$$

19.15. Force on a current at other than a right angle to a magnetic field

The results in the previous sections have depended upon the current direction being at right angles to the direction of the magnetic field. The force exerted on the current will be less than that given by the formula of Section 19.13 if the current direction is not perpendicular to the direction of the magnetic field.

First consider the special case where the current direction is *parallel* to the direction of the magnetic field. Diagrams 245 (a) and (b) show an end view and a side view of the two magnetic field-maps in this case (the combined 'resultant' magnetic field is not shown on these diagrams, to avoid over-complication of the picture). It is seen from these diagrams that the lines of force representing the magnetic field of the current are at right angles to the lines of force representing the 'external' magnetic field in which the conductor is placed. In this case, then, there is no direct addition or subtraction of the strengths of the two magnetic fields, as there was in the first case considered, in Section 19.11.

Imagine that a compass needle is placed near the current. The north pole of the compass needle will have two forces exerted on it. One force will be exerted by the external field, and will tend to make it point in a direction parallel with this field, and hence with the current. The second force will be exerted by the field due to the current, and will tend to make the compass needle point in a direction parallel with that field; i.e. at right angles to the current. The result will be that the compass needle will point along a spiral path round the current. Whilst the 'pitch' of this spiral path around the current will depend on the relative strengths of the two magnetic fields, the resulting combined field will have the same strength at corresponding points all round the current. In this case,

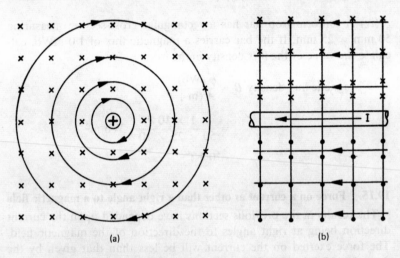

(a)   (b)

245. Current direction parallel to that of external magnetic field

(a) End view—the small crosses represent the 'cross-section' of the lines of force of the external magnetic field

(b) Side view—the vertical lines represent the side view of the circular lines of force around the current, the small crosses and dots representing the 'cross-section' of these lines of force

then, there is no strong field on one side of the current and weak field on the other side, and so there will be no force acting on the current trying to move it sideways in any particular direction.

Thus:

'There is no force acting on a current flowing parallel to the direction of a magnetic field.'

If a current is now considered as flowing in a direction at some angle between 0° and 90° to the direction of a magnetic field, the results for the two special cases of 0° and 90° may be combined. In the same way as any force may be resolved into two components at right angles to each other (Section 3.9, page 62), a magnetic field, which exerts a force on the poles of a magnet, may also be resolved into two component magnetic fields at right angles. Thus, for the case shown in diagram 246, where a current I flows in a direction inclined at an angle θ to the direction of the magnetic field of uniform strength B, the magnetic field can be considered as being the resultant of the two components shown. One component, equal to $B \sin \theta$, acts in a direction at right angles to the current direction, while the other component, equal to $B \cos \theta$, acts parallel with the current direction.

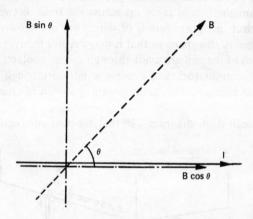

246. Current direction inclined to direction of magnetic field

The two components of flux density shown may be considered equivalent to—i.e. to replace—the original flux density B

The component $B \cos \theta$ parallel to the direction of the current will not react with the magnetic field of the current to produce any force on the current. The component $B \sin \theta$ perpendicular to the current direction will, however, react with the magnetic field of the current to produce a force

$$F = B \sin \theta . l . I \text{ newtons} \qquad . \qquad . \qquad \text{(iii)}$$

The direction of this force will be given by the rules already mentioned, with the component $B \sin \theta$ considered instead of the total field strength. It might prove convenient to remember that the direction of the force will always be perpendicular to the plane containing the vectors representing current and magnetic flux.

19.16.   Practical applications of force exerted on a current in a magnetic field

The fact that a current flowing across a magnetic field experiences a force has very many practical applications. Two of these are mentioned below, while others are discussed in Chapter 21, page 687, on electrical measuring instruments.

(a) Electric motors

Perhaps one of the most important applications of this principle is in the action of the electric motor. Diagram 247 indicates this basic principle. A magnetic field is set up across the space between the two poles of an electromagnet (details of which are not shown). A coil of wire is arranged in this space so that it may revolve freely. Connections to the two ends of the coil are made through sliding contacts by a device known as a 'commutator', and current is passed through the coil by means of these contacts. This arrangement is shown in cross-section in diagram 248.

It will be seen from diagram 248 that the two conductors forming

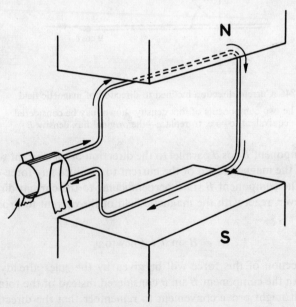

247. Diagrammatic sketch of coil between poles of electro-magnet, showing current direction round coil

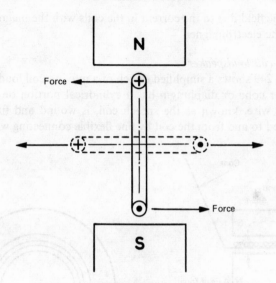

248. Simplified diagram of cross-section through
coil between poles of electromagnet

the sides of the single-turn coil will carry current in opposite directions in the gap between the poles of the electromagnet, so that the force developed on each side of the coil will be in opposite directions, as shown. Since the coil is pivoted about its axis, the two forces produce torques acting in the same direction, and the coil will rotate. If the coil were in the position shown dotted in diagram 248, the forces on the coil sides would only try to expand the coil, and no torque would be developed (since the two forces act in opposite directions along the same line of action through the axis of rotation). A practical motor has several coils spaced at different angles round the axis and so overcomes this disadvantage. In order to prevent the torque from reversing as the coil rotates through 180°, it is necessary to reverse the direction of the current through the coil every half-revolution. This current reversal is achieved by the sliding contacts on the commutator, which are arranged to always pass current in the same direction in the conductor 'passing under' a particular pole.

Perhaps it should be mentioned here that the theory of torque production in a practical motor is rather more complicated, since iron is used to provide more convenient and easier flux paths between the poles. However, the torque is fundamentally produced by the interaction of the magnetic field due to the current in the coils with the magnetic field set up by the electromagnet.

(b) Moving-coil loudspeaker

Diagram 249 shows a simplified sketch of a moving-coil loudspeaker. The speaker cone or diaphragm has a cylindrical portion on which a coil of fine wire, known as the speech coil, is wound and fixed. The current is led to and from the coil by fine flexible connecting wires. The

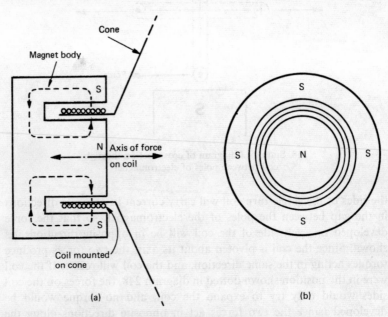

249. Simplified diagrams of moving-coil loudspeaker:

(a) Section through a diameter (b) End view

speech coil is then arranged in the radial air-gap of a cylindrical magnet body, shaped as shown in the diagram and magnetized so that the central core forms one pole and the outer ring forms the other. The arrangement is very similar to the magnetic circuit already described for a lifting magnet (page 605), although it is much smaller. The moving-coil loudspeaker magnet will usually contain a permanent magnet, but may be energized by a current in a suitably-wound coil. The paths taken by the magnetic flux are indicated by the dotted lines in diagram 249, and it will be seen that the speech coil lies in a radial magnetic flux. The direction of the force exerted on the speech coil will depend on the current direction round the coil, but will always be directed along its axis.

The current fed to the speech coil is 'alternating'—i.e. its direction is changing regularly—so that the direction of the force on the speech coil changes, and it vibrates backwards and forwards in the magnet air-gap. These vibrations are passed on to the cone or diaphragm, which then causes sound waves to be generated.

19.17. Force between parallel currents

Since it is known that an electric current is surrounded by a magnetic field, it seems likely that any other electric current close to it will experience a force, since this second current would be in the magnetic field of the first current. The second current will also exert an equal and opposite force on the first current. The direction of the force between two currents will depend on their relative directions. Diagram 250 (a) shows a map of the magnetic fields for two currents in the same direction while diagram 250 (b) shows a map for currents in opposite directions.

These diagrams illustrate the fact that the field between two currents flowing in the same direction is weakened, so that the currents will tend to move together, while the field between two currents flowing in opposite directions is strengthened and the currents will tend to move apart. The same result is given by the application of Fleming's left-hand rule to either of the currents lying in the magnetic field of the other.

The result may be remembered by the idea that parallel currents in the same direction will experience a force which will try to 'amalgamate' them into one larger current. Indeed, the magnetic field at some distance from two closely-spaced parallel currents flowing in the same direction cannot be distinguished from the magnetic field that would be obtained if both currents were flowing along the same wire.

This effect can be demonstrated by passing a large current (say about 20 A or so) along two straight, parallel wires suspended about 10 mm or so away from each other. The wires will be seen to move together when the currents are in the same direction along the wires, and to move apart when the currents are in opposite directions. The force involved is fairly small for values of current readily obtainable in a laboratory, but it can be large enough to cause damage to heavy-current bus-bars at a power station in the event of short-circuit faults.

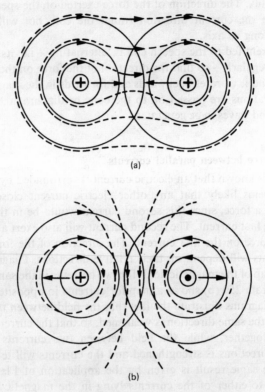

(a)

(b)

250. Magnetic field maps for parallel currents

(a) Currents in same direction (b) Currents in opposite direction

Another way of demonstrating the force between parallel currents is to suspend two similar coils of wire a little apart from each other. If current is passed in the same direction round each coil, they will swing towards each other. If the currents are in opposite directions round the coils, they will swing away from each other. This demonstration can be made more striking than the demonstration using parallel lengths of straight wire, since a large number of turns on the coils will give the effect of much longer conductors than could otherwise be obtained.

This attraction or repulsion between two parallel current-carrying coils provides the principle of action of the 'current balance' which will be mentioned at the end of the next section.

An interesting result of the force between currents is that a coil of wire carrying a current will experience forces tending to burst the coil sideways—for example, current in a square coil will set up forces tending to make the coil circular. Once again, the forces are fairly small under normal conditions, but coils used in power stations may be physically damaged in the event of heavy short-circuit currents flowing through them.

19.18. The ampere

The definition given for the unit of electric current in Section 16.7, page 443, showed that a current of 1 A is equal to a rate of flow of electric charge round a circuit of 1 C/s. The force between parallel currents described in the previous section gives an alternative method of measuring an electric current, in terms of the force exerted between equal parallel currents. The International Definition of the ampere accepts this property of an electric current as its basis, and defines the ampere as follows:

'The ampere is that value of electric current which, when flowing in each of two infinitely long parallel conductors separated in a vacuum by 1 metre between centres, causes each conductor to experience a force of 2×10^{-7} newton per metre length of conductor.'*

In practice, the substitution of air for the vacuum mentioned in the definition makes very little difference to the force between the conductors. Of course, the 'infinitely long' part of the definition cannot be achieved in practice. What happens is that the definition is used to calculate what the force should be between two currents flowing in other parallel paths which can be obtained for practical experiment, such as that between two parallel circular coils. These calculations are too complicated for details to be given at this stage, but it may be mentioned that an apparatus known as a 'current balance' can be used to measure the force between two parallel coils, and so to obtain a precise measurement of an electric current for use as a standard. Another fact worth mentioning here, although no proof will be given, is that the force between parallel currents varies inversely as the square of the

* The number 2×10^{-7} may seem an unusual number to appear in a definition, since definitions of units are usually carefully arranged so that all quantities are numerically equal to unity. This is one of the very few exceptions, and arises from the value of what is known as the 'magnetic space constant' or the 'absolute permeability of free space'. This quantity, which is usually written as μ_0, has the value $4\pi \times 10^{-7}$. The student specializing in electrical engineering will learn more about this quantity later.

distance between them. For example, it would need only 0·25 A in parallel wires 0·5 m apart to give a force on each of 2×10^{-7} N/m.

19.19.   Electromagnetic induction

If a conductor is moved across a magnetic field, an electromotive force will be produced along the conductor. If the conductor forms part of a closed electrical circuit, then the e.m.f. produced will set up an electric current round the circuit. This effect is known as 'electromagnetic induction', and the e.m.f. is said to be 'induced' in the conductor as a result of its motion across the magnetic field. The effect was investigated by Michael Faraday, whose name appears so frequently in the history of electrical science that many people consider him to be the father of electrical engineering.

A simple experiment will show the presence of this induced e.m.f. If the two ends of a coil of wire are connected to the terminals of a galvanometer, a deflection will be observed on the galvanometer when a bar magnet is brought up to the coil. A galvanometer deflection in the opposite direction will be observed as the magnet is taken away again, but no deflection is obtained as long as the magnet is held stationary, whether it be near to or far away from the coil. Deflections in the opposite directions to each of those noticed in the first case will be seen if the opposite pole of the bar magnet is brought up nearer to the coil. Large deflections of the galvanometer will be seen if the magnet is brought up to, or taken away from, the coil quickly, while smaller deflections result from the slower movement of the magnet. These results are so important, and the apparatus required to obtain them should be so easily available, that every student ought to carry out this experiment for himself. If possible, the student should also investigate the effects of using a coil having a larger number of turns, and of using magnets of different strengths.

Since an electric current flowing in the coil of an electromagnet also provides a convenient method of obtaining a magnetic field, the effects of electromagnetic induction could also be investigated in the following ways. A wire connected across a galvanometer may be moved rapidly between the poles of an electromagnet. Again, a deflection on the galvanometer will be observed as the wire moves across the gap between the poles, and if the direction of the wire's movement is reversed the deflection on the galvanometer will also be reversed. Rapid movement of the wire will give larger galvanometer deflections than will slower movement of the wire, and no deflection at all will be obtained if the wire is held stationary, even if it is then in the strongest part of the magnetic field between the poles.

Another interesting experiment using an electromagnet can be carried out if a few turns of wire are wound on top of (one of) the energizing coil(s) of the magnet and the coil so made connected across a galvanometer. If the energizing coil of the electromagnet is then switched on, a deflection will be observed on the galvanometer. An opposite, and probably greater, deflection will be observed when the energizing coil is switched off. Once again, however, when the conditions are unchanging —in this case either when the current in the energizing coil has a steady value or when it is zero—there will be no deflection on the galvanometer. The effect of using a coil with a different number of turns should also be investigated. It should be mentioned here that much greater deflections are likely during the tests just described than for the earlier tests. If the same galvanometer is used throughout, it would be wise to shunt it before carrying out these last tests (see Section 17.13, page 536).

In each test a magnetic flux has been made to pass through a coil of wire. This flux is said to 'link' the circuit containing the coil, and the term FLUX LINKAGES is used to measure the product of the magnetic flux and the turns of wire with which this flux has linked. The unit of flux linkage is the WEBER-TURN. It may be that not all the flux passing into one end of a coil will come out at the other end, since some of the flux entering may leave through the side of the coil. In this case, the flux linkages will be less than those that would have been produced if all the flux had linked with all the turns.

In practice it may sometimes be rather difficult to decide exactly what is the value of flux linkages in a particular case, but simple approximations are often possible. Diagram 251 illustrates the meaning of flux linkages.

The results of the various experiments to investigate the effects of electromagnetic induction may now be summarized as follows:

(i) The value of the induced e.m.f. is proportional to the rate at which the flux linkages for the circuit change.

(ii) The direction of the induced e.m.f. depends on whether the flux linkages are being increased or decreased.

Before these summaries are expressed as statements of natural laws (which they represent), they will be viewed against the experimental results obtained.

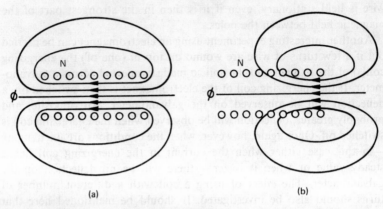

(a)   (b)

251. Flux linkages

(a) All the flux φ weber links with all the N turns of the coil, to give φN weber-turns flux linkages

(b) *Not* all the flux φ weber links with all the N turns of the coil, so that the flux linkages will be *less than* φN weber-turns

Diagram 252 (a) indicates the conditions of the first test, in which a magnet is brought up close to a coil of wire connected across a galvano-meter. Before the magnet approaches, there will be no flux linking the coil. Therefore, as the N-pole of the magnet nears the coil the flux linkages will increase as long as the magnet is moving. The faster the magnet moves, the greater will be the rate of increase of flux linkages. Note that since magnetic flux is associated with a particular direction, flux linkages also must be associated with a direction. By taking the flux linkages as increasing positively as flux enters the coil in the direction shown in this particular instance, the positive direction has been chosen for flux linkages. The stronger the magnet, the greater will be the flux and hence the flux linkages produced; the more turns on the coil, the more flux linkages will be produced for the same flux. As the magnet moves away from the coil, the flux linkages are again changed; this time they are reduced. The statements (i) and (ii) above are fair summaries of these results. The reversal of the galvanometer deflection which occurs if the S-pole of the magnet is brought near the coil first follows from the fact that flux-linkage increase in the opposite sense can be considered to be a negative value. The flux linkages for the coil then change from 0 to $-\varphi N$; i.e. they 'decrease' mathematically. (See diagram 252 (b).)

Diagram 253 illustrates the second test described.

Here again, movement of the wire through the air-gap of the electro-magnet is seen to change the flux linkages with the galvanometer circuit (in this case the flux passes through only one turn). Movement from position (a) to position (b) represents an increase in flux linkages,

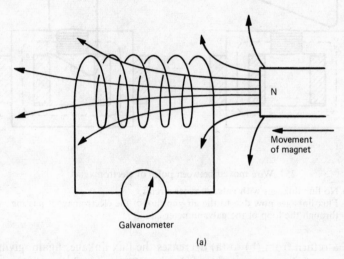

Galvanometer

(a)

Galvanometer

(b)

252. Magnet and coil experiment

(a) Flux linkages increase as flux from right to left increases—taken as positive

(b) Flux linkages decrease as flux from left to right increases—taken as negative

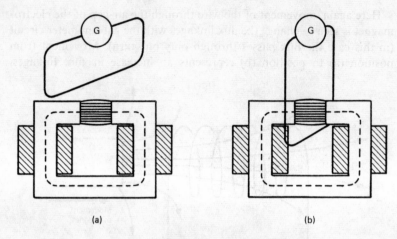

(a)   (b)

253. Wire moved between poles of electromagnet

(a) No flux linkages with galvanometer circuit
(b) Flux linkages now due to the air-gap flux of the electromagnet passing
    through the loop of the galvanometer circuit

whilst a return from (b) to (a) decreases the flux linkages again, giving
a reversal of the galvanometer deflection. Similarly, if the whole galvanometer circuit were turned round before the wire was again passed
between the poles, flux linkages would increase in the opposite direction

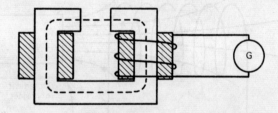

254. Coil wound to link with flux of electromagnet

through the loop, which would be considered a 'negative' increase; i.e.
mathematically a decrease.

Diagram 254 illustrates the third test described.

Here, perhaps, the change of flux linking with the galvanometer
circuit is rather more obvious. When the energizing coils of the electromagnet are switched off, there will be no flux round the 'magnetic circuit'
of the electromagnet (neglecting any retention of magnetic effect by the

iron core), and therefore no flux linkages with the galvanometer circuit. When the supply is switched on to the energizing coils, magnetic flux will become established round the circuit. This setting up of the magnetic flux is not instantaneous, and while the flux is being established, flux linkages with the galvanometer circuit increase and a deflection is observed on the galvanometer. Once established, the flux is constant; there are no further changes in flux linkages and no galvanometer deflection. If the energizing current is changed, the flux and the flux linkages will also change, and a deflection will be observed while the change is taking place. If the energizing current is switched off the flux will collapse, almost certainly more quickly than it was established, and a large reversed deflection of the galvanometer will be observed.

The arrangement shown in diagram 255 is of interest. In this case,

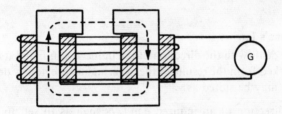

255. Coil wound round both limbs of electromagnet

the galvanometer-circuit coil embraces both limbs of the electromagnet, and no galvanometer deflection should be observable, whatever changes are made in the energizing current of the electromagnet. The reason for this is that the flux round the electromagnet—a typical flux path is shown dotted in the diagram—passes through or links with the galvanometer circuit twice, once in each direction. Since the flux in the two limbs will be the same, the *total* flux linkages will be zero, and there will be no induced e.m.f.

All this evidence points towards the truth of the two earlier summarizing statements, which will now be given under the names by which they are usually known.

19.20. Faraday's law of electromagnetic induction

'An e.m.f. is induced in a circuit whenever the magnetic flux linking with that circuit changes. The value of this induced e.m.f. is directly proportional to the rate of change of flux linkages with the circuit.'

In symbols, if the flux linkages with a circuit change by φN in time t, and this change takes place at a uniform rate, then the induced e.m.f. is

$$E \propto \frac{\varphi N}{t} \qquad . \qquad . \qquad . \qquad . \qquad \text{(iv)}$$

If φN is measured in WEBER-TURNS and t is measured in SECONDS, then E, measured in VOLTS, will be *equal* to the rate of change of flux linkages. In other words,

$$1 \text{ VOLT} = 1 \text{ WEBER-TURN PER SECOND}$$

and
$$E = \frac{\varphi N}{t} \text{ volts} \qquad . \qquad . \qquad . \qquad \text{(v)}$$

19.21. Lenz's law

This law deals with the direction of the induced e.m.f. and its validity can be checked from the results of the experiments previously described. Lenz's law may be stated as:

'The direction of an induced e.m.f. is such as to set up currents which cause a force opposing the change responsible for inducing the e.m.f.'

This sounds very involved, but the basic idea is relatively simple, and is not very far removed from the basic idea behind the law concerning equal action and reaction. It would be possible to generalize Lenz's law as follows:

'Every action tending to produce a change sets up a reaction opposing the change.'

To take a specific case, consider the wire connected across a galvanometer. When the wire is pushed through the air-gap of the electromagnet (page 625) the induced e.m.f. in the wire will set up a current round the galvanometer circuit, which gives rise to the deflection on the galvanometer. The wire then becomes a current-carrying conductor at right angles to a magnetic field, and so will experience a force produced by the interaction of the magnetic field with the magnetic field set up by the current (Section 19.11, page 605). Lenz's law states that the current will be in such a direction that this force opposes the original motion of the conductor, as shown in diagram 256. This is really another instance of the principle of conservation of energy (Section 22.2, page 706). The current flowing in the resistance of the galvanometer circuit will cause the wires to heat up, however slightly. This heat energy is first of all delivered to the system as mechanical energy produced when the conductor is pushed down against the upwards resisting force.

Lenz's law may be combined mathematically with Faraday's law of electromagnetic induction. From Lenz's law, it may be said that the

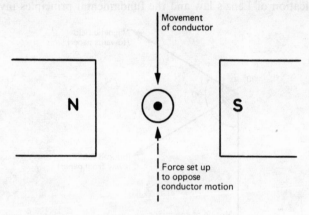

256. Illustrating Lenz's law

e.m.f. induced when the flux linkages through a circuit *increase* (i.e. when φN is *positive*) will be in such a direction as to pass current which will try to *decrease* the flux linkages. If positive current (and so positive e.m.f.) is taken to be that direction of current which would give positive flux linkages, it follows that if the *change* in φN is *positive*, the e.m.f. must be in a negative direction. Therefore, the resulting negative current would try to decrease the flux linkages again. Of course, if the change in φN is negative, then the e.m.f. will be positive. All this can be stated as

$$E = -\frac{\varphi N}{t} \text{ volts} \qquad . \qquad . \qquad . \qquad (vi)$$

As long as the sign convention outlined above is understood and followed, this equation can be interpreted to give both the magnitude *and* direction of E.

It should be noted that this equation is only strictly true provided that the rate of change of flux linkages remains constant over the time interval t. If the rate of change of flux linkages varies during the time interval t, then the e.m.f. will similarly vary during this time. The equation then gives only the time-average of the induced e.m.f.

19.22. Fleming's right-hand rule

The direction of the induced e.m.f. is perhaps best worked out from an application of Lenz's law and the fundamental principles involved,

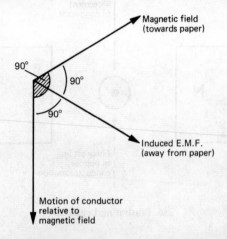

Magnetic field
(towards paper)

90°

90°

90°

Induced E.M.F.
(away from paper)

Motion of conductor
relative to
magnetic field

257. Relative directions of magnetic field, conductor motion relative to magnetic field, and induced e.m.f. (Note: this diagram is intended to represent directions in three dimensions)

as shown above. However, a rule giving the direction of this e.m.f. has been stated by Fleming, and may be found helpful. Fleming's right-hand rule states that:

'If the thumb and first two fingers of the right hand are held at right angles to each other, and the first finger pointed in the direction of the magnetic field, with the thumb pointing in the direction of motion of the *conductor relative to the field*, then the second finger will point in the direction of the e.m.f. induced in the conductor.'

This arrangement of the directions is also shown in diagram 257. As with Fleming's left-hand rule for the direction of the force on a current at right angles to a magnetic field (Section 19.12, page 609), great care should be exercised in the use of this rule. It might be a useful memory aid to notice that the right-hand rule deals with the direction of Induced e.m.f.

The student might like to compare the left-hand and right-hand rules for the same directions of magnetic field and current (or e.m.f.). The thumbs will be found to point in opposite directions, as required by the opposing nature of reaction force and conductor movement in the induction case.

19.23. Flux-cutting rules

Faraday's law of electromagnetic induction as stated in Section 19.20 is very useful for direct application to certain electrical engineering problems. There are some cases, however, for which the idea of flux linkages is not so convenient. For these cases an alternative statement of Faraday's law may be derived, using the concept of the 'cutting' of flux by a conductor. These two versions of Faraday's law should be considered, however, only as two ways of looking at the same thing, rather as if they were the two sides of the same coin. Either of them may be derived from the other. In this case since the 'flux-linkage' form has already been stated, the 'flux-cutting' form will now be derived from it.

Diagram 258 indicates two parallel conducting rails arranged so that a magnetic field of uniform flux density B T is at right angles to

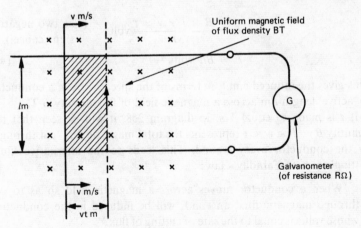

258. Model generator (vertical arrow gives direction of induced e.m.f.)

them. The small crosses on the diagram represent a 'cross-section' through typical lines of force representing this field, the direction of which is into the paper. The parallel conducting rails are spaced l m apart and are connected at one end to the terminals of a galvanometer. Another conductor is laid at right angles across the parallel rails, and completes the galvanometer circuit. The rails are assumed to have zero resistance so that all the resistance R of this circuit is concentrated in the galvanometer and its connecting leads. If the conductor lying across the parallel rails is moved in the direction shown at a constant speed of v m/s, after a time t s it will have covered a distance of vt m, to reach the new position shown dotted in diagram 258.

The magnetic flux threading through, or linking with the shaded area on this diagram, which previously linked with the galvanometer circuit, is now excluded from this circuit. Since there is only one turn in the circuit, this flux also represents the change (decrease) in flux linkages with the circuit. Then

change in flux (linkages) = flux density × area now excluded

or $$(\varphi N) = - B \times l \times vt \text{ weber (turn)}$$

(φN is negative since it is a decrease here)

But by the statement of Faraday's law given in Section 19.21,

induced e.m.f. $$E = - \frac{\varphi N}{t} \text{ volts}$$

$$E = \frac{B \times l \times v \times t}{t} \text{ volts} \quad \text{(The two negative signs cancel)}$$

or $$\underline{E = Blv \text{ volts}} \qquad . \qquad . \qquad . \quad \text{(vii)}$$

This gives the induced e.m.f. in terms of the speed v m/s of a conductor of 'active' length l m across a magnetic field of flux density B T.

If t is made to equal 1 s, in diagram 258, it will be seen that the quantity $B \times l \times v \times 1$ represents the total magnetic flux 'cut through' by the conductor every second. This leads to the alternative 'flux-cutting' form of Faraday's law:

'When a conductor moves across a magnetic field so as to cut through magnetic flux, an e.m.f. will be induced in the conductor, whose value is equal to the rate of cutting of flux.'

The direction of the e.m.f. can, of course, still be found from an application of Lenz's law, or of Fleming's right-hand rule. It can also be found from the sign convention of Section 19.21, by which the e.m.f. in this case has been seen to be positive. In the case of the device shown in diagram 258, the direction of the e.m.f. is as shown, and this will also be the direction of the current I. In the terms of the problem,

$$I = \frac{E}{R} = \frac{Blv}{R} \text{ amperes}$$

The total electrical energy converted into heat energy in the resistance of the galvanometer circuit in a time t is:

energy converted to heat in t s $= I^2Rt$ joules

$$= \frac{B^2l^2v^2}{R^2} . R . t \text{ joules}$$

$$= \underline{\underline{\frac{B^2l^2v^2t}{R}}} \text{ joules}$$

Now, when the conductor carries current I A across a magnetic field of flux density B T, it will experience a force

$$F = BlI \text{ newtons}$$

$$= B . l . \frac{Blv}{R} \text{ newtons}$$

$$= \underline{\underline{\frac{B^2l^2v}{R}}} \text{ newtons}$$

By Lenz's law, this force will oppose the motion of the conductor, and so an equal and opposite force must be applied to the conductor to make it move at the required speed of v m/s. The mechanical agency which provides this force must then expend an amount of mechanical energy in time t s of:

mechanical energy
      supplied in t s $=$ force $\times$ distance moved in the direction of the force

$$= \frac{B^2l^2v}{R} \times vt \text{ newton metre}$$

$$= \underline{\underline{\frac{B^2l^2v^2t}{R}}} \text{ joules} \qquad \Big| \quad \begin{array}{l} \text{Since 1 joule} = \\ \text{1 newton metre} \end{array}$$

Comparing these results shows that the mechanical energy input in a given time is equal to the electrical energy converted into heat energy in the same time. As expected, no energy is either lost or gained. Whilst a device such as this is barely practical, it works on the same basic principle as a practical generator.

19.24. Examples

(i) A coil of 2000 turns gives rise to a magnetic flux of 4 mWb when carrying a current of 5 A. What average e.m.f. will be induced in the coil if a current of 5 A in it is reversed in direction in one-tenth of a second?

Flux linkages set up when a current of 5 A is established in the coil

$$= \text{flux} \times \text{turns (assuming all the flux links}$$
$$\text{with all the turns)}$$

$$= 4 \text{ mWb} \times \left(\frac{1 \text{ Wb}}{1000 \text{ mWb}} \right) \times 2000 \text{ turns}$$

$$= 8 \text{ Wb-turns}$$

When a current of 5 A is reversed in the coil, the flux linkages change from, say, $+ 8$ Wb-turns to $- 8$ Wb-turns, a total change of $- 16$ Wb-turns (i.e. a reduction). (The negative sign has little significance here, as no sign is either given or implied for the current and flux before the current reversal.)

$$\text{Average value of e.m.f.} = \frac{\text{total flux-linkage change}}{\text{total time taken}}$$

$$= \frac{16}{0 \cdot 1} \text{ V}$$

$$= 160 \text{ V}$$

This effect due to the magnetic field of the coil is very important in later work. It is known as a 'self-induced e.m.f.' or the 'e.m.f. or self-inductance', and will be present whenever a current changes in a coil. It is this e.m.f. which provides the reason for the fairly slow growth of current and magnetic flux in an electromagnet, already mentioned in Section 19.19 on page 622. It would not be appropriate to discuss this point any further here.

(ii) If the flux set up by the coil in the previous example is assumed to be proportional to the current in the coil, find the flux set up by a current of + 2 A in the coil. Hence find the average e.m.f. induced in the coil when a current of + 5 A through the coil is reduced to a current of + 2 A in one-fiftieth of a second. What is the direction of this e.m.f.?

If flux is proportional to current, then a current of + 2 A produces a flux of $+ \frac{2}{5} \times 4 = + 1.6$ mWb.

Then, when a current of + 5 A is reduced to a current of + 2 A, the total flux changes from + 4 mWb to + 1.6 mWb, a change of − 2.4 mWb (negative since it is a *reduction*).

The total change in flux linkages is

$$\varphi N = - 2.4 \text{ mWb} \times \left(\frac{1 \text{ Wb}}{1000 \text{ mWb}} \right) \times 2000 \text{ turns}$$

$$= - 4.8 \text{ Wb-turns}$$

The average self-induced e.m.f. in the coil is

$$E = \frac{\text{total flux-linkage change}}{\text{total time taken}}$$

$$= - \frac{\varphi N}{t} \text{ volts}$$

$$= \frac{(- 4.8)}{\frac{1}{50}} \text{ V}$$

$$= + 240 \text{ V} \qquad \text{(Greater value than before due to shorter time interval)}$$

Since the e.m.f. is positive, it is in the same direction as the current flow in the coil, and will try to maintain the current at its steady value of + 5 A.

These answers mean that an additional applied voltage equal and opposite to the self-induced e.m.f. must be applied to the coil in order that the current should change as stated in the specified time.

(iii) A jet air-liner flies along a horizontal route at a steady speed of 800 km/h. It is built of metal and its wing-span is 45 m. If the vertical component of the earth's magnetic field can be taken as 0.04 mT, find the e.m.f. developed between the wing-tips.

For this example, the 'flux-cutting' concept is best.

$$v = 800 \text{ km/h}$$

$$= 800 \text{ km/h} \times \left(\frac{16 \cdot 7 \text{ m/s}}{60 \text{ km/h}}\right)$$

$$= \frac{800 \times 16 \cdot 7}{60} \text{ m/s}$$

$$= 222 \text{ m/s}$$

$$B = 0 \cdot 04 \text{ mT}$$

$$= 4 \times 10^{-5} \text{ T}$$

Substituting in the 'flux-cutting' formula,

$$E = B.l.v \text{ volts}$$

$$= 4 \times 10^{-5} \times 45 \times 222 \text{ V}$$

$$= \underline{\underline{0 \cdot 4 \text{ V}}}$$

Perhaps two points should be made concerning this question and its answer. Firstly, this e.m.f. could never be measured in practice, since any wires connecting the wing-tips to a voltmeter on board the 'plane would have an equal e.m.f. induced in them. These two e.m.f.'s would be in opposition round the local circuit of the voltmeter, and so no deflection would be observed on the meter.

Secondly, because of the low value of the flux density due to the earth's magnetic field, this e.m.f. is very small even at quite high speeds in 'planes of large wing-span. A much more important effect is the collection by the outside surfaces of the 'plane of a 'static' charge due to its friction with the air rushing over its surface. (See Section 16.1, page 436.) The accumulation of this charge could have serious consequences, and arrangements have to be made to 'discharge' the body of the aeroplane in flight.

19.25. Practical applications of the effects of electromagnetic induction

(a) Electrical generator

Perhaps the most important application of the effects of electromagnetic induction is in the electrical generator. The principle of action of a generator can be seen from the behaviour of a coil of wire which is rotated in a uniform magnetic field, in much the same sort of arrangement as already described in Section 19.16, page 613, in connection with the electric motor. In fact, there is little practical difference in the construction of an electric motor and an electrical generator, and each machine performs the functions of both during its normal action, one effect merely predominating over the other. The fundamental factor governing the function of the machine is the direction of energy transfer. If electrical energy is supplied to the machine, it acts as a motor. If electrical energy is obtained from the machine (originating from some form of energy input to the machine), it acts as a generator.

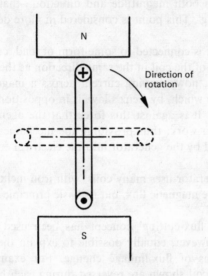

259. Simple generator

Again with practical constructional details omitted, diagram 259 shows a simplified cross-sectional view of a single-turn coil being made to rotate in a uniform magnetic field.

While the conductors of the coil pass 'under' the poles producing the magnetic field their speed across the field is at a maximum, and so the e.m.f. induced in the conductors is a maximum at this instant. The directions of these induced e.m.f.'s are given by Lenz's law—or by Fleming's right-hand rule—and are as shown on the diagram. It will be seen that the conductor e.m.f.'s are additive around the coil. When the coil reaches the position shown dotted in diagram 259, the conductors are for that instant moving parallel with the magnetic field, so that they do not 'cut' any magnetic flux, and no e.m.f. is induced in them. As the coil continues its rotation, the conductor which was previously passing under the N-pole of the magnet system will next pass under the S-pole. The direction of the induced e.m.f. thus reverses for every half-revolution of the coil. If a commutator is used for the coil, as described for the motor in Section 19.16, page 616, the output of the generator will be a unidirectional e.m.f., although its value will change continuously as the conductors move round each half-revolution. If other arrangements are made for connections to the coil, the output e.m.f. will be varying in both magnitude and direction—that is, the output will be 'alternating'. This point is considered in more detail in Chapter 20, page 646.

If the generator is connected to some form of load, current will flow in the conductors of the coil in the same direction as the induced e.m.f. These conductors, now carrying current across a magnetic field, will experience a force which, by Lenz's law, is in opposition to the motion of the conductor. It is against this force that the agency driving the generator must do work, thus providing the mechanical energy input which is converted by the generator into the electrical energy output of the machine.

A practical generator uses many coils, with iron included to provide easier paths for the magnetic flux, but its basic principle of operation is as described here.

Note that the 'flux-cutting' concept has been used here for convenience. It is, however, equally possible to explain the action of the generator in terms of flux-linkage change. For example, the flux-linkages with the coil shown are reversed during each half-revolution, and this fact could be used to calculate the average e.m.f. induced in the coil.

(b) Eddy-current brake

If a conducting disc, say of copper or aluminium, is rotated between the poles of a magnet as indicated in diagram 260, the relative movement between the conductor and the magnetic field will cause an e.m.f. to be induced in the disc. This may be seen more clearly if a radius of the disc is thought of as a conductor moving across the magnetic field. For the directions shown in diagram 260, the direction of the induced e.m.f. is from the centre of the disc to its outer circumference. This e.m.f. could be measured by means of suitable sliding connections between the axle and circumference of the disc.

Since the disc is solid, the induced e.m.f. will set up circulating cur-

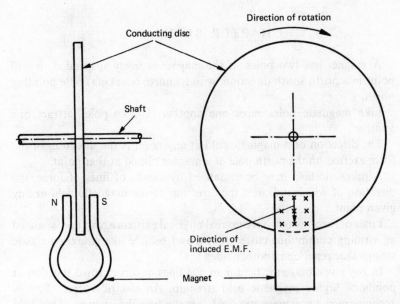

260. Principle of eddy-current brake

rents, known as 'eddy currents', in many parallel paths in the disc. These currents, flowing across the magnetic field, experience forces which oppose the motion of the disc, and thus give a breaking action. This effect may be demonstrated if such a disc is set spinning freely, and then a magnet is brought up to it. The disc will be found to slow down much more rapidly in the presence of the magnet. If the resistance of the eddy-current paths is increased, perhaps by use of a thinner disc, or a disc of material having a higher resistivity, or by holes or slots being cut in the disc, the value of the eddy-currents will be reduced, the resulting force opposing the motion will be reduced, and the braking effect will become less.

Since the induced e.m.f.'s, the eddy-currents, and the braking forces will decrease as the speed of the disc decreases, an eddy-current brake alone would not be very effective to give braking down to standstill. Nevertheless, the principle has quite wide applications. For example, the well-known electrical energy meter (or kWh-meter) used for domestic premises includes an eddy-current brake in its mechanism. The disc in such a meter is also driven round by the reaction of eddy currents and a second magnetic field across the disc, although no further details of the theory of its operation will be given here.

CHAPTER SUMMARY

A magnet has two poles. If the magnet is freely suspended, it will point in a north-south direction, with its north (-seeking) pole pointing north.

Like magnetic poles repel one another. Unlike poles attract one another.

The direction of a magnetic field at any point is the direction of the force exerted on the north pole of a magnet placed at that point.

A magnetic field may be visualized by means of lines of force, the direction of which indicates the direction of the magnetic field at any given point.

Lines of force, which have no real physical existence, can be visualized as forming continuous closed loops, and behave like stretched elastic strings that repel one another sideways.

In any given magnetic field map, the lines of force crowd together at points of higher magnetic field strength. An electric current flow is accompanied by a magnetic field surrounding the current. This field can be visualized as cylindrical in form so that the lines of force around a cross-section of the current are circular. The direction of these lines is the direction in which a right-handed screw must be turned in order to advance it in the direction of the current. If electric current flows round a loop, the magnetic field threads through the loop. The direction of current flow round the loop is that in which a right-handed screw must be turned in order to advance it in the direction of the lines of force through the loop.

The presence of an iron core inside a current-carrying coil greatly increases the strength of the resulting magnetic field.

This effect can be used in electromagnets of various types.

If a current flows at right angles to a magnetic field, it will experience a force at right angles to both field and current, such that the current will move towards regions of weaker magnetic field. (Or, see Fleming's L.H. rule, page 609.)

The value of this force is given by

$$F = B.l.I \text{ newtons}$$

where
B = magnetic field strength, in T
l = active length of conductor, in m
I = current, in A.

If the current direction makes an angle θ with the direction of the magnetic field, the force will be

$$F = B.l.I \sin \theta \text{ newtons}$$

If two currents flow along parallel paths in the same direction, a force is set up tending to bring the currents together.

If the parallel currents are in opposite directions, the force will tend to separate them.

This force between parallel currents is used for the definition of the ampere (see page 621).

Whenever the magnetic flux linking with a circuit is changed, an e.m.f. is induced in the circuit. The value of this induced e.m.f. is equal to the rate of change of flux linkages in weber-turns per second.

$$E = -\frac{\varphi N}{t} \text{ volts}$$

where
$\varphi N = $ flux-linkage change, in weber-turns
$t = $ time taken for the change, in seconds

It follows that

1 volt = 1 weber-turn per second

The negative sign is included to indicate that the direction of the e.m.f. will be such as to tend to set up current opposing the change in flux linkages.

When a conductor moves across a magnetic field so as to cut magnetic flux, an e.m.f. is induced in the conductor. The value of this induced e.m.f. is equal to the rate of cutting of the flux. In other words,

$$e = B.l.I \, v \text{ volts}$$

where
$B = $ magnetic field strength, in T
$l = $ active length of conductor, in m
$v = $ speed of conductor perpendicular to flux, in m/s.

QUESTIONS

1. Suppose you place two bar magnets, in a straight line and about 100 mm apart, under a thin card, then scatter iron filings over the card and tap gently. Draw the lines of force shown by the filings (a) when like poles are facing, (b) when unlike poles are facing.

W

2. What is a solenoid?

You are given a cell, a bar of iron and some insulated wire. Draw a diagram, with the usual sign for a cell, to show how the bar could be made into a magnet. Mark the polarity of the magnet.

3. Describe with the help of a diagram a method of magnetizing an iron bar, AB, by means of an electric current, so that the end B becomes a south pole.

State how you would prove that the end B is a south pole. Give a sketch of the magnetic field due to the magnetized iron bar. How could the bar be demagnetized after the experiment?

4. What is understood by a magnetic material?

With the use of a length of wire and a battery, show how you would make a bar magnet with a N-pole at each end, and give a sketch to show the distribution of the magnetic field.

With the aid of a diagram show how you would magnetize an iron ring with a N-pole at one point on the circumference and a S-pole diametrically opposite.

5. Explain with the aid of a suitable sketch how to make an electromagnet. What would be the most suitable materials for this magnet and upon what factors would the strength of the magnet depend?

Sketch the field set up by this magnet.

6. Draw neat diagrams to show the shape of the resulting magnetic field when direct current is passed through each of the following: (a) a straight wire, (b) a flat circular coil, (c) a solenoid. In each case indicate by arrows the directions of the current and the fields. Describe the rule used for the determination of these directions.

7. Two similar bars of magnetic material are placed in a solenoid and magnetized as shown in the diagram. Both bars are then removed from the solenoid and freely suspended to hang horizontally in the same plane. The distance between their points of suspension is just sufficient to prevent the magnets touching. Give diagrams, using the lettering given, to show the ways in which the two magnets could lie in relation to each other, stating the reasons for your conclusions.

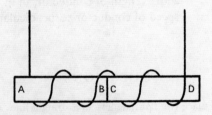

8. What is meant by a 'magnetic line of force' and a 'magnetic field'? Sketch the magnetic field in the neighbourhood of:

(a) an air-cored solenoid carrying a current

(b) two parallel conductors carrying equal currents in the same direction.

In each case show clearly the directions of the currents in the conductors and the lines of force.

9. What magnetic effects are produced when a current flows in one direction along a length of straight wire? State also what happens if the direction of the current is reversed. Describe a simple experiment to show this, illustrating your answers with sketches.

10. Describe, with the aid of a sketch, how to demonstrate that a magnetic field exists around a current-carrying conductor. Sketch the magnetic field due to two parallel conductors carrying current in the same direction. Indicate directions of current and magnetic field.

11. With the aid of a diagram show how a current-carrying conductor is affected when it is placed in a magnetic field. Clearly mark the direction of the current, the resultant magnetic field and the direction of motion. Give a sketch of a moving-coil galvanometer and describe its construction and action. If the galvanometer is required to indicate a current in excess of its capacity, what modification would you make?

12. State the expression for the force acting on a current-carrying conductor lying in and at right angles to a magnetic field.

A rectangular former has a mean width of 15 mm and a mean axial length of 20 mm. It is wound with 50 turns of wire and is situated in an air-gap of uniform flux density 0·2 T. When the current in the coil is 0·01 A, calculate:

(a) the force acting on one side of the coil

(b) the maximum torque on the coil

(c) the work done when the coil turns through an angle of 30°, assuming the torque to remain constant.

13. The force developed by a conductor l m long, carrying a current of I A and situated in a magnetic field of flux density B T is given by BIl N. Apply this formula to an electric motor whose armature has 600 conductors situated in a magnetic field of average density 0·8 T. The armature has a core length of 300 mm, and the conductors lie on an effective diameter of 250 mm.

Determine (a) the torque, (b) the power developed when each conductor is carrying a current of 6 A and the motor speed is 1500 rev/min.

14. Two coils of wire are wound face to face, and parallel to each other, on a short wooden core. One coil is connected to a battery and switch, and the other to a centre-zero galvanometer. Make a sketch of the arrangement and mark the direction of the windings. Explain what happens when the switch (a) is closed, (b) remains closed, (c) is opened. Indicate clearly the direction of the currents for each case, and give an explanation of the results obtained. How would the above results be affected if the core were (a) air, (b) soft iron?

15. A current of 4 A produces a flux of 1 mWb in a coil of 1000 turns. Calculate the induced e.m.f. in the coil if the current increases from 2 A to 10 A in 20 ms at a uniform rate.

16. Two coils, A and B, of 1200 turns and 750 turns respectively, are wound side by side on the same former. A current of 1 A in coil A produces a magnetic flux of 0·06 mWb in A. Assuming that 60% of any flux in A links with coil B, calculate the e.m.f.'s in millivolts induced in A and B if a current in A changes from 2 A to 2·1 A in 50 m/s.

17. Explain what is meant by 'electro-magnetic induction'. Describe experiments in which (a) a magnet is produced by means of an electric current, (b) an electric current is produced by means of a magnet.

A careful diagram is to be drawn in each case showing the polarity of the magnet and direction of the current.

18. (a) State Lenz's law.

(b) A coil of 1200 turns is wound on an iron former and, with a certain value of current flowing in the circuit, a flux of 0·004 Wb is produced. When the circuit is opened the flux falls to its residual value of 0·001 5 Wb in 0·04 s. Calculate the average value of the induced e.m.f.

19. A well-known law of electro-magnetic induction may be expressed in the following way:

'The direction of the induced e.m.f. produced by the motion of a conductor in a magnetic field is such that, if induced current could flow it would produce a force opposing that causing motion.'

With the aid of a clear diagram, describe an experiment which could be performed to verify the law.

The diagram must show the direction of (a) the magnetic field, (b) the motion of the conductor, (c) the reacting force, (d) the induced current.

20. A conductor, 200 mm long, is moved at a uniform velocity of 40 m/s at right angles to its length and to a magnetic field. Find the e.m.f. induced between the ends of the conductor if the density of the magnetic field is 1·2 T.

If the ends of this conductor are joined through an external resistance so that a current of 50 A flows, find the retarding force. Find also the power required to keep the conductor moving.

21. Four conductors, each 100 mm long, connected in parallel, move at a uniform velocity of 5 m/s at right angles to their length and to a magnetic field of density 2 T. This arrangement of conductors is connected to an external circuit of a resistance such that a current of 20 A flows through each conductor.

Find the total force, in newtons, on the conductors and hence show that force × velocity = e.m.f. × current.

22. A conductor lies perpendicular to a magnetic field of flux density 0·7 T such that 500 mm of its length lies within the field. If the conductor carries a steady current of 10 A, calculate:

(a) the e.m.f. induced if the conductor is moved perpendicularly across the field at a uniform velocity of 12 m/s

(b) the force in newtons required to maintain this velocity

(c) the energy in joules absorbed in moving the conductor in this manner for one minute.

23. (a) Define the ampere in terms of the force between two parallel conductors.

(b) A straight conductor 200 mm long is moved at a uniform speed of 6 m/s at right angles to its length and to a uniform magnetic field. Calculate the flux density of the field if the e.m.f. induced in the conductor is 1·8 V. If this conductor forms part of a closed circuit having a total resistance of 0·1 Ω, calculate the force on the conductor in newtons.

20. Alternating Currents

In the preceding chapters, an electric current has been seen to be the steady drift of electric charge around a circuit (Section 16.6, page 442). In the cases considered so far, this movement of charge was in one direction, under the influence of a 'uni-directional' electromotive force acting round the circuit. Such a current is called a 'direct current', and such circuits are called direct-current circuits, or d.c. circuits. There is, however, widespread use of circuits in which the electric current is not uni-directional, but is continually reversing. In these circuits the electric charge starts to move in one direction, then stops and re-starts to move in the opposite direction, only to stop and again reverse. In fact, any individual electron may never get right round the circuit, but may simply drift backwards and forwards around one point. Since the current then flows in alternate directions, it is known as an 'alternating current', and such circuits are called alternating-current circuits, or a.c. circuits. It follows that the direction of the e.m.f. in an a.c. circuit is also alternating.

Considerable advantages are to be gained for many purposes by the use of such a.c. systems, and the electrical supply to the vast majority of installations, domestic and industrial, in this country is an a.c. supply. Before a full appreciation of these advantages can be grasped, it will be necessary to deal with some of the theory of alternating currents.

20.1. Generation of alternating e.m.f.

It was seen in Section 19.25, page 636, that if a coil of wire is rotated in a uniform magnetic field an e.m.f. is induced in the coil, and that the value of this e.m.f. will vary from instant to instant as the coil position changes. Diagram 261 (a) shows a sketch of the physical arrangements of, and diagram 261 (b) shows a sketch of the cross-section through, a coil which is made to rotate at constant speed in a uniform magnetic field. These diagrams are similar to those in Sections 19.16 and 19.25 on pages 613 and 637, but have been slightly modified to suit the present purpose. In this case, connections to the ends of the coil have been made by sliding contacts to devices known as 'slip-rings', so that any one terminal is always connected to the same coil side.

Diagram 261 (c) shows a portion of the coil at the instant when it

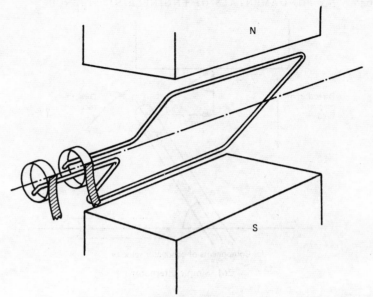

(a) Sketch of physical arrangement of coil
arranged to rotate in a uniform magnetic field

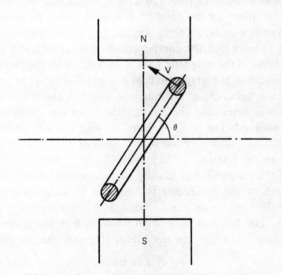

(b) Sketch of cross-section through coil indicated in (a)

261. Simple alternator

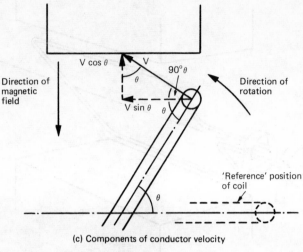

(c) Components of conductor velocity

261. Simple alternator

has turned through an angle θ from the reference position shown, midway between the magnetic poles. The diagram also shows that the instantaneous velocity of the conductor v, which will be tangential to the circle described by the rotating conductor, may be considered to have two components at right angles. From the geometry of this diagram it follows that the component of this velocity at right angles to the direction of the magnetic field is $v \sin \theta$, whilst the component of velocity parallel to the magnetic field is $v \cos \theta$. The speed with which the conductor 'cuts across' the magnetic flux will, then, be $v \sin \theta$, and this speed will determine the e.m.f. induced in the conductor at the instant considered. The component of velocity $v \cos \theta$, parallel to the magnetic flux, does not give rise to any induced e.m.f., since it does not contribute to the 'cutting' of any flux.

Thus, if the magnetic flux density is uniform and equal to B T, the active length of the conductor is l m, and its tangential velocity is v m/s, the instantaneous e.m.f. induced in the conductor when the plane of the coil has moved through an angle θ to the reference plane (where the coil embraces the maximum magnetic flux) is given by

$$e = B.l.(v \sin \theta) \qquad \text{(see page 632)}$$

The maximum or 'peak' e.m.f. (E_{max}) will be induced in the conductor at the instant when the conductor cuts the flux at a maximum rate.

This will be when the tangential velocity is perpendicular to the direction of the magnetic flux; i.e. when $\theta = 90°$—so that this maximum e.m.f. is given by

$$E_{max} = B.l.v$$

Combining this result with the previous equation ($e = B.l.v \sin \theta$), the instantaneous e.m.f. induced in the conductor is then given by the equation

$$e = E_{max} \sin \theta \qquad . \qquad . \qquad . \qquad (i)$$

Note that although the coil is rotating at a constant speed, so that its tangential velocity v is always the same, it is the component of this velocity which is *across* the magnetic field that determines the rate at which the conductor cuts the magnetic flux, and so determines the value of the induced e.m.f. It is this component of the conductor velocity across the magnetic field that varies as the coil position varies from instant to instant.

This point may be seen more clearly from diagram 262. Here, the uniform magnetic field between the poles is represented by a number of equally-spaced parallel lines of force, and one conductor of the coil is shown in various positions as it moves round.

Since the conductor is assumed to be moving at a constant speed, and each point shown numbered on the diagram represents a 15° movement from the next point, the time taken for the conductor to move from one point to the next will be the same in each case. The number of lines of force 'cut' by the conductor in moving from one point to the next, which represents the flux cut by the conductor in the time taken, will then represent the rate of cutting of flux; that is, the average e.m.f. induced during this time.

If these lines are counted on the diagram, the results are as shown in the following table:

As conductor moves from 1 to 2, it cuts   0 lines*

from 2 to 3,	7 lines
from 3 to 4,	13 lines
from 4 to 5,	18 lines
from 5 to 6,	23 lines
from 6 to 7,	25 lines
from 7 to 8,	26 lines
from 8 to 9,	25 lines

* (The conductor will actually cut some flux in moving between 1 and 2, but since 2 is vertically above 1, the same amount of flux is cut in opposite directions, so that the average e.m.f. will be zero for this movement.)

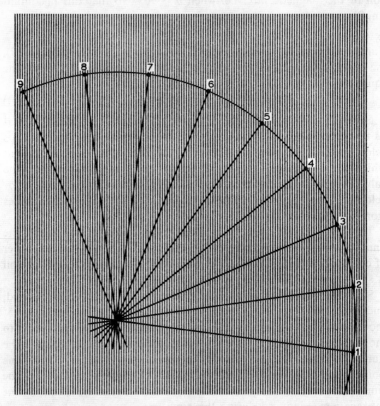

262. Flux cut by conductor moving round circular path in a uniform magnetic field

This table shows that although the time interval for each movement is the same, the flux cut during each movement in this time increases up to a maximum as the average position of the conductor reaches a point directly under the pole. If these values of flux cut in equal times, which are proportional to the e.m.f. induced in the conductor, are plotted against average conductor position, the result is as shown in diagram 263.

It can be seen that this graph, which represents the instantaneous e.m.f. induced in the conductor at different conductor positions, has the same shape as a graph of $\sin \theta$ against θ.

Both the equation $e = E_{max} \sin \theta$, and the graph in the above

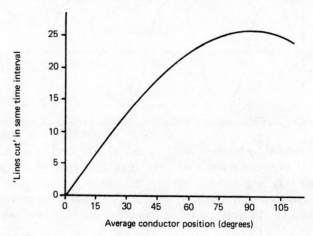

263. Graph showing variation in rate of cutting of flux as conductor
position varies

example, show that the e.m.f. induced in the conductor varies in the
same way as does a sine 'wave' as the angle θ increases during the
rotation of the coil. When the coil has been all the way round one
complete revolution, the instantaneous values will be repeated in the
same sequence for the next revolution. This fact is expressed rather
neatly by the mathematician, who says that

$$\sin \theta = \sin (\theta + n\ 360°)$$

where n is a whole number, or what is called an 'integer'.

This is simply another way of saying that, for the present case, when
the coil has been round one complete revolution from any instantaneous
position considered, it will be back again in the same position relative
to the magnetic field. It will still have the same instantaneous velocity
across the magnetic field, and so will have induced in it at that instant
the same e.m.f. as when it was there before.

This type of sine wave variation is known as SINUSOIDAL, so that the
e.m.f. induced in the conductor is said to be a 'sinusoidal, alternating
e.m.f.'. A graph of instantaneous conductor e.m.f. against values of the
angle θ is shown in diagram 264, for three revolutions of the coil. Note
that in this diagram the scale for the angular position of the coil, as
measured by the angle θ, goes on beyond 360°. Each complete 360°
represents one complete revolution, so that $1\frac{1}{4}$ revolutions from zero

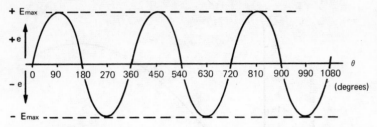

264. Graph of instantaneous conductor e.m.f. against angular position of coil

is represented by an angle of $1\frac{1}{4} \times 360°$ or $450°$, and so on. If the coil is made to rotate many times, the angle θ, defined in this way, can become very large indeed. Nevertheless, the actual position of the coil after it has turned through any angle θ at all, however large, can always be found by subtracting a whole number of $360°$ from the value given, until an angle less than $360°$ is arrived at.

For example, suppose the coil has turned through $10\,000°$ from its starting point along the reference axis between the poles. Then, since $10\,000$ divided by 360 is $27\frac{280}{360}$, an angle of $10\,000°$ represents 27 complete revolutions and $280°$ over. The coil position will be as shown in diagram 265, exactly the same as it would have been if it had only turned through $280°$.

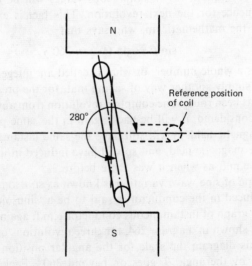

265. Coil position after turning through $10\,000°$

Perhaps it should be mentioned here that alternating waveforms other than sinusoidal may sometimes be encountered in practice. However, the sinusoidal waveform has many advantages over all other kinds for supply purposes, and a great deal of effort is made in electricity supply systems to try to ensure a purely sinusoidal waveform for alternating voltages and currents.

20.2. A cycle of an alternating waveform

Practical rotating generators of alternating e.m.f. are usually called 'a.c. generators', or 'alternators'; these have many coils, and use iron wherever possible to provide easier paths for the magnetic flux. Their principle of operation is, however, as described in the previous section, although, since the e.m.f. is induced as a result of the *relative* movement between the conductors and the magnetic field, it is usually found more convenient for large alternators to keep the conductors stationary and to arrange for the magnetic field poles to rotate. This enables the output voltage and current (which may both be quite large, of the order of thousands of volts and several hundreds of amperes) to be taken from stationary contacts, and so avoids complications at the slip-ring connections.

To return to the simple alternator of diagram 261, the speed at which the coil is made to rotate in the magnetic field is important in two ways. Firstly, the coil speed will determine the maximum induced e.m.f. ($E_{max} = B.l.v$). Secondly, the coil speed will determine the time taken for one complete revolution, and hence the time required for the induced e.m.f. to go through one complete set of values before these values are repeated again in the same order during the next revolution.

The complete set of values of induced e.m.f. in the coil of the simple alternator as it makes one complete revolution is called a CYCLE. It is not necessary to count the start and finish of a cycle from any particular value such as zero. The only requirement is that the finish of the cycle should be at the instant when the coil is back in the same position relative to the magnetic field as it was at the instant taken as the start of the cycle. This is illustrated in diagram 266, where the complete set of values between A and B, or between P and Q, or between X and Y, are all known as one cycle of the waveform. It should be noticed that the same values are obtained during any one cycle as during any other cycle, the only difference being in the starting point chosen. Each cycle will contain a zero, a steady rise to a maximum value, a steady fall

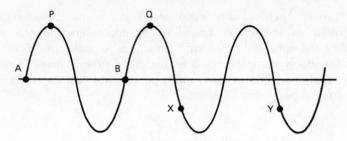

266. Meaning of the term 'cycle'

again to zero, a steady rise to a maximum value in the opposite direction and a steady return to zero again. It is almost as if the letters KLMNO were to be written after one another repeatedly, giving KLMNOKLMNOKLMNOKLMNOKLMNO. Any five consecutive letters taken from this sequence, whatever the starting point, would represent one cycle, and would contain all five letters of the basic sequence, in the same basic order (for example, MNOKL or OKLMN).

Thus it can be said that the e.m.f. output of an alternator undergoes one complete cycle for each time the conductors move from one position relative to the magnetic field to the next corresponding position—which takes one complete revolution for the simple alternator. The case of slightly more complex arrangements will be considered a little later—see Section 20.6, page 663.

20.3.   Period

The time required for an alternating waveform to go through one complete cycle of values is known as the PERIOD of the waveform (usually represented by the symbol T). The basic unit of period is the second, although if the periods are short the millisecond or the microsecond may be used. The period will depend on the speed of rotation of the coil between the poles of the magnetic field. Again, for the simple alternator shown in diagram 146, the period of the waveform of the induced e.m.f. will be the time required for the coil to go through one complete revolution. If the coil is rotating at a speed of n rev/min, the time for one revolution will be $\frac{1}{n}$ min, or $\frac{60}{n}$ s.

(If n revolutions take 1 min, or 60 s, then 1 revolution will take $\frac{1}{n}$ min, or $\frac{60}{n}$ s.)

Thus if the coil were rotating at 600 rev/min, the time for one revolution would be $\frac{60}{600}$ s, or $\frac{1}{10}$ s. The period of the waveform of the induced e.m.f. would then also be $\frac{1}{10}$ s for this alternator.

In practice, it is this time scale which is of importance, rather than the angle turned through by the coil. The horizontal axis of the graph of the waveform is therefore almost always marked off in seconds or in parts of a second, rather than in degrees. The conversion from the angle scale to the time scale depends on the speed of rotation of the coil. Since an angle of 360° corresponds to one revolution or one cycle, the conversion scale is simply

distance represented
by 360° = distance representing the period of the
waveform in seconds.

For example, if a sinusoidal waveform has a period of $\frac{1}{50}$ s, or 0·02 s, and a graph is to be drawn of this waveform having a horizontal time-scale of 20 mm to represent 0·01 s, then a horizontal distance of 40 mm will represent the period of the waveform (and also an angle of 360°). The graph of one complete cycle would then be as shown in diagram 267.

For various mathematical reasons which will become apparent later, angles turned through by the coil are more usually measured in radians than in degrees. This need cause no difficulty as long as it is remembered that an angle of 360° is equivalent to an angle of 2π rad. Thus, if the speed of the coil is n rev/min, its angular velocity (see Section 10.3, page 277) is given by

$$\omega = \frac{2\pi n}{60} \text{ rad/s}$$

(The coil goes through n revolutions every minute, or $\frac{n}{60}$ revolutions every second. But in each revolution it goes through an angle of 2π rad, so that its angular velocity is

$$\omega = 2\pi \frac{n}{60} \text{ rad/s)}$$

If the angular velocity of the coil is ω rad/s, then the angle turned

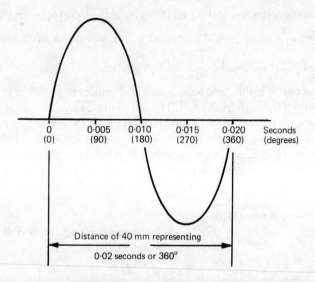

267. Graph of sinusoidal waveform having a period of 0·02 s

through by the coil in any time interval t s will be $\omega \times t$ rad. The angle turned through by the coil has so far been called θ, and so it is now seen that

$$\theta = \omega t \text{ rad}$$

where the coil has been rotating at a constant angular velocity ω rad/s for a time t s.

This value of θ may be substituted in equation (i) to give the more general equation for the instantaneous e.m.f. in terms of time:

$$e = E_{\max} \sin \omega t \qquad . \qquad . \qquad . \qquad \text{(ii)}$$

The period of this waveform may now also be expressed in general terms, using the angular velocity of the coil.

Period T = time for 1 revolution at ω rad/s
or T = time for 2π rad at ω rad/s

or $T = \dfrac{2\pi}{\omega}$ seconds $\qquad . \qquad . \qquad . \qquad . \qquad .$ (iii)

20.4. Frequency

The basic time information concerning an alternating waveform may be given in another, and sometimes more useful, way. Instead of the period of the waveform, which, as seen above, gives the time required for a complete cycle, the total number of cycles passed through in a given time may be stated. In other words, instead of being given the 'seconds per cycle' for a waveform, the 'cycles per second' may be given.

This measure of the number of cycles passed through in a given time (usually in 1 s) is called the FREQUENCY of the waveform (usually represented by the symbol f). The basic unit of frequency is the HERTZ (written Hz where 1 Hz = 1 cycle/s) although for cases where the frequency is high, the units kilohertz (kHz) or megahertz (MHz) may be used. (The prefixes 'kilo-' and 'mega-' have the usual significance.)

The frequency is very simply related to the period, and perhaps some examples will make this clear. If the period of a waveform is 0·1 s, there will be 10, or $\dfrac{1}{0\cdot1}$, cycles in 1 s. If the period of the waveform is 2 s, there will be only $\dfrac{1}{2}$ a cycle in 1 s. If the period of a waveform is T s, there will be $\dfrac{1}{T}$ cycles in 1 s.

In other words, cycles per second is the reciprocal of seconds per cycle

$$\text{or} \qquad f = \frac{1}{T} \qquad . \qquad . \qquad . \qquad \text{(iv)}$$

A waveform having a long period will have a low frequency.
A waveform having a short period will have a high frequency.
In terms of the angular velocity of the coil,

$$\text{since} \qquad T = \frac{2\pi}{\omega} \text{ s} \qquad \text{(equation (iii))}$$

$$\text{then} \qquad f = \frac{\omega}{2\pi} \text{ Hz} \qquad . \qquad . \qquad . \qquad \text{(v)}$$

This equation is also very important in its transposed form

$$\omega = 2\pi f \,\text{rad/s} \qquad . \qquad . \qquad . \qquad \text{(vi)}$$

This last relationship also gives an alternative form of the fundamental equation for a sinusoidal e.m.f., for substituting for ω in equation (ii) gives

$$e = E_{\max} \sin 2\pi ft \quad . \qquad . \qquad . \quad \text{(vii)}$$

It is usually the frequency, rather than the period or the angular velocity of the generator coil, which is quoted for an alternating waveform. For example, the standard frequency of the alternating power supply in this country is 50 Hz. Other countries use other frequencies as standard for supply purposes—for example a frequency of 60 Hz is often used in the U.S.A., and in some parts of Europe a frequency of 25 Hz is used.

20.5. Examples

(i) Draw a graph of one cycle of a sinusoidal voltage waveform having a peak value of 100 V and a frequency of 50 Hz. Use scales of 20 mm = 50 V and 60 mm = 0·02 s.

Since frequency $\qquad\qquad f = 50 \text{ Hz}$

then period $\qquad\qquad T = \dfrac{1}{f} = \dfrac{1}{50} = 0\cdot 02 \text{ s}$

A horizontal distance of 60 mm will then represent the time for one cycle of the waveform. In building up a table of values for such a graph, it is much more convenient to work in degrees than in radians. With degrees, then:

60 mm represents 0·02 s or 360°

An angle of 30° would therefore be represented by 5 mm, and would be equivalent to a time interval of $\dfrac{1}{600}$ s. (Although a 30° interval may seem a little wide for a graph to be drawn, practice in drawing sine waves will usually enable a fairly accurate graph to be drawn even through such widely-spaced points.) With the help of tables of sines of angles (or, better, by remembering the important results that sin 0° = 0, sin 30° = 0·5, sin 60° = 0·866, sin 90° = 1), the following table of values may be constructed. Note that since the peak value of the voltage is 100 V, the equation can be written $e = 100 \sin \theta$.

$\theta°$	0	30	60	90	120	150	180
t s	0	$\dfrac{1}{600}$	$\dfrac{2}{600}$	$\dfrac{3}{600}$	$\dfrac{4}{600}$	$\dfrac{5}{600}$	$\dfrac{6}{600}$
$\sin\theta$	0	0·5	0·866	1·0	0·866	0·5	0
$e = 100\sin\theta$	0	50	86·6	100	86·6	50	0

$\dot{\theta}°$		210	240	270	300	330	360
t s		$\dfrac{7}{600}$	$\dfrac{8}{600}$	$\dfrac{9}{600}$	$\dfrac{10}{600}$	$\dfrac{11}{600}$	$\dfrac{12}{600}$
$\sin\theta$		−0·5	−0·866	−1·0	−0·866	−0·5	0
$e = 100\sin\theta$		−50	−86·6	−100	−86·6	−50	0

The required graph can then be drawn as shown in diagram 268.

An examination of the table of values shows a constant repetition, with appropriate changes of sign, of the numerical values obtained for the first quarter-cycle. This indicates that very little extra work would

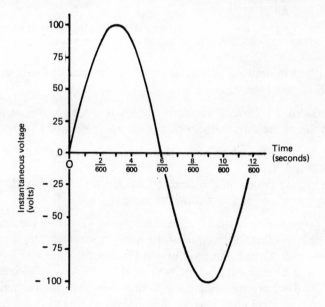

268. Graph of voltage waveform for example (i)

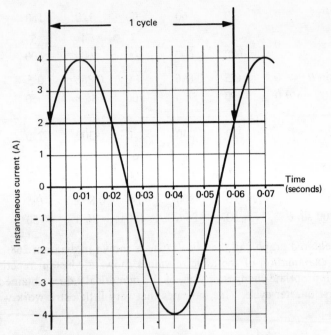

269. Graph of current waveform for example (ii). Inspection of the graph shows that the peak current reached during the cycle is 4 A

be involved in drawing up a table of values for smaller intervals than the 30° chosen here.

(ii) Given the current waveform shown in diagram 269, state the peak value of the current, the period of the waveform and its frequency.

Inspection of the graph shows that the peak current reached during the cycle is 4 A.

The arrows drawn on the diagram indicate corresponding points at the beginning and end of a complete cycle.

Note (a) rather more than one cycle has been included in the diagram
(b) the other intersection of the heavy horizontal line, drawn at +2 A, with the waveform is discounted, since although the instantaneous current here is also +2 A, it is decreasing. The corresponding point to that shown for the beginning of the cycle must have an instantaneous value of +2 A and be increasing.

(There are two other pairs of corresponding points that might almost equally conveniently have been chosen. Which are they?)

From the time scale, the time interval between these corresponding points on the waveform is 0·06 s. In other words, period $T = 0·06$ s.

Then
$$\text{frequency } f = \frac{1}{T}$$

$$= \frac{1}{0·06} \text{ Hz}$$

$$= 16\tfrac{2}{3} \text{ Hz or } 16·7 \text{ Hz}$$

(iii) What is the peak value, the period and the frequency of the current waveform shown in diagram 270? Is this waveform sinusoidal?

From the diagram, peak current = 0·5 A.

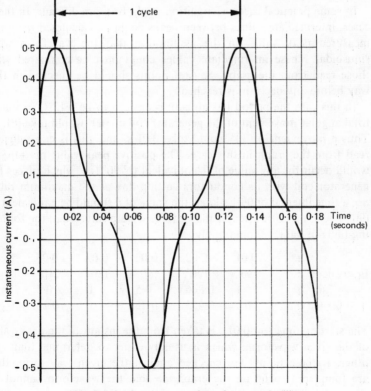

270. Graph of current waveform for example (iii)

Taking consecutive positive peaks as convenient corresponding points at the beginning and end of a complete cycle,

$$\text{period } T = 0.13 - 0.01 \text{ s}$$
$$\text{or } T = \underline{\underline{0.12 \text{ s}}}$$

$$\text{Frequency } f = \frac{1}{T}$$

$$= \frac{1}{0.12} \text{ Hz}$$

$$= \underline{\underline{8.3 \text{ Hz}}}$$

If the shape of this waveform is compared with the sinusoidal waveforms shown previously, it can be seen that this is *not* a sinusoidal waveform.

In some practical cases, recognition might be more difficult. In these cases, intermediate values between peaks could be calculated from the measured peak value on the assumption that the waveform were sinusoidal. These intermediate values could then be compared with those read from the graph. Several points should be checked in this way before any decision is reached.

In this case the period has already been seen to be 0.12 s, so that a total angular movement of the generator coil of 360° would take 0.12 s. Thus a movement of 30° would take 0.01 s, and this is conveniently read from the graph in this case. The positive peak value of +0.5 A would occur for any value of θ 'equivalent to' 90° (i.e. which places the generator coil with its conductors cutting flux at the maximum rate). So, a time interval of 0.01 s later, the value of θ should be equivalent to (90° + 30°), or 120°. Then, if the waveform were sinusoidal, the following table of values should apply:

t	0.01	0.02	0.03	0.04	0.05	(s)
Equivalent θ	90°	120°	150°	180°	210°	
$\sin \theta$	1	0.866	0.5	0	−0.5	
$i = 0.5 \sin \theta$	0.5	0.433	0.25	0	−0.25	(A)

The starting time $t = 0.01$ s is taken from the instant of the peak value of the given waveform, which is usually easier to determine than any other. If these points are checked against the given waveform, they are found not to lie on the graph, so that the waveform cannot be sinusoidal. (Strictly, rather more points should be taken, and they should preferably be at rather irregular intervals, but a more complete treatment of this problem would be out of place here.)

20.6. Multi-polar alternators

Many alternators in practical use have a slightly more complicated arrangement of the magnetic field than has so far been discussed. This could be said to be due to the choice of 50 Hz as a standard supply frequency for this country. It has been seen that for the simple alternators shown in previous diagrams, the induced e.m.f. goes through one complete cycle for every revolution of the coil, so that for a frequency of 50 cycles every second, the coil must make 50 revolutions every second, or $50 \times 60 = 3000$ revolutions per minute.

Now, although alternators can be, and are, built to rotate at 3000 rev/min, this is a very high speed, and requires special arrangements in the design of the alternator. Furthermore, some machine must be available to drive the alternator at this speed (a machine used to drive an alternator or generator is sometimes called the 'prime mover'). Again, although some high-speed drives capable of this speed are available, notably steam turbines, these are economical only in very large sizes. Many prime movers conveniently available have speeds of much less than the 3000 rev/min required for the 'one cycle per revolution' type of 50 Hz alternator. Consequently, slower-speed alternators are made in which the induced e.m.f. goes through two or more cycles for each revolution.

The principle of these machines can be seen from the alternator sketched in diagram 271, where the coil rotates between four magnetic poles as indicated. Such machines are, not unnaturally, referred to as 4-pole alternators, to distinguish them from the 2-pole alternators previously described.

In this arrangement, each conductor of the coil 'cuts' the magnetic flux leaving, or entering, a magnetic pole four times during each revolution, the conductor passing under these poles in the sequence N, S, N, S, – – –.

In order that the e.m.f. induced in each side of the coil shall be in the same direction round the coil, and so add up to give the total coil e.m.f., the two coil sides must be arranged so that when one is under a N-pole, the other will be under a S-pole. Each coil will then 'span' the distance between poles, as shown.

As conductor A, diagram 272, passes under a N-pole, the e.m.f.

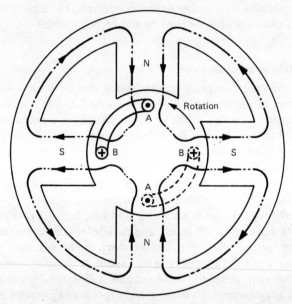

271. Simplified 4-pole arrangement of alternator. (Typical paths of magnetic flux shown — · · →. Note that the coil 'span', A to B (or A′ to B′), is roughly equal to the distance between pole centres)

induced in it will be at a maximum value, and will be directed out of the paper towards the reader for the given direction of rotation. It will then move on until it reaches position B under the next S-pole, where its e.m.f. will again be at a maximum, but in the opposite direction. Further rotation brings it to position A′ under the next N-pole, where the conditions of position A are repeated, in that the e.m.f. is again at a maximum and is directed out of the paper. It follows that the induced e.m.f. has gone from one peak value to a corresponding peak value in only half a revolution, so that the e.m.f. will go through two complete cycles for each revolution of the coil. Thus, in order to provide a 50-Hz e.m.f., this machine would have to be driven at only half the speed of that for a 2-pole machine; i.e. at 1500 rev/min.

This idea can be extended to any number of pole-pairs. The induced e.m.f. in the conductor will go through one complete cycle for each pair of N and S magnetic poles, so that if there are 3 pole-pairs provided (i.e. 6 poles altogether; 3 North poles and 3 South poles), the e.m.f. will go through 3 complete cycles for each revolution of the coil.

Note that the poles must be arranged so that they are alternately North and South round the conductor path, in order that the conductor passes under the poles in the correct N—S—N—S sequence.

For example, diagram 272 shows the arrangement of the magnetic field system for a 16-pole (or 8 pole-pairs) machine. Such a machine would give 8 complete cycles for each complete revolution of the coil. A simple formula connects the frequency, number of pole-pairs and speed of rotation. For each *pair* of poles there is 1 cycle per revolution,

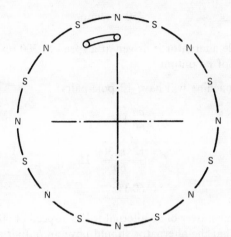

272. Diagram of 16-pole magnetic field, indicating approximate coil span that would be required

so that for p pole-pairs there would be p cycles per revolution. If the speed of rotation is n revolutions per minute, then there will be pn cycles per minute, or $\frac{pn}{60}$ cycles per second,

or
$$f = \frac{pn}{60} \text{ Hz}$$ . . . . . (viii)

where
f = frequency of induced e.m.f.
p = number of *pole-pairs*
n = speed in rev/min

20.7. Examples

(i) At what speed must an 8-pole alternator be driven in order to provide a 50-Hz output?

An 8-pole machine will have 4 pole-pairs:

$$f = \frac{pn}{60} \text{ Hz}$$

or

$$50 = \frac{4 \times n}{60} \text{ Hz}$$

or

$$n = \frac{50 \times 60}{4} \text{ rev/min}$$

$$= 750 \text{ rev/min}$$

(ii) A 24-pole alternator is driven at a speed of 300 rev/min. What is the frequency of its output?

A 24-pole machine will have 12 pole-pairs:

$$f = \frac{pn}{60} \text{ Hz}$$

or

$$f = \frac{12 \times 300}{60} \text{ Hz}$$

$$= 60 \text{ Hz}$$

(iii) The prime mover of an alternator has a speed of 500 rev/min and it is required that the alternator should have an output at a frequency of 50 Hz. How many poles are required on the alternator?

$$f = \frac{pn}{60} \text{ Hz}$$

or

$$50 = \frac{p \times 500}{60} \text{ Hz}$$

or

$$p = \frac{50 \times 60}{500} \text{ pole-pairs}$$

$$= 6 \text{ pole-pairs}$$

so that the alternator must have 12 poles

20.8. Average value of an alternating current

It has been seen that the instantaneous value of an alternating current varies continuously throughout its cycle. The current rises from zero to a maximum or peak value in one direction, falls again to zero, rises to a peak value in the reverse direction and again falls to zero. One method of measuring a quantity whose instantaneous value is continually changing would be to measure its average value over a given time interval, and this method may be used for an alternating current. It is important to notice, however, that the average value of an alternating current over a complete cycle is always zero, since the total movement of electric charge in one direction during one half-cycle is equal to the total movement of electric charge in the opposite direction during the next half-cycle. There is no overall movement of charge in any one particular direction, and so the average value over a complete cycle is zero.

There are applications, however, in which the average value of an alternating current over one half-cycle is of importance. For example, a device known as a rectifier may be used which allows current flow in one direction but prevents current flow in the reverse direction. In such a case there will be an overall resultant movement of electric charge in the permitted direction which will correspond to the average value of the current considered over one half-cycle. The average value of an alternating current (sometimes also called the mean value) has significance only in such cases, so that it may be defined as follows:

'The average, or mean, value of an alternating current is the average value of the current measured over a positive or negative half-cycle.'

Note that in this case, the half-cycle chosen must be such that it covers the movement of electric charge in one particular direction.

An electric current is measured as the rate of flow of electric charge, so that if a charge of Q C is displaced around a circuit in time t s, the current will be I A, where $I = \dfrac{Q}{t}$ (Section 16.7, page 444). If the rate of flow of electric charge varies during the time interval t, then this equation will give the average value of the current during this time. The problem of finding the average value of a varying current is then seen to be solved by finding the total electric charge displaced round the circuit in the given time. Although more advanced mathematical methods are available, graphical methods may be used for this calculation which are capable of giving reasonably accurate results.

Consider first the constant current I A flowing for a time t s as shown in diagram 273.

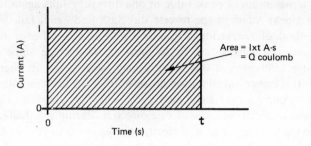

273. Constant current flow

The total electric charge Q C displaced around the electrical circuit in time t is given by

$$Q = It$$

But $(I \times t)$ represents the area enclosed by the graph of I against t, so that this area represents the electric charge displaced. This result is true in all cases, and may be summarized as follows:

'The total electric charge displaced around an electrical circuit in a given time is represented by the area enclosed by a graph of electric current against time for the time interval considered, measured in (units of current) × (units of time).'

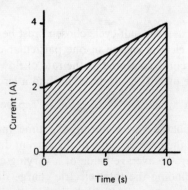

274. Steadily-increasing current flow

For example, if a current increases steadily from 2 A to 4 A in 10 s, the graph of current against time would be as shown in diagram 274.

The area enclosed by this graph is that of a trapezium having parallel sides equivalent to 2 A and 4 A and a perpendicular distance between these sides equivalent to 10 s.

Then

$$\text{area} = \tfrac{1}{2} \begin{pmatrix} \text{sum of parallel} \\ \text{sides} \end{pmatrix} \times \begin{pmatrix} \text{perpendicular distance} \\ \text{between them} \end{pmatrix}$$

$$= \tfrac{1}{2}(2 + 4)\,(\text{A}) \times 10\,(\text{s})$$
$$= 30\,\text{A} \times \text{s}$$
$$= 30\,\text{C}$$

The total charge displaced around the circuit is then 30 C, so that the average current during these 10 s is given by

$$\text{average current} = \frac{\text{total charge displaced}}{\text{time taken}}$$

$$= \frac{30\,\text{C}}{10\,\text{s}}$$

$$= \underline{\underline{3\,\text{A}}}$$

If the instantaneous current changes so that the current/time graph is a curve, the area enclosed by the graph can be found by any of the approximate methods, such as counting squares, mid-ordinate rule or Simpson's rule. In the case of a sinusoidal alternating current, careful measurement of this area gives the result that the average value of such a current is 0·637 times the peak value. Use of more advanced mathematical methods shows that the result is $\dfrac{2}{\pi}$ times the peak value. In other words:

Average, or mean, value of a sinusoidal alternating current is given by

$$I_{\text{av}} = \frac{2}{\pi} \times I_{\text{peak}} \simeq 0{\cdot}637\,I_{\text{peak}} \,. \qquad . \qquad . \qquad \text{(ix)}$$

20.9. Examples

(i) In a particular circuit, the value of the current remains constant at 2 A for 10 s. The current is then suddenly increased to 4 A for a period of 20 s, and is finally suddenly reduced to 1 A for a further period of 20 s. Find the average current for the whole 50-s period.

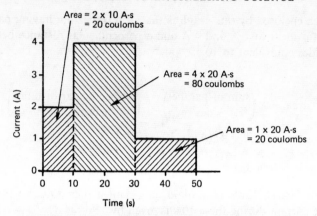

275. Current/time graph—numerical example

The graph of current against time is shown in diagram 275.

The total electric charge displaced is represented by the area enclosed by this graph, which is the sum of three rectangular areas. Then:

$$\text{Charge displaced} = (2 \times 10 + 4 \times 20 + 1 \times 20)\,(\text{A s})$$
$$= 20 + 80 + 20 \text{ C}$$
$$= 120 \text{ C}$$

$$\text{Average current} = \frac{\text{charge displaced}}{\text{time taken}}$$

$$= \frac{120 \text{ C}}{50 \text{ s}}$$

$$= 2 \cdot 4 \text{ A}$$

Average current over the 50-s period = 2·4 A

(ii) Find the average value of a sinusoidal alternating current having a peak value of 10 A.

Note: (a) The average value of an alternating current is measured over a positive or negative half-cycle only.

(b) The average value will be independent of the period of the waveform since the general shape of the graph is the same whatever scale is used for the time base. In this case it is often more convenient to scale the base in angles measured in degrees.

Diagram 276 shows the positive half-cycle of this sinusoidal alternating current.

Using the mid-ordinate rule to estimate the area enclosed by this graph, and with strips 20° wide,

area $\simeq$ (width of strip) × (sum of mid-ordinates)

$= 20$ (degrees) × $(1\cdot7 + 5 + 7\cdot7 + 9\cdot4 + 10 + 9\cdot4 + 7\cdot7$

$+ 5 + 1\cdot7)$ (A)

$= 20 \times 57\cdot6$ amp-degrees

$= 1152$ amp-degrees

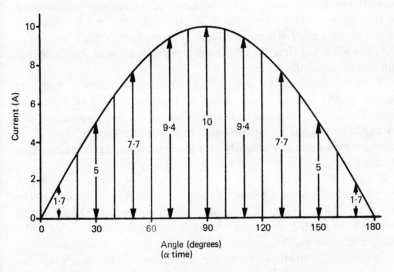

276. Positive half-cycle of a sinusoidal alternating current

$$\text{average current} = \frac{\text{area enclosed by graph}}{\text{base of graph}}$$

$$= \frac{1152 \text{ amp-degrees}}{180 \text{ degrees}}$$

$$= 6\cdot4 \text{ A}$$

Average value of sinusoidal alternating current of 10-A peak value $\simeq 6\cdot4$ A

(This answer should be compared with the more accurate result of $0\cdot637$ × peak value, given earlier.)

20.10.   Heating effect of an alternating current

If a steady current of I A flows for a time t s in a resistance of $R\,\Omega$, the total amount of electrical energy which is converted into heat energy in the resistance is given by:

energy converted

to heat $= I^2Rt$ joules (see Section 16.13, page 449)

This same amount of energy is converted to heat no matter what the direction in which the current flows through the resistance. The same resistor connected across the same battery for the same length of time will get just as hot when a particular end of the resistor is connected to the negative battery terminal as it will when that end is connected to the positive battery terminal. The important factors are the value of the resistance, the time for which the current flows, and the *value*, but not direction, of the current.

If the value of the current is suddenly changed after a time, the power, or the *rate* at which energy is being converted to heat, will change. A sudden increase in current through the same resistance will mean that energy is being converted to heat more rapidly. This effect can be shown quite conveniently on a graph of power against time, as in diagram 277.

Diagram 277 (a) shows the power/time graph for a current of 1 A being switched on for a period of 10 s through a resistance of 1 Ω. The power ($= I^2R$ watts) is 1 W. The total energy converted to heat ($= I^2Rt$ joules) is 10 J. This amount of energy is represented by the *area* under the power/time graph.

Diagram 277 (b) shows the power/time graph for the case where the 1-A current in the 1-Ω resistance is suddenly doubled after 5 s, the current again being switched off after a total period of 10 s. The total energy converted to heat during the first 5 s is 5 J ($1^2 \times 1 \times 5$ J) which is again represented by the area under that part of the graph. The total energy converted to heat during the last 5 s is 20 J ($2^2 \times 1 \times 5$ J), which is also represented by the area under the second part of the graph. The *total* energy converted to heat in the whole 10 s is thus 25 J, which is represented by the *total* area under the graph. Notice that when the current is doubled, from 1 A to 2 A, the power is four times as great, being 4 W instead of 1 W, so that energy is being converted to heat four times as quickly. This is because the power depends on the *square* of the current.

The graphical method outlined above gives a very convenient way of

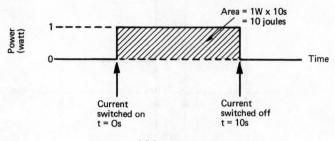

(a) Constant power

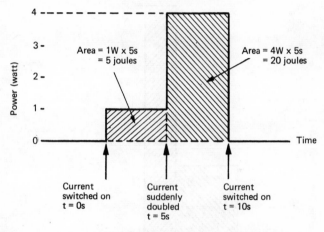

(b) Sudden change in power

277. Power/time graphs

finding the heating effect of a current which is varying. Since the heating effect of any current is directly proportional to the resistance of the circuit through which it flows, it is convenient to refer the heating effect to a resistance of 1 Ω. It is then easily possible to make a direct comparison between the relative heating effects of two currents. This method is indicated in the following examples.

Examples

(i) A current of 2 A is switched on in a circuit, and 10 s later its value is suddenly increased to 3 A. After a further 5 s, the current is suddenly decreased to 1 A, and is switched off after a further 15 s. What

x

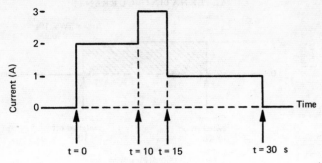

(a) Graph of current against time for given example

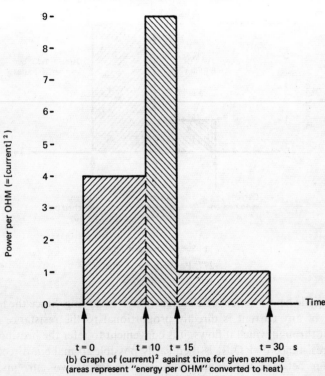

(b) Graph of (current)² against time for given example
(areas represent "energy per OHM" converted to heat)

278. Graphs for example (i)

steady value of current, flowing for the whole 30 s, would produce the same heating effect in the circuit?

Note that it is not necessary to know the resistance of the circuit to solve this problem. The heating effect can be compared per ohm of the circuit resistance. A steady current of I A produces a power of $(I)^2$ W/Ω in a resistance; i.e. 1 (A)^2 is equivalent to 1 W/Ω.

A current/time graph for this given case is as shown in diagram 278 (a). The graph of the power per ohm against time is shown in diagram 278 (b) and is obtained by squaring the currents shown in the first graph.

The shaded areas shown under the graph of (current)^2 against time will represent the 'energy per ohm' converted to heat, so that

$$\text{energy converted} = 4 \times 10 + 9 \times 5 + 1 \times 15 \text{ J}/\Omega$$
$$= 40 + 45 + 15 \text{ J}/\Omega$$
$$= 100 \text{ J}/\Omega$$

The same area, and hence the same energy converted per ohm, would be given by a rectangle having a 'base' of the total time of 30 s and a 'height' of $\frac{100}{30}$ W/Ω. In other words,

$$\text{height of equivalent rectangle} = \frac{100}{30} \text{ W}/\Omega$$
$$= 3{\cdot}33 \text{ (A)}^2$$

So that the value of the steady current which would give the same heating effect if it flowed for the same time would be given by:

$$\text{equivalent steady current} = \sqrt{3{\cdot}33} \text{ A}$$
$$\simeq 1{\cdot}83 \text{ A}$$

(ii) The current in a circuit is increased uniformly at a steady rate from zero to 5 A in 20 s, after which it is switched off. Find the equivalent steady current which would produce the same heating effect in the same time.

In this case, the graph of current against time is the sloping straight line shown in diagram 279 (a), so that the graph of (current)^2 against time is the curve shown in diagram 279 (b). Individual points on this second graph are found by squaring the corresponding current values.

Once again, the energy per ohm converted to heat will be represented

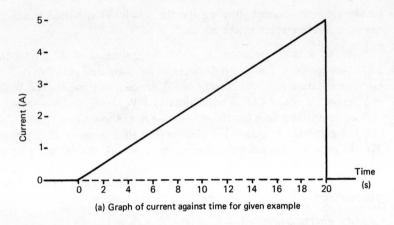

(a) Graph of current against time for given example

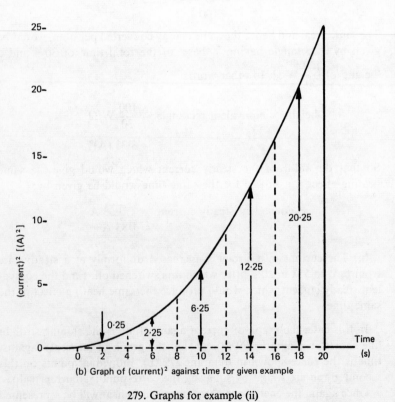

(b) Graph of (current)² against time for given example

279. Graphs for example (ii)

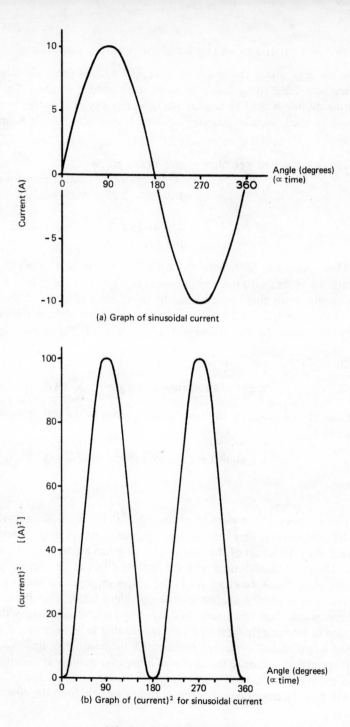

(a) Graph of sinusoidal current

(b) Graph of (current)² for sinusoidal current

280. Graphs for example (iii)

by the area under the graph of (current)² against time, although the area may have to be found by some approximate method. The mid-ordinate rule is used as an example here, but any of the other methods may be used, such as counting squares, trapezoidal rule or Simpson's rule.

$$
\begin{aligned}
\text{Energy converted per ohm} &= \text{area under graph} \\
&= (\text{width of strip}) \times (\text{sum of mid-ordinates}) \\
&= 4\,(0{\cdot}25 + 2{\cdot}25 + 6{\cdot}25 + 12{\cdot}25 \\
&\qquad\qquad\qquad\qquad + 20{\cdot}25)\ \text{J}/\Omega \\
&= 4 \times 41{\cdot}25\ \text{J}/\Omega \\
&= 165\ \text{J}/\Omega
\end{aligned}
$$

(This result has been obtained by mid-ordinate rule, using 5 strips each 4 s 'wide', with the mid-ordinates as shown on the graph. A more accurate result could be obtained by using more strips.)

The same area, and hence energy converted per ohm, is represented by a rectangle having a base of the total time of 20 s and a height of $\dfrac{165}{20}$ W/Ω:

$$
\text{height of equivalent rectangle} = \frac{165}{20}\ (\text{A})^2
$$

Equivalent current for the same heating effect in the same time is thus given by:

$$
\text{equivalent steady current} = \sqrt{\frac{165}{20}}\ \text{A}
$$

$$
\simeq \underline{2{\cdot}9\ \text{A}}
$$

The accuracy of the method of finding the area limits the accuracy of the final answer, here quoted to 2 significant figures only, although in fact the calculation of the area in this case has an error of about 1%.

The method of dealing with the heating effect of an alternating current should now be clear. As in the above examples, a graph may be drawn of (current)² against time from values taken from the current/time graph. The area under this 'squared-current' graph may then be used to estimate the heating effect. Notice that values of current during the negative half-cycle are represented by positive ordinates on the (current)² graph, since the square of a negative number is positive. This is merely a mathematical way of saying that a certain value of current will give the same power in a given resistance, whatever the direction of the current. The case of a sinusoidal alternating current is given in the following example.

(iii) Find the equivalent steady current which would give the same heating effect when flowing for the same time as a sinusoidal alternating current having a peak value of 10 A. The time for which the current flows may be assumed to be much greater than the period of the alternating current.

Provided the statement made in the last sentence of this question applies (which it very nearly always does in practice, because of the short periods commonly encountered—a 50-Hz current, for example, has a period of 0·02 s), then the actual period or frequency of the alternating current is not important in this sort of problem. It may be assumed that a large number of complete cycles of the alternating current would eventually be involved, and the comparison in heating effect may be considered for just one of these cycles. The result is then true for any whole number of cycles, and any error due to an odd fraction of a cycle 'left over' at the end of the period can be discounted. This fraction would have to be less than a quarter cycle for any error to be involved at all, because of the symmetry of the (current)² graph. Since this is the case, it is often more convenient to plot the graphs to a base of angles in degrees instead of time in seconds, so that the areas involved are proportional to, rather than equal to, the energy converted per cycle.

The graphs of current against angle, and (current)² against angle, are shown in diagrams 281 (a) and (b). Once again, the mid-ordinate rule will be used for estimating the area, but any other suitable method could be used.

Then

energy converted to heat per cycle $\propto$ area under (current)² graph

But

area under (current)² graph
$= 4 \times$ area under first quarter-cycle
$= 4 \times$ (width of strip) $\times$ (sum of mid-ordinates)
$= 4 \times 10 \times (0·8 + 6·7 + 17·9 + 33 + 50 + 67 + 81$
$\qquad\qquad\qquad\qquad\qquad\qquad + 93 + 99)$ (A)²-degree
$= 40 \times 448·4$ (A)²-degree
$\simeq 17\ 940$ (A)²-degree

(This takes 9 strips, each 10° wide, for the first 90°. The areas under each of the other quarters of the graph will be equal so that, as here, the total area is four times the area under the first 90°.)

The same area would be given by a rectangle having the full 360° as base and a height of $\dfrac{17\,940}{360}$ (A)^2:

$$\text{height of equivalent rectangle} = \frac{17\,940}{360}\ (A)^2$$

$$\simeq 50\ (A)^2$$

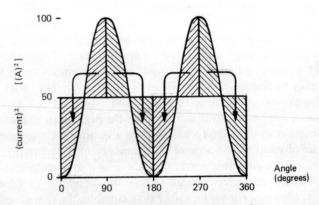

281. Rectangle having same area as that under a (sinusoidal current)^2 graph

Equivalent current for the same heating effect in the same time is therefor given by

$$\text{equivalent steady current} = \sqrt{50}\ A$$
$$\simeq 7\cdot 1\ A$$

In actual fact, because of the symmetry of the (current)^2 graph for a sinusoidal waveform, this result can be seen very quickly by the following trick. If the peaks of the (current)^2 graph are imagined as being cut off half-way up, they will fit exactly in the troughs, as shown in diagram 281. This indicates that the height of the equivalent rectangle in this case is exactly 50, and the equivalent current can be stated more accurately as 7·07 A, or even more accurately as $\dfrac{10}{\sqrt{2}}$ A.

This effective heating value of an alternating current is very important in a.c. theory, and is the value usually indicated by meters. For example, when the statement is made that the alternating voltage available at a consumer's supply terminals is 250 V, it is the effective value that is given. That is, the heating effect resulting from applying this voltage across a resistance would be the same as that resulting from an application of a steady voltage of 250 V for the same length of time. Notice that, since the effective value is less than the peak value for a sinusoidal waveform, a 250-V sinusoidal a.c. supply will have instantaneous values greater than 250 V for some part of the cycle, and will have a peak value of just over 350 V. Since it is calculated by finding the square root of the average value of (current)^2, the effective value is often known as the root mean square, or r.m.s., value.

20.11. Form factor

The waveform of an alternating voltage or current may not always be sinusoidal, and one method by which the departure from a sinusoidal waveform may be measured is by means of the form factor. This is defined as

$$\text{form factor} = \frac{\text{effective, or r.m.s., value}}{\text{average, or mean, value}}$$

For a sinusoidal waveform, as seen earlier, the effective value is $\dfrac{1}{\sqrt{2}} \times$ peak value, while the average value is $\dfrac{2}{\pi} \times$ peak value.

Then the form factor of such a waveform is

$$\text{form factor} = \frac{\dfrac{1}{\sqrt{2}} \times \text{peak value}}{\dfrac{2}{\pi} \times \text{peak value}}$$

$$= \frac{\pi}{2\sqrt{2}}$$

$$\simeq \underline{\underline{1 \cdot 11}}$$

If a waveform has a form factor of less than 1·11 this indicates that the shape is more flat-topped than a sine wave.

20.12. Crest, or peak, factor

A similar indication of the shape of a waveform is given by the crest, or peak, factor. This is defined as:

$$\text{crest, or peak, factor} = \frac{\text{peak value}}{\text{effective, or r.m.s., value}}$$

For a sinusoidal waveform,

$$\text{crest factor} = \frac{\text{peak value}}{\dfrac{1}{\sqrt{2}} \times \text{peak value}}$$

$$= \sqrt{2}$$

$$\simeq 1{\cdot}41$$

A crest factor lower than 1·41 indicates a waveform having a flatter top than a sine wave, while a crest factor higher than 1·41 indicates a waveform which is more peaky than a sine wave.

The crest factor is less frequently quoted than the form factor.

CHAPTER SUMMARY

An alternating current is one whose direction reverses periodically, so that it flows in alternate directions round the circuit.

The value of a sinusoidal, alternating e.m.f. can be expressed mathematically by the equation

$$e = E_{max} \sin \omega t$$

where

e = instantaneous e.m.f.

E_{max} = maximum e.m.f.

$\omega = 2\pi f$ = angular velocity of simple generator coil

f = frequency

t = time measured from an instant of zero e.m.f.

Note that $\omega = 2\pi f$ rad/s

or $f = \dfrac{\omega}{2\pi}$ Hz

Period of waveform = time for one cycle

$$= \frac{1}{f} \text{ seconds}$$

$$= \frac{2\pi}{\omega} \text{ seconds}$$

For a multi-polar machine, the frequency f Hz, number of pole-pairs p, and speed n rev/min, are related by the equation

$$f = \frac{pn}{60} \text{ Hz}$$

The average value of an alternating current is measured over a positive or negative half-cycle only. It is equal to the total charge displacement during this half-cycle divided by the time taken for the half-cycle. In other words,

$$\text{average value} = \frac{\text{charge displaced during positive half-cycle}}{\text{time taken for half-cycle}}$$

The total charge displaced is represented by the area enclosed by a current/time graph.

For a sinusoidal waveform,

$$\text{average value} = \frac{2}{\pi} \times \text{peak value} \ (\simeq 0{\cdot}637 \times \text{peak value})$$

The effective value of an alternating current is that steady current which would produce the same heating effect in the same resistance in the same time. It can be found from the area under a graph of (current)^2 against time, which represents the energy per ohm converted to heat in resistance. The effective value is then given by the square root of the average value of (current)^2, and so is also known as the 'root mean square' or r.m.s. value. For a sinusoidal waveform,

$$\text{effective, or r.m.s., value} = \frac{1}{\sqrt{2}} \times \text{peak value}$$

$$(\simeq 0{\cdot}707 \times \text{peak value})$$

$$\text{Form factor} = \frac{\text{r.m.s. value}}{\text{average value}} \ (= 1{\cdot}11 \text{ for a sine wave})$$

$$\text{Crest factor} = \frac{\text{peak value}}{\text{r.m.s. value}} \ (= 1{\cdot}41 \text{ for a sine wave})$$

QUESTIONS

1. A voltage wave is given by $v = 100 \sin \omega t$. Construct on graph paper without the use of tables one cycle of v plotted against ωt, marking also the ordinates corresponding to ωt equal to

$$\text{(a) } \frac{\pi}{6} \text{ rad, (b) } \frac{\pi}{3} \text{ rad, (c) } \frac{7\pi}{6} \text{ rad, (d) } \frac{4\pi}{3} \text{ rad}$$

If $\omega = 5000$ rad/s, calculate the value of t corresponding to these four angles and state the frequency of the waveform.

2. Explain the terms cycle, peak value, frequency, mean value, root mean square value of an alternating current. A 6-pole alternator is driven at 1000 rev/min. What is the frequency of its output voltage? At what speed should it be driven to give an output frequency of 60 Hz?

3. (a) Sketch the arrangement of the poles for the field system of a 6-pole alternator.

(b) The frequency of an alternating supply varies between 48·5 Hz and 51·5 Hz. Between what limits would the speed vary if the alternator had (i) 4 poles, (ii) 16 poles?

4. At what instant after passing through zero is the value of the alternating current represented by $i = 10 \sin 100t$ A first equal to (i) its average value, (ii) its r.m.s. value, (iii) its peak value? What is the frequency of this current?

5. Explain the terms (a) period, (b) peak value, (c) mean value, (d) r.m.s. value and (e) form factor, when used with reference to an alternating e.m.f. What are these values for a 240-V, 50-Hz, sinusoidal supply?

6. A coil of 200 turns is rotated at 1200 rev/min between the poles of an electromagnet. The flux density of the field is 0·02 T and the axis of rotation is at right angles to the direction of the field.

The effective length of the coil is 300 mm and the mean width 200 mm.

Assuming that the e.m.f. produced is sinusoidal, calculate (a) the maximum value of e.m.f., (b) the r.m.s. value, (c) the frequency and (d) the periodic time.

7. Explain the meaning of the following terms as applied to an alternating quantity: (a) instantaneous value, (b) form factor, (c) frequency.

An alternating current waveform is given by $i = 4 \sin 314 \, t$. Plot this waveform to a base of time (in seconds) and thence show, by graphical means, that the r.m.s. value is 2·83 A.

8. Explain the following terms relating to an alternating waveform:
(a) periodic time, (b) frequency, (c) form factor, (d) crest factor.

If an alternating current is given by $i = 100 \sin 314 \, t$ A, state the values of (i) the amplitude of the current wave; (ii) its r.m.s. value; (iii) its frequency.

9. What information can be obtained from the form factor of an alternating waveform? What is its value for (i) a sinusoidal waveform, (ii) a square waveform? When is the r.m.s. value of an alternating voltage equal to $\dfrac{2}{\sqrt{2}} \times$ the peak value?

10. The instantaneous value of an alternating voltage is given by $v = 100 \sin \theta + 20 \sin 3\theta$ volts. Draw a graph of instantaneous voltage, v, against angle, θ, for one complete cycle of this waveform (between $\theta = 0$ and $\theta = 360°$). Calculate the r.m.s. value of this voltage.

11. An alternating voltage has a stepped waveform which varies as follows for equal intervals of time: 2, 3, 4, 2, 1, −2, −3, −4, −2, −1 volts. Plot this and thence determine, for the complete wave, the r.m.s. value.

12. (a) An alternating voltage has a triangular waveform. The voltage rises from zero to a maximum value of 8 V in 0·001 s, falls back to zero in 0·004 s, rises again to 8 V in the opposite direction in the next 0·004 s, and falls back to zero in a further 0·001 s. Sketch a complete cycle and determine (i) the frequency, (ii) the r.m.s. value.

(b) An alternating current has a frequency of 200 Hz, an r.m.s. value of 10 A and a sinusoidal waveform. Calculate its instantaneous value 1 millisecond after passing through zero.

13. A triangular voltage wave increases linearly from 0 to 100 V in 1·0 ms and then decreases linearly to 0 in 100 μs. Calculate the (a) periodic time, (b) frequency, (c) average value, (d) r.m.s. value of the voltage.

14. The waveform of an alternating current is given in the following tabulation. Plot the wave by joining the points with straight lines, and calculate by using the graph (a) the average value, (b) the r.m.s. value and (c) the form factor.

Current in amp, i	0	3·0	4·0	4·5	4·0	3·0	0
Angle in degrees, θ	0	30	60	90	120	150	180

15. The following table gives values of an alternating voltage over a half-cycle. Assuming the voltage varies linearly between the points given, find the mean value and the r.m.s. value of the voltage.

Time, milliseconds	0	0·4	0·8	1·2	1·6	2·0
Voltage	0	50	66	70	44	0

21. Electrical Measuring Instruments

Electrical measuring instruments are required to measure the values of electric charge (or 'quantity of electricity') displaced in a circuit, electric current, difference in electric potential, electrical power, electrical energy, or other quantities dependent on these things. The instruments often give an indication of these values by the deflection of a pointer over a graduated scale, although other methods are possible. Some method of producing a deflection which is dependent on the quantity to be measured is thus required, and instruments are usually grouped in accordance with the method of deflection used. Some of these groups will be dealt with in the following sections. A few points which are common to many instruments can first be discussed here, however.

The moving part of the instrument to which a pointer is attached may either be mounted between bearings or suspended by means of a fine thread. Both kinds of instrument should be handled carefully, but the suspension type is obviously the more delicate, and is usually confined to use in a laboratory. Instruments which frequently have to be carried about by hand, or which are installed in positions where they are likely to suffer repeated mechanical shock, are usually of the pivoted type. In this type, the moving system is mounted on a spindle having polished and hardened points at the ends. The ends of the spindle rest in bearings which are usually of a very hard 'jewel' stone, such as sapphire, though they may sometimes be of hardened steel. This construction is designed to give the minimum friction to the movement of the spindle, and requires very careful and expert adjustment. The jewel (or steel) end-bearings are carried in adjusting screws, and if they are adjusted to press too heavily against the ends of the spindle, tremendous pressures—of the order of many MN/m^2—may be exerted on them (because of the very small area of contact), damaging them and adding friction to the movement. Alternatively, if the adjustment is too loose, the spindle will not rest properly on its points, and again friction is added to the movement. Furthermore, the possible sideways movement could also cause the moving parts to touch other parts near by, causing 'sticking'. In general, adjustment of meter bearings is best left to experts.

In addition to the deflecting device, a meter will require some device to control the deflection. This control is required to make the deflection dependent on the quantity being measured. (This point will be considered in more detail for each type of instrument described later.) Finally, since the moving parts of such an instrument will have inertia, it is usual to include some additional 'damping' device. Whilst there are instruments for which the minimum possible damping is necessary, the majority of indicating instruments are required to reach a steady indication as quickly as possible. When the deflecting force is first applied, the moving parts will accelerate towards the position of this steady indication. However, their inertia would tend to cause them to 'overshoot' the required position, and oscillate around this position for an appreciable time before coming to rest. The function of the damping device is to damp out these oscillations as quickly as possible without making the movement so sluggish that it cannot indicate fairly rapid changes in the quantity being measured.

Summary

Each electrical measuring instrument will usually have arrangements for

    (a) producing the deflection
    (b) controlling the deflection
    (c) damping the deflection.

21.1. Ammeters and voltmeters. General

It has been seen in earlier chapters (see pages 534 and 536) that ammeters and voltmeters are fundamentally made up from a similar instrument which measures small values of current, usually in the milli-ampere range or even less. (As with most generalizations, there are exceptions to this statement. An instrument known as an 'electrostatic voltmeter' does not work on this principle, but depends for its action on the force set up between electric charges.)

The way in which the range of an ammeter and a voltmeter is adjusted is described on pages 534-538, and the following descriptions apply to the basic meter movement used with either.

21.2. Ammeters and voltmeters. Moving-coil type

This type of meter uses the force exerted on a current-carrying conductor placed at right angles to a magnetic field (discussed in Chapter

19, page 605) to produce the deflecting force. The current to be measured is made to flow through a coil of fine wire suitably placed in a magnetic field. The resulting force causes the coil to move, and thus moves the pointer, which is attached to the coil, across the scale of the instrument. Although other controlling methods are possible, nearly all moving-coil instruments now use fine spiral springs (often called 'hair-springs' because of the thin material used to make them) to control the deflection of the pointer. The movement of the coil and pointer takes place against the opposing torque of these control springs, which are so designed that the torque which they exert is directly proportional to the angle through which they are deflected. Thus if the torque exerted on the springs by the moving coil of the meter is doubled, then the springs will allow the coil to move through twice the angle before their opposing torque again balances the coil torque and a steady indication is obtained. This system is seen to be equivalent to the 'weighing' of the torque exerted by the coil, in a manner similar to the way in which a force may be measured by a spring balance. The deflection of the pointer against the action of the spring is a measure of the torque exerted to cause the deflection. In practice, two control springs are used whose torques act in opposite directions, and cancel at the zero position of the pointer. Adjustment of the torque of one of these springs then gives adjustment of the zero point. The control springs are usually made of beryllium-copper or phosphor-bronze, and are also used to make the electrical connections to the moving coil. Each spring is connected to an end of the coil, and the fixed end of the spring, which is insulated from the rest of the movement, is then connected to the meter terminal. In this way, additional connection leads to the coil, and any consequent effect on its movement, are avoided.

Since the force experienced by the coil in the magnetic field is directly proportional to the current in the coil if the strength of the magnetic field is constant (see page 611), then the deflection of the pointer will also be proportional to the coil current. If the coil current were to be doubled, the angle moved through by the pointer would also be doubled. The scale on the meter will therefore be an 'even' one. For a moving-coil instrument then, the angle between marks on the scale for, say, currents of 0 and 1 A, will be the same as the angle between the scale marks representing 1 A and 2 A or representing 2 A and 3 A, and so on. This is very useful in that a deflection anywhere within the full range of the scale may be read to the same degree of accuracy. This feature depends on the fact that the strength of the

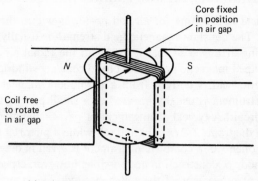

(a) Arrangement of coil and central cylindrical core in the air-gap of the magnet system of a moving-coil meter

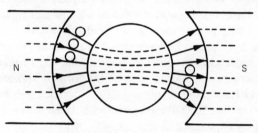

(b) Sketch of map of radial magnetic field in magnet air-gap, due to presence of cylindrical iron core (no coil current)

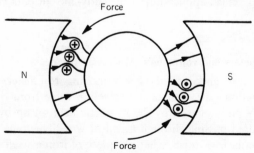

(c) Sketch of map of distorted field, due to current in the coil, and producing a torque on the coil

282. Moving-coil meter

magnetic field is the same for all coil positions within the limits of its movement. The constant magnetic field strength is usually obtained by the coil being arranged so that it moves in the radial air-gap between suitably-shaped magnetic poles and a fixed central cylindrical iron core. The magnetic field is derived from a permanent magnet, which in a modern instrument is usually inserted as a small part of the complete magnetic circuit. A typical arrangement of part of the magnetic circuit is shown in diagrams 282 (a), (b) and (c), while a pictorial sketch of the main components of a complete instrument is given in diagram 282 (d). Other methods of construction are possible, however, especially when a wide angle of movement of the coil is desired. The interested student is advised to consult manufacturers' literature, which usually gives sketches of constructional details.

The damping action in a moving-coil meter is usually obtained by the moving coil being wound on a light aluminium or alloy former, from which the coil is suitably insulated. This former then comprises a closed conducting path in the magnetic field. As the coil and its former move in the magnetic field under the action of the deflecting torque, e.m.f.'s are induced in the sides of the metallic coil former. These will be additive around the closed loop of the former, and, because of its low electrical resistance, circulating 'eddy' currents will be set up. By Lenz's law (see page 628), these currents will be in such a direction that the forces they experience in the magnetic field will oppose the movement producing them. These currents, and the forces resulting from them, are present only while the coil-former is moving. They thus set up opposition to the movement, and damp out oscillations in this movement, without affecting the final steady position of the coil. This is a simple practical application of the eddy-current brake discussed on page 638.

21.3. Ammeters and voltmeters. Moving-iron type

There are two fundamental types of moving-iron meter. One, known as the attraction type, derives its deflection force from the attraction exerted on a piece of iron by the magnetic field set up by the current to be measured passing through a coil of wire. This type may also be made in a 'polarized' form, when the piece of iron is itself permanently magnetized. The attraction force is then exerted on one or other of the magnetic poles of the iron, depending on the direction of the current through the coil. Very few attraction-type moving-iron meters are

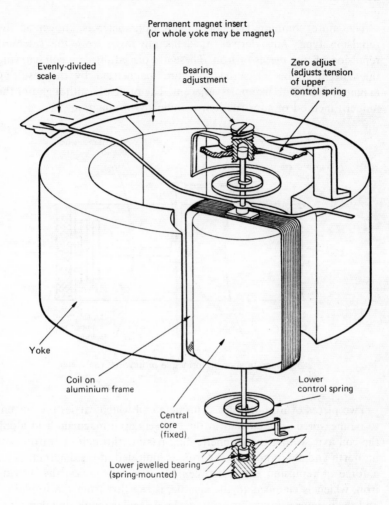

Permanent magnet insert
(or whole yoke may be magnet)

Evenly-divided
scale

Bearing
adjustment

Zero adjust
(adjusts tension
of upper
control spring

Yoke

Coil on
aluminium frame

Lower
control spring

Central
core
(fixed)

Lower jewelled bearing
(spring-mounted)

(d) Sketch of complete moving-coil instrument

282. Moving-coil meter

(The control springs, which are usually made of beryllium-copper, are often used
to lead the measured current into and out of the moving coil. If separate flexible
leads were used, difficulties would be encountered due to their 'drag' on the coil
movement)

now made, however, and no further description of them will be given.

The more common type of moving-iron meter is known as the repulsion type. This derives its deflecting force from the sideways repulsion of two pieces of iron. These are placed inside a coil carrying the current to be measured, and are magnetized by the resulting magnetic field, with like poles adjacent. The principle, although not the modern method of construction, is indicated in diagram 283.

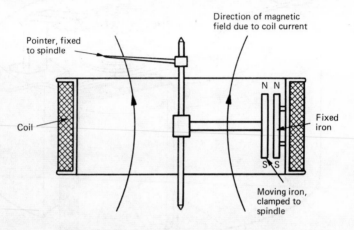

283. Diagram showing principle of moving-iron meter

Two pieces of iron are placed inside a coil which carries the current to be measured. The current in the coil sets up a magnetic field along the coil axis so that the magnetic flux, passing through each iron, sets up north and south poles in the iron as indicated in the diagram. Since a force of repulsion exists between like magnetic poles, the moving iron, which is clamped to the spindle, is repelled from the fixed iron and the pointer is moved over the scale. A similar repulsion takes place even if the coil current and hence the magnetic field is reversed, since the result will still be that adjacent ends of the irons have the same polarity.

The controlling arrangements are usually the same as those already described for the moving-coil instrument, although, of course, in the case of the moving-iron instrument the control springs are not rquired to carry any current. Once again it is common practice to use two opposing springs. In addition to the zero-adjust facility mentioned, this enables the spring, whose function it is to oppose the movement of the pointer and so make the final deflection proportional to the torque exerted, to start its operation from a partly wound-up state. This avoids errors due to slight irregularities at very low spring tensions.

It is not usual for a moving-iron meter to use eddy-current damping, as the magnetic field strength due to the operating coil is usually much less than in the moving-coil magnet system. The system of damping usually employed is by air vane. A flat, light, metal vane is fixed to the spindle, and the damping effect is obtained from the air resistance to the movement of the vane. A common practice is to arrange for this vane to move in a closed, or partially closed, chamber. The chamber restricts the flow of air round the vane and so increases the damping effect.

For the simple type of moving-iron meter using similar rods for the fixed and moving irons, the force set up between the irons, and hence the pointer deflection, is proportional to the square of the current in the coil. This means that if the current in the coil were to be doubled, the force and the pointer deflection would be four times as great. The scale for such an instrument is known as a 'square-law' scale, and is cramped at the lower end. For example, the angular distance between the points marking 0 and 4 A would be four times that between the points for 0 and 2 A, and sixteen times that between the points for 0 and 1 A.

In modern instruments, however, the fixed and moving irons are not simple rods. The fixed iron takes the form of a curved plate inside the coil, and the moving iron is also usually a (smaller) plate. By suitably shaping these irons, it is possible to greatly modify the basic square law for the deflection, and almost any scale shape can be obtained. Nevertheless, some cramping of the scale is usually still evident at the lower end, although a large portion of the scale can be made much more uniform than would be given by a square law.

A sketch of the construction of a modern moving-iron instrument is given in diagram 284; here spring control and air-vane damping are shown. A typical scale shape for a modern moving-iron meter is shown in diagram 285 (a), while a square-law scale is shown for comparison in diagram 285 (b). The scales have been 'straightened' for ease of comparison—they would normally, of course, be inscribed on the arc of a circle. Note that the modern scale has been adjusted to give maximum reading accuracy at values around the centre of the scale.

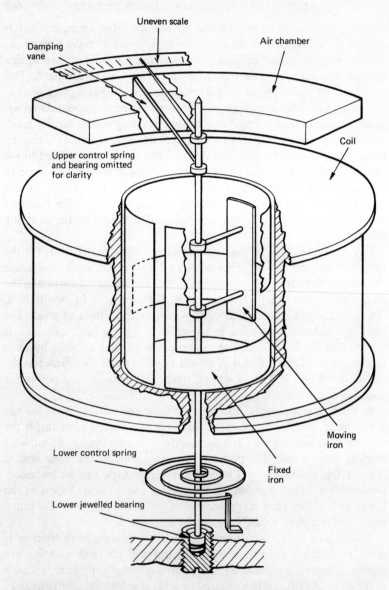

Uneven scale

Damping vane

Air chamber

Coil

Upper control spring
and bearing omitted
for clarity

Moving iron

Lower control spring

Fixed iron

Lower jewelled bearing

284. Diagrammatic sketch of moving-iron instrument
(Details of upper bearing, upper control spring, and zero adjuster omitted)

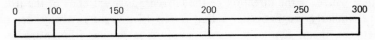

(a) Typical scale-shape for modern moving-iron
   instrument

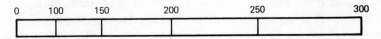

(b) Square-law scale corresponding to the range
of the scale shown in (a)

285. Comparison of scale-shapes for moving-iron instruments. (Note adjustment of scale in (a) to give comparatively even scale for readings over a chosen range of values)

21.4. Comparisons between moving-coil and moving-iron instruments

The majority of ammeters and voltmeters in common use are of either the moving-coil or moving-iron type, and a brief comparison of their relative advantages and disadvantages may be helpful. Broadly speaking, the use of each type is determined by whether the current to be measured is uni-directional (that is, a 'direct' current) or whether the current-direction is periodically changing (that is, an 'alternating' current). (See Chapter 20, page 646.)

The directions of the force exerted on a current-carrying conductor in a magnetic field will reverse if the direction of the current is reversed, (see page 605). This means that the deflection of the moving-coil instrument depends on current direction. If the current through the coil is reversed, the pointer will be moved backwards. This effect may be used to determine the direction of a direct current, for example in instruments having the zero point at the centre of the scale, of which the common form of d.c. galvanometer is typical. However, if the current direction is reversing periodically at other than very low frequencies, the inertia of the moving parts prevents the pointer from indicating the continual reversal of the deflecting force. The needle remains pointing at zero, although sometimes it can be seen to be trembling under the action of the alternating force. Consequently, unless special steps are taken to modify such a current (for example, by use of a 'rectifier', which ensures uni-directional current flow through the coil), the moving-coil meter cannot be used with alternating current.

This disadvantage does not apply to the moving-iron instrument, since whatever the direction of the current, adjacent ends of the irons are similarly magnetized, so that a repulsive force is always set up between them. Similarly, an attraction-type moving-iron instrument always gives the same direction of deflection, since the unmagnetized piece of iron will be attracted towards the centre of the coil for either direction of the magnetic field. This does not, however, apply to the polarized type. The moving-iron instrument may, then, be used on either direct or alternating current, since the direction of the deflecting force will always be the same. It can be shown that, when used on alternating current, the deflection depends on the effective, or r.m.s., value referred to on page 681.

The second major difference between the two instruments is in the convenient current range of the basic instrument. (The modification of this current range for particular purposes has already been discussed on pages 534-538.) Because a light moving coil is required, and because the coil current is usually carried by the control springs, the current which the coil of a moving-coil instrument is designed to carry is usually small—of the order of a few milli-amperes or less. This requirement does not apply in the case of a moving-iron instrument, and the coil of the moving-iron instrument can be wound for full-scale deflection currents of the order of several amperes. The use of a coil with tapping connections made at intervals in it enables several current ranges to be readily obtained without any need for the shunts discussed on page 536. However, since it is necessary to set up a magnetic field

Feature	Moving-coil meter	Moving-iron meter
Reversed current	Reversed deflection	Same deflection
Use	d.c. circuits only	d.c. circuits or a.c. circuits
Usual operating-coil current	5 mA or less	10 mA or more
Scale	Uniform	Non-uniform
Effect of external 'stray' magnetic field	Little effect (well shielded)	More easily affected (more difficult to shield)
Cost	Relatively expensive	Relatively cheap

Summary of relative features of moving-coil and moving-iron meters

of a certain minimum strength in order to produce the required deflecting force, it is more difficult to wind the coil of a moving-iron instrument for low current ranges (below about 10 mA or so).

This difference in minimum convenient operating current means that a moving-coil voltmeter can more easily be made to have a high sensitivity (low operating current) than can a moving-iron voltmeter. Typical values for instruments of comparable price would be about 1000 Ω/V for a moving-coil voltmeter and about 60 Ω/V for a moving-iron voltmeter (see page 535). These, and other characteristics of the two types of meter, are summarized in the table on page 696.

21.5. Dynamometer (or electrodynamic) instruments

In this type of instrument, a current-carrying coil is placed in the magnetic field set up by a current in another coil or set of coils. When used as an ammeter or a voltmeter the currents in the coils are the same, and depend on the current to be measured.

When used as a wattmeter, to measure the electrical power for a circuit, the current in one of the instrument coils is derived from the current in the circuit concerned, while the current in the other instrument coil is derived from the voltage across the circuit concerned. In this case the coils are usually referred to as the 'current' coil and 'voltage' (or 'pressure') coil, respectively.

The general arrangement of the coils in a dynamometer instrument is indicated in diagram 286. The moving coil (which in the case of the wattmeter is usually the pressure coil of the instrument) is arranged on a spindle which carries the pointer and which moves against the action of control springs as already described. Damping is usually obtained by air vane, as for a moving-iron instrument. Current flowing in the fixed coils (usually the current coils for a wattmeter) sets up a magnetic field along the axis of these coils, which is reasonably uniform in the gap between them provided this gap is not too wide. This gap is often just sufficient to insert the moving coil and its spindle. The moving coil is then of a small enough diameter to turn inside the fixed coils. This 'fixed-coil' magnetic field then interacts with the magnetic field of the current in the moving coil to produce a deflection torque which acts to move the pointer over the scale. The deflection torque is proportional to the product of the currents in the two coils, so that, because of the action of the control springs, the indication of the pointer on the scale is also proportional to this product of coil-currents. When used as a

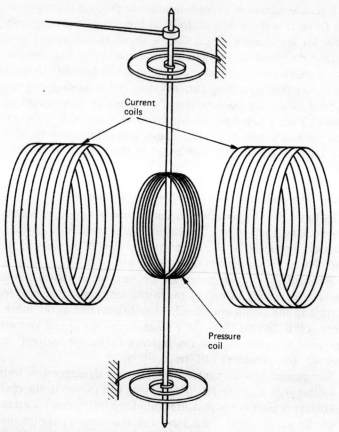

Current coils

Pressure coil

286. Diagrammatic sketch of coils in a dynamometer instrument

wattmeter, the current in the fixed coils is proportional to the current in the circuit concerned, while the current in the moving coil is proportional to the voltage across that circuit. In this case, then,

$$\text{deflection} \propto \text{voltage} \times \text{current}$$
$$\text{or} \qquad \text{deflection} \propto \text{power}$$

This means that the scale of a dynamometer wattmeter is uniform.

When used as a voltmeter or ammeter, the deflection will be proportional to the square of these quantities, and the instrument will have an uneven 'square-law' scale. It will indicate the effective or r.m.s. value of an alternating voltage or current.

The dynamometer instrument is most frequently used as a watt-meter, when it is connected as shown in diagram 287.

The indication of the wattmeter will give the power in the load resistance R_L. (For the connection shown the indication will also include the power in the current coils, but this is usually negligible, or, alternatively, allowance can be made for it.) The resistance r is the series 'range-adjusting' resistance for the pressure coil, whose value is determined in a similar way to that for a voltmeter.

In this connection it is most important to notice that the deflection depends on the values of both the current in the current coils *and* the

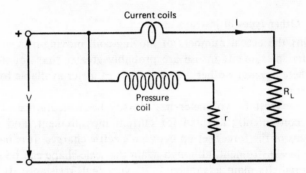

287. Circuit diagram of connections for a wattmeter

voltage applied across the pressure coil. If the current is doubled for the same voltage, or if the voltage is doubled for the same current, the deflection will be twice as great. If both the current *and* the voltage are doubled, the deflection is four times as great. If either the voltage or current is reversed, the deflection will be reversed, although the same deflection is obtained if both voltage *and* current are reversed. Many wattmeters include a reversing switch in the pressure-coil circuit.

If, however, the voltage applied to the pressure coil is zero, there will be no deflection, however great the current in the current coils. Similarly, no deflection will be obtained if the current coils are open-circuited, whatever voltage is applied to the pressure coils. What can be even more dangerous, however, is that only a small deflection may be obtained if either the voltage or current is low, even though the other quantity may be high. It would thus be possible for the pressure coil or the current coils to be overloaded (that is, to be carrying more current than the maximum safe value) even while the deflection was below its full-scale value. (On alternating-current circuits, this situation may arise even more readily.)

Consequently, although it is always important to avoid overloading any instrument, and care should always be taken to select an instrument of a suitable range for the circuit in which it is to be used, extra care is required in the use of a wattmeter. Evidence of overloading may not be given by the deflection of the pointer, and to avoid damage to the instrument coils the values of current and voltage should also be measured, and should be checked against the safe values for the wattmeter used.

21.6. Other types of instrument

Whilst the actual numbers of moving-coil, moving-iron and dynamometer instruments in use are probably greater than for any other type, there are many other different types of meter available for special applications.

The electrostatic voltmeter has already been mentioned. This type is not conveniently adapted for current measurement, and operates by means of the forces set up between electric charges. It is basically a square-law instrument, although again the scale-shape can be modified if required. Its main advantage is its very high resistance. It requires practically zero current for operation on direct voltages, and only extremely small currents on alternating voltages. This type is usually only available for relatively high voltage ranges.

The so-called 'rectifier' instrument, which is available as either an ammeter or a voltmeter, is really a moving-coil instrument suitably connected to a rectifier. A rectifier is a device for converting the alternate 'pulses' of an alternating current into uni-directional current pulses, as indicated in diagram 288. When these uni-directional current pulses flow in the moving coil of the meter, the deflection produced is given by the average value of the current, since the inertia of the moving parts prevents the needle from following the instantaneous current variations. The rectifier instrument is thus used for the measurement of alternating currents and voltages, and fundamentally measures their average value. The meter, however, may be scaled directly in terms of the effective or r.m.s. value on the assumption of a sinusoidal waveform.

'Thermal' instruments are available as either ammeters or voltmeters. These instruments measure the heating effect of a current.

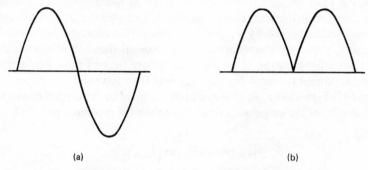

(a)   (b)

288. Current variations for rectifier instrument

(a) Sinusoidal alternating current
(b) Uni-directional current pulses in coil of moving-coil meter. Obtained from
    the current shown in (a) by means of a rectifier

Apart from the now obsolete 'hot-wire' ammeter, which operated by
the expansion of a wire heated by the current being measured, these
instruments are usually moving-coil milli-voltmeters which measure the
e.m.f. produced at the junction of two dissimilar metals when this
junction is heated. Such a junction is known as a 'thermo-couple',
and materials such as copper and iron, or copper and constantan (an
alloy of copper and nickel), are used to form the thermo-couple. This
junction is then attached to a small heating element, and the assembly
may then be enclosed in a glass bulb containing air or nitrogen at low
pressure, to shield the heater and junction from draughts and to
minimize loss of heat energy. The heat energy developed in the resistance of the heating element by the current to be measured is then used
to heat the thermo-couple junction, and the resulting e.m.f. is a measure
of the current through the heater. Since the heating effect is independent
of the direction of the current, these instruments may be used with
either direct or alternating currents. Their main function is as 'transfer'
instruments; that is, they are first calibrated with a direct current and
one of the accurate methods mentioned in Chapter 17, page 507, and
are then used as 'standard' instruments for the calibration of alternating-current meters.

The total electric charge, or quantity of electricity, passed round a
circuit in a given time is measured by an instrument basically similar to
a moving-coil meter, but without control springs. The deflecting force
will continue for as long as the charge-displacement is taking place,

and the total impulse (force × time) given to the moving-coil system is a measure of the total charge displaced. This impulse determines the total distance moved by the pointer, so that the scale can be calibrated in units of charge. The theory of the instrument shows that it is necessary for all the charge to be displaced before the coil moves by a significant amount. These instruments will then have a coil system of relatively high inertia, and, since damping should be kept to a minimum, are usually of the suspension type rather than the pivoted type.

CHAPTER SUMMARY

An electrical measuring instrument will usually have
  (i) a deflecting device
  (ii) a controlling device
  (iii) a damping device.

In a moving-coil meter,
  (i) the deflecting device consists of a coil suitably suspended in a uniform, radial magnetic field and carrying the current to be measured
  (ii) the controlling device consists of two control springs arranged so that they oppose the force developed on the moving coil. The deflection is thus made proportional to this force
  (iii) the damping device usually consists of a conducting former for the coil. Eddy currents set up in this coil-former give rise to damping forces.

In a moving-iron meter,
  (i) the deflecting device consists of two shaped pieces of iron within a coil carrying the current to be measured. One iron is fixed and the other iron is free to move and carries the pointer. Deflecting force is due to the mutual repulsion of the irons
  (ii) the controlling device consists of control springs, as for the moving-coil meter
  (iii) the damping device usually consists of a light metal vane fixed to the pointer spindle and arranged to move within a partially-closed metal surround. The air-resistance opposes the movement of the vane and so damps the movement of the pointer.

See page 696 for a comparison between moving-coil and moving-iron meters.

In a dynamometer, or electrodynamic, instrument,
(i) the deflecting device consists of a coil suitably suspended in the magnetic field of a second coil or set of coils. The moving and fixed coils may carry the same current (in ammeter or voltmeter applications) or different currents (in wattmeter applications)
(ii) and (iii) controlling and damping devices are usually as for moving-iron instruments.

QUESTIONS

1. Make a large and clear sketch to show the construction of a moving-iron, repulsion-type ammeter, and describe the action of this instrument. Explain how the movement is made to return to zero when the current is cut off, and how a steady reading is obtained. Has this type of instrument any advantages over a moving-coil instrument? Compare by means of a sketch the scale for each type of instrument.

2. Describe, with the aid of sketches, the construction of a moving-coil meter. The following points must be made clearly:
(a) The means by which current is taken to and from the coil
(b) The method of fixing the core piece
(c) The object of a core piece in such an instrument and why it is held in position by a non-magnetic material
(d) The method of damping.

3. Distinguish between (a) deflecting torque, (b) damping torque and (c) controlling torque, and explain clearly how each is produced in a moving-coil milliammeter.
A moving-coil instrument has a resistance of 50 Ω and gives a full-scale deflection with 5 mA. Show by means of a diagram how the instrument could be adapted to measure currents up to 1 A, and calculate the value of the resistance required.

4. (a) Explain why the coil of a moving-coil ammeter is wound on a metal frame.
(b) The coil in such an ammeter had an effective length of 30 mm and width of 15 mm and was wound with 400 turns. Calculate the torque on the coil when the current in it is 10 mA. The field strength is 0·8 T.

5. (a) Describe the principle of a moving-iron instrument (detailed constructional features are not required).
(b) An unmarked instrument has a removable back so that its interior may be inspected. What features would indicate that the instrument could be used (i) as an ammeter, (ii) as a voltmeter, (iii) on a.c. or d.c. supplies?

6. Describe with the aid of a diagram the construction and action of a moving-coil instrument with reference to how damping and control are effected. State the advantages and disadvantages of this type of instrument, and show by diagrams how it can be used for measuring current and voltage.

7. Sketch the main constructional features of a dynamometer wattmeter. Explain why it is possible to overload an instrument of this type without the pointer indicating a deflection greater than its full-scale value.

8. Use a diagram to describe the construction of a moving-iron repulsion-type meter. Indicate on this diagram the components used to produce (i) the controlling torque, (ii) the damping torque, and explain the function in each case.

22. Energy Conversion

22.1. Various forms of energy. Energy conversion

Energy may have several forms, and reference has already been made to forms of mechanical energy as the potential energy available from a body by virtue of its mass and position (Section 6.9, page 188), as the kinetic energy available from a body by virtue of its mass and speed of movement (Section 6.11, page 190), and as the strain energy available from a body by virtue of its distortion from its normal conditions (Section 6.10, page 190). Mention has also been made of the heat energy available from a body by virtue of its mass, specific heat capacity and temperature (Section 14.9, page 371), as well as the electrical energy available from an electric charge by virtue of its electrical potential (Section 16.2, page 438). Other forms of energy include chemical energy, light energy and pressure energy.

All these forms of energy are examples of the fundamental concept, or idea, that ENERGY IS THE CAPACITY TO DO WORK. For instance, the potential energy from a forge hammer is capable of doing work on the forging placed beneath it; the kinetic energy from a jet of water is capable of doing work on blades of a water-turbine as it strikes them; the strain energy from a wound-up clock-spring is capable of doing work in turning the gear-wheels of the clock; the heat energy released when a petrol–air mixture is burned is capable of doing work against the piston in a car engine; and the electrical energy supplied to an electric motor is capable of doing work in turning the motor shaft.

During each process quoted here, the form of the original energy is converted into some other form. Some of the potential energy from the forge hammer is converted into kinetic energy in the hammer as it falls down on to the forging; some of the kinetic energy from the water-jet is converted into another form of kinetic energy of rotation of the turbine wheel; some of the strain energy from the clock-spring is also converted into kinetic energy in the rotation of the gear-wheels of the clock; some of the heat energy from the petrol–air mixture is converted into kinetic energy of the moving piston; some of the electrical energy is converted into kinetic energy in the rotation of the motor shaft. In most cases, some of the available energy is also converted into the form of heat energy.

It follows then that energy may have many different forms, but that it is often quite easily possible to convert energy from one form to another. Of course, in some cases this conversion of the form of the energy is easier than in others.

Some mention should also be made of 'atomic' energy. This is a form of energy contained within an atom, although its release and conversion to other forms of energy is a very complicated process. Expressed very simply, the energy possessed within an atom is the energy required to hold it all together as an atom, and can be considered as a form of potential energy. If the nucleus of the atom can be broken apart, this energy may be released and converted to other forms, often to heat energy, as in a nuclear reactor. Einstein showed that mass is really another form of energy, although the large-scale conversion of mass to other usable forms of energy is not an easy process. This conversion is what takes place in a nuclear reactor. Incidentally, an atom can accept energy and give it out again, without anything as catastrophic as an atomic explosion occurring. For example, the operation of a fluorescent light fitting relies on this effect. The atoms of the fluorescent coating inside the tube accept light energy of one kind from the electrical discharge inside the tube and give out light energy of a different kind. The difference between this action and the atomic explosion is that in the fluorescent coating, the atomic nuclei are not disturbed. They are disturbed in the atomic bomb.

22.2. Conservation of energy

A very important fundamental principle which underlies all cases of energy conversion is that ENERGY CANNOT BE DESTROYED OR CREATED. This is known as the PRINCIPLE OF CONSERVATION OF ENERGY. Thus, although the form of the energy can be, and often is, changed, the *total* energy after conversion is the same as the *total* energy before the conversion took place.

Much of engineering is concerned with the conversion of energy from one form to another for a particular purpose. These practical methods of energy conversion are not ideal, in that not all the energy originally available in the first form becomes converted to the required form for further use. In this connection, engineers often refer to the energy 'lost'. In fact, what is meant is that this lost energy has been converted to some form other than that intended. It is impossible to 'lose' energy in the sense of destroying it, although the particular form in which it appears may not be capable of being directly used for the work for which the energy-converting machine was designed. The heat energy released by the fire under a boiler will not all be transferred to the water or steam obtained from the boiler; some will undoubtedly be transferred to the boiler walls, to the surrounding air, and to the gases going up the chimney. Although this energy is 'lost' to the engineer for his particular purpose, it is not lost in the sense of being destroyed.

It might be thought that energy is destroyed when it is used to do work. However, this is not the case, and perhaps a particular example will make this clear.

Take the case of the forge hammer. When the hammer falls on to the metal of the forging, its potential energy is first converted to kinetic energy, and this energy is used to do work in distorting the forging by pushing it into a new shape. The amount of work done is given by the product of the upwards resisting force of the metal, which must be overcome by the hammer, and the vertical distance by which the metal is distorted:

$$\text{work done} = \text{force} \times \text{distance moved in direction of force}$$

The work done, or energy 'consumed', in distorting the metal is converted into heat energy in the metal, and is not lost in any way. This point can very easily be verified. A small piece of metal vigorously hammered on a wooden bench will be found to be quite warm afterwards.

Thus, although it is said that energy (the capacity to do work) is used to do a particular amount of work, the energy will always be found to be converted in some way during the process—often into the form of heat energy—and not really used up in any way.

22.3. Stored energy

It is an interesting, and important, consequence of the principle of conservation of energy that all the energy available to do work for all time is already contained in the world—or, more broadly, within whatever limits the universe may have. As the more readily convertible forms of energy are converted into other forms—usually, ultimately, some form of heat energy—so new energy stores must be drawn upon to supply our needs for particular forms of energy. The point is being approached, although it is perhaps still remote, where energy derived from the sun in the form of light and heat energy, and stored as chemical energy in coal, will have all been converted into other forms. Fortunately, other energy stores such as oil, and, more recently, atomic energy have become available, as techniques of energy conversion have been developed and improved.

Energy can, then, be stored in many different ways. These ways vary from the chemical energy stored in a fuel by natural processes, to the potential energy stored in a forge hammer when it is lifted to the top of its stroke. The one is a natural store of energy fundamentally present in the world as it exists; the other is an energy store used by the engineer in much the same way as a bank is used to store money. The engineer arranges that a certain amount of energy is given to the forge hammer in order to lift it to the top of its stroke, knowing that this amount of energy will be available to do work on the forging when required. The fact that all the energy so stored will not do useful work in distorting the forging, but that some will be converted, say, into the energy in a sound wave, does not change the fact that the work done in lifting the forge hammer is stored as potential energy in the hammer.

Another example of stored energy is the kinetic energy stored in a rotating flywheel. Work is done on the flywheel by the torque required to accelerate it to its final speed, and most of this work will be stored in the flywheel. Some will be transferred as heat energy to the bearings of the flywheel shaft, and if the flywheel is allowed to slow down to a stop without any other load, all the stored energy will be transferred in this way. The stored energy in the flywheel may be used to supply energy to do some kind of work, as in a press-tool machine, or a flywheel may be used to store energy—for example, in between the firing strokes of an engine—in order that this energy may be released more smoothly to do work at the shaft of the machine.

Summary

Energy is the capacity to do work. It has many forms, and can be stored in most of these forms. It can be converted from one form to another, but it cannot be created or destroyed.

22.4. Efficiency of energy conversion

It has already been mentioned in Section 22.2, page 706, that practical forms of energy conversion are not ideal, in that not all the energy originally available is converted to the required form. The efficiency of an energy conversion is a measure of the success of the operation. The more the available energy that is converted to the required 'useful' form, the higher will be the efficiency of the process.

The percentage efficiency of any form of energy conversion can be defined as

$$\% \text{ efficiency} = \frac{\text{energy converted to useful form}}{\text{energy available for conversion}} \times 100\%$$

The value of the percentage efficiency gives the number of units of energy converted to useful form for every 100 units of energy originally supplied or available. It will always be less than 100. Sometimes the PER UNIT efficiency is given in a particular case. This will always be less than 1 and gives the number of units converted to useful form for each unit of energy originally supplied or available. The per-unit efficiency is simply the percentage efficiency divided by 100.

The efficiency achieved by different types of energy conversion may vary widely. For example, the overall efficiency of a steam engine viewed from the mechanical energy available at the shaft, compared with the energy stored in the fuel, may be of the order of 20% or so, while the efficiency of an electrical transformer viewed from the electrical energy supplied to an electrical load, compared with the electrical energy supplied initially to the transformer, may be of the order of 98%.

Sometimes energy conversions take place in series, with energy being converted from the initial input form to another form, before the final conversion to the output form. For example, a petrol engine may be used to drive an electrical generator. The petrol engine converts the chemical energy of the fuel into heat energy and then into mechanical energy. It supplies this mechanical energy to the electrical generator, which then converts it into electrical energy. At each stage of this sequence of energy conversion, not all the energy available from the previous stage will be converted into useful form. In other words, the efficiency of each stage will be less than 100%. In cases of this type, THE OVERALL PER-UNIT EFFICIENCY IS THE PRODUCT OF THE INDIVIDUAL STAGE PER-UNIT EFFICIENCIES. In other words, the overall efficiency is obtained by multiplying the separate efficiencies by one another, provided that, if percentage values are used, they are first divided by 100. This result could be obtained in the following way.

Suppose there are 100 units of energy available in the first place, and suppose the first device has an efficiency of 80%. This means that only 80 units of the original 100 units are converted to useful form, the other

20 units being converted to some other form and used, say, to heat up the surrounding air. If these 80 units are passed on to a second device having an efficiency of 75%, then only 75% of the 80 units received will be converted into the final useful form. That is, the final useful energy output of the two devices together is

$$75\% \text{ of } 80 \text{ units}$$

or
$$\frac{75}{100} \times 80 \text{ units}$$

$$= 60 \text{ units}$$

These 60 units of useful energy output have been obtained from the original 100 units of energy supplied, so that the overall percentage efficiency is given by

$$\% \text{ efficiency} = \frac{\text{useful energy output}}{\text{total energy input}} \times 100\%$$

$$= \frac{60}{100} \times 100\%$$

$$= \underline{\underline{60\%}}$$

Using the idea of per-unit efficiency,

$$\text{overall per-unit efficiency} = \frac{75}{100} \times \frac{80}{100} = 0.6$$

and this corresponds to a percentage efficiency of 60%.

$$(\text{percentage efficiency} = \text{per-unit efficiency} \times 100)$$

For the petrol-engine/electrical generator arrangement mentioned earlier, if the efficiency of the petrol-engine is 35% and the efficiency of the electrical generator is 85%, then the overall efficiency is given by

$$\text{overall per-unit efficiency} = \frac{35}{100} \times \frac{85}{100} = 0.297 \text{ p.u.}$$

or $$\text{overall percentage efficiency} = \frac{35}{100} \times \frac{85}{100} \times 100 = 29.7\%$$

22.5. Mechanical equivalent of heat

Mechanical energy has been seen to be capable of being converted into heat energy, so that a direct relationship must exist between the units in which these two forms of energy are measured. This relationship is known as the MECHANICAL EQUIVALENT OF HEAT, or, sometimes, as 'Joule's equivalent', after the scientist who first measured its value. The numerical value of the mechanical equivalent of heat is unity in that 1 newton metre of mechanical work done equals 1 joule. The joule is the unit of energy in all its forms: mechanical, heat, electrical, chemical and atomic.

There are various methods of determining the value of the mechanical equivalent of heat. The method used by Joule (which incidentally gave him a result which was about 1% below the value found by later, more accurate experiments) was to measure the amount of work done by a system of falling weights driving a paddle wheel round in water. The heat energy released in the water could be calculated from its mass, specific heat capacity and rise in temperature. Allowances had to be made for the heat energy absorbed by the water-container, work done against bearing-friction, heat energy transmitted to the surrounding air and so on.

Whilst the rise in temperature of a known mass of water remains the easiest way of calculating the heat energy obtained, now other methods of supplying the mechanical energy are usually used. One common method is to use a friction belt, under known constant tension, round a metal cylinder containing the water. Mechanical work is done when the cylinder is revolved against the frictional forces exerted by the belt. If the belt tension is T N and the diameter of the cylinder is d m, a torque of $\frac{Td}{2}$ Nm is required to rotate the cylinder—neglecting any additional torque to overcome bearing friction, which is not measured and which does not effect the result. The mechanical work done in one revolution is then

$$\frac{Td}{2} \times 2\pi \text{ Nm}$$

or, for n revolutions, is

$$\pi n T d \text{ Nm}$$

This mechanical energy input can then be equated to the heat energy absorbed by the water and its container.

22.6. Electrical equivalent of heat

Since electrical energy is also convertible to heat energy (and also to mechanical energy) a relationship similar to that between the units of mechanical energy and heat energy must exist between units of electrical energy and heat energy. This is known as the ELECTRICAL EQUIVALENT OF HEAT or, again, as 'Joule's equivalent'. Since electrical energy is also measured in joules, its value is again unity.

The most common method of determining the value of the electrical equivalent of heat is to measure the heat energy absorbed by a known mass of water when a known electric current flows for a measured time through a known value of resistance placed in the water. Allowances are made, as before, for the heat energy absorbed by the container and the material of the resistor, and for the heat energy transmitted to the surrounding air and along the electrical conductors. (If a current I A flows for a time t s through a resistance of $R \Omega$, the electrical energy delivered to the resistor is I^2Rt joules.)

22.7.   Examples

(i) An oil-fired boiler is used to provide steam to drive a steam-engine. The boiler is supplied with 3 kg/h of oil with a calorific value of 42 MJ/kg. The steam-engine drives a load requiring a torque of 300 Nm at a speed of 200 rev/min. Find the overall efficiency of the engine and boiler.

Heat energy input per second
$$\text{to the boiler} = 3 \left(\frac{\text{kg}}{\text{h}}\right) : 42 \left(\frac{\text{MJ}}{\text{kg}}\right) \times \left(\frac{1 \text{ h}}{3600 \text{ s}}\right)$$

$$= \frac{126}{3600} \text{ MJ/s}$$

$$= \frac{126\,000}{3600} \text{ kJ/s}$$

$$= 35 \text{ kJ/s}$$

The mechanical energy ouput of the steam engine is

$$\frac{2\pi n T}{60} \text{ J/s}$$

$$= \frac{2\pi \times 200 \times 300}{60} \text{ J/s}$$

$$= 6284 \text{ J/s}$$

$$= 6 \cdot 284 \text{ kJ/s}$$

∴ Overall efficiency of engine and boiler is

$$\frac{\text{useful energy output}}{\text{total energy input}} \times 100\%$$

$$= \frac{6\cdot284}{35} \times 100\%$$

$$= \underline{18\%}$$

(ii) An electric boiler is required to raise the temperature of 90 l of water per hour by 35°C. Find the cost of operating the boiler for a period of 5 h if electrical energy costs 0·8 p/kWh, and the efficiency of the boiler is 85%.

Heat energy required per hour to raise the temperature of the water
$$= mc\theta$$
$$= 90 \times 4\cdot186 \times 35$$
$$= 13\ 200 \text{ kJ/h}$$
$$= 13\cdot2 \text{ MJ/h}$$

Then the equivalent electrical power input to the water is

$$= 13\cdot2 \left(\frac{\text{MJ}}{\text{h}}\right) \times \left(\frac{1\ \text{h}}{3600\ \text{s}}\right) \times \left(\frac{1000\ \text{kJ}}{1\ \text{MJ}}\right)$$

$$= 3\cdot67 \text{ kJ/s (kW)}$$

Since the boiler efficiency is 85% (or 0·85 per unit) the electrical power input required to the boiler is given by

$$\text{input} = \frac{\text{output}}{\text{efficiency (p.u.)}}$$

$$= \frac{3\cdot67}{0\cdot85} \text{ kW}$$

$$= 4\cdot31 \text{ kW}$$

Total electrical energy input in 5 h is given by
$$\text{energy} = \text{power} \times \text{time}$$
$$= 4\cdot31 \text{ (kW)} \times 5 \text{ (h)}$$
$$= 21\cdot55 \text{ kWh}$$

Cost of electrical energy at 0·8 p/kWh is
$$0\cdot8 \times 21\cdot55 \text{ p}$$
$$= \underline{17\cdot2 \text{ p}}$$

(iii) A pump driven by an electrical motor raises 4·5 m³ of water per minute through a height of 15 m.

If the pump has an efficiency of 80%, what is the power output of the motor? If the motor has an efficiency of 85%, what is the electrical power input to the motor, in kW? If electrical energy costs 0·8 p/kWh, what is the cost of using this pump to fill a 450-m³ water tank (the tank being at the top end of the delivery pipe; i.e. 15 m above the water intake to the pump)?

Work done on water every minute by pump

$$= \text{mass of water per minute} \times \text{gravitational acceleration} \times \text{height raised}$$

$$\text{power output of pump} = 4·5 \times 1000 \times 9·81 \times 15 \text{ J/min}$$

$$= \frac{662\,000}{60} \text{ J/s}$$

$$= 11\,020 \text{ J/s} = 11·02 \text{ (kJ/s) kW}$$

Since pump efficiency is 80% (or 0·8 per unit),

$$\text{power input to pump} = \frac{\text{output}}{\text{efficiency (p.u.)}}$$

$$= \frac{11·02}{0·8} \text{ kW}$$

or

$$\text{power output of motor} = \frac{11·02}{0·8} \text{ kW}$$

$$= \underline{\underline{13·78 \text{ kW}}}$$

Since the motor efficiency is 85% (or 0·85 per unit),

$$\text{power input to motor} = \frac{\text{output}}{\text{efficiency (p.u.)}}$$

$$= \frac{13·78}{0·85} \text{ kW}$$

$$= \underline{\underline{16·2 \text{ kW}}}$$

In order to fill the 450-m³ water tank, the pump would have to be operated for $\frac{450}{4·5}$ min, or 100 min.

Then, total electrical energy input to the pump motor is

electrical energy input = power × time

$$= 16 \cdot 2 \text{ (kW)} \times \frac{100}{60} \text{ (h)}$$

$$= 27 \text{ kWh}$$

If the energy costs $0 \cdot 8$ p per kWh, cost of operation is $27 \times 0 \cdot 8$ p = $\underline{\underline{21 \cdot 6 \text{ p}}}$

(iv) An electrical generator delivers a load current of 25 A at a terminal voltage of 250 V. The generator is driven by a motor whose output power is $7 \cdot 5$ kW. What is the efficiency of the generator?

$$\text{Output power of generator} = V.I \text{ watts}$$
$$= 250 \text{ (V)} \times 25 \text{ (A)}$$
$$= 6250 \text{ W} = 6 \cdot 25 \text{ kW}$$
$$\text{Input power to generator} = 7 \cdot 5 \text{ kW}$$

$$\text{Then, generator efficiency} = \frac{\text{output}}{\text{input}} \times 100\%$$

$$= \frac{6 \cdot 25}{7 \cdot 5} \times 100\%$$

$$= \underline{\underline{83 \cdot 4\%}}$$

CHAPTER SUMMARY

Energy is the capacity to do work. It can have many different forms, and may frequently be converted from one form to another.

Principle of conservation of energy:

'Energy cannot be created or destroyed.'

Energy may be stored in many different forms, and released or converted into other forms as required. The efficiency of an energy conversion is given by

$$\text{efficiency} = \frac{\text{useful energy output}}{\text{useful energy input}} \text{ per unit}$$

$$\% \text{ efficiency} = \text{per-unit efficiency} \times 100\%$$

If several stages are involved, the overall efficiency is given by:

overall efficiency (p.u.) $= \eta_1 \times \eta_2 \times \eta_3 \times \ldots$ p.u. where η_1, η_2, η_3, etc. are the per-unit efficiencies of each individual stage.

QUESTIONS

1. (a) State the principle of the conservation of energy.

(b) A body having a mass of 1 tonne is raised vertically through a distance of 12 m in 15 s. How much work is done, and what average power is required? If the supporting rope now breaks, determine the kinetic energy of the body when it is 3 m from the ground.

2. A flywheel of a shearing machine has 300 kJ of kinetic energy stored in it when its speed is 300 rev/min. What amount of kinetic energy will be stored when its speed is reduced to 240 rev/min?

If 80% of the energy lost by the flywheel is supplied to the blades of the shearing machine during a stroke of 50 mm, what is the average force on the blades?

3. What is meant by 'kinetic energy' and how is it measured?

A machine has a flywheel of mass 2 tonne which may be considered concentrated at a radius of 0·85 m. During a working stroke the speed of the flywheel is reduced from 140 rev/min to 130 rev/min in 2 s. Calculate:

(a) the change in the kinetic energy of the flywheel

(b) the power absorbed by the machine from the flywheel during the working stroke.

4. State the principle of the conservation of energy.

A man lifts a stone having a mass of 250 g from the ground to a height of 1·650 m. He then throws it horizontally with a velocity of 6 m/s. Calculate the potential and kinetic energies gained by the stone and the work done by the man.

5. Define the terms 'potential energy' and 'kinetic energy', and show how these are involved in the case of a simple pile-driver.

A pile-driver uses a mass of 125 kg which is allowed to fall freely from rest through a vertical height of 6·6 m on to the pile which decreases the velocity of the mass on impact to 1·5 m/s. Calculate the energy lost by the mass on impact.

6. A train having a mass of 100 tonne is travelling at 8 km/h when it strikes the buffers, which are of the spring-loaded type. Each of the two buffers has a spring rate of 80 MN/m. Calculate the kinetic energy of the train before striking the buffers and the maximum compression of the buffers during impact.

7. A tank 4·5 m by 3·3 m contains water to a depth of 3 m. The water has to be pumped from the tank and discharged at a height of 18·3 m above the bottom of the tank. The tank is emptied in 20 min by means of a pump driven by an electric motor. Calculate:

(a) the power expended on the water

(b) the power supplied to the pump by the motor if the efficiency of the pump is 63%

(c) the electrical power in kilowatts supplied to the motor if its efficiency is 88%.

8. A 230-V, 1·5-kW, d.c. motor drives a pump whose efficiency is 65%. The input power to the motor is 1·7 kW. Determine:

(a) the current taken by the motor

(b) the efficiency of the motor

(c) the pump output

(d) the overall efficiency of the plant.

9. A conveyor belt is driven by an electric motor, a force of 40 kN being required to move the loaded belt at a steady speed of 75 mm/s. If the overall efficiency of the drive and the motor is 60%, calculate:

(a) the least input power required at the motor,

(b) the cost per 7-hour day if electricity costs 0·8 p/kWh.

10. (a) State the relationship between power, energy and time.

(b) When operating on a 240-V supply, a 5-hp, d.c. motor takes a current of 19 A.

Calculate (i) the efficiency of the motor, expressing it as a percentage; (ii) the energy consumed if the motor is used for 5 h.

11. Define the unit of energy.

A motor-driven pump delivers 9 m³ of water per min through a height of 30 m. The combined efficiency of the motor and pump is 50%. Calculate:

(a) the work done each second

(b) the power supplied to the motor

(c) the cost of running the pump for 1 h if energy costs 0·75 p/kWh.

12. An electrically-driven lubricating oil pump is required to pump 45 m³ of oil per hour to a height of 9 m. Calculate (a) the power rating of the electric motor, and (b) the energy input to the motor if it is in use for a period of 130 h. Assume that the efficiencies at this loading are 65% and 78% for the pump and motor respectively. The oil has a relative density of 0·8.

13. An electrically-driven pump lifts 585 litres of water per min through a height of 7·5 m. Allowing an overall efficiency of 63% for the motor and pump together, calculate the input current to the motor if the supply is 230 V.

If this pump is in operation for an average of 2 h per day, calculate the number of kWh consumed in a 7-day week.

14. A pump is required to lift 450 litres of water per min against a total head of 15 m. If the efficiency of the pump is 70%, calculate the current taken by the electric motor driving the pump if the motor efficiency is 90% and the supply voltage is 230 V. What is the overall efficiency of both motor and pump?

15. Upon what factors does the heating effect of an electric current depend?

The heating element of an immersion water heater has a resistance of 60 Ω and a current of 3 A flows through it. If the tank contains 20 kg of water at an initial temperature of 15°C, calculate the temperature after the current has been flowing for 3 h. The heat losses may be neglected.

16. Explain the terms (a) energy, (b) work, and give units in which each is measured.

Calculate the electrical power required to raise the temperature of 9 litres of water from 10°C to boiling point in 50 min if the heater used has an efficiency of 80%.

17. An immersion heater having a resistance of 180 Ω is immersed in a jar containing 3·5 litres of water. A current of 2 A is passed through the heater for 5 min. Calculate the increase in the temperature of the water.

18. A tank containing 135 litres of water has an immersion heater of 3 kW loading. If 80% of the power of the heater is usefully employed, find the time taken to raise the temperature of the water from 10°C to 77°C.

19. Express the power P absorbed when a current of I A flows through a conductor of R Ω resistance (a) in terms of current and resistance, (b) in terms of voltage and resistance. Write down an equation giving the energy W in joules absorbed in t s.

It is required to design a heater unit suitable for an electric boiler to raise the temperature of 4·5 kg of water from 15°C to 100°C in 20 min. Assuming a supply voltage of 240 V and the efficiency of the heater to be 100%, determine the resistance of the unit.

20. An ice rink of area 500 m² is prepared by freezing a water layer of uniform depth 50 mm at a temperature of 17·5°C, so that a layer of ice at −5°C is produced. If the overall efficiency of the electrical refrigeration plant is 10%, calculate the cost of preparing the rink, given that 1 kWh of electricity costs 0·6 p.

Specific enthalpy of fusion of ice = 335 kJ/kg
Relative specific heat capacity of ice = 0·5.

21. An electrode boiler is required to produce sufficient heat to raise the temperature of the water in a large thermal system from 25°C to 93°C in 9 h. The total amount of water in the system is 77 m³ and the pipes and tanks are so lagged that the overall efficiency is 95%.

Calculate the rating of the boiler in kilowatts and the cost of performing the above operation if electricity for such purposes costs 0·6 p/kWh.

22. A certain power station has an overall thermal efficiency of 32%, a rated capacity of 600 MW, and coal conveyors capable of a delivery rate of 960 tonne/h.

If this station were operating at its full rated load, calculate, in MJ/kg, the calorific value of a low-grade coal, such that the conveyors would have to work to the fullest extent of their delivery rate.

23. Determine the full load efficiency of a 6-MW turbo-alternator on the assumption that the whole of the losses appear in the cooling air and that the volume and temperature of the cooling air have been obtained and are as stated below. Test figures at full load:

Volume of cooling air at outlet, 12 m³/s; outlet temperature, 40°C; inlet temperature, 15°C.

Assume that over this range of temperature the relative specific heat capacity of air is 0·2 and that 1 kg of air occupies 0·75 m³.

24. Given the following data, compare the cost of heating a room 3·3 m × 3·3 m × 2·4 m by burning coal in an open grate of 20% efficiency, with the cost of using an electrical heater of 90% efficiency, reckoning a heating requirement of 53 W/m³:

Price of coal: £14 per tonne
Price of electricity: 1·2 p per kWh
Calorific value of the coal: 23 MJ/kg.

25. (a) Define the 'joule'.

(b) A 2-kW immersion heater raises the temperature of 90 litres of water from 15°C to 65°C.

Calculate the time taken if the equipment is 80% efficient.

26. (a) Explain what is meant by 'Mechanical Equivalent of Heat'.

(b) A gas-engine is developing 9·5 kW. If the calorific value of the fuel is 18·8 MJ/m³ and 20% of the available heat is converted into work, calculate the quantity of gas used per hour.

27. The calorific value of a certain fuel oil is 35 MJ/kg. If an engine uses 10 kg/h when working at 22 kW, what percentage of heat is turned into useful work?

28. Describe how you would determine experimentally the mechanical equivalent of heat.

An engine develops 19 kW. Calculate the heat equivalent of the work done in 15 min.

29. (a) Explain what is meant by 'mechanical equivalent' of heat.

(b) Cooling water is supplied to an oil engine at 9°C and leaves at 60°C; 9 kg of cooling water are circulated per min. Calculate the power equivalent to this rate of loss of heat.

30. An oil engine is used to drive an electric generator. The oil used has a heat value of 41 MJ/kg and the engine transforms 25% of this heat into useful work in driving the generator. The generator in turn transforms 80% of the energy it receives into electrical energy.

If the engine uses 2·5 kg of fuel per hour, calculate:
(a) the power output of the engine
(b) the electrical output of the generator.

31. A boiler generates steam at the rate of 60 kg/h at a pressure of 18 bar and 0·96 dryness. The complete output of steam is used in running an engine which in turn drives a generator. If the thermal efficiency of the engine including any pipe losses is 73%, what will be its power output?

If the generator efficiency is 90%, what will be its output?

Pressure bar	Temp °C θ	Enthalpy kJ/kg		
		h_f	h_{fg}	h_g
18	207·1	885	1912	2797

32. (a) What is meant by the terms 'specific liquid enthalpy', 'specific enthalpy of evaporation' and 'dryness fraction' when these are applied to steam?

(b) The exhaust from a steam plant enters a condenser at the rate of 600 kg of steam per hour at a pressure of 0·34 bar and 0·8 dry. The condensate leaves the condenser at 32°C. Calculate the heat extracted per hour from the exhaust steam. If all the heat extracted could be converted into mechanical work, by how much would the power output of the plant increase?

Pressure bar	Temp °C	Enthalpy kJ/kg		
		h_f	h_{fg}	h_g
0·34	72·0	302	2328	2630

23. Engineering Materials

A vast range of materials is used in modern engineering practice. In this book it will be possible to consider only broad groups of materials, the ways in which they are applied and the properties that make them suitable for these applications. This subject is a very wide one, but it is felt that all students of engineering science should have at least some knowledge of it.

Solid materials can be conveniently grouped under four main headings:

> Ferrous metals
> Non-ferrous metals
> Plastics
> Ceramics

Each group has special properties which make materials within the group suitable for particular applications. The following sections will discuss the main properties of a material which are of importance in engineering applications, and will then discuss these properties for each of the groups mentioned.

23.1. Mechanical properties of materials

(i) *Elasticity*

The ability of a material to return to its original dimensions after suffering a deformation, or strain, due to stress resulting from some applied force. The 'elastic limit' represents the greatest stress that may be applied without the material suffering permanent deformation.

(ii) *Plasticity*

The ability of a material to retain any deformation produced in it by a stress. Thus for a perfectly plastic material, no strain disappears when it is relieved from stress. Some important engineering materials go through a plastic stage at stresses beyond the elastic limit. They then exhibit the property of 'flow' in much the same way as does a viscous liquid, in that particles of the material may be physically moved from one position to another under the action of unequal stresses.

(iii) *Ductility*

The ability of a material to be drawn out to a small cross-section by a tensile force. A ductile material will have a significant plastic stage before it fractures under increasing stress. Ductility may be measured in terms of the percentage elongation obtained during a tensile test to destruction. This is a measure of the permanent strain produced during the plastic or ductile stage beyond the elastic limit. The greater the percentage elongation, the greater the ductility of the material.

(iv) *Brittleness*

This is a lack of ductility. A brittle material will have a negligible plastic stage, and will fracture at stresses much beyond the elastic limit. A brittle material will tend to fracture when subjected to a sudden blow, or other 'shock' load.

(v) *Tenacity*

The ability of a material to resist fracture under the action of a tensile force. It is measured in terms of the ultimate tensile stress; i.e. in terms of the maximum stress measured before fracture during a tensile test.

(vi) *Toughness*

The ability of a material to resist fracture under impact loads; i.e. loads suddenly applied. This may be measured by means of an impact test, which determines the mechanical energy required to fracture a standard shape of sample of the material.

(vii) *Malleability*

This is a property very similar to ductility. A malleable material may be beaten or rolled into plates without fracture. The malleability of a material may be affected by such treatment, because of a phenomenon known as 'work hardening'. The permanent deformation produced tends to set up internal stresses so that further strain causes fracture. These internal stresses can often be relieved by suitable heat treatment known as 'annealing', which also restores malleability.

(viii) *Hardness*

The ability of a material to resist penetration or wear. The hardness of the surface of a material may be made greater than that of the main body of the material by suitable heat treatment in the presence of certain other materials. The hardness may be measured in terms of the penetration of the surface by a standard pointed shape of a standard hard material such as diamond. There is a close relationship between hardness and ultimate tensile strength.

(ix) *Softness*

The reverse of hardness. The ability of a material to suffer indentation or penetration without fracture.

The 'machinability' of a material; i.e. the ease with which it can be cut, drilled, turned in a lathe, milled, shaped, etc., will depend on its ductility, tensile and shear strength and hardness.

Many of the properties listed here are inter-dependent, and much information can be obtained concerning a particular material from the results of tensile, impact and hardness tests. In nearly all cases, these properties can be very greatly modified by heat treatment, work hardening, etc. They can vary even in material from the same batch; i.e. produced under the same conditions. Any values given in the following sections must, therefore, be taken as typical approximate values.

23.2. Electrical properties of materials

It has been seen in Chapter 16, page 439, that materials can be grouped as conductors, semi-conductors or insulators as far as the property of electric current-flow along or through them is concerned. Another, but overlapping, method of grouping uses the magnetic property of materials. For most practical purposes, materials may be grouped as either 'magnetic' or 'non-magnetic'.

In this book certain electrical properties have been dealt with, and these are briefly summarized below. Other important properties for other applications will be met by the student during more advanced stages of his studies.

(i) *Resistivity*

This is a measure of the property of a material by which it impedes the flow of electric current through it. It is measured in terms of the electrical resistance between the opposite faces of a unit cube of the material.

(ii) *Conductivity*

This is the reciprocal of resistivity, and is a measure of the ease with which electric current may flow through a material. If the resistivity of a material is low, its conductivity will be high.

(iii) *Temperature-coefficient of resistance*

This is a measure of the change in resistance that takes place with a change in temperature. It is measured as the change in unit resistance at a given temperature for unit rise in temperature. For most metals its value is positive, indicating an increase of resistance with temperature. Certain materials and some metal alloys, however, have a negative temperature-coefficient of resistance, so that, for these, the resistance decreases with increasing temperature.

(iv) *Dielectric strength*

This is a measure of the ability of an insulating material to withstand physical 'breakdown' due to applied electrical forces. At normal temperatures, the electric current through an insulator is negligible until a voltage is applied across it sufficiently high to cause physical changes in its structure. The dielectric strength is measured in units of the electric potential difference which causes this breakdown across unit thickness of insulator.

(v) *Relative permeability*

This is a measure of the ease with which magnetic flux can be established through the material, compared with a vacuum. For 'non-magnetic' materials its value is 1 for most practical purposes. For 'magnetic' materials its value is not constant, but can be of the order of 1000 or more in special cases.

Other dielectric and magnetic properties of materials are omitted here, as no mention of them has been made in the theoretical discussions reached at this stage.

23.3.   Ferrous metals

Ferrous metals all contain some proportion of iron. It is very difficult to obtain absolutely pure iron in commercial quantities, but iron of a high purity is very ductile, of fairly low tensile strength (154 N/mm^2) and resists rust formation. Other substances such as carbon, manganese, silicon, sulphur, phosphorus, nickel and molybdenum may be added to iron, and will have considerable effects on the properties of the resulting material. However, it is not intended to discuss here the various methods of manufacture of these materials or their internal structure. The aim is to give an indication of the general properties of the more common materials with indications of their main fields of application.

(i) Cast iron

Cast iron is an alloy mainly of iron and carbon. It may contain up to 4% of carbon, although other elements, or impurities, may also be present. The various types of cast iron differ in the exact structure of the metal and the way in which the carbon mixes with or combines with the iron.

In broad terms, however, cast iron has a fairly low ultimate tensile stress, of the order of 150–225 N/mm^2, although this may be increased by the addition of suitable elements and by heat treatment. The compression strength is between 3 and 4 times the tensile strength, being about 770 N/mm^2, while the shear strength is of about the same order as the tensile strength (150–225 N/mm^2). As cast, there is usually a hard 'skin' on the surface of cast iron. Under this skin the material is more readily machinable, but is usually rather brittle. It may break under uneven heating conditions because of distortion produced by internal stresses which exceed the ultimate at the temperature concerned.

Under reasonable operating conditions, cast iron offers excellent resistance to corrosion compared with many other ferrous metals. It is an electrical conductor, having a resistivity of about 15×10^{-8} Ωm, and normally also has good magnetic properties.

Cast iron is used, as the name implies, in 'castings', for which the molten metal is poured into suitable moulds and allowed to solidify. This method makes it possible for intricate shapes to be formed without the expense and waste of material that would be involved in machining them from a solid block of material. Limitations in the shape and use of such castings are imposed by the relatively low tensile and shear strength of the material. These could lead to cracks in the cast iron as it cools down in the mould, or to the breaking-off of thin projections when it is in use.

(ii) Steel

Steel is also an alloy mainly of iron and carbon, although special steels may have amounts of other elements present in excess of the carbon content. These other elements, which include nickel, chromium, molybdenum and tungsten, considerably modify the properties of the resulting steel. The carbon content of steel is lower than that of cast iron, and does not exceed 2%.

As has been said, the physical properties of steel can be varied over a wide range by control of its content of carbon and alloying metals, and by heat treatment. For example, as the carbon content is increased the tenacity and hardness of the steel is increased, with a corresponding reduction in its ductility and toughness. Similarly, the addition of nickel increases the material's tensile strength, yield point and hardness, with a corresponding decrease in its ductility. Steels containing a high proportion of nickel have excellent corrosion-resisting qualities.

The addition of both nickel and chromium, to form nickel-chrome steels, ensures considerable hardening properties, with suitable heat treatment, with a corresponding tendency to brittleness. The addition of molybdenum and tungsten also increases the hardness and strength of the steel. Considerable research has been done, and is continuing, into the production of steels suitable for particular applications.

In broad terms, however, steel is a ductile material of high tensile strength, the ultimate tensile stress being of the order of 750–1500 N/mm^2. Its hardness and machinability vary widely with composition and heat treatment. Steel is an electrical conductor, having a resistivity of about 20×10^{-8} Ωm, and is also a magnetic material. Its resistivity and permeability may vary considerably, however, for different compositions.

Steel is used, for example, in structures where its high strength and resistance to impact loads may be of importance, and for tools for machining purposes. The so-called 'high-speed' steels retain their hardness to a marked degree even at higher temperatures, so that cutting tools of this steel will retain a sharp cutting edge under conditions of high-speed machining and at high temperatures. 'High-tensile' steels have a high value of ultimate tensile stress and are used to make springs or to sustain high-tensile loads.

23.4. Non-ferrous metals

The more common non-ferrous metals are listed below, together with some of their properties and applications. Once again, only a broad treatment is possible, and considerable variations in properties may be achieved by variation in the composition and heat treatment of the various alloys.

(i) *Aluminium*

Pure aluminium is a soft and ductile material. Its distinctive property is its light density—it has a relative density of about 2·7. It is a good electrical conductor but is non-magnetic. Its resistivity is about $1\frac{1}{2}$ times that of copper, being about $2 \cdot 6 \times 10^{-8} \, \Omega$m.

Aluminium has a low tensile strength, the ultimate tensile stress being of the order of 75 N/mm². It is soft, malleable and very readily machinable, but it is susceptible to work hardening, which increases its strength and reduces its ductility.

It is resistant to corrosion in normal atmospheric conditions, although serious corrosion takes place in sea water or when it is in contact, in moist air, with a dissimilar metal.

The practical uses of pure aluminium are limited by its softness and low tensile strength, but it has many applications when alloyed with other elements. These other elements include chromium, copper, iron, magnesium, manganese, silicon and zinc. Such alloys have much higher tensile strengths although rather less ductility than pure aluminium. They are used, for example, for light structural work, and in various electrical applications as conductors. Aluminium alloys are also used for castings, and special die-casting methods are available to produce precision castings requiring little or no subsequent machining. Aluminium can be soldered, but requires special arrangements to remove the very thin film of oxide present on the surface of the metal.

(ii) *Copper*

Pure copper is a soft and ductile material. Its distinctive property is its low electrical resistivity, which is about $1 \cdot 7 \times 10^{-8} \, \Omega$m, and it is very frequently used as an electrical conductor. It is non-magnetic. Copper has a fairly low tensile strength, the ultimate tensile stress being of the order of 150–225 N/mm². It is soft, malleable and very readily machinable, but is susceptible to work hardening, which increases its strength and reduces its ductility.

The practical applications of copper include those associated with the conduction of electricity and heat. It is also valuable for various plumbing applications, because of its ductility and the ease with which soldered joints may be made. Copper is also very often used in alloys in conjunction with other materials.

(iii) *Brass*

Brass is an alloy of copper and zinc containing over 50% of copper. Various proportions of copper and zinc, and the addition of other elements such as tin and lead, give brasses of different mechanical properties. In broad terms, however, brass is a soft material of lower ductility than copper, and having an ultimate tensile stress of the order of 225 N/mm^2. It is readily machinable, but also is subject to work hardening, with a corresponding increase in strength and decrease in ductility. The stresses set up by work hardening may be relieved by suitable heat treatment (annealing), when the ductility will be improved again. The tensile strength may also be reduced from its work-hardened value by annealing, but to a value higher than in the pre-stressed state. Brass is also resistant to corrosion, and it can be readily soldered. It is a non-magnetic conductor, having a resistivity of about 8×10^{-8} Ωm.

Brass may be used for nuts and bolts of various sizes, for bearing surfaces and in the form of castings, because it may be easily cast into complex shapes, and because it will give fairly high values of strength.

(iv) *Bronze*

Bronze is an alloy of copper and tin, together with certain other elements such as zinc and lead. Gun-metal is a bronze containing about 90% of copper, with mostly tin and a little zinc making up the remainder. Bronzes have a high tenacity and elasticity, although the ultimate tensile stress—of the order of 225–300 N/mm^2—is less than that for steel. Bronze is a comparatively soft, ductile material which is readily machinable, but it is also subject to work hardening. It can be readily soldered, and is a non-magnetic conductor having a resistivity of about 4×10^{-8} Ωm.

It is used for pumps, valves, general castings and pressings, and may also be used for bearings, gears, cams, etc. Phosphor-bronze, containing a small proportion of phosphorus (about 0·25%), is used for springs and castings, and is relatively non-corrodible.

It is of interest that the annealing process for copper, brasses and bronzes involves rapid cooling or 'quenching' from a high temperature. Such treatment has the effect of *hardening* a steel; i.e. producing the reverse condition.

(v) *Nickel*

Pure nickel is a soft ductile material having an ultimate tensile stress of about 450 N/mm^2. It is used mostly in alloys with other materials, but commercially 'pure' nickel may be used in certain electrical applications; for example, for alkaline cells. It has a resistivity of about 14×10^{-8} Ωm.

Copper-nickel alloys also have electrical applications as 'resistance alloys', with resistivities of $30-50 \times 10^{-8}$ cm. They can also be used for such applications as require resistance to high temperatures without undue deterioration of mechanical properties.

Iron-nickel alloys are tough and strong, and are very resistant to corrosion in air, fresh water and sea water. They can also be made to have exceptionally good magnetic properties, with relative permeabilities of the order of 20 000 or more.

Nickel-silver (so-called because of its silvery appearance) is an alloy of copper, nickel and zinc. It is often used for decorative purposes or as the basis of electroplated items such as spoons and forks. It has many electrical applications, such as for contacts and resistance wires in electrical equipment.

(vi) *Zinc*

Zinc is a soft, ductile material having good electrical properties. Its resistivity is roughly 4 times that of copper, being about $6·5 \times 10^{-8}$ Ωm, and its electrical uses include the cathodes of dry Leclanché cells. It is also used as a protective coating on the surfaces of iron and steel; for example, in the process known as galvanizing. Commercial zinc usually contains traces of cadmium, the presence of which tends to harden the material and to make it more brittle.

Zinc is very often used as an alloying material, and zinc alloys are used in the production of pressure die-castings. Such castings are usually superior to aluminium alloy castings, and can readily be nickel- or chromium-plated.

(vii) *Lead*

Lead is a very soft, ductile material. Its distinctive property is its heavy density, its relative density being about $11·4$. It is very easily cut and is extremely malleable, tending to be 'self-annealing', so that it recovers its original softness soon after deformation. It has a very low tensile strength, the ultimate tensile stress being of the order of 15 N/mm². It is a non-magnetic conductor having a resistivity of about 22×10^{-8} Ωm.

When alloyed with small amounts of materials such as cadmium, antimony or tin, lead is used for pipes and for covering electrical cables. Here, and elsewhere, the property of lead to suffer deformation without hardening is valuable. The lead grids of lead-acid accumulators usually contain about 10% of antimony, which increases the acid-resisting properties of the lead, and prevents local action between the lead plates and the sulphuric acid.

Lead is used in alloys with other materials to form white-metal bearing alloys, leaded bronzes and fusible alloys for use, for example, in electrical and other protective fuses.

(viii) *Tin*

Tin is a soft material having a low tensile strength—its ultimate tensile stress being of the order of 30 N/mm². Its distinctive property is its resistance to corrosion under many different conditions. For this reason, it is used as a coating on other metals such as steel to make 'tin-plate', which is used, for example, in the canning of food. Copper wires are also tin-coated to protect the copper from attack by the sulphur present in the vulcanized rubber used for insulation.

Tin is also used with lead as the basis of 'soft' solders; i.e. low melting-point solders. This gives the name 'tinning' to the process of combining the surface to be soldered with some of the solder before a joint is made, to ensure good bonding of the solder to both parts of the joint.

23.5. Plastics

This group covers a large and increasing range, from the natural materials such as rubber to the various man-made materials which have been comparatively recently developed and are already in widespread use, such as nylon, terylene and P.V.C. A plastics material could be simply defined as a material based on organic compounds, of which carbon is a main constituent, and which, on the application of sufficient heat and temperature, can be made to flow and take up a desired shape. If the temperature and pressure are relieved, the new shape is retained. As a result of the organic nature of a plastics material, it cannot usually withstand very high temperatures, and will often begin to decompose at about 200°C or so.

Plastics materials can be broadly divided into two groups: (i) thermosoftening or 'thermoplastic' materials and (ii) thermohardening or 'thermosetting' materials.

Thermoplastic materials can be softened and resoftened indefinitely by the application of the required heat and pressure. An object made of a thermoplastic material can be distorted by being heated to below its decomposition temperature and distorting pressure then being applied.

Thermosetting materials, however, undergo chemical changes during the initial process of being shaped, and thereafter further heat and pressure do not affect the shape, provided always that the temperature does not reach the decomposition temperature. The general characteristics of common plastics materials in each group are considered below.

(i) *Thermoplastics*

These materials generally behave like ductile metals, and they can be readily machined. They are, however, capable of being permanently deformed by quite small forces at temperatures of the order of 100°C or so. They can be joined by means of solvents, or in some cases they can be welded by means of a hot-air jet or low-temperature flame.

They can be moulded from powder form at relatively low temperatures (100°C or so) by comparatively small pressures. Air pressure, applied by 'blowing' or 'vacuum' techniques, can be used to mould sheets of the material into the shapes desired.

(*a*) *Celluloid* is a nitro-cellulose material, and is tough and water resistant. It is, however, very highly inflammable.

Its tensile strength is of the order of 45 N/mm² and compressive strength is about twice as great.

(*b*) *Cellulose acetate* has physical properties similar to those of celluloid, but is much less inflammable. (It is comparable with wood or paper in this respect.) Its tensile and compressive strengths are each of the order of 15–75 N/mm². It has a high electrical resistivity, of about 10^8–10^{10} Ωm. Its dielectric strength is of the order of 12–24 MV/m.

This material is widely available in the form of thin sheets for covers and so on, and a similar material is used as a base for photographic film.

(*c*) *Polythene* is a wax-like material that is chemically inert to most liquids. It is very tough and slightly elastic. It has an ultimate tensile stress of about 15 N/mm² and a value for Young's modulus of about 150 N/mm².

It has a high electrical resistivity, of the order of 10^{15} Ωm, and a dielectric strength of about 40 MV/m. It is used for moulded containers of various types and is of particular value as an electrical insulating material.

(*d*) *P.V.C.* (*Polyvinyl chloride*) is a tough, rubber-like material which is practically non-inflammable. It has a tensile strength of about 45–60 N/mm², a dielectric strength of about 16 MV/m, and an electrical resistivity of about 10^{13} Ωm. It is one of the cheapest of the plastics materials, and is widely used as an insulating cover on electrical cables.

It is also available in flat sheets, from a few hundredth's of a milli-metre upwards in thickness, and is also used for covers of various types.

(e) *Polystyrene* flows readily at temperatures of about 180°C, and is used for 'injection' moulding in which the material is injected under pressure into a pre-heated mould or die. It has a tensile strength of about 45 N/mm², but tends to be rather brittle. The electrical resistivity is high—about 10^{15} Ωm—and its dielectric strength is about 20 MV/m. It is often used as an electrical insulating material.

(f) *Perspex* may be used as a substitute for glass, since it is lighter in weight and transmits light even more readily. It is also used for electrical insulation purposes. Like the other thermoplastic materials, it can be readily bent, cut or machined. It is unaffected by dilute acids or con-centrated alkalis. It has a resistivity of more than 10^{11} Ωm, and a dielectric strength of about 14 MV/m. It has an ultimate tensile strength of the order of 75 N/mm², but tends to be rather brittle.

(g) *P.T.F.E.* (also known as *Teflin* or *Fluon*) is a wax-like material which has a very low coefficient of friction against itself—of the order of 0·1, which is roughly that of ice against wet ice. It can be used to give adherent coatings to metals and other materials. It does not absorb water at any temperature, and is resistant to nearly all chemicals.

Its electrical resistivity is about 10^{15} Ωm, and its dielectric strength is of the order of 20 MV/m. Its ultimate tensile strength is of the order of 15 N/mm². It is used, among other things, for electrical insulation, and mechanical applications in which its low coefficient of friction is an advantage.

(h) *Nylon* is a wax-like material very commonly used in the form of fibres. It is also moulded for other uses, however, since it is tough and has a low coefficient of friction with itself or with polished steel. It is used for gear wheels, bearings or other applications using its toughness and low frictional properties.

It has an ultimate tensile stress of about 60 N/mm² and is much less brittle than, say, perspex. It has an electrical resistivity of about 10^{11} Ωm and a dielectric strength of about 12 MV/m.

(i) *Terylene* is also frequently used in the form of fibre. It has a high tensile strength, of the order of 150 N/mm². It has an electrical resistivity of the order of 10^{11} Ωm and a high dielectric strength, of the order of 60 MV/m. For most practical purposes it is non-inflammable, although it can, with difficulty, be made to ignite and burn. Its high melting point makes the fibre, especially when suitably impregnated, extremely useful for high-temperature electrical insulation.

It is worth noting that, for garments made from plastics materials such as nylon or terylene, significant electrical charge can be produced on them by the friction in normal wear. Because of its high resistivity, these charges are not conducted very rapidly through the material, and electrical discharges can be made to take place between different points of the material, in the form of sparks.

(ii) *Thermosetting plastics*

As has already been stated, these materials undergo chemical changes at high temperatures, which means that they cannot then be resoftened by heat. They are thus more suitable for higher-temperature applications than the thermoplastic materials.

The moulding powder or resin may be shaped by compression moulds as required or, in another very important type of application, the resin may be used to bond together layers of paper or cloth. The sheets of paper, cloth or other fibrous material are impregnated with the resin and then pressed under heat to form rigid flat sheets or other required shapes. These materials are called 'laminates' and are very important. They can be cut or machined rather as wood can be, but have better electrical properties and are less affected by water.

(*a*) *Bakelite* was the first type of plastics material to be made artificially. The resin is usually mixed with a 'filler' of non-plastics material, which is added as a powder or in a fibrous state. So-called 'wood-flour' fillers give more brittle mouldings, which crack readily under shock loads or impact. Cotton or shredded fabric fillers give tougher mouldings, whilst asbestos fillers can be used to produce heat-resistant mouldings.

The material has a tensile strength of about 45 N/mm² and a compressive strength of about 150 N/mm². Its electrical resistivity is about 10^6 Ωm and its dielectric strength is about 10 MV/m.

(*b*) *Urea formaldehyde*. These resins, used with paper-pulp or wood-pulp fillings, give odourless, transparent mouldings resistant to surface tracking by electrical arc discharges. The mouldings are stronger than bakelite (tensile strength about 75 N/mm²), compressive strength about 225 N/mm²) and so may be of rather thinner section. They may therefore be used to make such things as 'plastic' cups. The mouldings are still rather brittle, however.

(*c*) *Laminates* are made under various trade names such as 'Paxolin' or 'Tufnol'. Sheets of fibrous material are bonded into a solid mass by the thermosetting resin. The surface is usually polished and can have very good resistance to surface tracking by electrical arc discharges.

The mechanical and electrical properties vary with the type of resin and filler used, but in broad terms these laminates combine good electrical insulation properties with mechanical strength. They are also extensively used, under various trade names, in the building industry, and as 'surface materials' for benches and table tops. They are usually relatively brittle, especially in unsupported thin sections.

(d) *Silicon plastics—silicones.* These differ from many other plastics in having silicon and oxygen as their base, with carbon and hydrogen 'attached'. A wide range of materials is possible. One of their important uses is as an additive to oils, waxes, rubbers, etc. Silicones are water repellent, and can withstand high temperatures, which makes them very useful for high-temperature electrical insulation applications.

(e) *Epoxy resins* (e.g. (Araldite') are used for 'potting' electrical components; i.e. for sealing them against ingress of moisture, etc. They are also used as the basis of adhesives. They have good electrical properties and are resistant to heat, moisture and surface tracking by electrical arc discharges.

It should be noted that some natural organic materials and resins exhibit thermosetting properties. For example, shellac products such as micanite can be moulded by a thermosetting process, and the process of vulcanizing natural rubber and sulphur is similar in type.

Development work on plastics materials is continuing, and it can be expected that additional materials will become available which have special properties suited to particular applications. The potentialities of plastics in engineering seem very great.

23.6. Ceramics

These are inorganic materials whose main industrial use is as electrical insulating materials, or in high-temperature applications. They include:

(a) *Asbestos-cement compositions*, for applications where high heat resistance is required, and especially as 'arc-chutes' on electrical switchgear.

(b) *Porcelain* and *steatite*, for applications where dust and moisture readily collect. These materials can be moulded into special shapes before being fired and glazed rather as crockery is. The porcelain-type insulators on high-voltage transformer and switchgear 'bushings', and on high-voltage transmission and distribution overhead lines, will probably be familiar to the student.

(c) *Special ceramics* are available for such applications as motor-vehicle sparking-plug insulators or special electrical components.

(d) *Glass*, for out-door insulators and other applications.

(e) *Mica-glass compositions* for high-temperature insulation applications.

Typical electrical resistivity of a ceramic material is of the order of 10^{12} Ωm, with dielectric strengths in the region of 12 MV/m or more. Tensile strength is about 45 N/mm^2, and compressive strength about 750 N/mm^2. Ceramics are almost always very hard and brittle, and can withstand high temperatures.

APPENDIX A: BOW'S NOTATION

Systems involving a number of forces acting at the same point commonly occur in structural engineering, for example in framed structures such as bridges or roof supports ('trusses'). The various members of these structures are pin-jointed or riveted together and will be in tension or compression under the action of the forces loading the structure. Those in tension are called *ties* and those in compression are called *struts*.

The determination of the forces in these members usually requires the investigation of conditions at each junction in the structure, and this could be done by drawing separate vector polygons for each junction. An adaptation of the vector polygon is available, however, which enables a complete force diagram for the whole structure to be obtained. Although the examples of structures considered here will be planar—all the members could be contained in the same flat surface—it should be noted that the forces in the members will not in general be concurrent—they will not all pass through the same point. Consequently a special method must be used, and this is illustrated in the following example.

Example

Find the force in each member of the structure shown in diagram 289 (a) and state whether the member is a tie or a strut.

The first step is to draw a space diagram of the structure to scale and to insert letters in the spaces between and around the structure so that every member or external force (including the reactions at the supports) has a letter on each side of it. This is shown in diagram 289 (b).

This system of lettering is known as BOW'S NOTATION and enables any one member or force to be represented by the letters on each side of it. Thus AB refers to the vertical reaction force R_1, CF refers to the horizontal member at the top of the frame, and so on.

The reaction forces R_1 and R_2 may be determined by taking moments in the usual way. Thus, taking moments about the extreme lower right-hand junction, and noting that the line of action of the 20 kN force is

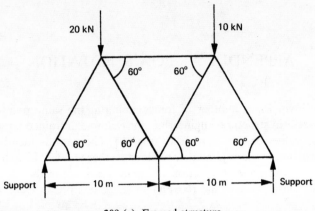

289 (a). Framed structure

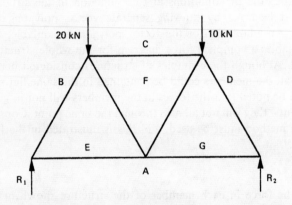

289 (b). Space diagram of framed structure

at a perpendicular distance of 15 m from the lower right-hand junction while the line of action of the 10 kN force is 5 m perpendicularly from this junction,

$$R_1 \times 20 = 20 \times 15 + 10 \times 5$$

or $$R_1 = 17 \cdot 5 \text{ kN}$$

so that $$R_2 = (20 + 10) - 17 \cdot 5 = 12 \cdot 5 \text{ kN}$$

Now consider conditions at the extreme lower left-hand junction. There are three forces acting at this point; the reaction R_1 and the forces in the members *BE* and *EA*. A triangle of force vectors may be drawn to scale for this point since the magnitude and direction of R_1 are known, as are the lines of action of the forces in *BE* and *EA*. (These forces must act along the members because of the pin-jointing.) This triangle of forces is shown in diagram 289 (c).

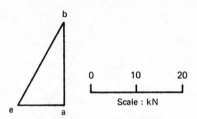

289 (c). Force diagram for lower left-hand junction

Note that no arrows are put on this diagram and that small letters are used to correspond with the capital letters on each side of the force or member concerned. The direction of a force represented on this diagram is indicated by these small letters. Thus, moving around the junction in a clockwise direction, movement from space *A* to space *B* passes an upwards force (R_1), and this is represented on the force diagram by an upwards movment from *a* to *b*. If we continue round the junction in a clockwise direction, it follows that, *at this junction*, the force in *BE* (represented by *be*) is pushing downwards at 60° to the horizontal, and the force in *EA* (represented by *ea*) is pulling away in a horizontal direction. These conditions are represented in the partial space diagram shown in diagram 289 (d).

Since the frame is in equilibrium, there can be no resultant force acting on it, and forces must exist at the other ends of the members *BE* and *EA* as shown by the dotted arrow-heads.

Now consider the member *BE*. It is seen that internal forces exist in this member pushing against the pin-joints at each end; i.e., it must be resisting external forces pushing on those ends, and so must be in compression. *BE* is therefore a strut.

The internal forces in *EA* are pulling at the pin-joints at each end; i.e., it must be resisting external forces pulling on those ends, and so must be in tension. *EA* is therefore a tie.

Consider conditions at the upper left-hand junction. There are four forces at this point, two of which (force in *BE* and the 20-kN force) are known in magnitude and direction, and the other two are along known

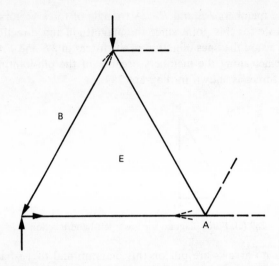

289 (d). Partial space diagram showing directions of internal forces in members

lines of action. The force diagram can then be extended as shown in diagram 289 (e).

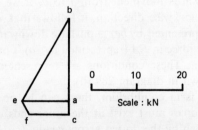

289 (e). Extended force diagram to include junction BCFE

As before, go round the junction in a clockwise direction. Thus the internal force in *EB* is represented by *eb* and is pushing on the junction. *BC* is a downwards force of 20 kN and is represented by *bc* vertically downwards. The internal forces in *CF* and *FE* must act along the directions of these members, so that lines drawn in these directions on the force diagram from *c* and *e* respectively must intersect at *f*. Note that a clockwise circulation round the junction indicates from the force diagram that the internal force in *CF* (represented by *cf*) is pushing horizontally to the left on the junction while the internal force in *FE* (represented by *fe*) is pushing upwards at 60° to the horizontal.

This process may be continued, considering in turn the junctions *AEFG* and *GFCD*. In each case a clockwise movement round the junction is considered, and vectors drawn on the force diagram in the direction of the force exerted. The completed force diagram will then be as shown in diagram 289 (f).

It will be noted that the force diagram now includes all the forces in the framework. A final check on the directions of the forces may be made by considering a clockwise movement round junction *DAG*.

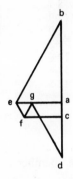

289 (f). Complete force diagram

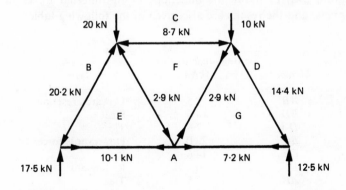

289 (g). Space diagram showing internal forces in members

Measurements to scale from this completed force diagram will give the magnitudes of the forces in the members and, as already discussed, clockwise movement round each junction will indicate the directions of the internal forces in each member. These results are indicated in the space diagram 289 (g) and are also given in the following table:

Member	Magnitude of force (kN)	Type
AB	17·5	Upwards reaction
BE	20·2	Strut
EA	10·1	Tie
BC	20·0	Downwards force
CF	8·7	Strut
FE	2·9	Strut
FG	2·9	Tie
GA	7·2	Tie
CD	10·0	Downwards force
DG	14·4	Strut
DA	12·5	Upwards reaction

Example

Find the force in each member of the structure shown in diagram 290 (a) and state whether the member is a tie or a strut.

Diagram 290 (a) has been lettered in accordance with Bow's notation and the corresponding force diagram is shown in diagram 290 (b). Diagram 290 (c) shows the directions of the internal forces in the members, and the results are also given in the following table:

Member	Magnitude of force (kN)	Type
AB	7·5	Upwards reaction
BD	10·6	Strut
DA	7·5	Tie
BC	20·0	Downwards force
CE	14·6	Strut
DE	0	Redundant
AE	7·5	Tie
CA	12·5	Upwards reaction

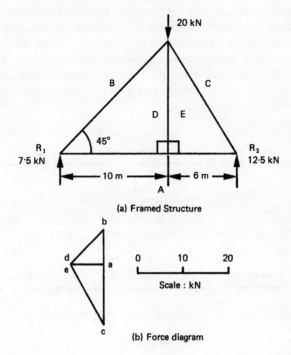

20 kN

B

C

D E

45°

R₁
7·5 kN

R₂
12·5 kN

10 m

6 m

A

(a) Framed Structure

b

d
e a

0 10 20

Scale : kN

c

(b) Force diagram

20 kN

B
10·6 kN

0

C
14·6 kN

D E

7·5 kN

7·5 kN A 7·5 kN

12·5 kN

(c) Space diagram showing internal forces in members

290 (a, b, c)

Note that in this case, member *DE* has no force in it; i.e., it is a redundant member not carrying any load, and the loads on the other members would be unaffected if it were to be removed. This fact is indicated by the superposition of points *d* and *e* on the force diagram.

Note again that the *internal forces* in the members at a junction are given from the force diagram. These determine whether the member is acting as a tie or as a strut. Diagram 292 shows internal and external forces for a tie and a strut.

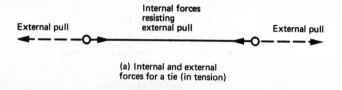

(a) Internal and external forces for a tie (in tension)

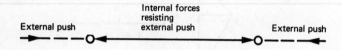

(b) Internal and external forces for a strut (in compression)

291. Ties and struts

QUESTIONS

1. A simply supported roof truss is shown in the diagram, and is loaded as indicated. Determine graphically the forces in the members, stating whether they are in compression or tension.

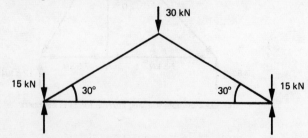

[*Answer*: Horizontal member: 26 kN, tension (tie)
Each sloping member: 30 kN, compression strut)]

2. A pin-jointed structure is secured by frictionless hinges at (1) and (2) to a ramp, as shown in the diagram. The spaces are lettered according to Bow's notation. For the loading shown, draw the force diagram to a scale of 10 mm to 2 kN. Hence determine:

(a) the nature and magnitude of the forces in all the members,

(b) the magnitude and direction of the reaction at hinge (1).

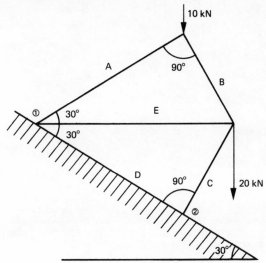

[*Answer*: (a) AE; 5 kN, compression (strut)
BE; 8·7 kN, compression (strut)
DE; 20·2 kN, tension (tie)
CD; 31·7 kN, compression (strut)
(b) 16·1 kN at 171° to horizontal]

3. Find the force in each of the members of the loaded framework shown in the diagram, using a graphical method. State which members are ties and which are struts.

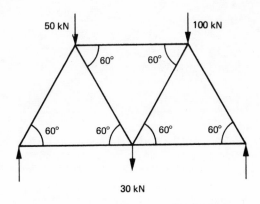

[*Answer*: Sloping members in sequence from left-hand support:
89·4 kN, strut; 31·8 kN, tie; 2·9 kN, tie; 118·4 kN, strut
Lower horizontal members in same sequence:
44·7 kN, tie; 59·2 kN, tie
Upper horizontal member: 60·6 kN, strut]

APPENDIX B: NOTE ON UNITS

The U.K. Government has expressed the view that British industry must adopt the *Système International d'Unités*, for which the abbreviation is SI in all languages.

This system is based on the following six fundamental units

length	*metre*	(m)
mass	*kilogramme*	(kg)
time	*second*	(s)
electric current	*ampere*	(A)
temperature	*Kelvin*	(K)
luminous intensity	*candela*	(cd)

A full discussion of unit systems in general, and of SI units and their advantages in particular, would be out of place here but, as further illustrations, the derived SI units (recommended for increasingly wide use) for some of the quantities discussed in this book are

area	*square metre*			(m^2)
volume	*cubic metre*			(m^3)
linear acceleration	*metre per second squared*			(m/s^2)
angular acceleration	*radian per second squared*			(rad/s^2)
force	*newton*	(N)	where	$N = kg\ m/s^2$
work, energy, quantity of heat	*joule*	(J)	where	$J = Nm$
power	*watt*	(W)	where	$W = J/s$
electric charge	*coulomb*	(C)	where	$C = A\ s$
electric potential	*volt*	(V)	where	$V = W/A$
electric resistance	*ohm*	(Ω)	where	$\Omega = V/A$
frequency	*hertz*	(Hz)	where	$Hz = s^{-1}$
magnetic flux	*weber*	(Wb)	where	$Wb = Vs$
magnetic flux density	*tesla*	(T)	where	$T = Wb/m^2$

Other derived units follow a similar pattern, and indeed one of the advantages of SI units is that a derived unit is obtained by the straightforward combination of the units from which it is derived. Thus, unit area is obtained when unit length is multiplied by unit length, or unit force is obtained when unit mass is multiplied by unit acceleration. Such a unit system is known as a *coherent* system. It should be noted that only the SI units themselves are used to form derived units and that multiple or sub-multiple units (such as the centimetre or the millisecond) should not be used for this purpose.

Further reference may be made to B.S. 3763:1964 *The International System (SI) units.*

Trigonometrical Ratios

Angle		Sine	Tangent	Cotangent	Cosine		
Degrees	Radians						
0	0	0	0	∞	1·0000	1·5708	90
1	0·0175	0·0175	0·0175	57·2900	0·9998	1·5533	89
2	0·0349	0·0348	0·0349	28·6363	0·9994	1·5359	88
3	0·0524	0·0523	0·0524	19·0811	0·9986	1·5184	87
4	0·0698	0·0698	0·0699	14·3007	0·9976	1·5010	86
5	0·0873	0·0872	0·0875	11·4301	0·9962	1·4835	85
6	0·1047	0·1045	0·1051	9·5144	0·9945	1·4661	84
7	0·1222	0·1219	0·1228	8·1443	0·9925	1·4486	83
8	0·1396	0·1392	0·1405	7·1154	0·9903	1·4312	82
9	0·1571	0·1564	0·1584	6·3138	0·9877	1·4137	81
10	0·1745	0·1736	0·1763	5·6713	0·9848	1·3963	80
11	0·1920	0·1908	0·1944	5·1446	0·9816	1·3788	79
12	0·2094	0·2079	0·2126	4·7046	0·9781	1·3614	78
13	0·2269	0·2250	0·2309	4·3315	0·9744	1·3439	77
14	0·2443	0·2419	0·2493	4·0108	0·9703	1·3265	76
15	0·2618	0·2588	0·2679	3·7321	0·9659	1·3090	75
16	0·2793	0·2756	0·2867	3·4874	0·9613	1·2915	74
17	0·2967	0·2924	0·3057	3·2709	0·9563	1·2741	73
18	0·3142	0·3090	0·3249	3·0777	0·9511	1·2566	72
19	0·3316	0·3256	0·3443	2·9042	0·9455	1·2392	71
20	0·3491	0·3420	0·3640	2·7475	0·9397	1·2217	70
21	0·3665	0·3584	0·3839	2·6051	0·9336	1·2043	69
22	0·3840	0·3746	0·4040	2·4751	0·9272	1·1868	68
23	0·4014	0·3907	0·4245	2·3559	0·9205	1·1694	67
24	0·4189	0·4067	0·4452	2·2460	0·9135	1·1519	66
25	0·4363	0·4226	0·4663	2·1445	0·9063	1·1345	65
26	0·4538	0·4384	0·4877	2·0503	0·8988	1·1170	64
27	0·4712	0·4540	0·5095	1·9626	0·8910	1·0996	63
28	0·4887	0·4695	0·5317	1·8807	0·8829	1·0821	62
29	0·5061	0·4848	0·5543	1·8040	0·8746	1·0647	61
30	0·5236	0·5000	0·5774	1·7321	0·8660	1·0472	60
31	0·5411	0·5150	0·6009	1·6643	0·8572	1·0297	59
32	0·5585	0·5299	0·6249	1·6003	0·8480	1·0123	58
33	0·5760	0·5446	0·6494	1·5399	0·8387	0·9948	57
34	0·5934	0·5592	0·6745	1·4826	0·8290	0·9774	56
35	0·6109	0·5736	0·7002	1·4281	0·8192	0·9599	55
36	0·6283	0·5878	0·7265	1·3764	0·8090	0·9425	54
37	0·6458	0·6018	0·7536	1·3270	0·7986	0·9250	53
38	0·6632	0·6157	0·7813	1·2799	0·7880	0·9076	52
39	0·6807	0·6293	0·8098	1·2349	0·7771	0·8901	51
40	0·6981	0·6428	0·8391	1·1918	0·7660	0·8727	50
41	0·7156	0·6561	0·8693	1·1504	0·7547	0·8552	49
42	0·7330	0·6691	0·9004	1·1106	0·7431	0·8378	48
43	0·7505	0·6820	0·9325	1·0724	0·7314	0·8203	47
44	0·7679	0·6947	0·9657	1·0355	0·7193	0·8029	46
45	0·7854	0·7071	1·0000	1·0000	0·7071	0·7854	45
		Cosine	Cotangent	Tangent	Sine	Radians	Degrees
						Angle	

Properties of Materials

APPROXIMATE VALUES

Material	Density kg/m³	Young's Modulus of Elasticity kN/mm²	Modulus of Rigidity kN/mm²	Relative Specific Heat Capacity	Coefficient of Linear Expansion ×10⁻⁶/°C	Resistivity At 0°C ×10⁻⁸Ωm	Resistance-Temperature Coefficient At 0°C ×10⁻⁴Ω/Ω°C	Electro-chemical Equivalent ×10⁻³ g/C
Aluminium	2700	70	27	0·21	23	2·45	45	0·093
Copper	8900	96	38	0·09	17	1·56	43	0·329
Gold	19 300	79	27	0·03	14	2·04	40	0·681
Iron	7830	205	82	0·11	12	8·9	65	0·193
Lead	11 300	15·7	—	0·03	29	19·0	42	1·074
Mercury	13 600	—	—	0·03	60	94·1	10	1·039
Nickel	8800	198	—	0·11	13	6·14	68	0·304
Platinum	21 500	164	51	0·03	9	9·81	39	0·506
Silver	10 500	78	29	0·06	19	1·51	41	1·118
Tungsten	19 300	410	—	0·03	4·5	4·9	48	0·318
Zinc	7100	86	38	0·09	30	5·5	42	0·339
Constantan (or Eureka)	—	164	61	—	16	48	± 0·2	—
Manganin	—	123	46	—	—	42	0·1	—

Many of these values are affected by purity, method of production, temperature, etc., and the figures given should be taken as typical rather than absolute

Prefixes used with Metric Units

Term	Abbreviation	Unit multiplied by
tera or megamega ..	T or MM	10^{12} (= 1 000 000 000 000)
giga or kilomega ..	G or kM	10^9 (= 1 000 000 000)
mega	M	10^6 (= 1 000 000)
kilo	k	10^3 (= 1000)
deci	d	10^{-1} (= 0·1)
centi	c	10^{-2} (= 0·01)
milli	m	10^{-3} (= 0·001)
micro	μ	10^{-6} (= 0·000 001)
nano or millimicro	n or mμ	10^{-9} (= 0·000 000 001)
pico or micromicro	p or $\mu\mu$	10^{-12} (= 0·000 000 000 001)

Answers to Questions

1. 2700 kg/m^3
2. (a) 0·649 kg, (b) (i) 35 ml, (ii) 0·97
3. 27·2 kg
4. 48 kg
5. 20·8 mm, 1·6 kg
6. 25·7 mm
8. 0·8, 800 kg/m^3

1. (a) 3·75 N at − 127° to 2·25 N
   (b) 3·75 N at + 53° to 2·25 N
2. Jib: 57 kN (compression); Tie: 37 kN (tension)
3. (a) 2700 N, (b) 2580 N, (c) 600 N
4. 1·79 m from A, T_A = 255 N, T_B = 360 N
5. 21·5 kN, 26·5 kN
6. R = 400 N at 58° to horizontal; T = 230 N
7. 5 N at 60° S of W
8. (i) 39·24 kN, (ii) 27·8 kN
9. 52 N, 270°
10. 12·2 N, $4\frac{1}{2}$° S of E
11. Tie rod tension, 10·3 kN; Beam thrust, 10 kN
12. 40·8 kN, 117·7 kN
13. (a) 98·1 N, (b) 113·2 N
14. AC, 89·6 N (tension); BC, 51·5 N (compression)
15. 18·1 kN, 14·3 kN; 33 kN
16. (i) 25·4 N, $117\frac{1}{2}$°; (ii) 21 N, $236\frac{1}{2}$°
17. (i) 2·15 N, $274\frac{1}{2}$°; (ii) 4·68 N, 333°
18. 1·15 N to left; 21·64 N upwards
19. 168 kg, 1·75 kN
20. 2·89 N
21. 17·9 N; 66·9°
22. (a) 1225 N, (b) 1275 N

753

23. $14\frac{1}{2}°$, 2·06 N
24. (i) 40·4 N, 17·1 N, (ii) 44·1 N, 34·8 N
25. 1·36 MN, 332 kN

Chapter 4 (p. 139)

1. 20 N
2. 0·894 kg
4. 53 kN, 67 kN
5. 55·9 mm, 84·7 mm
6. (a) 50 N, (b) 25 N
7. 80 mm, 52·5 mm
8. 424 mm, 40·6 kg
9. 1·055 m from A
10. A, 1·35 kN; B, 900 N
11. (a) 41·25 kN, 48·75 kN; (b) 140 kN at C
12. 107 mm, 94·6 mm
13. (a) 382·5 N, (b) 541 N
14. (i) 1·02 kg, (ii) 27·5 N
15. 15·9 kg
16. Up to 1·25 m from overhanging end
17. 1·025 m
18. (a) 2·155 N, 1·275 N, (b) 0·531 m
19. 0·694 from A (force downwards); 0·106 m from A (force upwards)
20. 495 N; 1065 N reaction at A
21. 19·96 kN, 13·96 kN; 2·0 m from A
22. 195·5 mm below A, pointing to left
23. 11·65 kg
24. 125 mm from face, 20·2 mm from axis
25. 86 mm along axis from flat end
26. 26·7 mm from 125 mm edge; 39·3 mm from 100 mm edge
27. 366 mm
28. 456 mm from drilled end
29. 2·59 kN
30. F = 63·9 N; R = 76·5 N at 59·6° below horizontal towards end D
31. (a) 0·6 kN, (b) 2·25 m from A, (c) 0·4 kN, 0·75 kN

Chapter 5 (p. 169)

1. 150 N
2. 67 kN/mm²
3. 39·05 mm, 1·755 mm
4. 19·1 N/mm²

5. (a) 76·8 kN, (b) 202 N/mm²
6. (a) 39·7 N/mm², (b) 0·024 2 mm
7. 205 kN/mm²
8. 13 mm
9. (a) 196 kN/mm², (b) 0·8 N/mm²
10. (a) 9100 mm², (b) 14 mm; 2·4 mm
11. 39 mm, 200 kN/mm²
12. (i) 0·06 mm, (ii) 206 kN/mm²
13. (i) 1462 mm², (ii) 13·65 N/mm²
14. a = 33·3, b = 510; (a) 510 mm, (b) 960 mm
15. 11·25 mm, 60 N
16. 3·001 755 m
17. 50·79 mm
18. 67·8 mm, 1·375 mm
19. 203·5 kN/mm², 0·118 mm
20. 225 kN, 0·675 mm
21. 416 kN
22. 123·7 kN, 28 N/mm²
23. 200 kN/mm²; Stress just beyond elastic limit
24. 18·8 mm, 249·807 mm
25. (a) 208 kN/mm², (b) 280 N/mm², (c) 452·5 N/mm², (d) 40%, (e) 57%
26. 31 N/mm², 200 kN/mm²
27. 109·5 N/mm², 4·1

Chapter 6 (*p.* 192)

1. 784 J, 270 J, 61·8 kJ
2. 131·25 J, 35 N
3. 28 J; 467 N
4. 3 kN/m; 21·6 J
5. 2·7 kJ
6. 96·8 kJ
7. (a) 1·6 kJ, (b) 4·8 kJ
8. (a) 12·45 kJ, (b) 24·45 kJ
9. 9·87 kg; 564 J
10. 17·6 J
11. 48 m
12. 29·8 kJ; 26·5 kJ
13. 2·53 J
14. 57 mJ
15. 20 N/mm; 21·2 mm

Chapter 7 (*p.* 216)

1. (i) (a) 2·165 kN; (b) 1·25 kN; (ii) 2·165 kJ; (iii) 6·3 kN; (iv) 0·344; (v) 0·181
2. (a) 705 N, (b) 4648 N, (c) 0·151 5
3. 44·2 N, 884 J
4. 455 N; 53·8 kg
5. 1 kN
6. 125 N
7. (a) 30 Nm, (b) 628·4 J
8. 577 J
9. 1885 kJ
10. (a) 1370 N, (b) 154 N; 1510 N
11. (a) 65·6 kN, (b) 1 kN, (c) 1·605 MJ
12. (a) 76 N, (b) 79 N parallel to plane
13. 0·213, 199 N
14. 141 N
15. 7·3°, 0·257

Chapter 8 (*p.* 254)

1. 0·25 m/s², 20 s
2. (a) 9·27 s, (b) 129 m; 0·54 m/s²
3. 120 m, 48 s, 68 s, 460 m
4. (a) 99·4 m, (b) 44·1 m/s, (c) 2·68 s
5. (a) 20·4 km, (b) 34·3 m/s, 122·5 m
6. (a) 1·2 m/s, (b) 12·05 m/s, 5·7° above horizontal
7. 5·96 m; 12·7 m/s at 66·9° to horizontal
8. (a) 0·36 m/s², (b) 5·4 m/s, (c) 40·5 m
9. (a) 50·7 km/h, (b) 81·7 km/h, (c) 39·2 s
10. (b) 3·2 min, (c) 83 km/h
11. 1·84 km
12. (a) 43·2 km/h, (b) 0·4 m/s², (c) 0·6 m/s²
13. (a) 9·55 km/h, (b) 1·39 m/s², (c) 994 m
14. (a) 118 m, (b) 211 s, (c) 237·6 s
15. (a) 6·08 km, (b) 65·8 s, (c) 34·2 km
16. 33 km/h, 0·261 m/s², 0·453 m/s², 390 m
17. (a) 86·5 km/h, (b) 10·63 km
18. (i) 24 km/h, (ii) 52·8 km, (iii) 52·8 km/h, (iv) 37·6 km
19. 34·4 km/h, N 17·3° W
20. 98 m, 44·7 s
21. (a) A – B, 11·55° S of W; B – C, 26·8° N of E; C – A, due S, (b) 0·824 h, (c) 53·9 km/h

Chapter 9 (p. 268)

1. 27·8 s
2. 13·8 m/s², 604 m
3. (a) 180 500 kgm/s, (b) 9·03 kN, 13·55 kN
4. 13·87 kN
5. 208 500 kg m/s, (a) 40·2 kN, (b) 1·45 MJ, (c) Decreases from 1·45 MJ to zero
6. (a) 81·9 kN, (b) 90 kN
7. (a) 250 000 kg m/s, (b) 9·96 kN, (c) 218 m
8. (a) 27·8 s, (b) 193 m
9. (i) 0·616 m/s², (ii) 2·46 N, at 77° to original direction
10. (i) 12 m/s, (ii) 7·35 m, (iii) 30 kg, (iv) 1·225 s
11. (a) 0·277 m/s², (b) 105·7 kN
12. 73·4 kN
13. 102·2 kN, 1 in 28·1
14. 37·8 kN, 3 m 47 s
15. (a) 5·6 kN, 3·17 MJ, (b) 37·4 km/h, (c) 69·5 s
16. (a) 154·5 m, (b) 22·2 s, (c) 0·625 m/s²
17. (i) 35 N, (ii) 2 m/s², (iii) 131·25 m, (iv) 17·5 s
18. (a) 931 N
19. (a) 307·5 N, (b) 245 N, (c) 182·5 N, (d) 20 m
20. 27·6 m/s, at 27° to original direction

Chapter 10 (p. 288)

1. (a) 492 rev/min, (b) 27·5 m/s
2. 382 rev/min
3. (a) (i) 8·33 s, (ii) 13·28°, (iii) 261 J; (b) 0·002 95 rad/s²
4. (i) 251 rad/s, (ii) 25·1 m/s
5. 15·7 rad/s, 7·855 m/s
6. (a) 86·2 s, (b) 13·9 rad/s, (c) 0·161 rad/s²
7. (a) 0·111 m/s², (b) 139 m, (c) 17·05 rad/s, (d) 0·342 rad/s²
8. (a) 5·24 rad/s², (b) 41·6 rev
9. 19·6 J
10. (a) 26·2 rad/s, (b) 1·75 rad/s², (c) 197 rad, (d) 29·5 kJ
11. 12·6 kJ
12. 1·57 kJ

Chapter 11 (p. 299)

1. 188 kW, 246 kW
2. 3·53 MJ, 35·3 kW

3. (a) 706 kJ, (b) 2·35 kW
4. 540 N
5. 2·25 kW
6. (a) 450 Nm, (b) 350 W
7. (a) 23·6 W, (b) 562·5 W
8. 1·51 kW
9. 247 W
10. 39·24 kJ, 3·924 kW
11. (a) 72·5 kJ, (b) 1·335 kN, (c) 9·3 kW, (d) 17·35 rad/s
12. (a) 13·5 kW, (b) 2·7 kJ
13. (i) 9·42 kJ, (ii) 1·57 kW
14. 10·1 kN
15. 4·905 MJ, 49·05 kW, 65·5 kW
16. 5·45 kW
17. 4·25 kW
18. 14·32 kNm
19. (a) 6·47 kNm, (b) 10·76 kN
20. 72·1 kW
21. 516 W

Chapter 12 (p. 346)

1. 585 N
2. 10
3. (a) $E = 0·05 F + 1$, (b) 230 N, 0·293 p.u. (29·3%)
4. 0·707 m/s
5. $P = 0·065 F + 15$
6. $E = 0·45 F + 1$
7. $E = 0·25 F + 17$
8. (a) 10, (b) (i) 6·53, (ii) 0·653 p.u. (65·3%)
10. 283 N
11. 0·485 p.u. (48·5%)
12. 6, 0·80 p.u. (80%)
13. 254 N, 300 J
14. 863 N, 300 rev/min
15. 82 mm
16. $P = 0·03 F + 175$; 700 N, 25, 0·625 p.u. (62·5%)
17. 0·485 p.u. (48·5%)
18. (a) 0·335 p.u. (33·5%), (b) 0·219 p.u. (21·9%)
19. (a) $P = 0·03 F + 150$, (b) 825 N, 27·3, 0·546 p.u. (54·6%)
20. 3·97 kN, 1·59 kN, 165·5 mm

22. (a) 239 mm, (b) 15·9 N/mm²
23. 24, 4·23 N, 0·787 p.u. (78·7%)
24. (a) $P = 0.014\,2\,F + 2.7$, (b) 5·9 N, (c) 0·59 p.u. (59%)
25. 80·6 mm
26. (a) $P = 0.04\,F + 12.5$, (b) 0·5 p.u. (50%)

Chapter 14 (p. 412)

5. 876 kJ
6. 39·5°C
7. (b) 314 kJ, (c) 1·25 kg
8. (i) 15·1 MJ, (ii) 2·093 MJ
9. (i) 12·56 MJ, (ii) 50°C
10. (a) 50·3 kJ, (b) (i) 66·7°C, (ii) 13·95 MJ
11. 369°C
12. 0·03
13. 24·7°C
14. 66 g
15. 0·098
16. 16·6°C
17. 0·132
18. 13·27 MJ
19. 0·41 kJ/kg°C
20. 7·775 MJ
21. 10·68 kJ
22. 2260 kJ/kg
23. 75·7°C
24. 63·8%
25. 41·25 g
26. 304 kJ
27. 30·3 MJ
28. 11·24 tonne/h
29. 0·9 mm
31. (a) 184·5 kJ, (b) 7·78 mm
32. 2·4 mm
33. (a) 182°C, (b) 325 kJ
34. 34·1 mm
35. (a) 1·999 52 m, (b) 2·003 12 m
36. (i) 0·9 mm, (ii) 1·8 mm
37. 1·002 m, 0·040 054 4 m²
38. 0·000 012/°C

39. (a) 2·381 MJ, (b) 80 kg
40. 29·8°C
41. 55·8 m³
42. 2·529 MJ, 412 kg/h
43. 2 l
44. (i) 0·42 m³, (ii) 0·399 m³
45. (a) 9 bar, (b) 0·034 6 m³
46. 13·5 mm
47. (a) 394°C, (b) 9·67 bar gauge
48. 356 ml
49. 575°C
50. 204°C
51. (b) 8·13 kg, (c) 43°C
52. (a) 4·91 bar, (b) 5·27 bar
53. 5·6 m³, 6·79 kg
54. 0·712 kg
55. (a) 106°C, (b) 0·034 6 kg
56. 0·162 5 m³

Chapter 15 (p. 433)

3. 120·9 kN/m²
4. 6·43 N
5. 40·5%
6. Length should exceed 0·76 m
7. 14 ml, 3·5 g
8. 33 kN, 424 N
9. 240 mm; Yes
10. 132·7 kN/m², 50 kN/m²
11. 0·875
12. (a) 100 g, (b) 2·7
13. 0·965 m
14. 56·25, 1·125 MN, 2·54 N/mm²
15. 234·5 mm
16. 450 ml
17. (a) 51·8%, (b) 15·2 g/ml

Chapter 16 (p. 497)

6. (a) 75 C, (b) 18 000 J
7. (i) 5 V, 10 V, 15 V, (ii) 30 V
8. 11 V

9. 1·28 Ω, 4·7 A
10. 10·9 Ω
11. 19·2 Ω
12. 2·4 A
13. 3
14. 25 Ω, 4 A, 40 V, 60 V, 100 V
15. 2·5 Ω, 1 Ω
16. (i) 0·725 A, 0·149 A, (ii) 7·25 V, 1·49 V
17. 3·75 V, 2·82 A
18. 0·25 A, 360 J
20. 33 A, 22 A, 11 A, 6 A
21. 6 A, 3 A
22. 18 Ω, 6 V, 1·5 A
23. (a) 1 A, (b) 1·25 A, (c) 42·5 V, (d) B positive to C, (e) 30 Ω
24. (a) 0·25 A, (b) 20·25 V, F positive to D; 21·25 V, F positive to H; 1·0 V, D positive to H
25. (a) $R_1 = 20$ Ω, $R_2 = 15$ Ω, (b) 2 A, (c) 8 A
26. 18·8 Ω
27. 3·93 m
28. $1·725 \times 10^{-8}$ Ωm
29. 0·507 Ω
30. 19·5 Ω
31. (a) 556 mm², (b) Aluminium cable is 0·512 × weight, and 1·69 × cross-section, of copper cable
32. 244 V
33. $V_x = V_y = 236$ V
34. 525 V, 462·5 V, 362·5 V
35. 242 V, 236 V, 232 V, 230 V
36. 41·7 A, 10·4 kW
37. 347 W
38. (i) 576 W, (ii) 1150 W, (iii) 2300 W
39. 20 k Ω, 4 k Ω, 800 Ω, 80 Ω; 80 Ω
40. (a) (i) 1·25 A, 20 A, (ii) 312·5 W, 5000 W, (b) 0, 15 A
41. (a) 3·75 kW, (b) 12·5 A, (c) 24 Ω, (d) 36 p
42. (a) 177 V, 2·85 A, 1·07 A, (b) 95 W
43. 0·023 1 A, 0·154 V, 0·004 26 A, 0·008 9 W
44. (a) 1·6 Ω, (b) 0·288 kW, 2·69 kW
45. 86·2 mm²
46. 3·53 V
47. 2·5 A, 576 Ω, 13·2 p

48. (a) 1·0 A, 174 W, (b) 0·062 5 A, 10·9 W
49. 100 Ω, £1·56
50. 132 Ω, 109 W
51. 15 A
52. 7900 kWh, 480 A
53. 445 W
54. 10 m
55. (a) 340 W, (b) 62·25 V, (c) 31·12 Ω, (d) 6·07 Ω
56. (i) 99·4 kW, (ii) 795 kWh, (iii) £3·98
57. 76 p
58. (a) 20 mm², (b) 15·7 V (19/1·32)
59. 34°C
60. 0·004 3/°C at 0°C
61. 84°C
62. 0·004 3/°C at 0°C
63. 0·000 249, 591 m, 1025 Ω

Chapter 17 (p. 547)

1. 12·5 V, 0·25 Ω
2. 0·1 Ω
3. 1·53 V
8. 210 V, 0·395 A; 532 Ω
10. 1·25 Ω, 146 mA
11. 7·31 Ω
12. (a) 0·01 Ω to 2·10 Ω, (b) 100 Ω to 21 000 Ω
13. (i) 0·075 2 Ω, (ii) 39 970 Ω
14. (a) 19 995 Ω, (b) 0·076 2 Ω
15. 1·546 Ω; Tapping at 0·155 Ω from common terminal
16. Voltmeter multiplier sections:
    1985 Ω + 8000 Ω + 10 000 Ω
    Universal shunt sections:
    0·3 Ω + 2·7 Ω + 27 Ω
17. 3 mA; Tapping at 2 Ω from common terminal

Chapter 18 (p. 581)

4. 5 Ω, 14 V
7. 24 Ω
8. 10·4 h
10. 4·62 Ω, 2 Ω; 15 h approx.
11. 17·2 Ω, 7·6 Ω, 15 h approx. (assuming Ah efficiency of about 80%)

12. 59 min 40 s
13. Ammeter reading 0·03 A low
14. 3·02 g, 2700 C
15. 1·2 A
16. 1·95 A
17. 0·001 cm

Chapter 19 (p. 641)

12. (a) 2×10^{-3} N, (b) 3×10^{-5} Nm, (c) $1·57 \times 10^{-5}$ J
13. (a) 108 Nm, (b) 17 kW
15. 100 V
16. A, 144 mV; B, 54 mV
18. 75 V
20. 9·6 V, 12 N, 480 W
21. 16 N, 80 W
22. (a) 4·2 V, (b) 3·5 N, (c) 2520 J
23. 1·5 T, 5·4 N

Chapter 20 (p. 684)

1. (a) 0·105 ms, (b) 0·210 ms, (c) 0·733 ms, (d) 0·838 ms; 795 c/s
2. 50 Hz, 1200 rev/min
3. (i) 1455–1545 rev/min, (ii) 364–386 rev/min
4. (i) 0·006 9 s, (ii) 0·007 9 s, (iii) 0·015 7 s; 15·9 Hz
5. (a) 0·02 s, (b) 340 V, (c) 153 V, (d) 240 V, (e) 1·11
6. (a) 30·2 V, (b) 21·4 V, (c) 20 Hz, (d) 0·05 s
8. (i) 100 A, (ii) 70·7 A, (iii) 50 Hz
9. (i) 1·11, (ii) 1·0; Sinusoidal waveform
10. 72 V
11. 2·6 V
12. (a) (i) 100 Hz, (ii) 4·6 A, (b) 13·45 A
13. (a) 2·2 ms, (b) 455 Hz, (c) 50 V, (d) 57·7 V
14. (a) 3·1 A, (b) 3·3 A, (c) 1·07
15. 46 V, 50·4 V

Chapter 21 (p. 703)

3. 0·252 Ω
5. 0·001 44 Nm

Chapter 22 (p. 716)

1. 117·5 kJ, 7·85 kW, 88·3 kJ
2. 192 kJ, 1·728 MN

3. (a) 21·45 kJ, (b) 10·72 kW
4. 4·05 J, 4·5 J, 8·55 J
5. 7·95 kJ
6. 247 kJ, 55·5 mm
7. (a) 6·11 kW, (b) 9·71 kW, (c) 11·03 kW
8. (a) 7·4 A, (b) 0·883 p.u. (88·3%), (c) 975 W, (d) 0·57 p.u. (57%)
9. (a) 5 kW, (b) 28 p
10. (i) 81·7%, (ii) 22·8 kWh
11. (a) 44·1 kJ/s (kW), (b) 88·2 kW, (c) 66 p
12. (a) 1·36 kW; (b) 227 kWh
13. 4·95 A, 15·95 kWh
14. 7·62 A, 0·63 p.u. (63%)
15. 85°C
16. 1·41 kW
17. 14·7°C
18. 4·38 h
19. 43·2 Ω
20. £174·5
21. 677 kW, £36·5
22. 7·03 MJ/kg
23. 0·948 p.u. (94·8%)
24. Cost of coal heating: Cost of electrical heating: 1 : 1·095
25. 3·28 h
26. 9·1 m³/h
27. 22·65%
28. 17·1 MJ
29. 32 kW
30. (a) 7·12 kW, (b) 5·7 kW
31. 33·1 kW, 29·8 kW
32. 1·22 GJ/h, 339 kW

Index

ABSOLUTE pressure, 402
Absolute temperature scale, 405
Absolute zero, 405
Acceleration, 227, 242, 258
Accumulator, 560
Alkaline secondary cells, 567
Alternating current, 646
Alternator, 653
Aluminium, 726
Ammeter shunt, 536, 540
Ampere, 443, 621
Ampere-hour, 563
Ampere-hour efficiency, 567
Aneroid barometer, 426
Angle of friction, 204
Angular acceleration, 282
Angular velocity, 277
Anode, 551
Archimedes' principle, 427
Atmospheric pressure, 425
Atomic energy, 706
Atomic structure, 355
Average value, 666

BAKELITE, 733
Barometer, 425
Battery, electric, 470
Beams, simply supported, 109
Belt drives, 336
Board of Trade Unit, 493
Boyle's law, 401
Brass, 727
Brittleness, 165, 722
Bronze, 728

CALORIMETER, 377
Capacity of secondary cell, 563
Cast iron, 725
Cathode, 551
Cells, electric, in parallel, 471
Cells, electric, in series, 470
Cells, electric, internal resistance, 473
Celluloid, 731
Cellulose acetate, 731
Celsius temperature scale, 369
Centre of gravity, 118
Centroid, 120
Ceramics, 736
Chain drives, 338
Characteristic equation of a gas, 409
Charge, electric, 436

Charles' law, 403
Chemical effect of electric current, 445, 568
Coefficient of expansion, 392
Coefficient of friction, 197
Components of a force, 62, 71
Compression, 148
Conductance, 455
Conduction of heat, 366
Conductors, 439, 478
Conservation of energy, 706
Convection, 367
Copper, 727
Corkscrew rule, 590, 593
Coulomb, 438
Couple, 116
Creep, 166
Crest factor, 682
Cycle, 653

DANIELL cell, 554
Density, 30
Depolarizing agent, 554
Dielectric strength, 724
Direct current, 646
Domain (magnetic), 602
Dry cell, 557
Ductility, 165, 722
Dynamometer instruments, 697

EDDY-CURRENT brake, 638
Effective value, 681
Efficiency, 295, 304, 492, 567, 708
Elastic limit, 164, 721
Elasticity, 721
Electric bell, 604
Electric cells, 469–472
Electric charge, 436
Electric current, 442
Electric generator, 636
Electric motor, 616
Electric potential, 438
Electric potential difference, 438
Electrical equivalent of heat, 711
Electrical power, 489
Electro-chemical equivalent, 571
Electrode, 551
Electrolysis, 568
Electrolyte, 551
Electromagnet, 603
Electromagnetic induction, 622

Electromotive force, 441
Electron, 353, 436
Electroplating, 573
Elongation (percentage), 164
Energy, 188, 449, 705
Enthalpy, 382
Epoxy resins, 734
Equilibrium, 51
Expansion of gases, 399
Expansion of liquids, 397
Expansion of solids, 396

FACTOR of safety, 165
Faraday's law of electromagnetic induction, 627
Faraday's laws of electrolysis, 571
Fatigue, 165
Faure process, 165, 561
Ferromagnetic materials, 584, 601
Fleming's left-hand rule, 609
Fleming's right-hand rule, 630
Fluid pressure, 421
Flux (-density), magnetic, 598, 611
Flux linkage (magnetic), 623
Flywheel, 191
Force, 25, 39, 258
Force Ratio, 303
Form factor, 681
Frequency, 657
Friction, 195
Fulcrum, 95

GALVANOMETER, 509
Gas constant, 409
Gas laws, 400
Gauge pressure, 402
Gear drives, 329
Gravitational force, 26

HARDNESS, 722
Heating effect of electric current, 444, 450, 672
Hertz, 657
Hoffman voltameter, 570
Hooke's law, 154
Hydraulic press, 422
Hydrometer, 428

IDEAL gas, 403
Inclined plane, 80, 208, 323
Induced e.m.f., 622
Inertia, 259
Insulators, 440, 478, 484
Internal resistance of cell, 473, 507
Ion, 552
Iron, 724

JOULE, 174, 438, 451, 490
Joule's equivalent, 710, 711

KELVIN scale of temperature, 409
Kilowatt, 491
Kilowatt-hour, 493
Kinetic energy, 190, 264

LAMINA, 119
Laminates, 733
Lead, 729
Lead-acid accumulator, 560
Leclanché cell, 556
Lenz's law, 628
Levers, 102, 306
Limit of proportionality, 156
Line of force, 586
Local action, 552
Lubricants, 196

MACHINABILITY, 723
Magnet, 584
Magnetic effect of electric current, 444, 588
Magnetic field, 585
Magnetic flux, 598
Malleability, 722
Mass, 24
Mean value, 666
Mechanical advantage, 303
Mechanical equivalent of heat, 710
Metre bridge, 524
Modulus of elasticity, 156
Modulus of rigidity, 156
Molecule, 358
Moment of a force, 94
Momentum, 259
Movement ratio, 304
Moving-coil loudspeaker, 618
Moving-coil meters, 688
Moving-iron meters, 690
Multi-polar alternator, 663

NEUTRON, 354
Newton, 27, 262
Newton's laws of motion, 259
Nickel, 728
Nickel-iron alkaline cell, 567
N.T.P., 409
Nucleus, 355
Nylon, 732

OHM's law, 445

PARALLELOGRAM of forces, 43
Peak factor, 682
Peak value, 648
Period, 654
Permeability (magnetic), 600, 724
Perspex, 732
Planté process, 561
Plasticity, 721

Plastics, 730
Polarization, 553
Polygon of forces, 48
Polystyrene, 732
Polythene, 731
Porcelain, 734
Potential difference, 438
Potential divider, 528
Potential energy, 188, 264, 449
Potentiometer, 509
Power, 290, 489
Pressure, 27
Pressure—absolute, 402
Pressure—atmospheric, 425
Pressure—fluid, 421
Pressure—gauge, 402
Primary cell, 560
Projectiles, 250
Proton, 354
P.T.F.E., 732
Pulley systems, 312
P.V.C., 731

RADIAN, 272
Radiation of heat, 367
Reaction force, 51
Relative density, 31, 428
Relative permeability, 600, 723
Relay (electromagnetic), 604
Resistance alloys, 484
Resistance (electrical), 445
Resistance-temperature coefficient, 482, 487, 723
Resistivity, 475, 722
Resistors in parallel, 454
Resistors in series, 452
Resolution of vectors, 62, 71, 247
Retardation, 227
R.m.s. value, 681

SCALAR quantities, 38
Screw-jack, 324
Secondary cell, 560
Semi-conductors, 441, 478
Sensitivity of voltmeter, 535
Series-parallel circuits, 465
Shear, 149
Shunt, ammeter, 536, 540
Siemen, 455
Silicon plastics, 734
Simple voltaic cell, 550
Siphon, 426
Slide-wire bridge, 524
Slide-wire potentiometer, 509
Softness, 722
Solenoid, 593
Specific heat capacity, 371
Speed, 219
Speed cones, 339
Square-law scales, 693

Steatite, 734
Steel, 724
Steelyard, 131
S.T.P., 409
Strain, 152
Strain energy, 190
Stress, 150
Sulphating, 563

TEMPERATURE-COEFFICIENT of resistance, 482, 487, 723
Temperature scale, 369
Tenacity, 721
Tension, 148
Terylene, 732
Tesla, 599, 611
Thermal capacity, 374
Thermal conductivity, 366
Thermo-couples, 371, 701
Thermometers, 370
Thermoplastics, 731
Thermosetting plastics, 733
Tin, 730
Toroid, 596
Torque, 116, 283, 291
Toughness, 721
Transmission of heat, 366
Triangle of forces, 43

ULTIMATE stress, 164
Universal shunt, 540
Urea formaldehyde, 733

V-BELTS, 337
Vector quantities, 38
Velocity, 221, 277
Velocity ratio, 304
Viscosity, 196, 421
Volt, 438
Voltaic cell, 550
Voltameter, 569
Volt-box, 531
Voltmeter multiplier, 534, 538
Voltmeter sensitivity, 535

WATER equivalent, 376
Watt, 291, 490
Watt-hour efficiency, 567
Wattmeter, 699
Weber, 598, 611
Weston standard cell, 511, 558
Wheatstone bridge, 522
Wheel and axle, 308
Work, 174, 285

YIELD point, 164
Young's modulus, 156

ZINC, 729